Conversion Factors

1 unified atomic mass unit u = 1.66053×10^{-27} kg = 931.48 MeV/c^2

1 eV = 1.60219×10^{-19} J

1 kg = 5.6095×10^{29} MeV/c^2

1 (thermochemical) calorie = 2.613×10^{19} eV = 4.184 J

Energy (in eV)-wavelength (in Å) conversion $E\lambda = 12398.5$ eV·Å (≈ 12345)

1 year = 3.1558×10^7 s $\approx \pi \times 10^7$ s

1 inch = 2.5400 cm

1 statute mile = 1.609 km

1 pound (mass) = 0.4536 kg

1 radian = 57.296°

1 Å = 10^{-10} m

1 fm = 10^{-15} m = 1 fermi

1 curie (Ci) = 3.700×10^{10} disintegrations/s

Numerical Values

$e = 2.71828$ $\qquad$ $1/e = 0.367879$ $\qquad$ $e^3 \approx 20$

$\pi = 3.14159$ $\qquad$ $\sqrt{\pi} = 1.772454$ $\qquad$ $\pi^2 = 9.870$

$\ln 2 = 0.69315$ $\qquad$ $\log x = \ln x / \ln 10 = 0.4343 \ln x$ $\qquad$ $\ln x = 2.303 \log x$

$\sin 30° = \cos 60° = 0.500$ $\qquad$ $\tan 30° = \cot 60° = 0.577$

$\sin 45° = \cos 45° = 0.707$ $\qquad$ $\tan 45° = \cot 45° = 1.000$

$\sin 60° = \cos 30° = 0.866$ $\qquad$ $\tan 60° = \cot 30° = 1.732$

FIELDS AND PARTICLES

An Introduction to
Electromagnetic Wave Phenomena and Quantum Physics

The Fifth Solvay Physics Conference

Brussels, Belgium, 23–29 October 1927

Sponsored by the Solvay International Institute of Physics.

1. A. Piccard
2. E. Henriot
3. P. Ehrenfest
4. Ed. Herzen
5. Th. De Donder
6. E. Schrödinger
7. E. Verschaffelt
8. W. Pauli

9. W. Heisenberg
10. R. H. Fowler
11. L. Brillouin
12. P. Debye
13. M. Knudsen
14. W. L. Bragg
15. H. A. Kramers
16. P. A. M. Dirac

17. A. H. Compton
18. L. de Broglie
19. M. Born
20. N. Bohr
21. I. Langmuir
22. M. Planck
23. Mme. Curie
24. H. A. Lorentz

25. A. Einstein
26. P. Langevin
27. Ch. E. Guye
28. C. T. R. Wilson
29. O. W. Richardson

Absent: Sir. W. H. Bragg,
H. Deslandres et E. Van Aubel

FIELDS AND PARTICLES

An Introduction to
Electromagnetic Wave Phenomena and Quantum Physics

Francis Bitter
>   Late Professor of Physics   Massachusetts Institute of Technology

Heinrich A. Medicus
>   Professor of Physics   Rensselaer Polytechnic Institute

American Elsevier Publishing Company Inc. New York London Amsterdam

AMERICAN ELSEVIER PUBLISHING COMPANY, INC.
52 Vanderbilt Avenue, New York, N.Y. 10017

ELSEVIER PUBLISHING COMPANY
335 Jan Van Galenstraat, P.O. Box 211
Amsterdam, The Netherlands

International Standard Book Number 0-444-00129-8
Library of Congress Card Number 72-87209

Library of Congress Cataloging in Publication Data

Bitter, Francis, 1902–1967.
Fields and particles.

Earlier ed. by F. Bitter published in 1956 under
title: Currents, fields, and particles.
1. Electromagnetic waves. 2. Particles (Nuclear
physics) I. Medicus, Heinrich, 1918–   joint author.
II. Title.
QC661.B437   1973   530.1'41   72-87209
ISBN 0-444-00129-8

Manufactured in the United States of America

Contents

Chapter 3. Wave Mechanics

Chapter 4. Atoms and Molecules

Chapter 5. Waves In Solids

Chapter 6. Nucleons and Nuclei

Chapter 7. Particles and Symmetries

Appendix I The Poynting Vector and Electromagnetic Waves

Appendix II The Special Theory of Relativity

Appendix III The Complex Notation of Trigonometric Functions

Appendix IV Elements of Statistical Mechanics; Boltzmann, Bose, and
          Fermi Statistics

Preface

In 1956, Francis Bitter's efforts in bringing fresh ideas into the teaching of introductory physics courses at the Massachusetts Institute of Technology to students of engineering and science resulted in the publication of his textbook, "Currents, Fields, and Particles." It was a pioneering achievement in its integrated treatment of electromagnetism and quantum physics and was probably the first American textbook written on the sophomore level in which wave mechanics occupied a principal role.

In the mid-sixties the question of a revision of this book arose. Francis Bitter, who had transferred from MIT's Physics Department to the Department of Geophysics and Geology, now was devoting most of his efforts to getting the National Magnet Laboratory started, which, shortly after his death, was named after him. He asked me if I might help him with the book because I had closely worked with him in educational matters during the time when he was writing his textbook, thus we both were familiar with each other's ideas about the teaching of physics. We soon reached the decision to write a new book, retaining, however, extensive portions of the original one. Whereas the original work included a discussion of stationary or quasi–stationary electromagnetic phenomena, we now chose as a point of departure Maxwell's equations which explains the change of the original title to "Fields and Particles."

Prerequisites are introductory courses in mechanics, electricity and magnetism up to Maxwell's equations, and a little bit of thermodynamics. It would be desirable if the Special Theory of Relativity, the wave differential equation and the Poynting vector had been treated in these preceeding courses. However, since this is often not the case, Appendices I and II serve to fill these gaps.

We have tried to show on an elementary level how limitations of the classical concepts of waves, fields, and particles in the description of microscopic phenomena have been overcome by wave mechanics. Because we wanted to tell the story of fields in their relationship to particles, other important concepts of modern physics were de-emphasized in our treatment. Some of the material which usually is found in texts with titles like "Modern Physics" is therefore not in our book. Relativity is only covered here insofar as it applies to optical phenomena, because we feel that a much better place for an introduction to the Special Theory of Relativity is in a mechanics course. Furthermore, for those who disagree with us and are not satisfied with the additional material in the appendix, there are numerous excellent introductions to this subject in paperback. Also statistical mechanics, because it represents such a different approach to physics, is treated in an appendix rather than in the main body of the text.

Our line of thought is developed as follows: Starting with electromagnetic waves of macroscopic dimensions, such as radio waves, we then proceed to light waves and x radiation. In view of the important role of boundary conditions in wave mechanics, this concept is first introduced in macroscopic electromagnetic waves and again taken up in the discussion of reflection and transmission in optics. We then make the transition to matter waves, quanta of light, and wave mechanics. The square well, the harmonic oscillator and the rotator appear like a musical *thema con variazoni* here and later on in atomic, molecular, solid state, and nuclear physics. Also the chapter on particle physics is not bare of wave-mechanical concepts. The similarities in the spectroscopies of atoms, nuclei, and particles are given particular attention. We hope our treatment will convey to science and engineering students the unity of physics and the power and usefulness of quantum mechanics.

Throughout, we have tried to incorporate new results as much as possible in order to dispel the misconception that most of modern physics was created in the first third of this century, and to give the student some feeling for present-day physics and the importance of, and need for, further research.

Although considerable care was taken with the historical aspects of physics, our approach does not cling to an historical development. It might perhaps come as a shock to some colleagues that Bohr's atomic model, although of great significance in the history of physics, is discussed only in passing and this only after the wave-mechanical treatment of the hydrogen atom! The reason for this somewhat unorthodox procedure is our conviction that it is better if students learn to think about atoms in terms of particles in a (somewhat distorted) box than in terms of a planetary model.

In general we have endeavored to keep the mathematics as simple as possible even if it meant in several cases to forego a more elegant approach. An example is the hydrogen atom which we (and also Bitter in his earlier book) treated in cartesian coordinates, not in spherical ones with which the student might not be so familiar. We also resorted frequently to simplifying assumptions and rough order-of-magnitude estimates so that the main ideas would not be lost in all the details. At times, however, we changed pace to treat more advanced material in order to give the student a taste of what physics can do. The problems at the end of each chapter and appendix range from simple to very challenging.

Unfortunately, Francis Bitter passed away after we had completed the first version which was tried out at Rensselaer with a small class of sophomore students. Subsequent revisions were tested with increasingly larger sophomore classes of science and engineering students. We believe, however, that this book can also serve in many instances as an introduction to modern physics in junior and senior courses.

The candid and strong feedback which I received over the years from our students was of utmost value. I also gratefully acknowledge the help and advice of many of my colleagues at Rensselaer. In particular, Profs. H. B. Huntington, M. Leon, J. S. Levinger, R. M. Lichtenstein, K. Min, H. C. Ohanian, and P. Stoler endeavored to point out flaws in earlier versions. After the untimely death of Francis Bitter, M. Gilder improved and extended the draft on the chapter of solid state physics, an area in which I confess to have no real expertise. Several pages towards the end of this chapter are indeed mostly of his writing. I was very lucky indeed that my former colleague, Herta R. Leng, after her career as a highly regarded and successful teacher, read the whole manuscript, much of it in several versions, and offered many excellent suggestions. Profs. L. Philip Howland of Whitman College and Warren Blaker of Vassar College also provided much valuable constructive criticism. Among the students and assistants, I want to mention specifically Beth Stoeckly, Dean Nairn, and David Swedlow and thank all of them for their valuable contributions. The job of typing the various versions of the manuscript was most diligently performed mainly by Mrs. Cassie Young and Mrs. Jeanette Murphy. We gratefully acknowledge the kindness of the MIT Press to let us incorporate extensive parts of "Currents, Fields, and Particles" for which it holds the copyright. It also gives me great pleasure to mention the always helpful cooperation of Mr. R. L. Goodman and his staff at American Elsevier.

Finally, I want to thank my wife, who over these years not only endured my evening, weekend, and vacation hobby of writing this book, but also helped me with the proof reading.

Heinrich A. Medicus

Troy, New York

Electromagnetic Fields, Waves, and Quanta

All attempts to create a coherent model of the physical world are based on the propagation of waves and particles and their interactions with one another. There is a close relationship between waves and fields because the presence of a wave implies a modification of the physical properties of space which is described by the field concept. A considerable part of this book deals therefore with the interaction of electromagnetic fields with matter. In most cases these fields are oscillating and, as we shall see, travel with the velocity of light. The frequency ν of the oscillation may vary from 10^5 hertz (hertz = cycles/sec), as in broadcast waves, to 10^{30} hertz or more, as in the electromagnetic component of the cosmic radiation. The corresponding wavelengths λ according to the equation $\lambda\nu = c$, where c is the speed of light = 3×10^8 m/sec, run from $\lambda \approx 1000$ m for long radio waves to 10^{-22} m. Whereas from our daily life we have a good feeling for the magnitude of a kilometer, the dimensions of waves from the other end of this spectrum are far beyond our conceptions. These short wavelengths are much smaller than atoms, which are approximately 10^{-10} m in diameter, or even protons and neutrons, which are of the order of 10^{-15} m. In fact, neither these wavelengths nor their frequencies have been measured directly, but both are deduced from the energy associated with these waves.

Thus, it is certainly not surprising that for different ranges of wavelength or frequency, different experimental methods are needed to study their interactions with matter. However, it is not evident that the theoretical treatment of electromagnetic phenomena and interactions need be radically different for long waves as compared with short waves. Nevertheless such is the case. For the long wavelengths—or low frequencies—the methods of classical electromagnetic theory are highly satisfactory, but for the very short wavelengths such treatment turns out to be completely inappropriate. We shall see in Chapter 2, and again later on, that electromagnetic waves of short wavelengths behave much more like particles; energy and momentum are two of their most significant attributes, while wavelength and frequency play a secondary role. This particle aspect of electromagnetic waves is best described by the quantum theory. Our challenge is to delineate the regions of validity of classical electromagnetic theory and quantum

1

theory. We shall see that in a large middle range of wavelengths and frequencies which is of great physical importance both theories are necessary
for a complete description of physical phenomena. We think here particularly about the region of the visible light which has a frequency of the order
of 10^{15} hertz. We shall see that certain physical events, such as emission and
absorption of light by atoms, usually belong to the domain of quantum
theory, whereas the propagation of light through space may best be
described by electromagnetic theory.

This wave-particle duality is not limited to electromagnetic fields. We
shall see that what we commonly call particles also have wave aspects.
This is the fascinating, apparently self-contradictory phase of the subject
where particles, like protons or electrons or atoms, are not simply like
marbles. Conversely, waves are not merely the familiar undulations in
space, or the undulations of matter in elastically deformable media. We
shall find that waves are particles, just as particles are waves. Sound waves
are demonstrably particles called phonons, and electromagnetic waves
(e.g., light waves or x rays) are demonstrably quanta, also called photons.

Quanta were first postulated by Planck shortly before Christmas 1900.
It was known that the radiation emerging from a small hole in a furnace
had a frequency distribution depending only upon the temperature in the
furnace, and that the radiation was independent of the material of which
the furnace was made. The radiation inside the furnace, by absorption and
re-emission, comes into thermal equilibrium with the walls of the furnace.
At about 600°C the furnace glows red; over 1000°C it becomes "white
hot." The experimentally found distribution of the electromagnetic energy
as a function of the frequency of the electromagnetic waves is shown in
Fig. 0.1.1. The maximum of this distribution clearly moves to higher

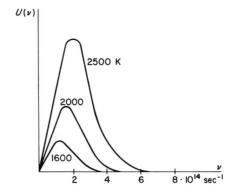

Fig. 0.1.1   The frequency distribution of the radiation in the cavity of a furnace at
three different temperatures.

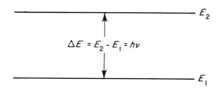

Fig. 0.1.2   Two energy levels in an atom.

frequencies with increasing temperature of the furnace. Planck was able to derive an expression for this observed frequency distribution, but only by assuming that the radiation was emitted or absorbed by "oscillators" in the walls of the cavity which vibrated with a frequency ν, but could take up or give off energy in little packets of energy, or quanta, of $E = h\nu$, where h is a constant of nature, Planck's constant

$$h = 6.626196 \pm 0.000050 \times 10^{-34} \text{ joule-sec.}$$

It should be noted here that quanta of energy were first introduced to account for the properties of the radiation fields and had little connection with the structure of matter. Matter was introduced in Planck's derivation only as a means of changing the frequency distribution in accordance with the temperature—by absorbing one frequency and emitting another.

However, soon after Planck's introduction of quanta in the oscillators, the concept of quanta was enlarged by Einstein, Bohr, and others, and shown to be inherent also in the radiation field itself and in the structure of atoms. One of the consequences of their ideas was the realization that atoms exist in certain energy states, each with its characteristic energy, and that radiation is emitted or absorbed in transitions between these states. Two energy levels are shown in Fig. 0.1.2. If the atom is in state 2 having an internal energy E_2, it can lose an amount of energy

$$\Delta E = E_2 - E_1$$

by making a transition to state 1 with internal energy E_1. This may occur by the radiation of an electromagnetic quantum of frequency ν and energy $\Delta E = h\nu$.[1] Conversely, if the atom is in state E_1, it can reach state 2 by absorbing an amount of energy $\Delta E = E_2 - E_1$. This may be as the result of absorbing a quantum of energy $\Delta E = h\nu$ from an electromagnetic field oscillating with the frequency ν. The rules for calculating the energies for atoms are established by quantum mechanics. At this point we wish to emphasize only the existence of quanta of radiation as an aspect of field

---

[1] We neglect here the small recoil energy of the atom caused by the emission of the quantum.

theory as well as a consequence of the mechanism of emission and absorption of radiation by atoms.

These two aspects of electromagnetic phenomena, the field concept and the quantum concept, may be reconciled by assuming that for a wave of frequency ν the electromagnetic energy is distributed in packets of energy $h\nu$ each with such a volume density that the classical expression for the electromagnetic energy density is satisfied. The situation is somewhat analogous to the distribution of matter in a gas. Even though we speak of a mass density of so and so many grams per unit volume, mass is actually distributed in the form of discrete atoms, and their number per unit volume determines the macroscopically observed density. Electromagnetic quanta play a corresponding role in electromagnetic fields. Their density and their movement in space are determined entirely by the fields; but in interactions with matter, as well as in statistical aspects of the fields themselves, which determine the most probable frequency distribution of electromagnetic energy confined to a box, the quanta must be considered.

Chapter 1

The Propagation of Electromagnetic Energy

1.1 A SHORT REVIEW OF MAXWELL'S EQUATIONS

Electric and magnetic fields are generally introduced in physics courses in terms of demonstrable effects on charged bodies (Coulomb's law) or current-carrying conductors (law of Biot and Savart). This approach is particularly suited to discussion of the problems involving static or slowly varying fields and electrical apparatus. However, we shall here be concerned almost exclusively with oscillating fields and their effects on atoms and their constituents. This will require rethinking the procedures and definitions which at first seemed completely adequate. Obviously, we cannot use a pith ball or a current element in a metallic circuit to measure electric or magnetic fields that change sign over distances of the order of 10^{-7} m and in times of the order of 10^{-15} sec as we shall find that they do in a beam of light. We can, and in order to make sense we must, replace our macroscopic test body by an electron. But when we do, we must also change our manner of making observations. We cannot observe the position of an electron or the force acting on it as we can for a macroscopic object.

However, a reasonable way of proceeding is open to us. The starting points are the basic equations of electromagnetic theory.[1] There is, first, the force $\mathbf{F}$ on a charge q exerted by an electric field $\mathbf{E}$ and a magnetic field $\mathbf{B}$:

$$\mathbf{F} = q(\mathbf{E} + \mathbf{v} \times \mathbf{B}). \qquad (1.1.1)$$

We shall assume this to be valid without regard to the physical nature of the charge q or to the manner in which the equation is to be verified when the charge acted upon is that of an electron and $\mathbf{E}$ and $\mathbf{B}$ are rapidly varying fields. The energy density in space, U, and the flow of energy in space

---

[1] We use (rationalized) mks units throughout.

5

represented by the Poynting vector **S**, are given by[2]

$$U = \tfrac{1}{2}\mathbf{E}\cdot\mathbf{D} + \tfrac{1}{2}\mathbf{H}\cdot\mathbf{B} \qquad (1.1.2)$$

$$\mathbf{S} = \mathbf{E} \times \mathbf{H} \qquad (1.1.3)$$

where, in free space,

$$\mathbf{D} = \epsilon_0\mathbf{E}$$

$$\mathbf{E} = \mu_0\mathbf{H} \qquad (1.1.4)$$

$$\epsilon_0 = 8.85 \times 10^{-12}\,\text{farad/m and } \mu_0 = 4\pi \times 10^{-7}\,\text{henry/m.} \qquad (1.1.5)$$

Maxwell's four equations in the absence of material objects then are:

$$\text{Faraday's law of induction } \oint \mathbf{E}\cdot d\mathbf{s} = -\int_S \dot{\mathbf{B}}\cdot d\mathbf{A}$$

$$\text{Ampère's law for displacement currents } \oint \mathbf{H}\cdot d\mathbf{s} = \int_S \dot{\mathbf{D}}\cdot d\mathbf{A} \qquad (1.1.6)$$

$$\text{Gauss' law in the absence of charges } \int_S \mathbf{D}\cdot d\mathbf{A} = 0$$

$$\text{Absence of magnetic monopoles } \int_S \mathbf{B}\cdot d\mathbf{A} = 0$$

From these, the wave equations for **E** and **H** may be derived (see Appendix I)

$$\nabla^2\mathbf{E} = \frac{1}{c^2}\frac{\partial^2\mathbf{E}}{\partial t^2}$$
$$\qquad (1.1.7)$$
$$\nabla\,\mathbf{H} = \frac{1}{c^2}\frac{\partial^2\mathbf{H}}{\partial t^2}.$$

The solutions for plane-polarized waves traveling along the x-axis are

$$E_y = E_{y0}\sin\frac{2\pi}{\lambda}(x \pm ct)$$
$$\qquad (1.1.8)$$
$$H_z = H_{z0}\sin\frac{2\pi}{\lambda}(x \pm ct).$$

---

[2] **D** is the electric displacement, and **H** the magnetic field intensity. In general **D** = ϵ**E** and **B** = μ**H**. For a derivation of the Poynting vector see Appendix I.

In free space the waves are subject to the condition that the ratio of the electric field (volts/m) to the magnetic field (amperes/m) is

$$\frac{E_y}{H_z} = \sqrt{\frac{\mu_0}{\epsilon_0}} = 377 \text{ ohms (approx.)} \tag{1.1.9}$$

$$c = \frac{1}{\sqrt{\epsilon_0 \mu_0}} = 3 \times 10^8 \text{ m/sec (approx.).} \tag{1.1.10}$$

We are apparently justified in using these expressions for describing waves in free space with arbitrarily high frequencies and short wavelengths because in the above equations only the constants ϵ_0 and μ_0 enter which determine the relative amplitudes[3] of the electric and magnetic waves, and the speed with which they are propagated. The wavelength or frequency of the waves described is perfectly arbitrary.

Maxwell's classical equations (1.1.6) as they stand are correct and unchallenged. However, they do not tell the whole story. Advanced quantum-theoretical considerations—which again reflect the wave-particle duality of nature—have shown that electric and magnetic fields can never be static or even zero. There are always minimum "zero-point" fluctuations in these fields. (A rough analogy might be the noise level in a reasonably quiet room which also varies more or less randomly.) It was found necessary to revise the concept of empty space. A vacuum is never completely free of fields and of particles; the local fluctuations of the electromagnetic field imply a never ceasing presence of fields. There are also fluctuations of the electric charge distribution due to the perpetual creation and disappearance of pairs of negatively and positively charged electrons. We wish to point out that empty space also contains fluctuating fields related to particles other than electrons. Some of these particles interact with electromagnetic fields. We shall pass these by now, however and concentrate on difficulties that arise in accepting Eq. 1.1.6 when charges are introduced. These difficulties are resolved by the quantum theory. The existence of electromagnetic quanta supplements rather than contradicts the electromagnetic equations. In discussing the propagation of electro-

---

[3] Different transparent media not only transmit electromagnetic waves with different speeds, but require a changed ratio of electric to magnetic amplitudes, all because they have a permittivity differing from ϵ_0. The permeability μ, on the other hand, differs very little from μ_0 in media which are transparent for electromagnetic waves. In optics, this physical difference is called a change of index of refraction $n = (K_e)^{1/2}$, where the dielectric constant K_e is defined by $\epsilon = K_e \epsilon_0$. In the language of electromagnetic circuits, it is called a change of impedance. Impedance is the ratio of voltage to current and is expressed in ohms. The concepts of index of refraction and impedance will be considered in more detail later.

magnetic waves in later sections in this chapter the existence of quanta
may be neglected. They play no part in the phenomena of propagation.
It is only when we consider the absorption, scattering, and emission of
radiation by atomic systems that the existence of quanta is clearly re-
vealed, as we shall see in subsequent chapters.

1.2 THE FLOW OF ELECTROMAGNETIC ENERGY GUIDED BY CONDUCTORS

In this section we discuss the electromagnetic theory of phenomena that
belong to a wavelength and frequency range where the measurement of
electric and magnetic fields may proceed according to definition (e.g., Eq.
1.1.1) using conducting circuits and electrical instruments. In Chapter 2
we move on to a more general discussion of the electromagnetic spectrum
and the kinds of interactions with matter that characterize shorter wavelengths and higher frequencies.

We emphasized earlier that wave aspects are not limited to electromagnetic phenomena. The mathematical formalism which we are going to
develop is therefore also applicable to the description of other waves. In
particular, standing waves and partial and total reflection of waves at
boundaries will play an important role in later parts of this book.

To illustrate the flow of energy, we take up the transmission of energy

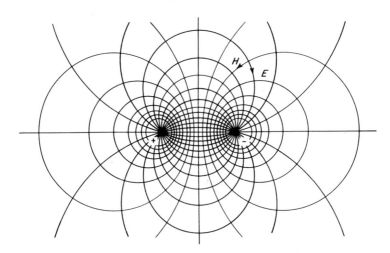

Fig. 1.2.1 The electric and magnetic fields around a two-wire cable of negligible
resistance carrying power from a battery to a load. The current flows into the paper in
the left wire and toward the observer in the right wire.

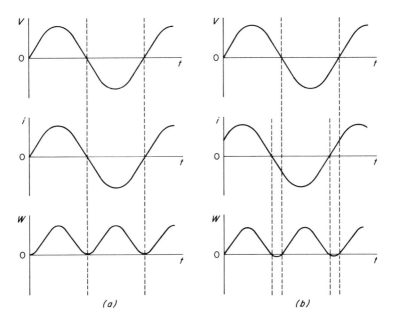

Fig. 1.2.2 Voltage, current, and power as a function of time at an arbitrary location in a cable connected to an a-c power supply. (a) Energy flow into a resistance chosen such that no energy is reflected back, that is, termination by the characteristic resistance. (b) Energy flow into a resistance which reflects some of the energy.

along a cable or transmission line consisting of two straight parallel wires from a battery to a load. We shall assume that the resistance of the cable is negligibly small. The difference in voltage between the terminals of the battery will then appear across the terminals of the load, and there will be no voltage drop along either wire, and therefore no electric field component parallel to the cable. The cross section of the cable, which we shall take to be composed of two straight wires, is shown in Fig. 1.2.1. The electric lines of force run from the positively charged wire at a high potential to the negatively charged wire at a lower potential. The current flows along the positively charged wire into the paper toward the load, and in the load from the high to the low potential wire, and back from the load to the battery along the negatively charged wire. The magnetic lines of flux surround the current into the page (toward the load) in a clockwise sense, and out of the page (toward the battery) in a counterclockwise sense, as shown. Note that the magnetic and electric fields are everywhere at right angles to each other, and that the Poynting vector, $\mathbf{S} = \mathbf{E} \times \mathbf{H}$ is everywhere in Fig. 1.2.1. away from the reader into the page, or from the battery toward the load. The numerical integration of the Poynting vector, $\int \mathbf{S} \cdot d\mathbf{A}$, over the entire plane is numerically equal to the power supplied by the battery to the load. The computation will not be attempted here, but the simpler case of a coaxial cable is given as a problem at the end of the chapter.

Traveling Waves in Cables

The movement of waves along a cable is very similar to the movement of electromagnetic energy in space. Let us now consider a two-conductor cable having some arbitrary length, one end being connected to a source of alternating emf. To begin with, we shall assume that the cable is so terminated at the far end that the energy delivered by the generator travels to the termination and is there absorbed, so that there is no reflection of energy from that end. Such a termination is usually realized by a pure resistance of appropriate value, the so-called characteristic resistance. (For further details see footnote 4.) Termination by the characteristic resistance has the same effect on the cable as if it were continued to infinity. In this case, illustrated in Fig. 1.2.2 (a), the current and voltage, or the current and voltage waves, are in phase with each other, and the energy delivered by the generator is always positive. In general, the phase relation between the current and voltage waves will depend on the impedance[4] of the cable and its termination, and there may be reflected energy coming back to the generator for part of a cycle, as illustrated in Fig. 1.2.2 (b).

A wave traveling along a two-wire cable terminated by a characteristic

[4] The impedance Z of a current is understood to be the ratio of the voltage amplitude to the current amplitude

$$Z = \frac{V_0}{I_0}.$$

It is measured in ohms. For example, the impedance of a series circuit containing the resistance R, inductance L, and capacitance C, for an angular frequency ω, is

$$Z = \sqrt{R^2 + \left(\omega L - \frac{1}{\omega C}\right)^2}.$$

The characteristic impedance Z of a cable is equal to the ratio of the voltage to the current in a traveling wave and is given by $Z = (L'/C')^{1/2}$, where L' and C' are the inductance and capacitance per unit length of the cable, respectively. This ratio is not only a function of the electromagnetic properties of the insulating medium but also depends on the shape of the conductors in the cable.

As stated earlier, if a cable is terminated by the characteristic resistance, all of the energy moving from a source towards this termination is absorbed there, and none of it is reflected. The value of the characteristic resistance is equal to the characteristic impedance of the cable.

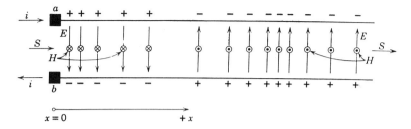

Fig. 1.2.3   A traveling wave in a cable.

resistance is schematically shown in Fig. 1.2.3. At the instant shown the terminal a is positive with respect to terminal b, the generator is doing work, a current is flowing out of the positive terminal a and into the negative terminal b. A wave of positive charge is moving down the upper cable and a wave of negative charge is moving up the lower cable with a velocity which we shall not compute. Associated with the moving charge is a current, equal to the charge per unit length times its velocity, which will have maxima where the charge density is greatest. There will therefore be a periodic electric field and a periodic magnetic field surrounding the cable. These two fields will be in phase with each other, as will also the voltage and current waves that move along the cable.

Cables in general may be called waveguides in the sense that they guide the flow of electromagnetic energy carried by the fields in their vicinity. The term waveguide is often reserved for a cable consisting of single tubular conductor, having a circular or rectangular cross section. In such a waveguide currents are set up not only along the axis of the guide but also with transverse components, as shown in Fig. 1.2.4. The Poynting vector will therefore in general be at an angle to the axis of the guide, and the electromagnetic energy may be thought of as bouncing to and fro as it moves down the guide as schematically shown in Fig. 1.2.5.

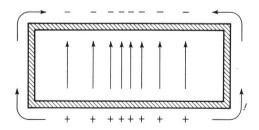

Fig. 1.2.4   Cross section of a rectangular waveguide showing transverse components of the current.

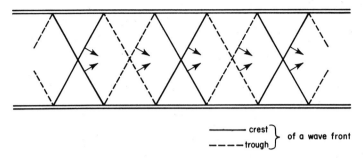

━━━ crest ⎫
 ─ ─ ─ trough ⎭ of a wave front

Fig. 1.2.5 Schematic representation of the flow of energy in a rectangular wave-guide as illustrated in Fig. 1.2.4. Note that the waves change phase on reflection. The arrows indicate the direction of propagation.

Standing Waves; Reflection

Standing waves are formed by the superposition of waves traveling in opposite directions. A wave traveling to the right, or in the direction of increasing x, may be written

$$V_{\text{right}} = V_0 \sin \frac{2\pi}{\lambda} (x - vt)$$

$$i_{\text{right}} = I_0 \sin \frac{2\pi}{\lambda} (x - vt).$$

(1.2.1)

A voltage wave having the same amplitude and frequency but traveling to the left would be

$$V_{\text{left}} = V_0 \sin \frac{2\pi}{\lambda} (x + vt). \tag{1.2.2}$$

The current wave traveling to the left would be in phase with the corresponding voltage wave, but if we agree to designate positive charges moving to the right in the upper cable of Fig. 1.2.3, for example, as positive currents, then for our current wave traveling to the left in phase with the voltage we must put

$$i_{\text{left}} = -I_0 \sin \frac{2\pi}{\lambda} (x + vt). \tag{1.2.3}$$

In adding the above expressions we make use of the trigonometric relations

$$\sin(a - b) + \sin(a + b) = 2 \sin a \cos b$$
$$\sin(a - b) - \sin(a + b) = -2 \cos a \sin b.$$

We then have the voltage and current along the cable when the two waves are present

$$V = 2V_0 \sin \frac{2\pi x}{\lambda} \cos 2\pi \nu t \qquad (1.2.4)$$

$$i = 2I_0 \cos \frac{2\pi x}{\lambda} \sin 2\pi \nu t. \qquad (1.2.5)$$

These standing waves are shown in Fig. 1.2.6. The time dependence is here such that, for $t = 0$, the voltage is a sine function of x, and the current is at this time everywhere zero, as shown by the heavy lines in Fig. 1.2.6(a) and (b). At this instant $t = 0$ there will be a charge distribution along the cable like that schematically shown in Fig. 1.2.6(c). The charges are at rest, and the currents are therefore everywhere zero. If we vary the time we find that the charges and currents are varying periodically along the cable with a frequency $\nu = v/\lambda$. The period of this oscillation is $\tau = 1/\nu$. Let us examine the condition of the cable a quarter of a cycle later, when $t = \tau/4 = 1/4\nu$. The voltage is now everywhere zero, because $\cos 2\pi\nu \cdot 1/4\nu = \cos \pi/2 = 0$. The current is now a negative cosine function, as shown in Fig. 1.2.6(b). The charge distribution along the cable has disappeared and has been replaced by a current distribution, shown in Fig. 1.2.6(d). Adjacent plus and minus charges move toward each other, producing maxima and minima in the current halfway between the previous charge maxima and minima. Another quarter of a cycle later, or for $t = \tau/2$, the currents have disappeared, and the charge maxima are reversed in sign from those initially on the cable.

The standing wave continues the above cyclic changes. Energy moves to and fro along the cable, but there is no net transport in any one direction. When the currents vanish, as at $t = 0$, the energy is located in the electric fields produced by the charge distribution of Fig. 1.2.6(c). A quarter of a cycle later the electric field is everywhere zero, but there are magnetic fields surrounding the currents a quarter of a wavelength from the electric field maxima. At the location of the nodes of V and i the Poynting vectors are always zero, since $\mathbf{S} = \mathbf{E} \times \mathbf{H}$. They have periodic maxima between the electric and magnetic field maxima and change their direction periodically.

The standing waves we have been describing are formed in an arbitrarily long cable in which waves of equal frequency and equal amplitude pass each other in opposite directions. Notice that, at $x = 0$, and at corresponding points along the cable a half wavelength apart, the voltage between the conductors is always zero. Notice also that at other points a half wavelength apart, such as A in Fig. 1.2.6, the current along the wire is zero at all times.

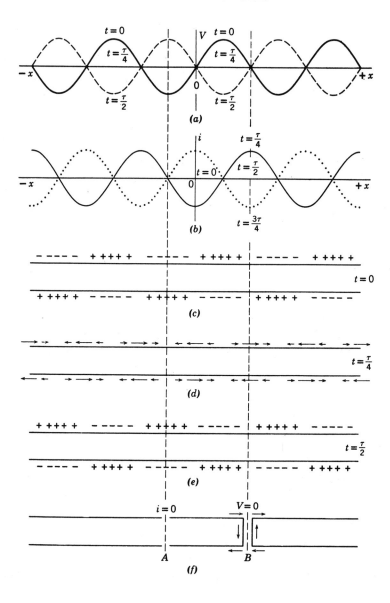

Fig. 1.2.6 A standing wave in a parallel-conductor cable. (*a*) Voltage distribution at the times $t = 0$, $\tau/4$, and $\tau/2$. (*b*) Current distribution at the times $t = 0$, $\tau/4$, $\tau/2$, and $3\tau/4$. (*c*) Charge distribution at the time $t = 0$. (*d*) Charge flow at the time $t = \tau/4$. Note that at this time positive and negative charges are evenly distributed. (*e*) Charge distribution at the time $t = \tau/2$. (*f*) Cutting the cable at A or cutting and short-circuiting the ends at B.

If at point A the cable is cut and the end of the right section is held close to the end of the left section, as shown in the Fig. 1.2.6(f), the current and charge distribution will not be affected. If the ends of the cable are pulled apart, it is true that the electric fields near the cut will be deformed, but, if the separation between the conductors is small compared to the wavelength, the alteration will not be important. We must think of the wave incident from the left as being reflected at the break, and the sum of the incident and reflected waves may be thought of as responsible for the standing wave pattern. Similarly, the right-hand side of the cable will have a traveling wave incident from the right and a reflected wave moving toward the right. The sum of these two will give rise to the standing waves in this half of the cable.

Similarly, if at B we short-circuit the two conductors and pull the two junctions apart as in Fig. 1.2.6(f), the voltage between the conductors will be zero and the currents which originally flowed longitudinally from one

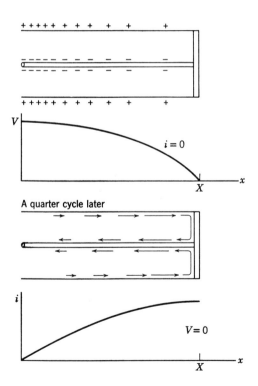

Fig. 1.2.7   Cross section of a coaxial cable shorted at one end oscillating at the lowest possible frequency.

part of the cable to the other now flow across from one conductor to the other.

In Fig. 1.2.6(f), the central section of cable open-circuited at one end and short-circuited at the other has a length $3\lambda/4$. It is easy to generalize this result. A system of standing waves may be maintained in a cable whose length is x and which has one end short-circuited and one end open-circuited provided $x = (\lambda/4) + (n\lambda/2)$, where n is any positive integer or zero. Similarly, a system of standing waves may be maintained in a cable whose length is x and which has either a short circuit at both ends or an open circuit at both ends, provided $x = n\lambda/2$, where n is any positive integer.

These results are precisely equivalent to corresponding results obtained for the natural frequencies of organ pipes. If x is put equal to the length of the organ pipe and $\lambda = v/\nu$, then the above equations give the natural frequencies. The fundamental mode for a cable open-circuited at one end and short-circuited at the other is shown in Fig. 1.2.7.

Partial Reflection

The foregoing discussion of standing waves and the following discussion of partial reflection are here given in some detail because they form an ideal introduction to corresponding situations involving waves of other frequencies, especially visible light, as we shall see further on, at an interface between two transparent media. It also serves to emphasize the great generality of electromagnetic theory. Furthermore, a number of the same concepts is also of importance in wave mechanics.

We have seen that a wave in a cable will be reflected at an open-circuited or a short-circuited terminal. An interesting extension of the ideas leading to this result is to consider what happens when a wave strikes the junction between two cables having differing characteristic impedances.* That is an important consideration in circuits involving interconnected cables and other pieces of apparatus.

Let us consider a junction at $x = 0$, in a cable having a characteristic impedance Z_1 for negative values of X, and Z_2 for positive values of x. A wave incident from the left may be partly reflected and partly transmitted. We shall determine the fraction of the incident energy that is reflected.

Let us assume that the amplitudes of the incident voltage and current waves are V_i and I_i and that the amplitudes of the transmitted voltage and current waves are V_t and

---

* See footnote 4 on p. 10.

I_t. These two waves may be written

$$V_i \sin \frac{2\pi}{\lambda} (x - vt), \qquad I_i \sin \frac{2\pi}{\lambda} (x - vt)$$

$$V_t \sin \frac{2\pi}{\lambda} (x - vt), \qquad I_t \sin \frac{2\pi}{\lambda} (x - vt).$$

Similarly for the reflected wave moving to the left, we should have

$$V_r \sin \frac{2\pi}{\lambda} (x + vt), \qquad -I_r \sin \frac{2\pi}{\lambda} (x + vt).$$

The minus sign in the above expression for the reflected current was discussed in connection with Eq. 1.2.3. We wish to examine the conditions at the junction, where $x = 0$. It is necessary that the voltages across the cable just to the left of the junction be equal to that just to the right of the junction, or that

$$V_i \sin \frac{2\pi}{\lambda} (0 - vt) + V_r \sin \frac{2\pi}{\lambda} (0 + vt) = V_t \sin \frac{2\pi}{\lambda} (0 - vt).$$

But since $\sin(-x) = -\sin x$, the above expression may be reduced to

$$- V_i + V_r = - V_t. \tag{1.2.6}$$

Similarly the currents into and out of the junction are equal, or

$$I_i \sin \frac{2\pi}{\lambda} (0 - vt) - I_r \sin \frac{2\pi}{\lambda} (0 + vt) = I_t \sin \frac{2\pi}{\lambda} (0 - vt)$$

or, after simplifying as above,

$$-I_i - I_r = -I_t. \tag{1.2.7}$$

In addition the voltages and currents in the two cables are related by the characteristic impedances,

$$V_i = I_i Z_1, \qquad V_r = I_r Z_1, \qquad V_t = I_t Z_2.$$

Substituting these expressions into Eq. 1.2.6 and rewriting Eq. 1.2.7 with plus signs, we have for the conditions to be met

$$-I_i Z_1 + I_r Z_1 = -I_t Z_2$$

$$I_i + I_r = I_t.$$

Dividing the first of these equations by Z_2, and adding this to the second, we get

$$I_i \left(1 - \frac{Z_1}{Z_2}\right) + I_r \left(1 + \frac{Z_1}{Z_2}\right) = 0,$$

or

$$I_r = \frac{Z_1 - Z_2}{Z_1 + Z_2} I_i. \tag{1.2.8}$$

In this equation I_r and I_i are amplitudes and must necessarily be positive. Our discussision therefore applies only if $Z_2 < Z_1$. A review of the assumptions we have made shows that the selection of sine rather than cosine functions requires justification. If, for example, we make Z_2 very small compared to Z_1, we have conditions approaching those to be expected at a short-circuited termination with regard to reflection properties. There will be a voltage node at the junction. We must also consider reflections when there are current nodes at the junction. It turns out that if we had written all our traveling waves as cosine functions, as is perfectly permissible, we should have found

$$I_r = \frac{Z_2 - Z_1}{Z_2 + Z_1} I_i \qquad (1.2.9)$$

which is applicable if $Z_2 > Z_1$. In this case if Z_2 is much greater than Z_1, we approach the condition of reflection at an open-circuited termination, with a current node.

In calculating the reflection coefficient R, or the ratio of the reflected to the incident power, we have, since in both traveling waves current and voltage are in phase,

$$R = \frac{I_r V_r}{I_i V_i} = \frac{I_r^2 Z_1}{I_i^2 Z_1} = \left(\frac{I_r}{I_i}\right)^2 = \left(\frac{Z_1 - Z_2}{Z_1 + Z_2}\right)^2. \qquad (1.2.10)$$

The reflection coefficient for a light wave normally incident at the interface between two dielectrics will be discussed further on. Its similarity to the above is emphasized if we replace the expressions for the characteristic impedance by the corresponding expressions for the properties of the dielectrics. The characteristic impedance of a coaxial cable is $Z = (L'/C')^{1/2}$, where the inductance and capacitance per unit length are

$$L' = \frac{\mu}{2\pi} \ln \frac{r_2}{r_1} \qquad (1.2.11)$$

$$C'' = \frac{2\pi\epsilon}{\ln r_2/r_1}. \qquad (1.2.12)$$

If the cables have the same dimensions and contain dielectrics having the permeability μ_0 and the permittivities $\epsilon_1 = K_{e1} \epsilon_0$ and $\epsilon_2 = K_{e2} \epsilon_0$, respectively, the substitution of Eqs. 1.2.11 and 1.2.12 into Eq. 1.1.10 results in the expression

$$R = \left(\frac{\sqrt{K_{e2}} - \sqrt{K_{e1}}}{\sqrt{K_{e2}} + \sqrt{K_{e1}}}\right)^2 \qquad (1.2.13)$$

to which we shall return in Section 2.2.

1.3   THE RADIATION OF WAVES INTO SPACE

We shall now consider qualitatively how energy can detach itself from the moving charges in conductors. A simple form of radiator is the dipole antenna shown in Fig. 1.3.1. It consists of two oppositely directed straight wires or bars connected to a high-frequency generator. These bars are given equal and opposite charges, and thus an electric field is created in their vicinity. The sign of the charge on either side of the antenna is periodically reversed. The charging and discharging of the antenna is brought about by currents which produce magnetic fields in the vicinity of the antenna.

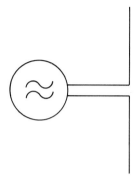

Fig. 1.3.1   A dipole antenna connected to a high-frequency generator.

We must follow the charging and discharging process in some detail. The fields around the antenna will be similar to those of a positive and negative charge performing linear oscillations around a common center. These fields are sketched in Fig. 1.3.2. Part a of this figure shows the initial state of the system in which the two charges are slightly separated and moving apart, the positive charge toward the top of the figure and the negative charge toward the bottom. The electric lines of force go from the positive to the negative charge. The magnetic lines of flux will be in the form of circles around the current. The cross section of a few lines of flux around the current is shown to indicate the presence of the magnetic field. The Poynting vector is directed outward. In b the charges have reached their maximum separation and have come to rest. As the charges come to rest, the magnetic field decreases and the Poynting vector near the charges vanishes. When the charges approach each other again, the magnetic field near the charges is reversed and the Poynting vector is directed inward. This sequence of events near the charges is shown in b and c. However, at the instant portrayed in b at which the charges are at rest, the magnetic field through all space cannot vanish instantly. It is because of the finite velocity of propagation in space of electromagnetic energy, just as we have already found in cables, that at distant points the magnetic field does not vanish until some later time. As a result these peripheral fields continue to move outward during b and c. Finally, the position of the charges is reversed, as in d, the nearby electric fields are reversed, and the Poynting vector is again directed outward everywhere. However, the electric lines of force, if they had remained unbroken, would have formed a loop and crossed each other, as indicated by the dotted lines. At the crossover point, however, the loop breaks away, and the electric lines of force in the loop close on themselves. This closed loop now moves out and forms the basis of the *radiation field*. The electric and magnetic fields in the radiation pattern are

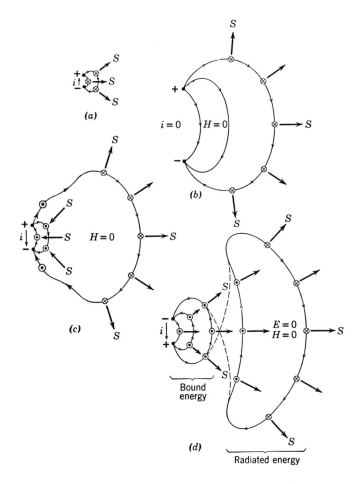

Fig. 1.3.2 The fields in the neighborhood of a radiating dipole. The lines of force have been drawn on one side of the dipole only.

schematically shown in Fig. 1.3.3. Note that, in the radiation field, the electric and magnetic fields are in phase with each other and the Poynting vector is everywhere directed outward, describing the radiation of energy away from the dipole. Near the dipole, on the other hand, the electric and magnetic fields have predominantly out-of-phase components, and most of the energy in the nearby bound fields pulsates to and fro.

This tendency for the energy in the field of an oscillating dipole to move in and out near the dipole can lead us to another conclusion. If we move the charge in Fig. 1.3.2 infinitely slowly, all the energy in the field when the charges are separated can be regained and none is radiated. (The same would happen if the speed of electromagnetic waves were infinite.) The faster we reverse the polarity of the dipole, the greater will be the tendency to form loops in the field, and consequently also the greater the tendency to radiate rather than reabsorb the energy in the field. For a dipole of this sort in which a total charge Q is oscillated through a distance x_0, the amplitude of the dipole moment is Qx_0. The total radiated energy is proportional to the fourth power of the frequency. This is easily understandable because the emitted energy is proportional to $\mathbf{S} = \mathbf{E} \times \mathbf{H}$. On the other hand, both $\mathbf{E}$ and $\mathbf{H}$ are proportional to the acceleration $\ddot{x}$ of the electric charges in the dipole, and consequently $\mathbf{S}$ must be proportional to the square of $\ddot{x}$. (In the radiation field $\mathbf{E}$ and $\mathbf{H}$ cannot be functions of the velocity $\dot{x}$ of the charge because according to the Special Theory of Relativity the choice of a particular frame of reference which moves with constant velocity cannot influence the result. It is well known that a stationary charge does not radiate energy; hence, a charge moving with constant velocity will not radiate either, because we can move a coordinate system together with this charge, such that this charge is a stationary one.) The acceleration $\ddot{x}$ of the oscillating charge is, according to the theory of simple harmonic motion,

$$\ddot{x} = -x_0\omega^2 \sin \omega t,$$

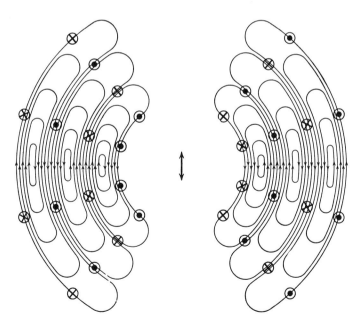

Fig. 1.3.3   The electric and magnetic fields in the radiation from an oscillating electric dipole.

that is proportional to the square of the frequency ω. Therefore the total radiated energy is proportional to ω^4. This energy flow is not uniformly distributed but has a maximum in the equatorial plane of the dipole. There is no radiation along the axis of the dipole. The polar diagram in Fig. 1.3.4 shows the energy emitted into a certain direction as a function of the angle α between that direction and the direction perpendicular to the dipole. The length of the vector represents the strength of the emitted radiation in that direction. Obviously, there is rotational symmetry about the axis formed by the dipole. The total energy radiated by an oscillating dipole per second, or the rate of emitted energy in watts, W_r, may be shown to be

$$W_r = \frac{\omega^4(Qx_0)^2}{12\pi\epsilon_0 c^3} \qquad (1.3.1)$$

where $\omega = 2\pi\nu$. For such an oscillating charge, the current amplitude will be $I_0 = Q\omega$, and the radiated power in terms of this current amplitude then may be written in the form

$$W_r = \frac{\pi}{3}\sqrt{\frac{\mu_0}{\epsilon_0}}\left(\frac{x_0}{\lambda}\right)^2 I_0^2. \qquad (1.3.2)$$

In the radiation field the amplitude of the electric and magnetic fields decreases as r^{-1}, and the Poynting vector as r^{-2}. Considering in Fig. 1.3.5 the areas A_1 and A_2 which are bounded by the walls of a cone and which are perpendicular to its axis, we see that the ratio of these areas is proportional to the square of the distance from the tip of the cone,

$$A_1{:}A_2 = r_1^2{:}r_2^2.$$

If an emitter of electromagnetic energy is located at the tip of the cone and its dimensions are negligible, the same amount of energy must flow

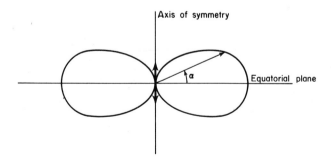

Fig. 1.3.4   Polar diagram showing the dependence of the radiated energy of a dipole antenna on the azimuthal direction.

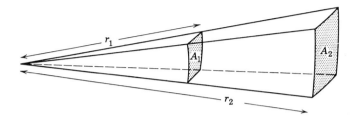

Fig. 1.3.5   A cone of radiated energy emerging from a point source.

through A_1 and A_2 since the radiated energy travels radially outward in straight lines. The Poynting vector must hence show a $1/r^2$ dependence. Apart from this, the propagation is described by Eqs. 1.1.8 to 1.1.10. As an interesting sidelight it might be mentioned here that in the emission of light by atoms and in that of γ rays by nuclei—both being electromagnetic radiation—a related situation exists. The rate at which energy is expended increases here also rapidly with the frequency of the emitted radiation.

The Interference of Electromagnetic Waves

We now propose to investigate the effects obtained when several antennas, simultaneously driven by a common oscillator, radiate. If the antennas are vertical, they radiate equally in all horizontal directions. The effect of the earth is simply to cut the waves in Fig. 1.3.2 in half, as shown in Fig. 1.3.6.

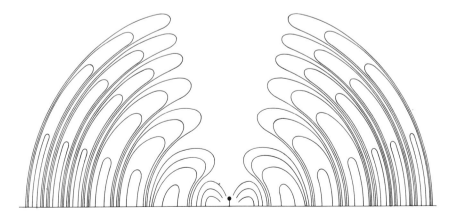

Fig. 1.3.6   "Snapshot" of the electric field lines of a radiating dipole.

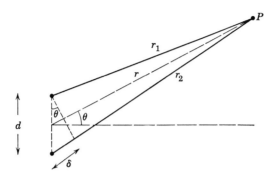

Fig. 1.3.7   Radiation from two antennas.

The earth below the surface is a sufficiently good conductor so that appropriate charges appear where the electric lines of force are terminated. These charges then move out with the wave. For points above the earth, however, the situation may be more complex, due to the presence of reflecting layers at high altitudes. We shall here neglect such effects.

Now, let us consider the interference of two beams from vertical antennas a distance d apart, and oscillating in phase with each other, shown in Fig. 1.3.7. Remember that electric and magnetic fields are vectorially additive. This holds for changing fields as well as static fields. The intensity of the radiation at P consequently depends on the resultant amplitude of the radiations from the two antennas. This resultant amplitude can range from twice the amplitude of the radiation from either one alone to zero, depending on the phase relation between the two. Furthermore, the resultant amplitude depends on the difference in the distance traveled by the two waves from the antenna to P. It is easy to see that, if the two antennas are synchronized, and if the path distances to P are equal, the radiations will be in phase at P. Furthermore, if the difference in path lengths r_1 and r_2 is some integral number of wavelengths, the two waves will likewise be in phase at P. If, on the other hand, the difference in path lengths is some integral number of wavelengths plus a half wavelength, the radiations will be out of phase and will produce what is called destructive interference. The waves cancel each other, and no energy will be received at P.

The conditions for constructive or destructive interference are easily established. Let us assume that the point P in Fig. 1.3.7 is far from the antennas compared to their separation, so that the two paths r_1 and r_2 are almost parallel. The path difference between the two rays is $\delta = d \sin \theta$. For a maximum at P, or for constructive interference, we must have

$$r_2 - r_1 = \delta = d \sin \theta = n\lambda \qquad n = 0, 1, 2, 3 \qquad (1.3.3)$$

and for a minimum at P, or for destructive interference, we must have

$$r_2 - r_1 = \delta = d \sin \theta = (n + \tfrac{1}{2})\lambda \qquad n = 0, 1, 2, 3, \ldots . \quad (1.3.4)$$

The intensity for any angle θ may be computed through writing for the resultant electric field at a point P

$$E_P = E_1 + E_2 = \frac{C}{r_1} \sin \frac{2\pi}{\lambda} (r_1 - ct) + \frac{C}{r_2} \sin \frac{2\pi}{\lambda} (r_2 - ct). \quad (1.3.5)$$

The same proportionality constant C is used for both beams on the assumption that the two antennas are identical and are driven not only in phase with each other but with the same amplitude. Since we limit our considerations to points far from the antennas compared to their separation, r_1 and r_2 are very nearly equal in length, the beams are traveling in essentially the same directions, the electric fields will be colinear, and their amplitudes will be equal. The same holds for the magnetic fields. We may then write

$$E_P = \frac{C}{r} \left(\sin \frac{2\pi}{\lambda} (r_1 - ct) + \sin \frac{2\pi}{\lambda} (r_2 - ct) \right). \quad (1.3.6)$$

We may not, however, make a similar simplification for the remaining expression involving r_1 and r_2, as will be clear from the following. From Fig. 1.3.7 we see that we may write

$$r_2 - r_1 = \delta$$

$$r - r_1 = \delta/2$$

$$r_2 - r = \delta/2$$

and consequently Eq. 1.3.6 may be put into the form

$$E_P = \frac{C}{r} \left[\sin \left(\frac{2\pi}{\lambda} (r - ct) + \frac{2\pi\delta}{2\lambda} \right) + \sin \left(\frac{2\pi}{\lambda} (r - ct) - \frac{2\pi\delta}{2\lambda} \right) \right].$$

But since

$$\sin(a + b) + \sin(a - b) = 2 \sin a \cos b,$$

we have

$$E_P = \left(2 \frac{C}{r} \cos \frac{\pi\delta}{\lambda} \right) \sin \frac{2\pi}{\lambda} (r - ct).$$

The amplitude of the electric field at the point P is

$$2 \frac{C}{r} \cos \frac{\pi\delta}{\lambda} \qquad\qquad (1.3.7)$$

and the intensity of the radiation, which is given by the Poynting vector, is proportional to the square of Eq. 1.3.7. We emphasize that it is the square of the amplitude and not the amplitude which is proportional to the intensity. By amplitude we may understand that of **E** or of **H**, since they are proportional to each other. Evidently the product of **E** and **H** is also proportional to the intensity. Quite generally intensities in waves are proportional to the square of the amplitude. We might mention here that in elastic waves (e.g., sound waves) similarly the square of the amplitude is proportional to the intensity.

If we call I_1 the intensity at P due to either antenna operated alone, we get

$$I = I_1 \cdot 4 \cos^2 \frac{\pi \delta}{\lambda}. \tag{1.3.8}$$

But from Fig. 1.3.7 we see that $\delta/d = \sin \theta$, so that the desired expression for the intensity of the beam of the two radiating antennas becomes

$$I = 4I_1 \cos^2 \left(\frac{\pi d}{\lambda} \sin \theta \right). \tag{1.3.9}$$

As before, we note that maxima are to be expected when $\sin \theta = n\lambda/d$, and that minima are to be expected when $\sin \theta = (n + \frac{1}{2})(\lambda/d)$. The distance r from the antennas determines the magnitude of I_1. The angular dependence is very different for antennas having various separations. Plots of I/I_1 as a function of θ are shown in Fig. 1.3.8 for separations of the antennas of a half wavelength, and of a full wavelength. The length of the dashed line drawn at an angle θ from the source to the curve is proportional to the intensity I of the radiation in this direction.

The correctness of these predictions concerning the interference of

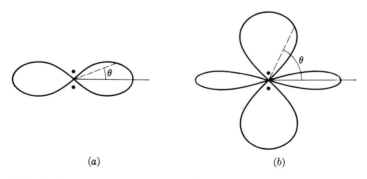

(a)   (b)

Fig. 1.3.8   Radiation pattern of two vertical antennas in phase with each other, with a separation of (a) a half-wavelength, and (b) a full wavelength.

beams, and concerning the velocity of propagation of electromagnetic energy, constitutes a major support of the classical theory of electromagnetic radiation.

We shall return to the subject of interference in more detail in Chapter 2.

1.4 THE SPEED OF LIGHT

The remainder of this chapter is devoted to those aspects of the special theory of relativity which have some bearing on the propagation of electromagnetic energy in space. Readers who are familiar with the special theory of relativity may therefore skip the rest of the chapter or at least parts hereof. For the others it should serve as a short introduction to this subject in conjunction with Appendix II. There the Lorentz transformations and the mass-energy relationship are derived, both being of considerable importance in nuclear and particle physics.

The actual measurement of the speed of light is a fascinating subject on which we shall dwell only briefly. When Galileo Galilei (1564–1642) set out to measure it, he was not the first who had considered the problem. For centuries before Christ philosophers had wondered whether or not light signals were transmitted instantaneously. The question could be answered only by speculation. It is true that Galileo must have known, as was pointed out centuries earlier by Pliny (A.D. 23–79), that the velocity of light was greater than the velocity of sound, even that it was much greater. This might have been established by measuring the speed of sound by timing echoes from distant objects, and noticing that the time elapsed between the arrival of light and sound signals from a distant noise-producing visible event was, within observable limits, the time required for the sound wave to travel the distance. But still, if one used considerable distances like a mile, the time required for sound to travel to a reflector and back would be 10,000 ft/1,000 ft/sec or 10 seconds, which is a long time even in terms of human reaction times. Could the time elapsed by a light beam in traveling from an observer to a distant mountain and back be measured? It was certainly worth trying, even though we now know that the measurement was not possible. The time required for light, moving with a speed $c = 3 \times 10^8$ m/sec, to travel three kilometers is $(3 \times 10^3 \text{ m})/(3 \times 10^8 \text{ m/sec})$, or 10^{-5} sec, which is too short for an eye to detect.

Since such short times could not be measured, it was by changing the scale of the experiment from miles to interplanetary distances that the time of travel could be made practically observable. Two years after Galileo's death Olaus Roemer,* a Danish astronomer, was born who, at

---

* Olaus (or Olaf) Roemer (1644–1710), professor of mathematics and astronomy in Copenhagen. Inventor of a number of astronomical instruments.

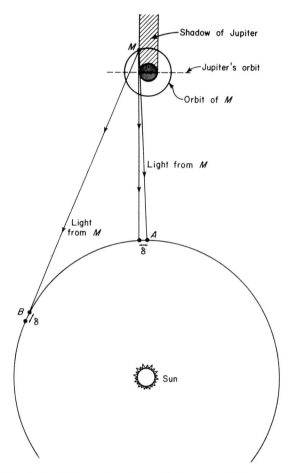

Fig. 1.4.1   The basis of Roemer's estimate of the speed of light.

the age of 32, in Paris in 1676 made the first reliable estimate of the speed of light. The nature of his method is illustrated in Fig. 1.4.1. One of Jupiter's moons here under consideration is designated to have a period τ. Its position in its orbit can be fixed by its emergence from Jupiter's shadow, as at M. During this time τ the earth moves a distance δ. When the earth is moving at right angles to the light beam from Jupiter, the observed period of M will be τ, since the delay in observing successive eclipses is the same for each. When, however, the earth is moving away from or toward Jupiter, as at B, Roemer observed that the time elapsed during successive eclipses is increased or decreased by δ/c. Measuring these apparent differences over a long span of time, he concluded that it took light 22 min. to cross the earth's orbit. Since the distance from the earth to the sun had been measured a few years before to be close to 1.4×10^8 km (the actual value is close to 1.5×10^8 km), and 22 min. $= 1.3 \times 10^3$ sec, the speed of light as measured by him is 2.8×10^{11} m$/1.3 \times 10^3$ sec $= 2.1 \times 10^8$ m/sec. However, Roemer's finding was not readily accepted by his colleagues, and only the discovery of the aberration of light in 1728, discussed in Sect. 1.7, changed their attitude.

The evolution of our knowledge of the value of c to its presently most precise determination at the National Bureau of Standards, Boulder, Colorado, by K. M. Evenson et al. [*Phys. Rev. Letters* **29**, 1346 (1972)],

$$c = 299,792,456.2 \pm 1.1 \text{ m/sec},$$

with even diminishing uncertainty in the last figure, is a long and intricate story. It involves not only improved technology in the measurement of distances of the order of meters, kilometers, orbits of satellites, and interplanetary distances, and times of more or less arbitrary duration with uncertainties of the order of nanoseconds, but also the measurement of completely different quantities. As we shall see in later discussions of relativistic phenomena, c is not only the speed of light, but also a universal constant. It is not only an essential part of electromagnetic theory, but also of the kinematics and dynamics of particles. Consequently it frequently appears as one of several theoretically interrelated constants that can be observed in a variety of combinations. If one requires internal consistency of all observations, a new approach to the determination of observational reliability is established. A reference leading to the considerable literature on this subject is B. N. Taylor, W. H. Parker, and D. N. Langenberg [*Rev. Mod. Phys.* **41**, 375 (1969)].

1.5 THE MICHELSON–MORLEY EXPERIMENT

Before 1887, when Michelson and Morley performed the experiment described below, there was one unsatisfactory aspect to Maxwell's prediction regarding the velocity of electromagnetic waves, particularly light waves, in space, namely: With respect to what coordinate system is the velocity to be measured? It was assumed that since other kinds of waves, like ripples on a pond, or sound waves, travel in a specified medium, such as water or air, for instance, this would presumably be true of light waves also. This medium was called the ether, and it became a challenge to measure experimentally what our motion on earth through the ether might be. Until this was done, no precise measurement involving light could be interpreted satisfactorily. As physicist with the U.S. Navy, Albert A.

Albert A. Michelson (1852–1931) with one of his interferometers (Courtesy of Niels Bohr Library, American Institute of Physics).

Michelson (1852–1931) earlier had measured the velocity of light. On a study leave in Europe he performed in Germany his very first, but not really conclusive, interferometer experiment for the detection of the motion of the earth through the ether. Later, at what is now the Case Western Reserve University in Cleveland, he teamed up with Edward W. Morley (1838–1923), a professor of chemistry, to do this famous experiment. In 1907 Michelson received the Nobel prize in physics.

The idea of the experiment is simplicity itself. If waves are moving across a pond in some direction, say along the $+x$ axis of a rectangular coordinate system, with a speed v over the surface of the water, then if an observer is in a motorboat moving in this same direction with a speed V, he will observe the waves going by him with a speed $v - V$. If he is heading into the waves, they will be going by him with a speed $v + V$. In mathematical language, the coordinates x, y, z with respect to the shore are transformed into the parallel coordinates on the boat x', y', z' by the relations

$$x' = x - Vt$$
$$y' = y \qquad\qquad\qquad (1.5.1)$$
$$z' = z$$
$$t' = t.$$

The last equation says that the times in both coordinate systems are identical. This is called a *Galilean transformation*. By differentiation we get for the speeds $dx/dt = v_x$, $dx'/dt' = v_x'$

$$v_x' = v_x - V \qquad v_x = v_x' + V$$
$$v_y' = v_y \qquad\qquad v_y = v_y' \qquad\qquad (1.5.2)$$
$$v_z' = v_z \qquad\qquad v_z = v_z'.$$

In terms of an experiment with light, v_x might be the speed of light with respect to the ether, v_x' the speed with respect to the earth, and V, the speed of the earth with respect to the ether. As a first assumption, it was supposed that the ether might be at rest with respect to the stars, or the sun. The speed of the earth in its orbit is about 30,000 m/sec, while the speed of light is about 3×10^8 m/sec, so that $V/c \sim 10^{-4}$.

As we have seen, the speed of light, because of its great value, is best measured on a "come and go" basis, for example as in a toothed wheel experiment, in which light travels a certain distance L to a mirror, and back, and this time $2L/c$ is related to the time it takes a toothed wheel to move from one transmitting aperture to the next. If the direction of motion of light is placed parallel to the direction of motion of the earth, we should have for a round trip as in Fig. 1.5.1 (a)

$$\Delta t_{||} = \frac{L}{c - V} + \frac{L}{c + V} = \frac{2L}{c} \frac{1}{1 - V^2/c^2}$$

$$\simeq \frac{2L}{c} \left(1 + \frac{V^2}{c^2} + \cdots \right). \qquad (1.5.3)$$

For the case of motion at right angles to the length of the optical path we should have, in accordance with Fig. 1.5.1 (b),

$$\Delta t_\perp = \frac{2L}{c} \left(\frac{1}{[1 - V^2/c^2]^{1/2}} \right)$$

$$\simeq \frac{2L}{c} \left[1 + \frac{1}{2} \left(\frac{V^2}{c^2} \right) + \cdots \right]. \qquad (1.5.4)$$

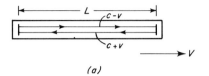

(a)

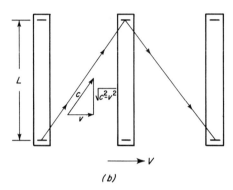

(b)

Fig. 1.5.1   The motion of light parallel or perpendicular to a path of length L.

The difference in elapsed time in the two cases is

$$\Delta t_{||} - \Delta t_{\perp} = \frac{L}{c} \frac{V^2}{c^2}.$$

For example, if $L = 15$ m, $c = 3 \times 10^8$ m/sec, $V/c = 10^{-4}$, the time difference is 0.5×10^{-15} sec. Notice that yellow light, $\lambda = 6 \times 10^{-7}$ m, has a period $\lambda/c = 2 \times 10^{-15}$ sec, so that the time difference to be measured corresponds to a quarter period.

Michelson had developed an interferometer, to be discussed further in Section 2.2, well suited to measuring "ether drift." Its essentials are shown in Fig. 1.5.2. Light is split by a half-silvered mirror M so that half of it travels along path A, half along B, to mirrors that reflect the two beams to be recombined by M to form the emergent beam C. Because of slight divergence or convergence of the beam along A and B, there will be slight differences of path length to adjacent points on M, and the emergent beam will show light and dark bands across M depending on whether the path lengths A and B differ by an even or odd number of half wavelengths. The situation is analogous to the interferences of radio beams discussed at the end of Section 1.3.

Suppose now that in some given orientation in the laboratory in which the ether drift is parallel to A there is some particular interference pattern in the beam C. If now the whole apparatus is rotated so that the ether drift is parallel to B, the pattern should have shifted so that bright zones and dark zones are interchanged, since Δt in A would have been increased and Δt in B would have been decreased by a half period.

Michelson and Morley performed an experiment along these lines in 1887 and obtained a null result. The experiment has been repeated by many observers at different times and places, always with the same result. The observed velocity of light is the same in all directions on earth regardless of the motion of the earth.

Table 1.5.1, taken from an analysis by R. S. Shankland et al.[5] on earlier measurements, summarizes experimental results of the Michelson–Morley experiment. There is always an observed fringe shift in any observation because it is impossible to hold experimental conditions absolutely constant during the rotation of the apparatus. The column marked A measures the amplitude of the second harmonic of the observed fringe shift, that is, the increase in intensity of the fringe pattern after rotation at the position of the intensity minima before rotation. The last column gives the ratio of the shift expected on the basis of a 30 km/sec ether drift (equal to the speed of the earth on its orbit) to $2A$. In 1964 a paper on a Michelson–Morley experiment, this time using lasers, was published which showed "that the

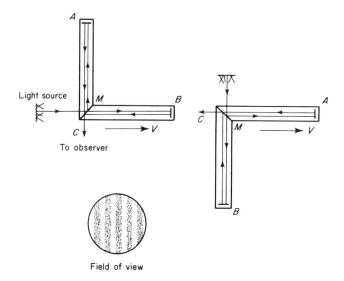

Fig. 1.5.2   Schematic diagram of a rotatable Michelson interferometer for measuring ether drift.

[5] *Rev. Mod. Phys.* **27,** 167 (1955).

TABLE 1.5.1
Trials of the Michelson-Morely Experiment

Observer	Year	Place	L	$(2L/\lambda)(v/c)^2$	A	Ratio
Michelson[a]	1881	Potsdam	120 cm	0.04 fringe	0.01 fringe	2
Michelson and Morley[b]	1887	Cleveland	1100	0.40	0.005	40
Morley and Miller[c]	1902–04	Cleveland	3220	1.13	0.0073	80
Miller[d]	1921	Mt. Wilson	3200	1.12	0.04	15
Miller[e]	1923–24	Cleveland	3200	1.12	0.015	40
Miller[f] (sunlight)	1924	Cleveland	3200	1.12	0.007	80
Tomaschek[g] (starlight)	1924	Heidelberg	860	0.3	0.01	15
Miller[h]	1925–26	Mt. Wilson	3200	1.12	0.044	13
Kennedy[i]	1926	Pasadena and Mt. Wilson	200	0.07	0.001	35
Illingworth[j]	1927	Pasadena	200	0.07	0.0002	175
Piccard and Stahel[k]	1927	Mt. Rigi	280	0.13	0.003	20
Michelson et al.[l]	1929	Mt. Wilson	2590	0.9	0.005	90
Joos[m]	1930	Jena	2100	0.75	0.001	375

[a] A. A. Michelson, *Am. J. Sci.* **22**, 120 (1881); *Phil. Mag.* **13**, 236 (1882).

[b] A. A. Michelson and E. W. Morley, *Am. J. Sci.* **34**, 333 (1887); *Phil. Mag.* **24**, 449 (1887).

[c] E. W. Morley and D. C. Miller, *Phil. Mag.* **9**, 680 (1905); *Proc. Am. Acad. Arts Sci.* **41**, 321 (1905).

[d] D. C. Miller, Data sheets of observations, Dec. 9–11, 1921 (unpublished).

[e] D. C. Miller, Observations, Aug. 23–Sept. 4, 1923; June 27–July 26, 1924 (unpublished).

[f] D. C. Miller, Observations with sunlight on July 8–9, 1924, *Proc. Nat. Acad. Sci.* **11**, 311 (1925).

[g] R. Tomaschek, *Ann. Physik* **73**, 105 (1924).

[h] D. C. Miller, *Rev. Mod. Phys.* **5**, 203 (1933).

[i] R. J. Kennedy, *Proc. Nat. Acad. Sci.* **12**, 621 (1926); *Astrophys. J.* **68**, 367 (1928); Kennedy and Thorndike, "Interferometer with Unequal Arms," *Phys. Rev.* **42**, 400, 1932.

[j] K. K. Illingworth, *Phys. Rev.* **30**, 692 (1927).

[k] A. Piccard and E. Stahel, *Compt. rend.* **183**, 420 (1926); **184**, 152, 451 (1927).

[l] A. A. Michelson, F. G. Pease, and F. Pearson, *Nature* **123**, 88 (1929); *J. Opt. Soc. Am.* **18**, 181 (1929).

[m] G. Joos, *Ann. Physik* **7**, 385 (1930); *Naturwiss.* **38**, 784 (1931).

effect of 'ether drift' is less than $1/1000$ of that which might be produced by the earth's orbital velocity."[6]

1.6   THE LORENTZ TRANSFORMATION

The Michelson–Morley experiment left a great gap in scientific thought and procedures. It meant that the Galilean transformation (Eqs. 1.5.1 and 1.5.2) could not be applied to the measurement of the speed of light in frames of reference moving relatively to each other. Attempts were of course made to rescue the ether concept because it seemed such a "natural" assumption. It was suggested that the ether in the laboratory was somehow dragged along by the earth. This was, however, inconsistent with the experimentally observed aberration of stars, their apparent displacement due to the earth's motion, to be discussed further in the next section. Another proposal by Fitzgerald and Lorentz[7] was that relative to a stationary ether, all bodies would be contracted in the direction of the ether drift. Thus a length L in a "stationary" condition would be changed to $L(1 - v^2/c^2)^{1/2}$. The times $\Delta t_{||}$ and $\Delta t_{\perp}$ given in Eqs. 1.5.3 and 1.5.4 now become equal, and a zero result would be expected. This is no longer true if the two arms of the interferometer have unequal lengths. This hypothesis was tested by Kennedy and Thorndike. The experiment gave a null result and, therefore, Fitzgerald and Lorentz' assumption had to be rejected. Finally there were several variations on the theme that the speed of light depended on the speed of the source, of intervening material media, and of mirrors. These all proved to be unacceptable. A recent experiment[8] performed with a very high-energy accelerator, the proton synchrotron of the CERN laboratory, indicates that the speed of light is, to a high degree of approximation, independent of the velocity of the source. With such accelerators different kinds of so-called elementary particles can be produced—neutral π^0-mesons, among others. These have a very short life, $\sim 10^{-16}$ sec, and thus even at the velocity of light they can move only $3 \times 10^8 \times 10^{-16}$ m $= 3 \times 10^{-8}$ m, or ~ 100 atom diameters. They decay into two photons. In the experiment mentioned, the π^0-mesons travel at about 99.98% of the speed of light. Short bursts of π^0-mesons were produced

[6] Jaseja, Javan, Murray, and Townes, *Phys. Rev.* **133**, A1221 (1964).

[7] G. F. Fitzgerald (1851–1901), professor of physics in Dublin; explained shortly before Lorentz the result of Michelson-Morley experiment. Hendrik Antoon Lorentz (1853–1928), Dutch physicist; professor in Leiden: 1902 Nobel prize; worked mainly in electromagnetic theory and the theory of the electron.

[8] Alväger, Farley, Kjellman, and Wallin, *Phys. Letters* **12**, 260 (1964); Alväger, Bailey, Farley, Kjellman, and Wallin, *Arkiv Fysik* **3**, 145 (1964).

which through their decay produced short bursts of photons. The velocity of those moving in the direction of motion of the π^0-mesons was determined by timing over a distance of 31 m. The time of flight was on the order of $31/(3 \times 10^8)$ sec $= 10^{-7}$ sec, or 100 nanoseconds [1 nanosecond (nsec) $= 10^{-9}$ sec] which can be measured accurately by electronic means. The measured speed of the photons was $2.9977 \pm .0004 \times 10^8$ m/sec, in close agreement with the speed of light from stationary sources, which is 2.9979×10^8 m/sec. Although the above result was not available to physicists in 1900, the hypothesis that the velocity of the light source might influence the speed of light was never taken seriously as an explanation of the Michelson–Morley experiment. It was in fact experimentally demonstrated to be false by the observation that, as determined by the Doppler effect, the apparent velocity of approach and recession of one of a pair of binary stars orbiting around this common center of mass, was accurately sinusoidal, which would not be true if the light emitted toward

Albert Einstein (1879–1955) ca. 1910 (Courtesy of Niels Bohr Library, American Institute of Physics).

the earth while approaching was traveling faster than the light emitted while receding from the earth.

The resolution of these difficulties came by the adoption of Einstein's[9] Special Theory of Relativity. This was based on the postulate that all the laws of physics, and in particular the speed of light, would be the same for observers in all coordinate systems moving with respect to each other at constant velocity, in other words, experiments performed within any two systems would yield identical results. Such coordinate systems are often referred to as equivalent inertial frames of reference. The first requirement of the Special Theory of Relativity was to find a transformation of coordinates from some one inertial frame x, y, z, t to another x', y', z', t' moving with respect to it, say with parallel axes at a speed V in the $+x$ direction, which would leave the velocity of light unchanged. The demands of the Special Theory of Relativity go much further, since they require not only a description of the motion of light, but of material objects, and also of electric and magnetic fields. Some more on the Special Theory of Relativity is contained in Appendix II. We shall confine ourselves here to considerations related to the propagation of electromagnetic radiation.

The required characteristic of the transformation for measurements made in the laboratory coordinate system x, y, z, t to one moving in the $+x$ direction with a speed V is that a light pulse started at the origin of the laboratory frame at the time $t = 0$ moves radially outward to a distance R with a speed c, so that $R^2 = x^2 + y^2 + z^2 = c^2t^2$, and that also in a moving frame whose origin coincided with the laboratory frame at $t = t' = 0$, $R'^2 = x'^2 + y'^2 + z'^2 = c^2t'^2$. The possibility that not only apparent lengths, but apparent times are changed by relative motion is included. Convenient standards of length and time in either frame are the wavelength and period of atomic radiations. If we assume that the properties of atoms are independent of any "absolute" motion, but are the same in all inertial frames, observers in all frames can construct equivalent meter-sticks and clocks.

The first requirement of the theory of relativity is a transformation that

---

[9] Albert Einstein (1879–1955) born in Germany. Studied physics at the Swiss Federal Institute of Technology. Patent examiner at the Swiss patent office in Berne 1902–1909. In 1905 published four famous papers, one on the theory of light quanta and the photoelectric effect (for which he received the Nobel prize in 1921), one on Brownian motion and two on the Special Theory of Relativity. (1905 Ph. D. from Univ. of Zurich with thesis on molecule size.) Between 1909 and 1914, professor at the Universities of Zurich and Prague and at the Swiss Federal Institute of Technology. 1914 Director of the Kaiser–Wilhelm Institute for Physics in Berlin and member of the Prussian Academy of Sciences. Had to leave Germany in 1933 and settled in Princeton, N.J. at the Institute for Advanced Study.

reduces to the Galilean for small relative speeds, but leaves the observed speed of light unchanged for any relative speed even approaching the speed of light. This transformation, called the *Lorentz transformation*, is as follows

$$x' = \gamma(x - Vt)$$

$$y' = y$$

$$z' = z \qquad (1.6.1)$$

$$t' = \gamma(t - Vx/c^2)$$

where

$$\gamma = (1 - V^2/c^2)^{-1/2}.$$

These equations may be solved for x, y, z, and t giving

$$x = \gamma(x' + Vt)$$

$$y = y' \qquad (1.6.2)$$

$$z = z'$$

$$t = \gamma(t' + Vx'/c^2).$$

By direct substitution we can verify that the transformation meets the requirement that in the laboratory frame the pulse of light emitted from the origin at $t = 0$ has traveled a radial distance $R = ct$, and in the moving frame a distance $R' = ct'$, which is equal to R if the clocks are equivalent.

There is fairly good evidence that the negative outcome of the Michelson–Morley experiment to detect the ether drift did not influence Einstein in his setting up the Special Theory of Relativity. Einstein only indirectly refers to the Michelson–Morley experiment in his early papers. In a short autobiographic note, written a few months before his death, he wrote (original in German): "During this year in Aarau [1895, when attending high school there] the question occurred to me: If one were to run with the speed of light along a light wave, one would see a wave field which does not change with time. But something like that does not seem to exist! This was the first youthful thought-experiment which deals with the Special Theory of Relativity. Discovery is not the work of logical thought, although the end product is tied to a logical frame work."[10] During that time he was intensively concerned with the role of the ether in electromagnetic theory and even wrote a small unpublished paper about it which only recently was discovered in his estate.

[10] *Schweizerische Hochschul Zeitung* **28**, special issue, p. 145 (1955); Einstein gave a similar account in his autobiographical notes written in 1946 for the book *Albert Einstein—Philosopher Scientist*, edited by P. A. Schilpp (Harper Torchbooks), p. 52.

1.7 MOVING LIGHT SOURCES AND TRANSMITTING MEDIA

The speed of light in vacuum is the same in all inertial frames of reference, but the direction of a beam, its intensity, its frequency, or its speed in a material medium are not the same. Approximately correct expressions for these effects can be obtained in a variety of ways for speeds small compared to the speed of light. In the nonrelativistic case which we exemplified earlier with the waves in a pond and a motorboat riding through these waves, we found that the velocity of the waves as seen from the observer in the motorboat was $U' = V + U$ if the boat was running against the waves. U is the velocity of the waves as seen from the shore, and V is the relative velocity between shore and boat, or more generally between the coordinate systems attached to shore and boat. If the speeds V and U are great, we need relativistic expressions. We might ask for example what the relative speed is between two protons which move in the laboratory system in opposite directions each with 0.8 times the velocity of light. The Galileo transformation immediately gives us a relative speed of $1.6c$ which, according to the postulate of the theory of relativity, cannot be correct since no object can move faster than the speed of light in any inertial system.

The Lorentz transformation, however, provides us elegantly and simply with answers that are correct for any attainable speed. In order to obtain these answers we need relativistic expressions for transforming velocities from one coordinate system to another. By taking differentials of Eqs. 1.6.1 and 1.6.2 we obtain

$$dx' = \gamma(dx - Vdt) \qquad\qquad dx = \gamma(dx' + Vdt')$$

$$dy' = dy \qquad\qquad dy = dy'$$

$$dz' = dz \qquad\qquad dz = dz'$$

$$dt' = \gamma(dt - Vdx/c^2) \qquad\qquad dt = \gamma(dt' + Vdx'/c^2),$$

again with $\gamma = (1 - V^2/c^2)^{-1/2}$. Now, dividing the space differentials by the corresponding time differentials, and putting $U_x = dx/dt$, $Ux' = dx'/dt'$, and so on, we obtain

$$U_x' = \frac{U_x - V}{1 - (U_xV)/c^2} \qquad\qquad U_x = \frac{U_x' + V}{1 + (U_x'V)/c^2}$$

$$U_{y,z}' = \frac{U_{y,z}}{\gamma[1 - (U_xV)/c^2]} \qquad\qquad U_{y,z} = \frac{U_{y,z}'}{\gamma[1 + (U_x'V)/c^2]} \qquad . \qquad (1.7.1)$$

Note that for small velocities this reduces to the Galilean transformation, but if $U_x' \to c$ in a frame moving in the $+x$ direction with a speed $V \to c$, then U_x approaches, not $2c$, but c. Note also that the y and z components of the velocity are changed, in contrast to the nonrelativistic case.

Aberration of Light

If light comes to an observer from a distant source, for example, a star, and he is moving at right angles to the direction of the incoming light, for example due to the motion of the earth, then he must tilt his telescope by an angle ϕ in order to see the star in the middle of his field of view. The situation is illustrated in Fig. 1.7.1. Nonrelativistically, one would say that in order for light to travel down the axis of the telescope, we should have $\tan \phi = V/c$, as in Fig. 1.7.1(a). Relativistically, in a coordinate system

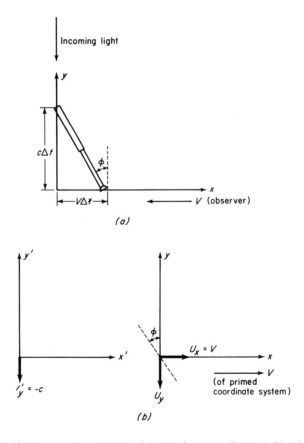

Fig. 1.7.1   Aberrations as interpreted (a) nonrelativistically, and (b) relativistically.

fixed with respect to the star, x', y', a light beam moving in the $-y$ direction has the velocity components $U_x' = 0$, $U_y' = -c$. The velocity components in the observer's unprimed system are, according to Eq. 1.7.1, $U_x = V$ and $U_y = -c/\gamma = -(c^2 - v^2)^{1/2}$, so that

$$\sin \phi = \frac{V}{c}. \tag{1.7.2}$$

We see that relativistically V cannot be greater than c. For small values of V/c, the nonrelativistic and relativistic results agree, since

$$\tan \phi = \sin \phi = \phi = \frac{V}{c}.$$

As long ago as 1728 Bradley[11] observed that stars lying near the axis of the earth's orbital motion around the sun seem to move in small orbits 41" of arc in diameter. The sine of half this angle is 10^{-4} which, according to Eq. 1.7.2, gives 30 km/sec for the velocity of the earth in its orbit, in close agreement with other observations.

Aberration was also used to test the earlier hypothesis of ether drag. It is quite clear that if the earth drags the ether surrounding it substantially along, the aberration should be much reduced. Since aberration was observed in the expected amount, the ether drag hypothesis had to be abandoned. Because of the smallness of the angle its sine and tangent are essentially equal. Stellar aberration could therefore not be used to test the validity of the Special Theory of Relativity; it only could give the death blow to the ether drag hypothesis.

The Headlight Effect

A more general discussion of aberration proceeds as follows. If light is emitted from a source at an angle θ' with the x' axis in its proper frame of reference, in which it is at rest, it will appear to move in a different direction in a coordinate system in which the light is moving. If the x' component of the motion is $c \cos \theta' = U_x'$ in the proper frame, and $c \cos \theta = U_x$ in the laboratory frame, we have from Eq. 1.7.1

$$\cos \theta = \frac{\cos \theta' + (V/c)}{1 + (V/c) \cos \theta'}. \tag{1.7.3}$$

---

[11] James Bradley (1693–1762), professor of astronomy in Oxford, later Astronomer Royal at Greenwich. Also discovered the nutation of the earth's axis.

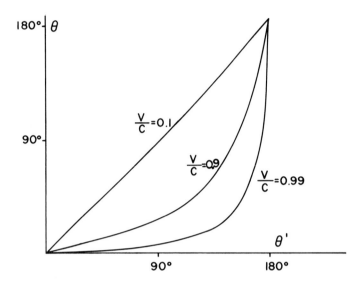

Fig. 1.7.2   The headlight effect.

The angle θ is plotted as a function of θ' in Fig. 1.7.2. This shows that at speeds approaching c, light from a moving light source is bunched in the forward direction of motion, even though in its proper frame it is emitting uniformly in all directions. This is known as the headlight effect, and applies to any form of radiation, not only electromagnetic, moving with speeds approaching c. It is amply borne out by observation on relativistic particles in high-energy physics.

The effect is being used in the production of nearly monochromatic photon beams. If a positron (a positively charged electron) meets an ordinary electron, the two can combine and annihilate by emitting two γ-quanta. Usually this process takes place when the electron and positron have little relative motion. This condition is fulfilled when the positron comes to rest in some material by losing kinetic energy in plowing through matter. Then both positrons and electrons have little kinetic energy. The two γ-quanta that are emitted in the annihilation process each have, in accordance to Einstein's $E = mc^2$ formula, 0.511 MeV energy, corresponding to the rest energy of 9.1×10^{-31} kg of the electron and the positron.

Because momentum has to be conserved, the two quanta fly away in opposite directions. The direction of their line in space is random and therefore the distribution is isotropic. In some rare cases positrons can also be annihilated in flight when they hit electrons at rest. In this case too, energy and momentum are conserved. The two photons will fly in opposite directions in the inertial system which is attached to the center-of-mass of the positron and the electron. In this system the two photons have equal energy and equal amounts of momentum, and the direction of emission is isotropic. In the laboratory system, however, the headlight effect makes it appear that one photon travels in the forward direction, the other one in the backward direction with respect to the original positron beam. Both photons travel according to the postulate of the Special Theory of Relativity with the speed of light also in the laboratory system. (The case is completely similar to the annihilation of the π^0-mesons discussed earlier.) The forward quantum, however, has nearly all of the energy available, and the backward flying quantum has very little energy.

The Doppler Effect

An approaching train whistle has a higher pitch than the same whistle when the train is receding. The same is true of light. An approaching source is perceived as emitting higher frequencies than a receding source. A quantitative relativistic calculation of this effect proceeds as follows. A source of light moving in the laboratory with a velocity V in the $+x$ direction (see Fig. 1.7.3) emits successive signals at times $t = 0$ and $t = \Delta t$ when the source is at x_1 and x_2; $(x_2 - x_1)/V = \Delta t$. These signals arrive at P at times r_1/c and $r_2/c + \Delta t$. The time interval observed at P we call

$$\Delta t_p = \frac{r_2}{c} + \Delta t - \frac{r_1}{c}.$$

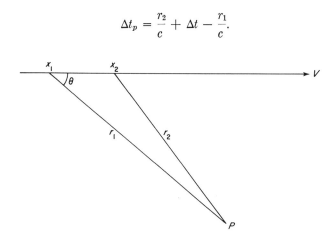

Fig. 1.7.3 Geometry describing emission and reception of signals from a moving source.

If P is far away compared to $x_2 - x_1$, we may put $r_1 - r_2 = (x_2 - x_1) \cos \theta$, or

$$\Delta t_p = -\frac{x_2 - x_1}{c} \cos \theta + \Delta t.$$

$$\Delta t_p = \Delta t \left(1 - \frac{V}{c} \cos \theta \right). \tag{1.7.4}$$

We wish to translate the interval Δt observed in the laboratory to $\Delta t'$, the corresponding interval observed in a "proper" coordinate system moving with the source. From Eq. 1.6.1 we have

$$\Delta t = \gamma (\Delta t' + V \Delta x'/c^2).$$

But since the source is at rest in its proper coordinate system, $\Delta x' = 0$, and we have

$$\Delta t = \gamma \Delta t'. \tag{1.7.5}$$

This is discussed further in Appendix II. Moving clocks appear to run slow. Substituting Eq. 1.7.5 into Eq. 1.7.4 we get

$$\Delta t_p = \Delta t' \cdot \gamma \left(1 - \frac{V}{c} \cos \theta \right) = \Delta t' \frac{1 - \frac{V}{c} \cos \theta}{\sqrt{1 - V^2/c^2}}.$$

Let us assume that $\Delta t'$ corresponds to 1 period at the source and that therefore $\Delta t' = 1/\nu'$. The corresponding time for the observations of a change of 1 cycle at P is $\Delta t = 1/\nu$. Substituting, we get

$$\nu = \nu' \frac{\sqrt{1 - V^2/c^2}}{1 - \frac{V}{c} \cos \theta}. \tag{1.7.6}$$

For the particular case of an approaching light source, $\theta = 0$, and

$$\nu = \nu' \frac{\sqrt{\left(1 - \frac{V}{c}\right)\left(1 + \frac{V}{c}\right)}}{1 - \frac{V}{c}} = \nu' \sqrt{\frac{1 + V/c}{1 - V/c}}. \tag{1.7.7}$$

This approaches the nonrelativistic relation

$$\nu = \nu'\left(1 + \frac{V}{c}\right) \quad \text{for} \quad \frac{V}{c} \ll 1. \tag{1.7.8}$$

If the relative direction of the light source and of the observed light beam do not coincide, there is still a Doppler effect, even if the two directions are at a right angle. In this latter case classically there should be none. The relativistic Doppler effect at right angles is called the transverse Doppler effect.

The frequency shift of this effect is given, according to Eq. 1.7.6, by

$$\nu = \nu'\sqrt{1 - \frac{V^2}{c^2}}$$

or by series expansion

$$\nu = \nu'\left(1 - \frac{1}{2}\frac{V^2}{c^2} + \cdots\right).$$

In contrast to the Doppler effect in the longitudinal direction, there is no term containing v/c.

Ives and Stilwell[12] in 1938 and 1941 were the first ones to detect in the laboratory the relativistic Doppler effect on a beam of fast moving hydrogen atoms. They measured the shift of a spectral line which was emitted from the atoms in direction of their motion, and simultaneously they also observed in the spectrograph, with the aid of a mirror, the shifted spectral line which was emitted in the opposite direction. Whereas for both directions the wavelength shift according to the nonrelativistic expression (Eq. 1.7.8) is opposite in sign but equal in magnitude, the series expansion of the relativistic formula (Eq. 1.7.7) also contains a term which is quadratic in v. This term yields for both directions a shift towards longer wavelengths. Hence, the arithmetical mean of the wavelengths of the Doppler-shifted lines which are emitted in the forward and backward direction will not coincide with the wavelength of the unshifted line, and it will depend on the speed of the atoms in the beam.

Plane Waves in a Moving Medium

As long ago as 1853 Fizeau, and more recently Michelson and Morley, verified the prediction of Fresnel that the velocity of light in a medium of

---

[12] H. E. Ives and G. R. Stilwell, *J. Opt. Soc. Am.* **28**, 215 (1938); also **31**, 369 (1941).

index of refraction n (see footnote 3 in Section 1.1, and Section 2.1) moving with a velocity V in or opposite to the direction of propagation of the light is

$$v = \frac{c}{n} \pm \left(1 - \frac{1}{n^2}\right) V. \tag{1.7.9}$$

This result is based on the assumption of elastic vibrations in a stationary ether. It can also be derived from Maxwell's equations if we assume a non-permeable liquid ($\mu = \mu_0$) in which Ampère's law in Maxwell's equations (1.1.6) is modified by the inclusion of a component of the magnetic field due to a moving polarization in the liquid produced by the electric field of the light wave. The complete relativistic result follows immediately from the transformation of velocities given in Eq. 1.7.1. If U_x', the speed of light in a liquid of index of refraction n is c/n, then the observed speed in the laboratory is

$$U_x = \frac{\dfrac{c}{n} \pm V}{1 \pm \dfrac{1}{n}\dfrac{V}{c}}. \tag{1.7.10}$$

For $V/c \ll 1$, and consequently neglecting terms in V/c, the above equation reduces to 1.7.9.

PROBLEMS

1. A *coaxial cable* carries direct current from a battery to a resistor. The resistance of the cable is negligible, so that there is no voltage drop along either conductor of the cable. Show that the power transmitted along the cable as computed from the *Poynting vector* in the dielectric between the conductors is equal to the power delivered by the battery to the resistor.

In order to carry out the required proof, it is useful to break the problem into several parts. The Poynting vector depends on E and H. It is therefore necessary to determine the magnitude and direction of E and H at any radial distance r from the axis of the cable. Since the fields are functions of only one variable, r, it is possible to write an expression for the total rate of energy flow through a ring-shaped area of radial width dr. With this done, it is possible to integrate dS from the inner conductor to the outer conductor. This integral is the total energy flow along the cable. It is equal to the power delivered from the battery to the resistor.

2. A *coaxial cable* of length x, open at both ends, is suspended with its axis parallel to a uniform constant *magnetic field B*. The inner and outer conductors are given equal and opposite charges so that the difference of potential between the two is V_{ab}. For simplicity, we may assume that the separation of d between the coaxial charged surfaces is small compared to the radius of either one. What are the magnitude and direction of S?

Compute the angular momentum of this circulating energy.

The inner and outer surfaces of the cable are now connected through a small length of wire having a resistance R.

What is the force on the small piece of wire of length d when a current i is flowing through it? What is the torque acting on the cable and wire? What is the total angular impulse imparted to the mechanical system as a result of the discharge? What is the change in angular momentum of the field?

3. A *capacitor* is connected in series with a switch and an inductor. A right-handed coordinate system having its origin halfway between the conductors and its y axis parallel to the conductors is set up as in the figure. The capacitor is charged with the upper plate positive, the switch is closed at the time $t = 0$, and an electrical oscillation is set up. The oscillating electric and magnetic fields at the origin of the coordinate system are parallel to the x and z axes, respectively, and have amplitudes E_0 and H_0. Plot E_x, S_y, and H_z at the origin for the first few cycles of the oscillation. What is the amplitude of S_y in terms of H_0 and E_0?

4. The *Poynting vector* for a traveling wave may be written in the form

$$\mathbf{S} = \mathbf{E} \times \mathbf{H} = (\tfrac{1}{2}\epsilon E^2 + \tfrac{1}{2}\mu H^2)\mathbf{v}$$

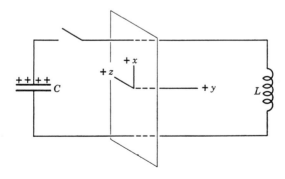

Figure P.1.1 (Problem 3)

for an electromagnetic wave. Show that at points midway between the two wires of the cable shown in Fig. 1.2.3 **E** and **H** are perpendicular to each other, and that the ratio of their magnitudes is

$$E/H = 1/\epsilon v$$

and that, on combining the above expressions, one gets $v = (\epsilon\mu)^{-1/2}$. Could this argument be applied to any point in the vicinity of any cable?

5. Plot a *traveling wave* in a cable for four instants a quarter of a period apart.

6. Plot a *standing wave* in a cable for four instants a quarter of a period apart.

7. Compute the three lowest *resonant frequencies* of a coaxial cable 3 m long, assuming that the properties of the insulation are given by ϵ_0 and μ_0, (*a*) when both ends of the cable are open (*b*) when one end is short-circulated.

8. Compute the amplitude of the current and voltage waves in a *coaxial cable* having an outer conductor whose radius is three times the radius of the inner conductor when it is delivering 100 watts to a resistance equal to the characteristic impedance of the cable. The insulation of the cable has a dielectric coefficient $K_e = 2.25$.

9. A *coaxial cable* is connected at one end to a 600-hertz oscillator having an amplitude of 100 volts. The insulation in the cable has a dielectric coefficient $K_e = 2.2$. The cable is terminated with its characteristic impedance, which is 55 ohms. (*a*) What is the amplitude of the current wave? Is it in phase with the voltage? (*b*) What are the frequency and wavelength of the traveling wave in the cable? (*c*) Plot the current and the instantaneous power dissipation in the load as functions of time for a few cycles. What is the average power delivered to the resistor?

10. A cable such as that shown in Fig. 1.2.3 carries a *single pulse*, in which the upper conductor is positively charged, toward a termination on the right. Draw this pulse and the fields surrounding it before and after reflection, first from an open end, and then from a short-circuited end. Note that in the first case i and H are reversed on reflection but V and E are left unchanged, whereas in the second case i and H are left unchanged but V and E are reversed. Note also that the Poynting vector is reversed in both cases by the reflection.

11. What are the *wavelengths* of electromagnetic waves in empty space having frequencies of 10, 30, 300 megahertz? What are the frequencies of electromagnetic waves having wavelengths of 100 m, 10 cm, 3 mm?

12. A *plane electromagnetic wave*, moving in the x direction, has a frequency of 150 megahertz. If its amplitude is such that the Poynting vector

at the plane $x = 0$ has a mean value of 10^{-12} W/m², what is the amplitude of the electric oscillations at the point $x = 100$ m?

13. A radio station broadcasts 4 kW at a frequency of 1.5 megahertz from an antenna 40 m long. What is the amplitude of the *antenna* current?

14. Assuming that the *electric dipole* whose total radiation is described by Eq. 1.3.1 consists of an electronic charge, $Q = 1.6 \times 10^{-19}$ coulomb, oscillating with an amplitude of atomic dimensions, $x = 10^{-10}$ m, how long would it take to radiate 1 eV of energy (*a*) if it radiated visible light with a wavelength 5×10^{-7} m? (*b*) in the far infrared with a wavelength of 10^{-4} m?

15. *Two antennas* radiating in phase with each other are 100 m apart. In what directions would the radiated intensities have a minimum if the frequencies of oscillation were (*a*) 1.5 megahertz? (*b*) 6 megahertz? (*c*) 12 megahertz?

16. A broadcasting station using vertical antennas is to be set up south of a town which it is to serve. *Two antennas* separated by a quarter of a wavelength are to be used and are to be operated not in phase but with a phase difference of a quarter of a cycle. How should the masts be oriented with respect to the town, and which antenna should lead in phase?

17. *Two* vertical radio *antennas* situated on a north-south line and 150 m apart oscillate at a frequency of 6 megahertz in phase with each other. At what angles from the north-south axis will the radiated signal be a minimum?

18. *Two* vertical radio *antennas* situated on a north-south line and 100 m apart oscillate at a frequency of 4 megahertz in phase with each other. At what angles from the north-south axis will the radiated signal be maximum?

19. *Three* vertical radio broadcasting *antennas* operating in phase with each other are placed in a straight line, the distance between adjacent antennas being 3 wavelengths. What are the directions for maxima and minima in the interference patterns at large distances?

20. *Three* vertical radio broadcasting *antennas* operating in phase with each other are located at the corners of an equilateral triangle. The distance between antennas is 2 wavelengths. Discuss the interference pattern at large distances.

21. *Two antennas*, radiating on the same wavelength and operating in phase, emit in certain directions four times the energy of one antenna, not only two times. From where does the difference come?

22. (*a*) Sketch the distribution of the energy radiated by *two antennas* that are separated by a half-wavelength and which are operating 180° out of phase. (*b*) Using the same scale show the radiation pattern if only one antenna is operating.

23. Roemer made the crucial observations about the *speed of light* on the moon of Jupiter, Io, which has a period of 1.769 days. What is the maximum difference of the apparent periods of Io for an observer on earth?

24. A river is 200 meters wide and flows from north to south. Assume that its velocity is uniformly 3 m/sec. A *boat* starts at the east shore across the *river* to a point directly opposite the starting point and returns immediately. The speed of the boat in standing water is 10 m/sec. (*a*) How much time will the round trip take? (Assume constant speeds throughout.) (*b*) The same boat goes 200 m upstream and returns immediately. What is its travel time? (*c*) In what direction must the boatsman aim for his trips across the river?

25. Verify that the *Lorentz transformation* meets the requirement that the velocity of light from a source which is moving with the velocity v against an observer is c in the coordinate system of the light source and also in that of the observer.

26. Show that for small velocities the *Lorentz transformation* reduces to the *Galileo transformation*.

27. *Kennedy* and *Thorndike* used for their experiment an interferometer with two arms of unequal length. (*a*) Show that the null result of this experiment rules out the existence of an ether which is stationary with the sun, even if one assumes a contraction of the kind Fitzgerald and Lorentz had proposed. (*b*) Show that the special theory of relativity agrees with the null result.

28. Somebody has a garage which was built for his 224″-long 1967 Cadillac which just fits into this garage. This car is traded for a 1973 model of the same make which is 228″ long. How fast must the owner drive his new car into the garage so that the *length* of the car *contracts* so much that it fits into the garage?

29. Charged *pions* (π^+ and π^- mesons) *decay* with a mean life of 2.6×10^{-8} sec. This is the time after which $1/e$ ($e = 2.71 \ldots$), or roughly one-third, of the initial number of pions are still left. If it is observed that in a mono-energetic pion beam the number of pions has dropped by a factor $2.71 \ldots$ when traveling through a distance of 50 m in the laboratory, what is the speed of the pions in the laboratory system?

30. An *electron moves* in the positive x direction with a velocity in the laboratory system of $0.1c$ and another with the velocity of $0.2c$. (*a*) What is the velocity of the second electron as seen in the reference system of the first electron? (*b*) What is the velocity of the first electron as seen in the reference system of the second electron? (*c*) How many percent is the error if the Galileo transformation is used?

31. An *electron moves* in the positive x direction with a velocity in the

laboratory system of $0.07c$ and another electron moves in the opposite direction with $0.03c$. (*a*) What is the velocity of the second electron as seen from the first electron? (*b*) What is the velocity of the first electron as seen from the second? (*c*) How many percent is the error if the Galileo transformation is used?

32. In high-energy physics experiments, one occasionally uses *colliding beams* in which protons approach each other head-on (details about colliding beam experiments are discussed in Sect. 7.2). If each of the protons has a velocity of $0.9990c$ in the laboratory system, what is the relative velocity of one proton as seen from the other proton?

33. A *K meson* having a velocity of $0.8c$ in the laboratory system *decays* into two pions (π mesons), each having a speed of $0.85c$ in the frame of reference moving with the K meson. (*a*) In order to conserve momentum, in what direction to each other must the pions be emitted in the system of the K meson? (*b*) What is the maximum speed and what is the minimum speed which these pions can have in the laboratory system? (*c*) What is the relative speed between the two π mesons as seen by one of the π mesons?

34. *Three objects, A, B,* and *C, move* in the positive x direction in the laboratory system. A moves with a speed of $0.5c$ against the laboratory system; B has in respect to A a relative velocity of $0.5c$ in the positive direction; and C has in respect to B a relative velocity of $0.5c$ in the positive direction. What is the speed of C relative to an observer in the laboratory system?

35. The π^0 meson, a *neutral π meson, decays* into two light quanta, or photons, which move in opposite directions in the frame of reference of the π^0 meson. If such a meson decays while moving with a speed of $0.9c$, what is the angle between the two quanta, assuming they are emitted symmetrically to the direction of the meson?

36. The mean radius of the orbit of the planet Mercury is 58×10^6 km and the period 88 (earth) days. Calculate the magnitude of the *stellar aberration* which an observer on this planet would measure.

37. The distance from the earth to the moon is about 400,000 km. In the Apollo flights the travel time was approximately 60 hours. How big is the *stellar aberration* which is observed at right angles to the path by the astronauts on their way to the moon if one assumes a constant velocity of the spacecraft?

38. The Pioneer X rocket on its way to Jupiter passed the moon, which is 4×10^5 km away from the earth, after approximately 10 hours flying time. What is the average *stellar aberration* in observations at right angles to the path of this rocket?

39. In the table below mark the boxes with a ($+$) sign where the *theory* agrees with the *experiment* and with a ($-$) sign where it disagrees.

	Experiment			
Theory	Michelson-Morley	Kennedy-Thorndike	Stellar aberration	Decay of π^0 mesons in flight
Stationary ether				
Ether drag by earth				
Lorentz contraction and stationary ether				
Special theory of relativity				

40. A light source that emits light uniformly in all directions in its reference frame moves with the velocity $v = 0.9c$ as seen by an observer. What is the half-angle of the *cone* into which half the *light* is emitted as seen by the observer?

41. In some runs of the experiment by Ives and Stilwell to detect the *relativistic Doppler effect,* singly charged H_2^+ molecule ions were accelerated by a potential of 13,700 V. The molecule ions later dissociated and some of the neutral H atoms emitted radiation of a wavelength of 4861 Å. (*a*) What is the shift in wavelength for radiation emitted in the same direction as the moving atoms? (*b*) in a direction opposite to that of the atoms? (*c*) What would be the shift in wavelength for light emitted perpendicular to the path of the atoms?

42. The *quasar* (quasi-stellar radio source) 4C 05.34 has been found [*Nature* **226,** 532 (1970)] to have a redshift of the spectral lines $z = 2.877$, where $z = \Delta\lambda/\lambda$. It is assumed that this redshift is a Doppler effect due to the expansion of the universe. Several lines have been identified, among them the Lyman α line of hydrogen, L_α, which has in the laboratory a wavelength of 1216 Å, and a spectral line originating from triply ionized carbon atoms, with $\lambda = 1550$ Å. (*a*) What is the observed, apparent wavelength of these two lines? (*b*) What is the velocity of the quasar relative to the earth?

Chapter 2

The Electromagnetic Spectrum

2.1 WAVE ASPECTS AND QUANTUM ASPECTS

Wavelength and Frequency

A sinusoidal wave has the property that the velocity of propagation is equal to the product of wavelength and frequency. This is a purely geometrical relationship. In the case of electromagnetic radiation in free space we have

$$\lambda \nu = c = 3 \times 10^8 \text{ m/sec.} \tag{2.1.1}$$

The names given to different ranges of frequency and wavelength are shown in Fig. 2.1.1. Note that the range of wavelengths extends from arbitrarily

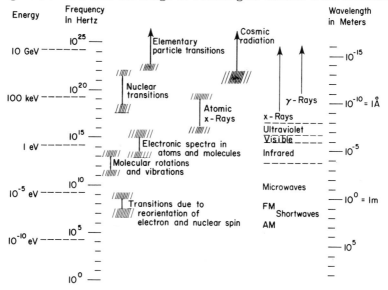

Fig. 2.1.1 The electromagnetic spectrum. Shaded areas represent fringe regions for the indicated types of transition.

long wavelengths made by man—hundreds of meters to millimeters—on through atomic sizes (10^{-10} m) and nuclear sizes (10^{-14}–10^{-15} m) and much further down, as found in the cosmic radiation. Out of this whole range, visible light extends for hardly an octave, 4–7 $\times$ 10^{-7} m. Dimensions in this range are often expressed in angstrom units, abbreviated Å, sometimes also A.U.

$$1 \text{ Å} = 10^{-8} \text{ cm} = 10^{-10} \text{ m}$$

or millimicrons, or nanometers,

$$1 \text{ millimicron (1 m}\mu) = 1 \text{ nanometer (1 nm)} = 10^{-9} \text{ m.}$$

Visible light, therefore, extends roughly from 4000 Å, or 400 mμ (violet), to 7500 Å, or 750 mμ (red), with blue centered around 470 mμ, green around 540 mμ, and yellow and orange around 610 mμ.

Figure 2.1.1 is also of interest from the quantum point of view. The energy of a quantum is $h\nu$ (in joules, or $h\nu/e$ in electron volts). In the range of frequencies used in electric circuits, the radio and microwave range, the energy of a quantum is less than kT at room temperature, or a few times 10^{-2} eV.[1] However, as we go to higher frequencies, we must adopt atomic or nuclear systems as radiators and absorbers, and emission and absorption processes involve single quanta. As we shall see, even in this range of frequencies, only the wave aspects of radiation determine the propagation of electromagnetic energy.

Polarization

The radiation pattern of a dipole antenna, as we saw in Fig. 1.3.3, is such that the E-vector always oscillates in planes which contain the dipole. Furthermore, at each point in space the H-vector is always perpendicular to the E-vector. The Poynting vector is obviously in the direction of the radius vector, or the propagation vector for the wave. Hence, we can define for each direction of propagation a plane of the E-vector and, perpendicular to it, one for the H-vector. Electromagnetic radiation for which we can define such a plane is called plane-polarized radiation, as shown in Fig. 2.1.2. The plane of polarization is usually understood to be the plane containing the E-vector.

We now consider the polarization of light. The radiating atoms, which are generally the source of light, can be considered in this respect as radi-

---

[1] It should be recalled that the average kinetic energy per degree of freedom of a molecule is $\frac{1}{2}kT$, k being the Boltzmann constant, 8.617 $\times$ 10^{-5} eV/°C, and T the absolute temperature.

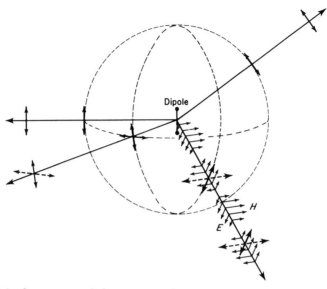

Fig. 2.1.2   Orientations of the E-vectors ($\updownarrow$) and H-vectors ($\leftrightarrow$) of the radiation emitted from a dipole into different directions in space.

ating dipoles. Therefore, for each atom emitting a quantum the above considerations are applicable. Usually the direction of these dipoles is assumed to be randomly distributed. In this case the light arriving at some point in space is unpolarized because the E-vectors originating from the differently oriented dipoles are not in the same plane. If, however, it can be arranged that all the dipoles oscillate in the same direction, our point in space would receive polarized light, just as in the case of only one radiating dipole.

A light beam of plane-polarized light may be pictured schematically as in Fig. 2.1.3(a), whereas unpolarized light beam is shown in Fig. 2.1.3(b); the two-headed arrows represent the orientation of the E-vector, which in the case of polarized light (a) determines the plane of polarization.

Polarized radiation can be produced in several ways from unpolarized radiation by eliminating from the beam the undesired components. One such possibility is by absorption. Some crystals (e.g., tourmaline) absorb light having its E-vector in a particular direction with respect to the orientation axis of the crystal much more than in a direction perpendicular to it. Certain man-made materials, the best known of them bearing the registered trademark Polaroid, also show this property; when light passes through such a material, it is polarized.

Scattering of light also can produce polarization. If unpolarized light falls on a slightly cloudy liquid, such as water containing a few drops of

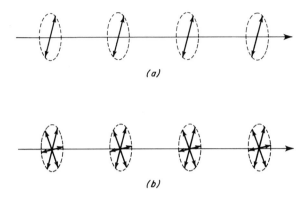

(a)

(b)

Fig. 2.1.3 (a) A plane-polarized light beam, the E-vector confined to one plane. (b) An unpolarized light beam, E-vectors lying in different planes. Only the E-vector is shown.

milk (in some communities the tap water is already dirty enough to produce the effect!), some of the light will be scattered by the particles suspended in the liquid. The scattered light may be thought of as reradiated by the oscillating dipoles that are induced in the particles in the liquid by the E-vectors of the incident beam. All the induced dipoles, therefore, oscillate in a direction perpendicular to the incident primary beam. The scattered, that is re-emitted, radiation is thus polarized in a direction also perpendicular to the primary beam. Figure 2.1.4 illustrates the situation for incident *polarized* light. The E-vectors for the incident beam and scattered light beams oscillate in a direction parallel to the plane of the paper. Only a few beams of scattered light are shown and this only for the horizontal and one vertical plane. If unpolarized light is used instead of polarized light, the figure should be thought to be rotated around the axis of the incident light beam. Since none of these induced dipoles have an oscillating moment in the direction of the beam, the light seen at right angles to the incident beam will be plane polarized, as shown in Fig. 2.1.5.

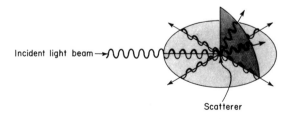

Incident light beam →

Scatterer

Fig. 2.1.4 The scattered radiation from an originally polarized beam.

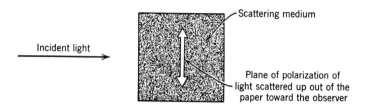

Fig. 2.1.5   Polarization by scattering.

The light from the blue sky, which is sunlight scattered on the air molecules (the short waves of the blue are scattered better than the red light of longer wavelength), is therefore considerably polarized.

Another form of polarization is circular polarization which originates from a rotating instead of an oscillating dipole. In a circular polarized wave the E-vector changes direction continuously, either in a right-hand or in a left-hand screw sense, as the electromagnetic wave proceeds.

It is evident that only transverse waves can be polarized. Sound waves, which are longitudinal, cannot be polarized.[2]

The Index of Refraction

An important aspect of the passage of electromagnetic radiation through matter is described by the index of refraction n. For example, in geometrical optics this aspect enters into *Snell's law of refraction* (Fig. 2.1.6)

$$n_1 \sin \alpha_1 = n_2 \sin \alpha_2.$$

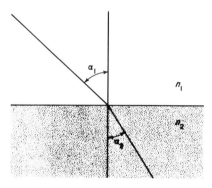

Fig. 2.1.6   Snell's law of refraction.

[2] Particle beams, e.g., of protons or electrons are called polarized if their spins all point in the same direction.

We shall give here a simplified theory of the index of diffraction. Let us consider matter as an assemblage of oscillators. These oscillators are the atoms in which one or several electrons can oscillate relative to the rest of the atom. From electrostatics it is known that an electric field can set up induced dipole moments in atoms. If the electric field alternates, the electrons and the rest of the atom undergo forced oscillations with respect to each other. If the frequency of the electric field is close to the natural frequency of the oscillating system (here the atom), in other words near resonance, the atom absorbs energy from the incident beam. This absorbed energy eventually is converted into heat or reradiated.

We recall from electrostatics that if a dielectric is placed in an electric field E, the induced polarization[3] P is equal to the induced dipole moment p per unit volume, where $p = qd$, that is, the product of charge q and distance d. P is furthermore proportional to the field intensity E, the proportionality constant χ being called the electric susceptibility of the material. Therefore, if N designates the number of induced dipoles per unit volume, we can write

$$P = pN = \chi E.$$

The oscillation of a dipole will, in general, lag behind the driving oscillation of the field by an angle ψ determined by the coupling of the dipole to other energy reservoirs, for example, the thermal agitation and collisions of the absorbing atoms. In the language of solid-state physics, in discussing the transmission of light through a dielectric medium such as glass, the oscillating induced dipole moment of amplitude P_0 will have a component $P_0 \cos \psi$ in phase with the applied field, and a component $P_0 \sin \psi$, 90° out of phase with the applied field. The corresponding components of the susceptibility, $\chi_{||}$ and $\chi_{\perp}$, are plotted in Fig. 2.1.7. They are also spoken

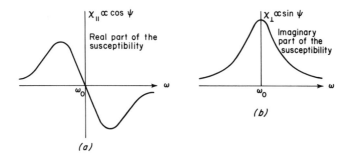

Fig. 2.1.7 The in-phase and out-of-phase components of the susceptibility of a dielectric near a resonance frequency.

[3] This polarization should not be confused with the polarization of waves! $D = \epsilon E = K_e \epsilon_0 E = \epsilon_0 E + P$, $P = \chi E$, $\epsilon = \epsilon_0 + \chi$.

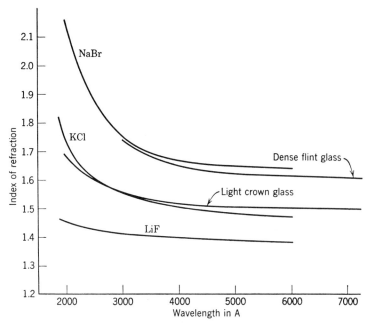

Fig. 2.1.8 The index of refraction of various substances in the ultraviolet and visible portion of the spectrum.

of as the real and imaginary parts of the complex susceptibility when the notation $e^{i\psi} = \cos\psi + i\sin\psi$ is used (see Appendix III). The real part of the susceptibility, $\chi_{||}$, which describes a polarization proportional to the applied field, leads to an increased dielectric coefficient, K_e, and so to a change in the velocity of light.

$$v = \frac{1}{\sqrt{\epsilon\mu_0}} = \frac{1}{\sqrt{K_e}}\frac{1}{\sqrt{\epsilon_0\mu_0}} = \frac{c}{\sqrt{K_e}} = \frac{c}{n} \qquad (2.1.2)$$

where n is the index of refraction and is connected with χ in the following way

$$n = \sqrt{K_e} = \sqrt{\epsilon/\epsilon_0} = \sqrt{1 + \frac{\chi_{||}}{\epsilon_0}}. \qquad (2.1.3)$$

In most transparent media, magnetic effects are negligible, and we have consequently assumed $\mu = \mu_0$ above. The electric effects produce a dependence of the index of refraction on wavelength or frequency. The measured index of refraction for various transparent solids as a function of frequency is shown in Fig. 2.1.8. This dependence of the index of refraction on frequency is called *dispersion*.

TABLE 2.1.1.

The Index of Refraction of Various Substances for Yellow Light Having
a Wavelength of 5890 Å[a]

Diamond	2.42
Glass	1.46–1.96
Quartz	1.544
Ethyl alcohol	1.361
Water	1.333
Air[b]	1.00028

[a] 1 Å (angstrom unit) = 10^{-10} m.
[b] Standard air (15°C, 760 mm Hg).

The strong increase of the index of refraction towards shorter wavelengths is due to resonances of the atoms in the ultraviolet. Because of these
the energy of the incident ultraviolet electromagnetic wave is easily
absorbed. This means that the material is less transparent to the waves in
the ultraviolet, or in the neighborhood of a resonance. The imaginary part
of the susceptibility, $\chi_\perp$, is a measure for the absorption coefficient and,
indeed, near the resonance it has a maximum as shown in Fig. 2.1.7(b).
The index of refraction of a few substances for yellow light is given in
Table 2.1.1.

The wavelength of a ray of light in different media is directly proportional
to the velocity of propagation of the ray, or inversely proportional to the
index of refraction. The frequency of a propagated wave is the same at all
points of its path regardless of the medium in which it is observed. Notice
that peaks and troughs of a traveling wave do not accumulate anywhere
along its path. Consider, then, two points along this path. In some long time
T the number of peaks that pass one of these points must be the same as
the number of peaks that pass the other. This is equivalent to saying that
the number of cycles per second, or the frequency at the two points, must
be the same. From this result, the wavelengths in the two media may be
computed. We have for media 1 and 2, having indices of refraction n_1 and
n_2, shown in Fig. 2.1.9,

$$\nu_1 = \nu_2$$

$$\lambda_1 \nu_1 = v_1 = c/n_1$$

$$\lambda_2 \nu_2 = v_2 = c/n_2$$

and, after dividing,

$$\frac{\lambda_1}{\lambda_2} = \frac{n_2}{n_1} \quad \text{or} \quad \lambda_1 n_1 = \lambda_2 n_2. \tag{2.1.4}$$

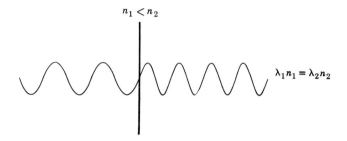

Fig. 2.1.9 A wave of constant frequency traveling with greater velocity in the medium on the left than in the medium on the right. In general, however, the amplitudes to the left and the right of the interface are not equal.

We have discussed the propagation of light in isotropic media only. The velocity of propagation is then independent of the direction in which the light travels and independent of the degree or kind of polarization. These results are no longer true when the light travels in anisotropic crystals. The complex phenomena encountered then can be explained by the fact that the polarizability of crystals is different in different directions, and that therefore the effective index of refraction for a plane-polarized wave will depend on the orientation of the electric vector in the crystal.

Absorption and Emission

Statistical aspects of absorption and emission can be equally well described in terms of wave or quanta. According to the wave picture an oscillating dipole that radiates for only a short time will not radiate at a single frequency, but the frequency spectrum will have a certain width. If the oscillator has a certain amount of energy which it can radiate at its natural frequency ν_0, the amplitude of oscillation will diminish in time due to loss of energy. This decrease can be described by the characteristic time τ, which is the time within which the amplitude falls to $1/e$ of its original value as shown in Fig. 2.1.10. Thus, $A(t) = A_0 e^{-t/\tau} \sin 2\pi\nu_0 t$. The radiated spectrum will not consist of the single frequency ν_0, but there will be a distribution around this frequency which is proportional to $1/\tau$. Such a spectrum is pictured in Fig. 2.1.11. Fundamentally, this distribution results because a pure sine wave has no beginning and no end. Qualitatively this broadening of the frequency spectrum can be made plausible in the following way: Periodic nonsinusoidal functions e.g., the square wave and the sawtooth function illustrated in Fig. 2.1.12 can, by so-called Fourier analysis, be decomposed into sinusoidal components of frequency ν, 2ν, 3ν, 4ν, ..., which constitute a Fourier series. The resulting frequency

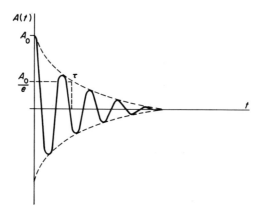

Fig. 2.1.10   A damped harmonic oscillation.

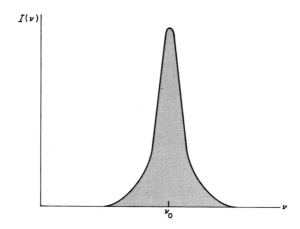

Fig. 2.1.11   The frequency spectrum emitted from a damped oscillator.

spectrum for these two functions is given in Fig. 2.1.13. Musical sounds usually have a rather complex spectrum with amplitudes that vary relatively irregularly with the frequency. The frequency spectrum of an oboe is shown in Fig. 2.1.14.

Similarly, a damped oscillation which by some external force has been excited again to the original amplitude after 2, 4, or 8 oscillations, for instance, can be analyzed into Fourier components, as shown in Fig. 2.1.15. The fundamental frequency ν_1 corresponds to the period T, with which the pattern repeats itself. The frequency ν_0 corresponds to the frequency of the undamped oscillation, or the period T_0. The other frequencies are necessary

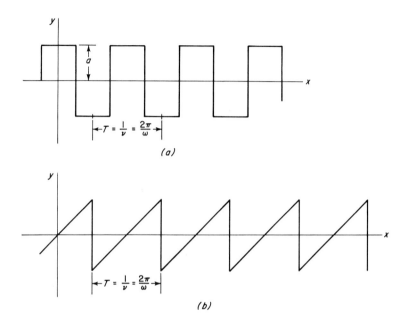

Fig. 2.1.12   Periodic functions that can be represented by a Fourier series.

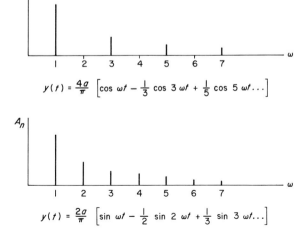

$$y(t) = \frac{4a}{\pi} \left[\cos \omega t - \frac{1}{3} \cos 3 \omega t + \frac{1}{5} \cos 5 \omega t \ldots \right]$$

$$y(t) = \frac{2a}{\pi} \left[\sin \omega t - \frac{1}{2} \sin 2 \omega t + \frac{1}{3} \sin 3 \omega t \ldots \right]$$

Fig. 2.1.13   Frequency spectrum and Fourier series of the functions of Fig. 2.1.12.

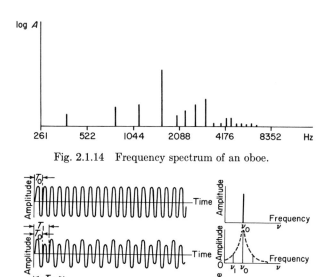

Fig. 2.1.14   Frequency spectrum of an oboe.

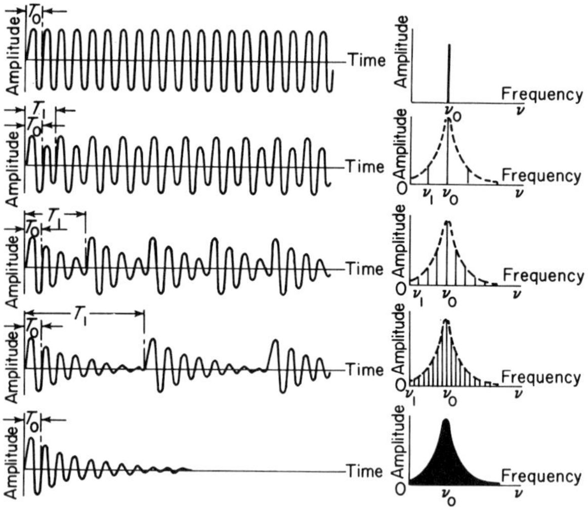

Fig. 2.1.15   Damped oscillations which are repeated after different intervals and their frequency spectrum. At the top is an undamped oscillation.

to give the damped wave its exponential envelope. The longer the time interval to rejuvenate the oscillations the more partial frequencies occur. It is therefore plausible that in the case where there is no repetition, a continuous frequency spectrum will be necessary. This will be described by a Fourier integral instead of a Fourier series. The relative intensities of the partial frequencies depend strongly on the degree of damping. It is obvious that if the damping were zero the frequencies different from ν_0 would be unnecessary. Conversely, the stronger the damping, the more important these frequencies become.

If an oscillating dipole can radiate at its natural frequency ν_0, and the amplitude of oscillation then diminishes with a characteristic time τ, the radiated spectrum will not consist of the single frequency ν_0, but will be distributed around this frequency with a distribution proportional to

$$\frac{1}{1/\tau^2 + (\nu - \nu_0)^2} \, .$$

Approaching our problem from the standpoint of quanta, we must point out that in quantum mechanics there is the well established "uncertainty principle," which relates to this problem (see Chapter 3). Applied to a radiating atom, the principle says that there is necessarily an uncertainty in the frequency that an atom will radiate in a transition to a perfectly sharp level (the undisturbed ground state) such that $\Delta\nu\Delta t \gtrsim 1$, where Δt is the uncertainty in the time, or the lifetime, that the atom spends in its excited state before radiating. Thus in an atomic beam of excited atoms emerging from an aperture, radiation of exponentially decreasing amplitude will be observed as a function of distance along the beam, or time after emerging from the slit. This is described in the language of quanta by saying that we cannot predict at exactly what time any one atom will emit a quantum, but the average number of atoms left in the excited state after a time t is given by $e^{-t/\tau}$. This then leads to the spectrum given by the wave picture if we assume that the excited state is not perfectly sharp defined in its energy E_0 but has a distribution in energy proportional to

$$\frac{1}{1 + [(E - E_0)/\Delta E]^2}$$

with $\Delta E = h\Delta\nu = h/\tau$, which of course, leads to the same spectrum previously obtained; h is Planck's constant, 6.62×10^{-34} joule-sec. Δt or τ is called the lifetime of the excited state. This need not be the lifetime of the excited state of the undisturbed atom, which is called the *natural lifetime* and leads to the *natural line width*. In the usual environment producing radiation, for instance a plasma, collisions with particles and quanta can lead to de-excitation, or removal of the excitation energy. The mean lifetime of the excited state is thereby decreased, and the radiated line consequently broadened. These processes are called collision broadening and radiation broadening, respectively.

Electromagnetic Pressure

Electromagnetic waves exert a pressure on a surface on which they impinge. If E_0 and H_0 are the amplitudes of the electric and magnetic waves, the average value of the Poynting vector is (see also Appendix I)

$$S_{\mathrm{av}} = \tfrac{1}{2}E_0H_0 = \tfrac{1}{2}E_0\left(\sqrt{\frac{\epsilon_0}{\mu_0}}\,E_0\right) = \frac{1}{2}\sqrt{\frac{\epsilon_0}{\mu_0}}\,E_0{}^2.$$

Remembering that the Poynting vector has the mks units volt/m·ampere/m = watt/m² = joule/sec − m² and can be thought of as the energy passing per second through a perpendicular unit area, the quantity

$$\frac{S_{av}}{c} = \sqrt{\epsilon_0\mu_0}\,\frac{1}{2}\sqrt{\frac{\epsilon_0}{\mu_0}}\,E_0^2 = \tfrac{1}{2}\epsilon_0 E_0^2, \tag{2.1.5}$$

represents the energy density in the wave. If such a wave impinges on a perpendicular surface and is absorbed, S_{av}/c represents also the energy which is absorbed per unit time and unit area. This quantity is also equal to the momentum transferred to the unit area per second, or the pressure. If the electromagnetic energy is not absorbed, but reflected, this is only half the pressure, because the change of momentum is now twice as great. A wave carrying 10^4 watts/m², on reflection, exerts a pressure $2 \times 10^4/(3 \times 10^8) \approx 10^{-4}$ newtons/m², or 10^{-9} atmospheres, or roughly 10^{-6} mm Hg. The above result, that the pressure exerted by a light wave on reflection is just twice the energy density divided by c, can also be derived as the interaction between the electromagnetic field at the surface of the reflector and the induced electric currents at the reflecting surface.

In the language of relativistic particles, their energy[4] E and momentum p are related by

$$E^2 = p^2c^2 + m_0^2c^4. \tag{2.1.6}$$

For quanta, the rest mass $m_0 = 0$. Taking the square root we have for a beam of quanta of density n, that is, the number of quanta per unit volume, the

$$\text{energy density} = nE = ncp. \tag{2.1.7}$$

In other words, the momentum carried by the radiation is the energy density divided by c.

Radiation pressure is a limiting factor in the size of stars. Whereas gravitational forces hold stellar matter together, radiation pressure tends to blow it apart. Therefore, stars with a mass $> 10^{32}$ kg would be unstable.

Quanta as Particles

Before closing this discussion, however, it is important to consider a little more thoroughly what properties we may expect small, invisible, "elementary" particles, especially quanta, to have. In terms of directly observable

---

[4] E, which stands for the energy, should not be confused with E_0, which stands for the amplitude of the electric field intensity.

particles, like pebbles, we should expect them to have mass, possibly charge and, as a consequence of their motion, linear and angular momentum, possibly a magnetic moment, and energy. If velocities approaching c are involved, we should expect the above quantities to be related relativistically. The energy E and momentum p would seem to be acceptably described by

$$E = h\nu \tag{2.1.8}$$

$$p = \frac{E}{c} = \frac{h\nu}{c} = \frac{h}{\lambda} \tag{2.1.9}$$

and for the mass m_q of a quantum we may, starting from $E = mc^2$, formally set

$$m_q = \frac{E}{c^2} = \frac{h\nu}{c^2}. \tag{2.1.10}$$

It must be emphasized that a quantum does not have a rest mass. If it had one, it could not travel with the velocity of light, because in this case its relativistic mass would be infinite. On the other hand, a quantum must by necessity travel with the speed of light. The "mass" m_q of a quantum is only an expression of its energy. Charge and magnetic moment also would seem to be reasonably acceptable as not present in quanta. However, we might expect to find angular momentum. We have said that rotating dipoles radiate circularly polarized light. In doing so, they lose angular momentum which they must impart to the radiation field. Linearly oscillating dipoles, on the other hand, lose no angular momentum in radiating plane-polarized waves. Since the constant h has the dimensions of angular momentum, it is not too surprising to find that the angular momentum carried by an electromagnetic quantum is

$$\hbar = \frac{h}{2\pi}, \quad \text{or a multiple of it.}$$

We shall return to this point in our discussion of atomic structure and the radiation of atomic systems in Chapters 3 and 4. But the question remains of the basic structure of particles, the *kinds* of particles that may exist, completely open. For instance, how can a particle be created or destroyed? What is the nature of collisions between particles? These questions have very different answers for different kinds of particles. For quanta, the answers are particularly simple. Subject to the laws of conservation of energy and momentum, quanta can disappear by being absorbed and destroyed by other systems, for instance an atom, which takes on the energy and momentum of the absorbed quantum. Similarly a quantum can be scattered by a collision with a free electron. The electron somehow interacts with the electromagnetic field which determines an average, or statistical aspect, of the motion of quanta, and after the interaction is over, has added momentum which it receives from the quantum. Thus the electron must have added energy which it received from the quantum. The quantum must therefore experience a decrease of frequency.

Because quanta have some particle aspects, they are also called photons, in analogy to electrons, protons, etc. The two names, quantum and photon, are interchangeably used. There is perhaps sometimes some preference for the term photon when particle aspects are in the foreground, and for the term quantum when the electromagnetic wave aspects play a role.

A final important point about quanta, or photons, is that they do not experience collisions with each other. Fields are additive, at least to the approximation that we are discussing here, and rays of electromagnetic radiation can penetrate each other without mutual interference. In other words, the E- and H-vectors of two light beams that cross each other superimpose on each other, but beyond the intersection the waves continue their travel unaffected by the encounter. Furthermore, in an enclosure containing many quanta each quantum is completely uninfluenced by the presence of others. This is entirely different from the behavior of electrons, for instance, and leads to important differences in the statistical behavior of large numbers of quanta in a furnace on one hand, and large numbers of electrons in a metal on the other hand. We shall discuss quantum behavior in Section 2.5 and electron behavior in Chapter 5.

2.2 WAVES—REFLECTION AND REFRACTION

The propagation of waves follows generally applicable rules and results in similar geometrical patterns, whether the waves are acoustic waves in solids, liquids, or gases, electromagnetic waves, electron waves, or other kinds of waves which we shall consider further on.

When an electric wave strikes a polarizable medium, it is reasonable to assume that the induced oscillating dipoles radiate, and that the resultant propagated wave must be considered the resultant of the attenuated incident wave and the added waves radiated by the induced dipoles. That a similar situation exists in a vacuum will not be new to the reader. Electrical currents are due not only to the motion of material charges but, in the case of displacement currents, also to the displacement of virtual charges in a vacuum. Similarly, we can account for the propagation of electromagnetic waves by assuming new waves generated by the polarization of a vacuum.

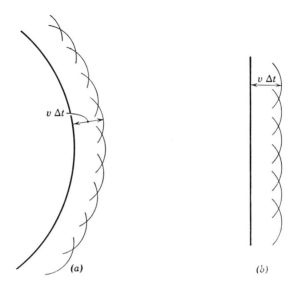

Fig. 2.2.1   The application of Huygens' principle to a spherical and to a plane wave propagated in free space.

This is described very generally, in a form applicable to all kinds of waves, by *Huygens' principle.*[5]

The rigorous formulation of Huygens' principle is beyond the scope of this discussion. Qualitatively, it says that any point on a wave front, such as shown in Fig. 2.2.1, may be thought of as a radiating source emitting a secondary wave, often called a Huygens' wavelet. The oscillation at some other point at later times may be computed by adding the effects of all the secondary waves from all points of the wave front. For spherical and plane waves in a homogeneous medium the propagation of the wave front in a time Δt may be easily computed through drawing all the secondary waves. Their envelope on the forward side of the old wave front is the new wave front whose position was to be computed. The nonappearance of a back wave becomes understandable only if we consider the dissimilarity of the disturbing wave in the forward and backward directions. This can be made plausible with the example of pulses traveling along a stretched string.

Consider two pulses generated in a stretched string by the movement of

[5] Christian Huygens (1629–1695), Dutch scientist; investigated problems in mechanics, e.g., pendulums, collisions. Inventor of the pendulum clock. Theory of waves (Traité de la Lumière, Leyden, 1690).

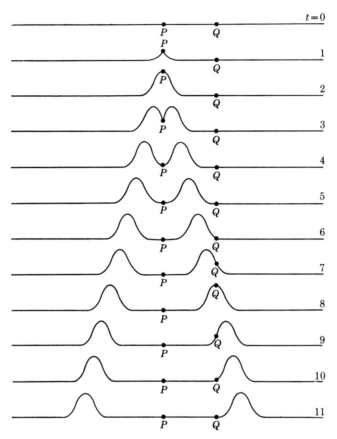

Fig. 2.2.2   The generation of two pulses in a stretched string. The curves represent the condition of the string after successive time intervals, starting at the top.

the point P in Fig. 2.2.2. For the moment we disregard point Q; it is simply another point in the string. As P is moved up and then back again to its original position, the string is distorted as shown, and two pulses are formed, one traveling to the right and one to the left. As the pulse passes point Q, Q undergoes the same motion that P did some time earlier and the string to the right of P is deformed in the same way. It is clear that we may think of the motion of Q as generating a pulse which moves off to the right. However, it is also clear that we would not expect the motion of Q to generate a pulse going to the left, since the deformation of the string on the left of Q is clearly not that required to produce a pulse. The shapes of the string immediately to the left of P at $t = 3$ and to the left of Q at $t = 9$ are very different, although the positions in the transversal direction and the directions of motion of these two points are similar. In fact, no pulse arises in the backward direction. If we think of the motion of Q as generating the propagated pulse, then we must think of the incoming pulse as just canceling the secondary back pulse.

The laws of reflection and refraction may be derived from Huygens' principle. We shall consider the plane surface shown in Fig. 2.2.3, with an

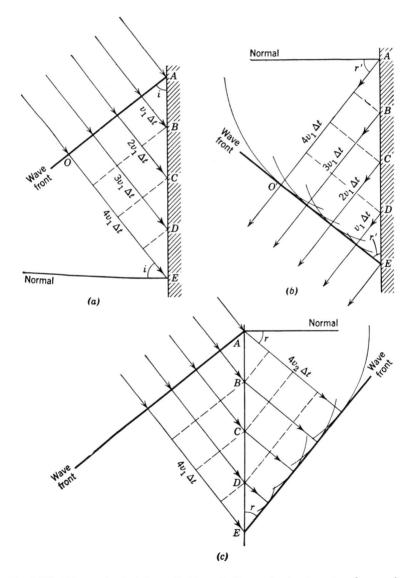

Fig. 2.2.3 Huygens' principle applied to reflection and refraction at a plane surface.

incident plane wave. The velocities in the two media are v_1 and v_2. For the case of electromagnetic radiation we shall say that the indices of refraction on the two sides of the surface are n_1 and n_2, respectively, so that the velocities of propagation in the two media are $v_1 = c/n_1$ and $v_2 = c/n_2$. We shall here concern ourselves only with the direction of propagation of the reflected and refracted waves.

Figure 2.2.3(a) is a representation of a wave front OA at some arbitrary time $t = 0$. The direction of propagation is normal to the wave front. The angle of incidence, i, is defined as the angle between the direction of the incoming rays and the normal to the surface. The position of the wave front at later times Δt, $2\Delta t$, $3\Delta t$, $4\Delta t$ is shown by the dashed lines. At these various times the incoming wave front intersects the reflecting surface at points B, C, D, and E. Let us now consider the Huygens' wavelets that originated at the points A, B, C, D, and E at times $t = 0$, Δt, $2\Delta t$, $3\Delta t$, and $4\Delta t$. These wavelets at the time $t = 4\Delta t$ are shown in Fig. 2.2.3(b). The wavelet originating at A has been growing for a time $4\Delta t$ and therefore has a radius $4v_1\Delta t$. The wavelets originating at B, C, D, and E have been growing for times 3, 2, 1, and 0. The wave front of all these wavelets is shown as OE in Fig. 2.2.3(b).

If the angle of reflection r' is defined as the angle between the reflected ray and the normal to the surface, we have

$$\sin r' = \frac{4v_1\Delta t}{AE}.$$

But from Fig. 2.2.3(a) we have

$$\sin i = \frac{4v_1\Delta t}{AE}$$

and therefore

$$i = r' \tag{2.2.1a}$$

which is the *law of reflection*.

The condition that a surface should reflect an electromagnetic wave is clearly that the envelope of the reflected Huygens' wavelets should be an adequate facsimile of the incident wave. A rough surface will introduce irregularities in the reflected wave. But there is a further requirement that the surface be flat and smooth over distances as measured in wavelengths. If it is not, interferences and diffraction effects (to be discussed in Sect. 2.3) will distort the reflected wave. One of the great surprises of the early days of radio was that signals were not limited to the horizon from the radiating source, but followed the curvature of the earth. This, it turns out, is due to an ionized layer in the atmosphere which is a relatively good conductor. It contains up to 10^6 ions and electrons per cubic centimeter at altitudes of a few hundred kilometers. Radio waves are reflected back and forth between the earth and the ionized layer, and so travel around the earth.

In deducting the law of refraction we must consider the Huygens' wavelets on the right side of the surface, or in medium 2, shown in Fig. 2.2.3(c). Calling the angle of refraction, r, that between the refracted ray and the normal to the surface, we have

$$\sin r = \frac{4v_2 \Delta t}{AE}$$

or, combining this with the above expression for the angle of incidence,

$$\frac{\sin i}{\sin r} = \frac{v_1}{v_2} = \frac{n_2}{n_1}.$$

The relationship between the angles of incidence and refraction and the indices of refraction of the two media involved is called *Snell's law*. If n_i is the index of refraction of the medium in which the incident ray is propagated, and if n_r is the index of refraction of the medium in which the transmitted ray is propagated, Snell's law, illustrated in Fig. 2.2.4, states that

$$n_i \sin i = n_r \sin r. \tag{2.2.1b}$$

Note that a ray is bent toward the normal in going from one medium into another having a greater index of refraction, as in going from air into water or glass.

Since the index of refraction is in general a function of frequency, or wavelength, different colors will be deviated by different amounts in going from one medium to another. This effect may be used to separate the

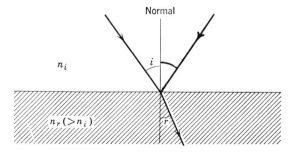

Fig. 2.2.4   An illustration of reflection and refraction at a plane surface.

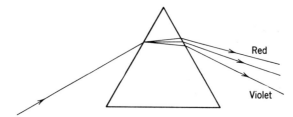

Fig. 2.2.5 The separation of rays of different wavelength in traversing a prism.

frequencies of colors which constitute any given ray, as in the case of the prism illustrated in Fig. 2.2.5.

A special case of importance occurs when n_r, the index of refraction of the medium in which the refracted ray is propagated, is less than n_i, the index of the medium in which the incident ray is propagated. Snell's law may be put in the form

$$\sin i = \frac{n_r}{n_i} \sin r$$

where according to our assumption the ratio n_r/n_i is less than unity. Now, obviously, since $\sin r$ cannot possibly be greater than unity, $\sin i$ cannot possibly be greater than n_r/n_i. This limiting value of the angle of incidence is called the critical angle, i_c. For greater angles of incidence, there is no way of satisfying Snell's law. There is consequently no refracted ray, only a reflected ray.

For angles of incidence greater than the critical angle, all the light must be reflected since none is transmitted. Reflection in these circumstances is called "total reflection," and the conditions are illustrated in Fig. 2.2.6.

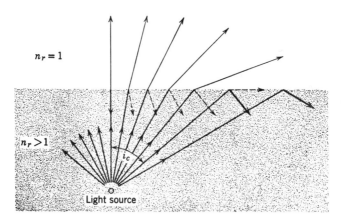

Fig. 2.2.6 The paths of light rays from an underwater light source.

Reflecting Power.

In the preceding discussion we made use of none of the electromagnetic aspects of light except its velocity. We must now reconsider the phenomena, particularly those affecting the electric and magnetic fields involved, that take place when a light ray strikes a boundary between two transparent dielectric media, for example, the interface between air and glass. We should expect to obtain not only the laws of reflection and refraction which we derived from Huygens' principle but also an interpretation of the fraction of the incident light which is reflected and the fraction refracted at an interface.

We shall begin with the simplest optical problem involving a surface, namely, normal incidence of a plane wave at a plane interface between two transparent dielectrics. We may expect that the incident wave will give rise to two other waves, one transmitted and one refracted, so that we shall have three in all to deal with. We shall need, for our discussion, the relationship between the electric and magnetic fields in a plane wave, which is derived in Appendix I,

$$\sqrt{\epsilon}\,E \;=\; \sqrt{\mu}\,H. \tag{I.20}$$

Using $v = (\epsilon\mu)^{-1/2}$ (Eq. I.15), we can write for the index of refraction

$$n = c/v = \sqrt{\frac{1}{\epsilon_0\mu_0}} \Big/ \sqrt{\frac{1}{\epsilon\mu}}.$$

Remembering that for substances transparent to light $\mu = \mu_0$, we have for the index of refraction $n = (\epsilon/\epsilon_0)^{1/2}$. We thus obtain

$$H = \sqrt{\frac{\epsilon}{\mu}}\,E = \sqrt{\frac{\epsilon}{\epsilon_0}\cdot\frac{\epsilon_0}{\mu}}\,E = \sqrt{\frac{\epsilon}{\epsilon_0}\cdot\frac{\epsilon_0}{\mu_0}}\,E = n\sqrt{\frac{\epsilon_0}{\mu_0}}\,E. \tag{2.2.2}$$

We need, furthermore, the boundary conditions to be satisfied at the interface between the normal and tangential components of the electric and magnetic fields.

$$D_{n1} = D_{n2} \qquad B_{n1} = B_{n2}$$

$$E_{t1} = E_{t2} \qquad H_{t1} = H_{t2} \tag{2.2.3}$$

The condition for D_n follows from Gauss's law

$$\int_S D_n dA \;=\; \sum q_i,$$

because there are no charges at the interface. The condition for E_t is a consequence of

$$\oint \mathbf{E} \cdot \mathbf{ds} = 0.$$

Because the lines of B cannot end at the interface, we have the condition for B_n. Finally, Ampère's law,

$$\oint \mathbf{H} \cdot \mathbf{ds} = i$$

yields, because there is no current at the interface, the boundary condition for H_t.

We shall apply Eqs. 2.2.2 and 2.2.3 to a normally incident wave using the notation and the geometrical relationships shown in Fig. 2.2.7, in which for the sake of clarity the three rays in question are shown slightly displaced with respect to each other. The vectors shown are instantaneous values of the boundary and may be thought of as varying with time as the waves move toward and away from the surface. The problem is to attempt to satisfy the boundary conditions (Eq. 2.2.3) and the relationship (Eq. 2.2.2) by the superposition of the three waves which we expect to find.

At the boundary, either the electric or the magnetic vector in the reflected ray must be reversed in order to reverse the direction of propagation, as specified by the Poynting vector. We shall assume, arbitrarily for the moment, that we are dealing with case (a) of Fig. 2.2.3, and that the electric vector is reversed whereas the magnetic vector is unchanged. The electromagnetic boundary conditions are particularly simple for the case of normally incident radiation, since we have only tangential vectors to consider. The normal components of B and D vanish, since they are in the direction of propagation of the wave, and the tangential components of E

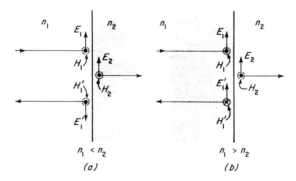

Fig. 2.2.7   Reflection and transmission at a surface.

and H must have the same values on either side of the boundary. Designating the absolute magnitude of the electric and magnetic vectors at the boundary in the incident ray by E_1 and H_1, in the reflected ray by E'_1 and H'_1, and in the transmitted ray by E_2 and H_2, we have to satisfy the boundary conditions by putting

$$E_1 - E'_1 = E_2 \tag{2.2.4}$$

$$H_1 + H'_1 = H_2. \tag{2.2.5}$$

But from Eq. 2.2.2 we see that

$$H_1 = n_1\sqrt{\frac{\epsilon_0}{\mu_0}}\, E_1 \qquad H'_1 = n_1\sqrt{\frac{\epsilon_0}{\mu_0}}\, E'_1 \qquad H_2 = n_2\sqrt{\frac{\epsilon_0}{\mu_0}}\, E_2. \tag{2.2.6}$$

Substituting these results into Eq. 2.2.5, we get

$$E_1 + E'_1 = \frac{n_2}{n_1} E_2 \tag{2.2.7}$$

and finally on combining this result with Eq. 2.2.4, thus eliminating E_2,

$$E'_1 = \left(\frac{n_2 - n_1}{n_2 + n_1}\right) E_1 \tag{2.2.8}$$

which specifies the magnitude of the electric vector in the reflected ray in terms of the magnitude of the electric vector in the incident ray. For the transmitted ray the corresponding result is, by eliminating E'_1,

$$E_2 = \left(\frac{2n_1}{n_2 + n_1}\right) E_1. \tag{2.2.9}$$

Notice that if n_2 is greater than n_1, according to Eq. 2.2.8, E'_1 is positive, as is to be expected for the magnitude of a vector if its orientation was properly chosen originally. We therefore conclude that a plane-polarized ray is reflected with a reversal of the electric vector at a boundary at which the reflecting medium has the greater index of refraction. An example is a beam of light in air being reflected at a glass or water surface. If, however, n_1 is greater than n_2, as would be the case for a ray traveling under water and being reflected at an air surface, the reflection takes place with a reversal of the magnetic rather than the electric vector. These points, though apparently of little significance at this stage, will be shown to be essential to an understanding of the optical properties of thin films which we shall discuss in Section 2.3.

The reflecting power of a surface for normal incidence is given by the ratio of the intensities, or of the Poynting vectors, describing the reflected and incident rays. Using the above results we have, for the reflecting power R,

$$R = \frac{S'_1}{S_1} = \left(\frac{E'_1}{E_1}\right)^2 = \left(\frac{n_2 - n_1}{n_2 + n_1}\right)^2. \qquad (2.2.10)$$

Compare this result with that obtained in connection with the discussion of partial reflection in a transmission line in Section 1.2.

If we had considered light incident at an arbitrary angle of incidence i, we should have had to specify the orientation of the E-vector in the incident ray and we should have had to assume arbitrary angles r' and r for the directions of the reflected and refracted rays. The solution of the problem would have proceeded as above, with the finding that for any orientation of the electric vector

$$i = r'$$

$$n_i \sin i = n_r \sin r$$

as in the previous discussion of Huygens' principle. In addition, we would have found, that if the electric vector in the incident ray is parallel to the reflecting surface, then the electric vectors in the reflected and refracted rays will also be parallel to the reflecting surface, and the ratio of the intensities of the reflected and incident rays, or the reflecting power R, is

$$R = \frac{\sin^2(i - r)}{\sin^2(i + r)}. \qquad (2.2.11)$$

This function is plotted in 'Fig. 2.2.8. If, on the other hand, the electric vector in the incident ray is in the plane of incidence, that is, the plane containing the incident ray and the normal to the surface, then the electric vector in the reflected and refracted rays will also be in this plane, and the

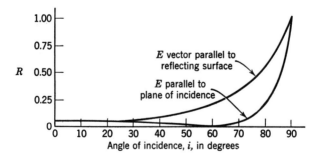

Fig. 2.2.8 The reflecting power of a surface for oblique incidence.

reflecting power is

$$R = \frac{\tan^2(i - r)}{\tan^2(i + r)}. \tag{2.2.12}$$

This discussion indicates how to use the expressions for the reflecting power of a surface for light incident at oblique angles. If the incident light is unpolarized, we may resolve it into two plane-polarized components. Each of these will be partly reflected and partly transmitted. But, from Fig. 2.2.8, we see that in general different fractions of these two rays will be reflected. In general, the reflected light and the transmitted light will be partly polarized. The reflected light will have its electric vector predominantly parallel to the plane of the reflecting surface. At one particular angle of incidence, the reflected light will be completely polarized. This is called Brewster's angle or simply the polarizing angle. In Fig. 2.2.8, it is in the vicinity of 60°. This situation arises when the denominator of Eq. 2.2.12 becomes infinite, or when $i + r = 90°$. We can express the polarizing angle in terms of the indices of refraction concerned by the following argument. We have from Snell's law

$$n_i \sin i = n_r \sin r.$$

If the angle of incidence is the polarizing angle i_p, we also have

$$i_p + r = \pi/2$$

and consequently

$$n_i \sin i_p = n_r \sin \left(\frac{\pi}{2} - i_p\right) = n_r \cos i_p$$

or

$$\tan i_p = \frac{n_r}{n_i}. \tag{2.2.13}$$

When light of any polarization is incident on a surface at the polarizing angle specified by Eq. 2.2.13, none of the component with the electric vector parallel to the plane of incidence is reflected. In other words, the electric vector in the reflected light can only be parallel to the plane of the reflecting surface. Reflection at the polarizing angle can be used to produce plane-polarized light.

Sunglasses with polarizing filters transmit light having its E-vector vertical and so absorb to a great extent the glare from highways or water surfaces, which is predominantly horizontally polarized. Reflection on metallic surfaces, including ordinary mirrors, is a considerably more complicated phenomenon and will not be treated here.

We have seen that the change in index of refraction, or of speed of light, at the interface of two adjoining media is the cause for the reflection of a fraction of the incident light. Later we shall meet analogous situations in wave mechanics, in particular in applications to nuclear physics. Similar considerations also apply for the reflection and transmission of sound waves at a boundary between two different media. Because the density and the speed of sound in water are so much greater than in air, essentially no sound wave energy will pass directly from one medium to the other; in the case of perpendicular incidence only one-thousandth will be transmitted. Nature, however, elegantly has overcome this problem in the ear. The spiral-shaped cochlea in the inner ear contains the auditory nerve endings. Although this portion is filled with liquid, sound waves are transmitted from the air-filled middle ear by way of an acoustical impedance matching device, the three small bones or ossicles—the hammer, anvil, and stirrup. These bones form a lever system by which the large amplitudes of the low-density air are transformed into small amplitudes of the high-density liquid.

The Formation of Images

We see objects because rays from points on the object enter the eye. We wish to emphasize that not only one ray but a small bundle of diverging rays from every point on the object enters the eye. It is this divergent bundle that gives us the sensation of seeing the point of origin of the bundle of rays. Such a bundle of rays entering an eye from two points on an object is shown in Fig. 2.2.9. In the process of seeing, the entire path of the light rays is not important. The eye takes into account only the nature of the rays as they enter the eye itself. Whether the rays actually come from the object, as shown in the figure, or whether they come out of some kind of optical instrument in these particular directions, is immaterial. The eye will see the same thing.

Two ways in which optical instruments can make· us see an object at a place where, in fact, it is not, are shown in Fig. 2.2.10. In (a) the optical instrument, a lens, takes rays diverging from a point and makes them

Fig. 2.2.9   Rays of light from two points on an object which are required for seeing these points.

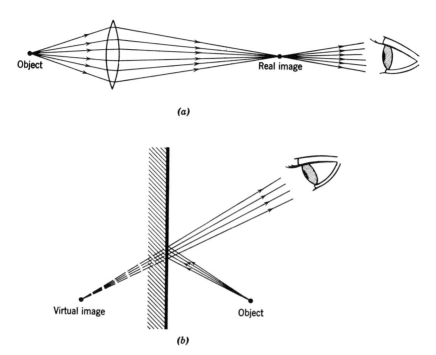

(a)

(b)

Fig. 2.2.10   Real and virtual images.

converge at some other point in their path. Beyond this point they again diverge, and an eye intercepting this diverging bundle will see the object at the point of divergence. This point of divergence is called an image of the object. It is called a real image, that is, one through which the rays actually pass, to distinguish it from the image in Fig. 2.2.10(*b*). Here the optical instrument used is a mirror, though in fact it need not be; similar effects can be produced with lenses. The rays entering the eye appear to diverge from a point behind the mirror, though in fact the mirror is opaque. The image at this point is called a virtual image, that is, one through which the rays do not actually pass.

Instead of delving deeper into ray optics, also called geometrical optics, we shall discuss the focusing properties of lenses in terms of wave optics.[6] In Fig. 2.2.11 a plane wave impinges perpendicularly on a plane-convex lens. Inside the glass the wave is slowed down; consequently, the wave

---

[6] Today, geometrical optics is sometimes looked down upon. However, it should be recalled that it still plays an important role. Zoom lenses, fish-eye lenses, and lenses of very great aperture are essentially post-World War II developments, made possible only by extensive use of computers and the creation of new glasses with the desired properties.

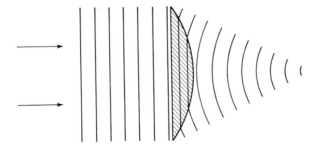

Fig. 2.2.11   Focusing of wave fronts of plane waves by a plane-convex lens.

fronts are closer together. Those parts of the wave front which are furthest away from the axis leave the lens first and under the greatest angle to the normal of the surface. According to the refraction laws which we have derived with Huygens' principle the wave front changes direction, and, since the angle between wave front and lens surface increases with the distance from the axis, the angle of refraction becomes bigger too. The wave front leaving the lens is therefore bent. The waves converge into a point, the focal point. It is left as an exercise to prove that these wave fronts are parts of circles, if the lens surface is spherical.

The important conclusion that can be drawn is that the wave fronts never were broken apart or disrupted by the lens, although they were distorted. If we want to use the picture of soldiers marching in step, the ranks may not be straight anymore after passing through an obstacle (the analog to the lens) but the soldiers still are in step with each other, and each soldier in the same row will reach the focal point at the same time. Reverting to light waves, a lens will distort the wave front, but it will not change the phase relationship within the wave front.

2.3   WAVES—INTERFERENCE AND DIFFRACTION

Introduction

Waves can be made to show interference. We have shown in Section 1.3 that radio waves from two (or more) synchronized antennas separated by distances of the order of wavelengths will produce interference effects, or nonuniform radiation patterns at distant points. The same is true for any wavelengths for which we can produce phase-related oscillating dipoles at suitable regular intervals. In the range of visible light, with wavelengths of 5×10^{-7} m or 5×10^{-4} mm, we can construct slits or reflecting surfaces with the required spacing. For x-rays, with wavelengths of the order of atomic dimensions, we can use the regular atomic spacing in atoms to produce the desired effects. These matters are taken up in detail here.

Diffraction is a related phenomenon that arises when part of a traveling wave is stopped, as shown in Fig. 2.3.1 for instance. In (a) we are dealing

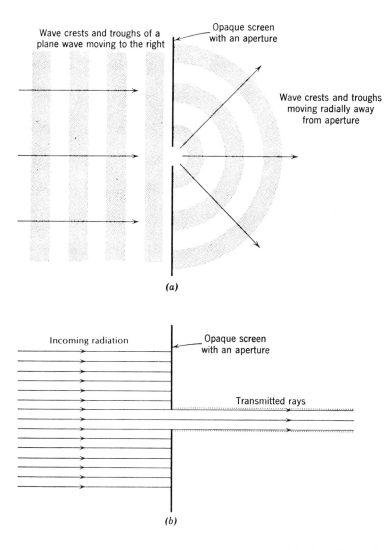

Fig. 2.3.1   The propagation of a wave through an aperture; (a) when the wavelength is comparable to the size of the aperture; (b) when the wavelength is small compared to the size of the aperture.

with a wave striking an aperture whose size is comparable to the wavelength, as for example, in the case of an ocean wave striking an opening in a breakwater. The wave inside spreads out fanwise and, as it spreads out, its amplitude decreases. When it has traveled many wavelengths, its amplitude is small compared to that of the original incident plane wave. In (b) it is assumed that the wavelength is small compared to the size of the aperture. Instead of shaded bands to indicate the crests and troughs of the wave, parallel lines are drawn in the direction of propagation. These are rays of radiation. The aperture now defines a beam. It is true that the edges of this beam are not perfectly sharply defined, as is indicated by the dotted line at the edge of the beam. Diffraction effects are most important not only in optics, but also in nuclear physics and will be discussed further.

Coherence

We have already discussed the interference pattern produced by two antennas (Section 1.3). The same arguments can readily be extended to any number of antennas in a linear or a two-dimensional array. Complete destructive interference at a point P in the field of the array will be achieved if the sum of the electric fields of all the waves passing through P adds to zero. For any two to interfere destructively we should require that they have (a) the same frequency, (b) the same amplitude, (c) the same polarization, and (d) that for complete cancellation, they are and remain 180° out of phase with each other.

Two independent sources of radiation, even if they satisfy conditions a, b, and c, but not d, will in general not produce interference phenomena, because no fixed-phase relationships between the two sources exist.[7] Such sources of radiation are said to be incoherent, whereas the two antennas coupled to the same oscillator are coherent.

The question of coherence (from the Latin *co*—together, *haerere*—to stick) in recent years has become of particular interest because of the lasers which can produce highly coherent light.

In the example of two antennas driven by the same oscillator operated at a constant frequency the two waves emerging have at any place in space a constant phase relationship. This means that at certain points there is always constructive interference between the two and at others always destructive interference. The two antennas are coherent sources of radiation and the waves emitted are coherent waves. It is not necessary that the two

---

[7] Two tuning forks of slightly different frequencies will produce beats, which are some kind of interference phenomenon, although neither condition a nor d is satisfied.

antennas radiate in phase with each other to produce interference. However, it is necessary that their phase relationship is fixed. If the two antennas emit waves that are 180° out of phase, the locations of constructive and destructive interference change place. If the phase relationship between the antennas becomes variable in time the interference phenomena wander or even disappear. This might happen if we replace the single oscillator driving both antennas by two independent oscillators which do not have quite the same frequency. If we now consider two transmitters which are turned on and shut off, each one operating in completely random bursts, no interference effects will be observed, assuming that the observations are averaged over a sufficient time span which includes a fair number of bursts.

However, if the random bursts are generated in an oscillator which feeds both antennas, the two antennas are coherent sources because their phase difference remains constant. A necessary condition for the occurrence of appreciable interference phenomena is that for the two beams the difference in path length Δ between source and point of observation is small against the length $c\tau$ of a wave train, τ being the duration of its emission and c the velocity of light. Obviously in order to interfere with each other, the two waves must sufficiently overlap in time at the point of observation, as shown in Fig. 2.3.2. The length of a wave train is called its coherence length.

Instead of radio antennas, we now consider sources of monochromatic light, say, a sodium vapor lamp. In such a device the sodium atoms are excited by some process (e.g., collisions) into higher energy levels and spontaneously return to their ground states with emission of light quanta. From the foregoing it should now be clear that two such lamps are not coherent sources, because the emissions of the atoms are uncorrelated.

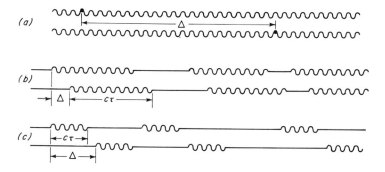

Fig. 2.3.2 (a)Two very (or infinitely) long wave trains can interfere even if the difference in phase, or path length, is very great. (b) For short wave trains the path difference must be shorter than the length of the wave trains to obtain interference. (c) No interference, although the two beams are coherent.

However, we can produce two coherent light beams from one single lamp by dividing the emitted light beam with the aid of a half-transmitting mirror into two light beams, therefore creating a situation similar to that discussed above, where one oscillator producing random bursts drove two antennas. The important point to remember is that the so-created two beams vary in amplitude, polarization, and phase in the same way. Two such light beams can be brought to interference if the difference in path length does not exceed the coherence length $c\tau$ of the emitted light. For atoms the time of radiation is of the order of 10^{-11} to 10^{-7} sec, so that the coherence length would be of the order of 0.003 to 30 m. If the length of the two arms of a Michelson interferometer (see Sects. 1.5 and 2.3) differs by more than half a coherence length, the interference fringes disappear. Much greater coherence lengths, up to 10^8 m, can be produced today by lasers, described toward the end of Section 2.5.

We have discussed coherence thus far always in terms of two sources, one of which could be a mirror image of the other, and both had to be in a constant phase relationship. Very often, however, the word "coherent" is used to characterize a single light beam, which means that between any two points of the wave which are separated by a certain time interval there is always the same phase difference. In this sense, a single wave as the one of Fig. 2.3.2(a) is a coherent wave, but obviously the single waves of Fig. 2.3.2(b) or (c) are not. Light with such a property is, so to speak, coherent with itself. A very good example of such coherent light is laser light. On the other hand, light from a single ordinary lamp is said to be incoherent.

One might be tempted to argue that in a source emitting incoherent but monochromatic light the individual wave trains that are emitted with random phases should cancel each other, with the result that no light at all should be observed. However, under such circumstances we have just as many situations of total destructive as of total constructive interference. These are the extreme cases, and in the average there is some partial constructive interference. The end effect is that in the case of incoherent light the intensity at a certain point in space is just the sum of the intensities of the individual light sources.

Interference

An experiment that contributed greatly to the recognition of the wave theory of light was Young's[8] famous interference experiment in 1801. At

---

[8] Thomas Young (1773–1829), physician in London. His wealth allowed him to devote much of his time to other interests. His scholarly endeavors were not limited to the wave theory of light; he also contributed substantially to the decipherment of the hieroglyphics of the Rosetta Stone.

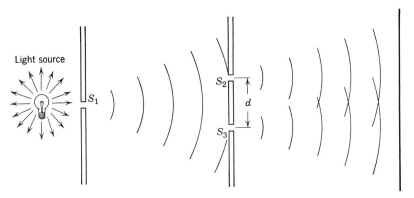

Fig. 2.3.3 Young's double-slit experiment.

that time Huygens' ideas, promulgated about a hundred years earlier, had nearly been forgotten. The essentials of the experiment are illustrated in Fig. 2.3.3. A monochromatic light source, for instance the yellow light of a sodium lamp, is used to illuminate a single slit S_1. The slit functions as a very small light source. Huygens' wavelets may be thought of as originating from this slit. Beyond this slit S_1 are two further slits S_2 and S_3, equidistant from S_1, from which two sets of Huygens' wavelets emerge. These wavelets have the same phase, amplitude, and polarization since they are stimulated by the same original wavelet from S_1. (Much greater intensities, however, may be achieved by using the coherent light from a laser to illuminate the slits S_2 and S_3.) Beyond these slits is an opaque screen on which a series of light and dark bands parallel to the slits appear. The position of the bright maxima may be computed from the condition that the difference in path length of the two rays to the point in question must be some integral number of wavelengths as discussed in Section 1.3. Using the quantities designated in Fig. 2.3.4, we see that the required condition for an interference maximum at a point P far from the slits is that

$$r_2 - r_1 = d \sin \alpha = n\lambda. \tag{2.3.1}$$

But for small angles

$$\sin \alpha \simeq x/r \tag{2.3.2}$$

and by combining Eqs. 2.3.1 and 2.3.2 we can compute the position of the maxima.

The distribution of intensity on the screen due to the interference of rays from two slits is given by the same expression derived in Section 1.3. If the intensity at the screen due to light from one slit alone is I_1 (which as

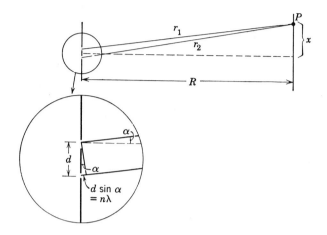

Fig. 2.3.4   The conditions to be satisfied for an interference maximum.

mentioned earlier, is proportional to $E_1{}^2$), the intensity of the combined beams, in the symbols of Fig. 2.3.4 is

$$I = 4I_1 \cos^2 \left[\frac{\pi d}{\lambda} \sin \alpha \right]. \qquad (2.3.3)$$

If the distance to the screen is large enough compared to x, $\sin \alpha \simeq \tan \alpha = x/R$, and the above reduces to

$$I = 4I_1 \cos^2 \left[\pi \frac{d}{\lambda} \frac{x}{R} \right]. \qquad (2.3.4)$$

As above, we see the intensity will have its maximum value, $4I_1$, when $(d/\lambda)(x/R)$ has an integral value, or is zero. The intensity vanishes when $(d/\lambda)(x/R)$ is an integer plus a half. The intensity distribution on the screen is shown in Fig. 2.3.5(a).

The interference patterns obtained with three or more equally spaced slits or sources are more complicated and are very important. We shall consider the case where the number N of slits or sources becomes very large. This is realized in an optical grating, which consists of a glass plate into which parallel grooves are ruled at regular intervals. The untouched strips between the grooves act as slits and transmit the light. If the lines are ruled on a metallized surface, the grating will work in reflection instead of transmission. The distance between lines, or the grating constant, in gratings used for research in the range of visible light, is of the order of magnitude of 10^{-3} to 10^{-4} cm. Large gratings might have more than 100,000 lines.

Monochromatic light coming from a grating does not show the broad interference maxima of Fig. 2.3.5(a) as was the case with two slits, but very sharp maxima, as in Fig. 2.3.5(b). Let us assume that we have a transmission grating with light falling onto it perpendicularly. These parts of the light waves that emerge from the slits perpendicularly are all in phase with each other, and will give rise to the zero-order maximum. The first-order maximum results when the path difference for light rays leaving neighboring slits is equal to λ. At the zero order there is a maximum for all wavelengths. The first-, second-, and higher-order maxima will come for values of x depending on the wavelength involved. Thus, if light containing two or more different wavelengths is incident on a grating, there will be two or more different maxima at each order of interference except the zero order, where the maxima coincide.

The position of the maxima is determined by the same condition for neighboring beams as in the case of two slits, shown in Fig. 2.3.4. The first-order maximum results from a phase difference of 360° between neighbors, which corresponds to a difference in path length equal to λ. To understand the sharpness of the lines we have to find at what angle the several beams cancel and thus produce the first minimum next to the

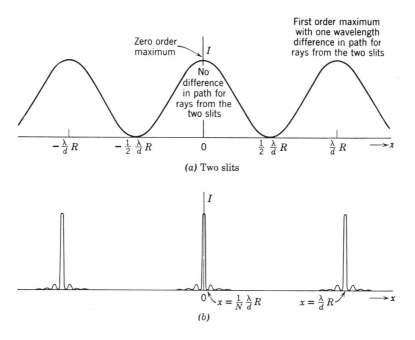

Fig. 2.3.5 (a) The interference pattern due to two slits. (b) The interference pattern due to N equally spaced slits ($N = 20$).

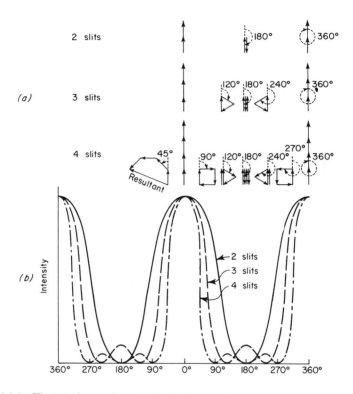

Fig. 2.3.6   The interference from 2, 3, and 4 beams. (a) Phase diagrams. (b) Intensity.

maximum. Since each beam has the same phase relation to its neighbor and has the same amplitude, we can construct a vector diagram in which each beam is represented by a vector. These vectors have equal length but different direction. Their sum represents the amplitude of the total light beam traveling in the direction under consideration. The square of the vector sum yields the intensity of the beam. Examples of phase diagrams for two, three, and four slits are given in Fig. 2.3.6(a). They are drawn for the minima between the zero- and first-order maximum, the first-order maximum, and also for some subsidiary maxima. Figure 2.3.6(b) gives the intensity as a function of angle. As shown in Fig. 2.3.6(a), two beams destroy each other when the phase angle is 180° and have again a maximum for 360°. Three beams can cancel each other when the phase angle is 120° or 240°, and will have a subsidiary maximum having $\frac{1}{9}$ the intensity of the main maxima at 0° and 360°. Similarly four slits will produce minima for phase shifts of 90°, 180°, 270°, with major maxima at 0° and 360°, and subsidiary maxima in between which are $\frac{1}{16}$ of the main maxima. Translating the phase angles shown in Fig. 2.3.6(a) to positions on the screen shown in Fig. 2.3.5, we see how the sharp lines produced by a grating evolve from the broad maxima resulting from two or a few interfering beams. It is therefore evident that the more lines taking part in an interference phenomenon the sharper the lines will be, because more and more roughly equally spaced subsidiary maxima must be accommodated between the main maxima which in all cases appear at phase differences of 0°, 360°, and integral multiples of 360°. If the spectroscopist wants to obtain sharp spectral lines he must see to it that the greatest possible number of lines of the grating are contributing.

We also can consider N equally spaced apertures of a grating, a distance d apart, shown in Fig. 2.3.7. In the forward direction all the rays to a sufficiently distant point P will have the same length, and we may expect a zero-order maximum as for two slits. If we consider rays making a small angle α with the forward direction, the first minimum will come not when the differences in path length of adjacent rays is $\lambda/2$ but at a much smaller angle. We divide the grating in two, with the lower and upper halves shown in the illustration having the same number of slits. When the path difference δ between the ray from the first slit and the central slit marked $N/2$ is one-half wavelength, these two rays will cancel each other. Similarly, for this same direction the second ray and that marked $N/2 + 1$ will cancel each other. Similarly, we can see that all the rays will cancel in pairs. The first minimum will therefore occur when

$$\delta = \frac{Nd}{2}\sin\alpha = \lambda/2 \tag{2.3.5}$$

$$\sin\alpha = \lambda/Nd \tag{2.3.6}$$

$$x \simeq R\sin\alpha = \frac{1}{N}\frac{\lambda}{d}R. \tag{2.3.7}$$

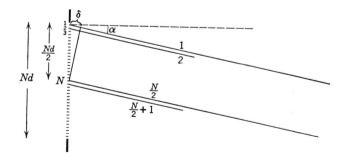

Fig. 2.3.7   Light transmitted by a grating.

There will be subsidiary maxima on each side of the central maxima, having smaller intensities. Thus, if we divide the grating into three zones, the rays from the first two will cancel when $\delta = (Nd/3) \sin \alpha = \lambda/2$ or for $\sin \alpha = 3\lambda/2Nd$. But this leaves the rays from the lower third of the grating uncanceled, and these rays are responsible for the adjacent maximum. The pattern for a grating having 20 lines illuminated with a single wavelength is shown in Fig. 2.3.5(b). The vertical scale is greatly reduced. The height of the intensity maxima is really very much greater than in Fig. 2.3.5(a), since the total area under the curve in both cases is simply the total energy coming through all the slits. There are not only more slits, but the energy flow is crowded into a narrower beam.

Like a refracting prism, a grating may be used to analyze or separate the wavelengths or frequencies present in any given bundle of light rays. Our eyes interpret these different frequencies as different colors. The order of the spectral colors as seen by the eye in order of increasing wavelengths and the corresponding range of the wavelength in millimicrons (1 mμ = 10^{-9} m) are approximately

Violet	390–420 mμ
Indigo	420–450
Blue	450–495
Green	495–570
Yellow	570–590
Orange	590–635
Red	635–770

It must be borne in mind, however, that color on the one hand and wavelength or frequency on the other are two different things. There is not even a unique correspondence between the two. Although we can say that a given frequency has a particular color, we cannot reverse the statement and say that a given color has a given frequency. There are many combinations of light of different frequency ranges that have the same color. The eye, unlike the ear, is not an analytical instrument. A trained ear can hear separately the individual frequencies that go into the combination called a chord. A sound having a single frequency cannot be duplicated by a combination of sounds having many different frequencies.

Thin Films; Interferometers

We now take up a somewhat more complicated case of interference, namely, that due to the interaction of light rays successively reflected by the surfaces of a thin film, as shown in Fig. 2.3.8. The complication arises

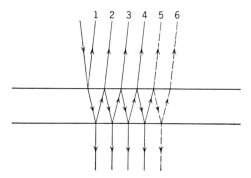

Fig. 2.3.8   Successive reflections in a thin film.

because we must take into account not only the phases of the successively reflected rays but also their intensities. The results obtained are maxima and minima whose positions depend on the direction of the incident light, and on the thickness of the film. We shall confine ourselves to a simple case which illustrates the points involved. First, we shall consider monochromatic light normally incident, or nearly so, as shown in Fig. 2.3.9. The angle of incidence is exaggerated in order not to confuse the figure by having the incident and reflected rays almost overlapping. It further turns out that the computation of the conditions for a maximum or a minimum in the reflected light, taking into account all the internal reflections, produces the same result as that obtained by using only the rays marked 1 and 2 in Fig. 2.3.8. We shall consequently limit ourselves to these two reflected rays, and shall consider the case of a thin film having an index greater than that of the medium on either side as, for example, in the case

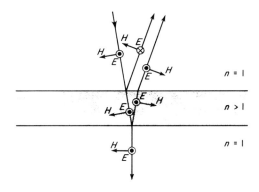

Fig. 2.3.9   Reflection of light from a thin film.

of a soap film in air. In Section 2.2 we gave the phase relationships for a ray reflected at a single surface. This is here applied to the successively reflected parts of the incident ray for the case that the film thickness is very small compared to the wavelength, so that all parts of the ray shown are in phase except for the reversals at the boundaries. In other words, the time taken for the wave to traverse the film is assumed to be very small compared to a period. It should be noticed that the electric vector of the incident ray is reversed at the first reflection and that the magnetic vector is unchanged. The transmitted ray remains in phase with the incident ray. At the lower surface the magnetic vector is reversed in the reflected ray and the electric vector remains unaltered. The net result is that both vectors in the two reflected rays are 180° out of phase and tend to cancel each other. There will therefore be a minimum intensity in the reflected light. In the limit as the film thickness diminishes, the reflection vanishes, and all the light is transmitted.

In considering thicker films, it should be pointed out that if the time required for the ray to traverse the film is an integral number of periods, the conditions outlined above are essentially unaltered. One of the reflected rays will be out of phase with the other, and there will be a minimum in the reflected intensity. Quantitatively, if T is the time required for a ray moving with a velocity $v = c/n$ to traverse a film of thickness t twice, once in each direction, we have

$$T = 2t/v = 2nt/c. \qquad (2.3.8)$$

But if this time T is to be an integral number, say k, of periods τ, we have, since the period is the inverse of the frequency,

$$T = k\tau = k/\nu = k\lambda/c. \qquad (2.3.9)$$

Combining Eqs. 2.3.8 and 2.3.9 and solving for the thickness, we have

$$t = \frac{k\lambda}{2n} \qquad (2.3.10)$$

as the condition for a minimum in the reflected intensity.

Maxima in the reflected intensity are obtained when the thickness of the film is halfway between the values given above, or when

$$t = \frac{(k + \frac{1}{2})}{2n} \lambda. \qquad (2.3.11)$$

The phase changes produced by the two reflections are then just canceled by the difference in path length of the two rays.

A particularly important application of the interference patterns produced by the thin films is in the inspection of optical surfaces. We shall here review the formation of dark and light interference bands, or fringes, between a plane and a spherical convex glass surface, illustrated in Fig. 2.3.10. These rings formed in the air film between the lens and the plate are called Newton's rings. The index of refraction of the air film being investigated is 1, and the thickness of the film required for a minimum in the reflected light is therefore, according to Eq. 2.3.10,

$$t = k\lambda/2.$$

But from the geometry of Fig. 2.3.10 we have

$$t = R(1 - \cos\theta) = 2R\sin^2(\theta/2).$$

For small angles θ we may set

$$\sin^2\frac{\theta}{2} = \left(\frac{\theta}{2}\right)^2$$

and

$$\theta = \frac{r}{R}$$

and consequently as the condition to be satisfied by the radius of a dark ring

$$t = \frac{k\lambda}{2} = 2R\left(\frac{r}{2R}\right)^2 = \frac{r^2}{2R}$$

or

$$r = \sqrt{kR\lambda}. \qquad (2.3.12a)$$

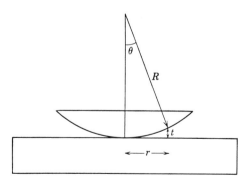

Fig. 2.3.10   Definition of symbols used in describing Newton's rings.

For a bright ring the radius is

$$r = \sqrt{(k + \tfrac{1}{2})R\lambda}. \qquad (2.3.12b)$$

If the surfaces are not accurately spherical or flat, Newton's rings will not be accurately round. The shape of these interference fringes can be used to detect imperfections in optical surfaces.

Today nearly all the lenses in photographic apparatus, field glasses, and so on are coated, which gives them a purple shine. The coating, usually a layer of evaporated fluorides which has an index of refraction between that of air and glass, has such a thickness that the reflected rays from the air-coating interface and coating-glass interface cancel for green light, which is approximately in the middle of the visible spectrum. Blue and red reflected light, therefore, are not so fully canceled and combine to purple. The light energy that is not reflected is transmitted. Since the reflection on one glass surface is of the order of 4%, high-powered photographic objectives which may have ten lens surfaces exposed to air would lose a considerable amount of light by reflection if they were not coated. Another reason for the coating is that the reflected light can be reflected a second time, and so produce a haze on the photographic plate.

Many devices for forming interference fringes are in use in optical laboratories. One of the best known is the Michelson interferometer already discussed in Section 1.5 and illustrated in Fig. 2.3.11. It can be used to measure distances directly in terms of the wavelength of light. Light from a source S is made parallel by a lens L and falls on a glass plate A inclined at 45° to the direction of the incident beam. The front surface of the plate has a coating of metal of just the thickness to transmit about half of the

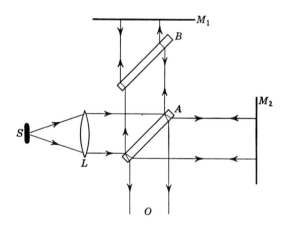

Fig. 2.3.11   The Michelson interferometer.

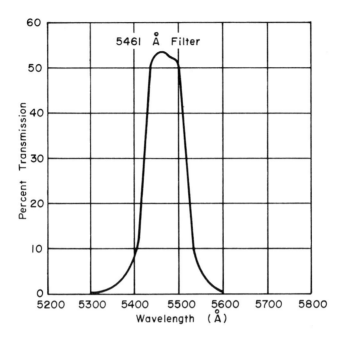

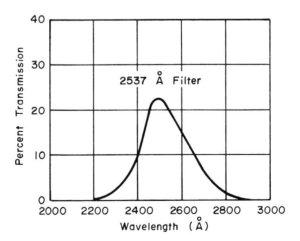

Fig. 2.3.12 Interference filters for transmission of narrow frequency bands at two spectral lines of mercury. (Courtesy of Oriel Corporation of America).

incident light and to reflect the remaining half. These two beams are reflected by the mirrors M_1 and M_2 back to A, where a part of the combined beams is transmitted to an observer at O. A second plate B having the same thickness as A is introduced so that both beams may traverse the same total thickness of glass. This is important if light of many different wavelengths is used, because of the dispersion of the glass. If the path length of the two beams is the same, they will recombine in phase and the beam transmitted to O will have a maximum intensity. If now one mirror is displaced by a quarter wavelength, so that one beam travels a half wavelength farther than the other, the two beams will recombine destructively and there will be a minimum in the intensity transmitted to O. As one of the mirrors is moved in the direction of its normal, alternate maxima and minima in the light transmitted to O will be observed. By counting these maxima, the displacement of the mirror can be expressed in wavelengths of light. This is of great importance not only in providing us with an absolute standard of length but also in making precise length measurements of many kinds, for instance, in establishing the uniformity of a threaded rod.

A further application of interference are the interference filters (Fig. 2.3.12) which can be made to transmit only a very narrow band of the spectrum, whereas the rest of it is reflected back. These devices consist of about twenty or many more layers of appropriate thickness and index of refraction. It also may be noted that the colors of butterflies are due to interference.

Diffraction

In the previous sections we have discussed the interference patterns produced by the interaction of individual point sources or rays of light. This involved the summation of the effects due to a usually small number of individual waves. The word interference is generally used to describe the interaction of a group of rays each of which has a constant phase relationship to the others. When the distribution of phases in an interacting group of rays becomes continuous, one speaks of diffraction rather than interference. Thus, for example, if we wish to estimate the light intensity at a point P on a screen which is receiving light through an aperture, as shown in Fig. 2.3.13, we must construct Huygens' wavelets originating from all points of the aperture and add their contributions to the field at P. But, as may be seen from the figure, the path length, and therefore also the phase of the wavelets, varies from point to point, and we may expect variations in the resultant amplitude, and therefore also in the intensity from point to point on the screen. If the screen is near enough to the aperture so that the

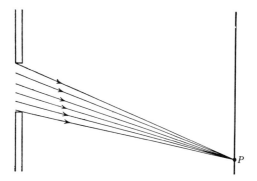

Fig. 2.3.13   Fresnel diffraction.

rays converge as in Fig. 2.3.13, one speaks of a *Fresnel diffraction*[9] pattern. If, on the other hand, the distance from the aperture to the screen is very large compared to the size of the aperture so that the rays combining to produce the illumination at point P on the screen are essentially parallel, the resulting pattern is called a *Fraunhofer diffraction*[10] pattern. A Fraun-

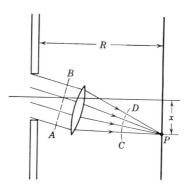

Fig. 2.3.14   Fraunhofer diffraction.

[9] A. Fresnel (1788–1827) earned his living as a civil engineer in the French government service. His systematic experiments dispelled the last doubts about the wave nature of light, and his theoretical work gave wave optics a solid mathematical foundation.

[10] J. Fraunhofer (1787–1826) started as an employee in an optical shop, finally was a professor in Munich. He improved the quality of optical glasses and lenses, constructed astronomical refracting telescopes, and made the first gratings. He investigated in great detail the dark lines in the spectrum of the sun which are named after him.

hofer pattern may be produced on a screen at relatively small distances by use of a lens, as in Fig. 2.3.14. We have seen in Section 2.2 that a lens will not alter the relative phases of the various rays that pass through it and, hence, will not alter the diffraction pattern. Any difference in phase between two points on a wave front approaching a lens is preserved for corresponding points on the wave front after traversing the lens. In other words, the lens does nothing more than bend the wave fronts without disrupting them. Thus, for example, if all points on the plane wave front AB in Fig. 2.3.14 are in phase, all points of the curved wave front CD will also be in phase and will reach point P in phase. This is a general characteristic of image formation by lenses.

Fraunhofer Diffraction Due to a Slit

We now take up the Fraunhofer diffraction pattern of a single slit. Plane waves of monochromatic light are assumed incident on a slit from the left, normally, so that the electric vectors at all points across the slit at any one instance are in phase with each other. The symbols to be used are shown in Fig. 2.3.15. The argument runs parallel to that previously used for the discussion of the interference pattern due to a grating. Instead of considering light from a finite number of small slits, we must add the contributions of an infinite number of infinitesimal sections. We proceed, as before, to determine the directions in which the radiated intensity is zero. For this purpose it is convenient to group the rays in pairs as 1 and 1′, 2 and 2′, etc., in the illustration. Rays 2 and 2′, for example, will cancel

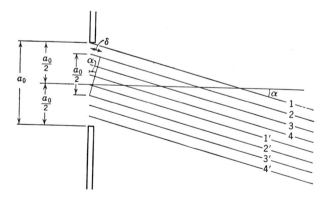

Fig. 2.3.15   Fraunhofer diffraction due to single slit.

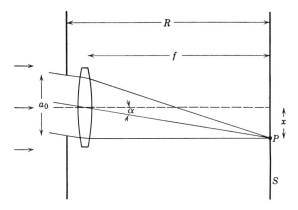

Fig. 2.3.16   One set of rays from a slit focused by a lens on a screen S. $R = f$ if the lens is at the aperture, here drawn a small distance away for clarity.

each other if their path difference δ is a half wavelength, or if

$$\sin \alpha = \frac{\delta}{a_0/2} = \frac{\lambda/2}{a_0/2} = \frac{\lambda}{a_0}. \tag{2.3.13}$$

Likewise the condition that any other pair of rays, such as 1 and 1' or 3 and 3', cancel is that given above. We conclude that, if Eq. 2.3.13 is satisfied, the sum of the fields due to all the rays at point P in Fig. 2.3.16, for instance, will be zero if

$$\sin \alpha = \lambda/a_0.$$

Similarly, if we divided the rays into any even number of groups, with a separation at the slit of $a_0/4$, $a_0/6$, etc., we should find destructive interference in pairs for directions given by

$$\sin \alpha = \frac{\lambda/2}{a_0/4} = \frac{2\lambda}{a_0}$$

$$\sin \alpha = \frac{\lambda/2}{a_0/6} = \frac{3\lambda}{a_0}, \text{ etc.,} \tag{2.3.14}$$

or intensity minima on the screen in Fig. 2.3.16 at the positions

$$x = R \tan \alpha,$$

where R is the distance between slit and screen. For sufficiently small angles, we may replace the tangent by the sine, and the above condition

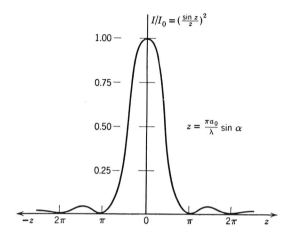

Fig. 2.3.17   Graph of the intensity distribution of the Fraunhofer diffraction pattern due to a slit.

becomes

$$x = \frac{R\lambda}{a_0}, \quad \frac{2R\lambda}{a_0}, \quad \frac{3R\lambda}{a_0}, \text{ etc.} \qquad (2.3.15)$$

Between these minima are intensity maxima, of which the central one is by far the most important. The actual distribution of light intensity in the Fraunhofer diffraction pattern due to a slit is derived below. It is

$$\frac{I}{I_0} = \left(\frac{\sin z}{z}\right)^2, \quad z = \pi a_0 \frac{\sin a}{\lambda}, \qquad (2.3.16)$$

where I_0 is the intensity maximum at the center of the central bright band. The intensity distribution is plotted in Fig. 2.3.17. The smallness of the secondary maxima may be qualitatively understood through dividing the slit into an odd, rather than an even, number of bands and noting that the effects of these cancel in pairs, leaving one band over. The higher-order maxima are then due to wavelets originating from a smaller area at greater angles to the incoming wave front and are therefore relatively weak.

Derivation of Eq. 2.3.16 for Diffraction from a Split

In the slit shown in Fig. 2.3.18, we are considering light diffracted at an angle α. The slit width is a_0, and we chose the origin of coordinates at the

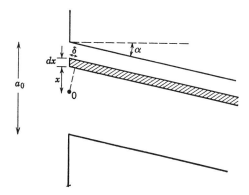

Fig. 2.3.18 Symbols used in deriving Eq. 2.3.16.

center of the slit. The Huygens' wavelets originating in a part of the slit of width dx will be proportional to dx. Let us choose the phase so that our measurements are with respect to the wave originating at $x = 0$. We would have for this wave

$$k dx \sin 2\pi\nu t$$

and for a wave originating at a distance x from the origin, as in Fig. 2.3.18,

$$k \, dx \sin \left(2\pi\nu t - 2\pi \frac{\delta}{\lambda} \right)$$

or, since $\delta = x \sin \alpha$,

$$k \, dx \sin \left(2\pi\nu t - 2\pi \frac{x \sin \alpha}{\lambda} \right).$$

The result of all the wavelets will be

$$\int_{-a_0/2}^{a_0/2} k \sin \left(2\pi\nu t - 2\pi \frac{x \sin \alpha}{\lambda} \right) dx.$$

If we put

$$z = \pi a_0 \frac{\sin \alpha}{\lambda}, \qquad (2.3.17)$$

the above integral becomes

$$\int_{-a_0/2}^{a_0/2} k \sin \left(2\pi\nu t - 2 \frac{z}{a_0} x \right) dx = \left[\frac{ka_0}{2z} \cos \left(2\pi\nu t - 2 \frac{z}{a_0} x \right) \right]_{-a_0/2}^{a_0/2}$$

$$= ka_0 \frac{\sin z}{z} \sin 2\pi\nu t. \qquad (2.3.18)$$

The intensity is proportional to the square of the amplitude. We therefore get for the ratio of the intensity of the wave diffracted through an angle α to the undiffracted wave at $\alpha = 0$

$$\frac{I}{I_0} = \left(\frac{\sin z}{z}\right)^2$$

which is Eq. 2.3.16.

Fresnel Zones

The diffraction pattern due to a slit consists of a series of light and dark lines, whereas that due to a circular aperture consists of light and dark concentric rings. By way of example, we shall discuss the Fresnel diffraction due to a circular aperture. The patterns formed by slits are qualitatively similar and are important in connection with the properties of gratings.

Let us consider the cumulative effect at P in Fig. 2.3.19 of all the Huygens' wavelets originating on the plane wave front which is moving in the direction of the arrows from left to right. Let the distance from P to the wave front be R, and let the normal to the wave front from P intersect it at O. Now construct concentric circles on the wave front about O having radii $r_1, r_2, r_3, \ldots, r_n$ such that the distances from P to these circles are

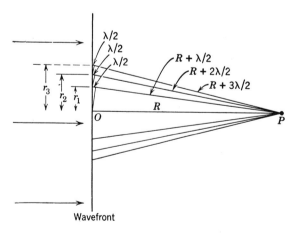

Fig. 2.3.19   The Fresnel zones of a plane wave for computation of the intensity at P.

$R + (\lambda/2)$, $R + (2\lambda/2)$, $R + (3\lambda/2), \dots, R + (n\lambda/2)$, respectively. These circles delineate the *Fresnel zones*. The equations for the radii r_n are

$$r_n{}^2 + R^2 = \left(R + \frac{n\lambda}{2}\right)^2$$

$$= R^2 + n\lambda R + \left(\frac{n\lambda}{2}\right)^2.$$

If we neglect the last term in comparison to the first two, which we may do if $\lambda \ll R$, and solve for r_n, we get

$$r_n = \sqrt{n\lambda R}. \tag{2.3.19}$$

Note that, since the path difference from any two points of the central zone to P is less than $\lambda/2$, the resultant phase difference of any two wavelets from that zone will be less than 180°. The wavelets will all interfere constructively, although not to the full extent, and we may therefore give them all the same sign and put for the resultant amplitude at P due to the first or central zone some positive number a_1. The resultant amplitude at P due to all the wavelets originating in the second zone will now necessarily be negative. The various wavelets originating in this zone will have distances to cover to P differing by less than $\lambda/2$, and will therefore differ in phase by less than 180°. The average path length, however, is $\lambda/2$ greater from zone 2 than it was from zone 1, and we conclude therefore that a_2 must be negative. The contributions due to wavelets from the successive zones will therefore be of opposite sign, and we may write

$$A = a_1 - a_2 + a_3 - a_4 + \cdots. \tag{2.3.20}$$

The magnitude of the various terms in this expression will vary because of three factors. First, the areas of the zones change slightly in going from one to the next. Second, the angle between the direction of propagation of the wave front and the direction to P changes from one zone to the next. Third, the distance to P changes. The net effect of all these factors is that the magnitude of the contributions from the successive zones gradually decreases as we go from smaller to larger radii.

In Fig. 2.3.20 the screen S is to be considered movable so that the distance R from screen to aperture is variable. Suppose a plane wave is incident on the circular aperture of radius r. We consider first the light intensity at the central point P. The difference in path length to P for rays from the center of the aperture and from the edge of the aperture is x, and the following relation must be satisfied:

$$r^2 + R^2 = (R + x)^2$$

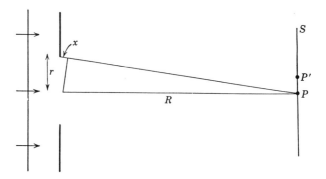

Fig. 2.3.20   A plane wave, circular aperture of radius r, and screen S.

$$= R^2 + 2xR + x^2$$

and, if $x \ll R$,

$$x = r^2/2R. \tag{2.3.21}$$

Now x may be written as some number n of wavelengths where n need not be integral. We have

$$n = r^2/2R\lambda \tag{2.3.22}$$

and we see that, as R increases, the number of wavelengths of path difference decreases, and therefore that the number of Fresnel zones exposed changes. In Fig. 2.3.21 (a) the distance R is such that $x = 3\lambda/2$, and three zones are exposed. At greater distances R, fewer zones are exposed. It may then happen that the intensity at P goes through successive maxima and minima as the distance R is varied.

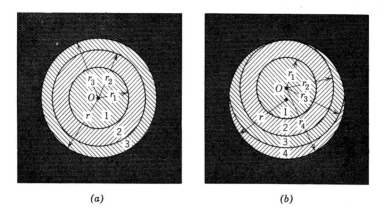

(a)   (b)

Fig. 2.3.21   The Fresnel zones in the circular aperture of Fig. 2.3.20: (a) for the point P on the screen S; (b) for the point P'.

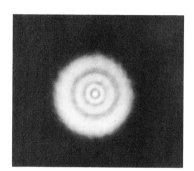
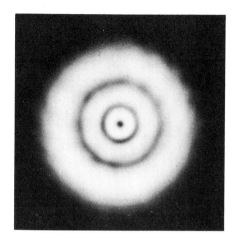

Fig. 2.3.22   Fresnel diffraction pattern for a hole of 2 mm diameter at two different screen distances. Light source was a neon-helium gas laser. (R.P.I. sophomore physics laboratory, courtesy of J. Starbuck.)

Now we focus our attention on point P', off the axis in Fig. 2.3.20, for some one fixed distance R. The Fresnel zones at the aperture are shown in Fig. 2.3.21(b). They are not all completely exposed, and, in calculating the amplitude at P', the changing exposed areas of the zones must be taken into account. When this is done, it is found that the light intensity at P' goes through successive maxima as the distance from the axially located point P is increased. Photographs of Fresnel diffraction patterns of a hole for different distances between hole and screen are shown in Fig. 2.3.22. Note that as the distance is varied the central spot may be either light or dark.

An interesting question is what happens if we replace the circular aperture in Fig. 2.3.13 by a system of concentric circular openings with radii of the Fresnel zones in which the odd zones (1, 3, 5) are transparent, and the even ones (2, 4, . . .) opaque. Such an arrangement is called a zone plate and is shown in Fig. 2.3.23. We have seen that the light coming from the odd zones is predominantly out of phase with the light from the even ones at point P in Fig. 2.3.19. By eliminating the even zones we will have only positive contributions and will see a central bright spot which has, as the detailed calculation shows, the fourfold intensity over that if there were no obstruction at all. We have therefore a focusing action. The zone plate acts as a lens. It can act as a lens not only for parallel incident light, as in Fig. 2.3.12, but also, if the zones are suitably constructed, for light diverging from a nearby source. However, in this case, as for a lens, the image distance is altered.

Fig. 2.3.23   A zone plate.

Holography

Another application of interference phenomena is known as holography (Greek *holos* = total, *graphein* = writing), which is a system of lensless photography that gives a truly three-dimensional view of the original object. Although it was discovered in 1948 by Gabor[11] in England, it became much more important in 1962 with the advent of lasers, which were able to furnish intense coherent light.

[11] Dennis Gabor (1900–   ), Hungarian-born British scientist. Made his discovery when in industry. Later professor for applied electron physics at Imperial College, London. Presently also staff scientist at CBS Laboratories. Nobel prize in physics 1971 for holography.

In order to form an image by holography one produces interference patterns with coherent light on a photographic plate. A portion of this light falls directly on the plate and serves as a reference beam, whereas another portion is directed to the object from which it is reflected on the plate. The object must be completely motionless during the exposure. Because the phase relationship between the two beams at each location on the plate is constant in time, the resulting interference pattern is a representation of the wave front of the light coming from the object. This wave front is "frozen" on the photographic plate. The frozen wave front can be reconstructed at a later time by illuminating the photographic plate containing the information with a reference beam. The reconstructed wave front will then produce an image of the original object.

To study this process in detail, let us first consider the holography of a point object. Coherent parallel light from a laser strikes a photographic plate and a point object at P shown in Fig. 2.3.24(a). The resulting interference pattern which is called a hologram will consist of a series of light

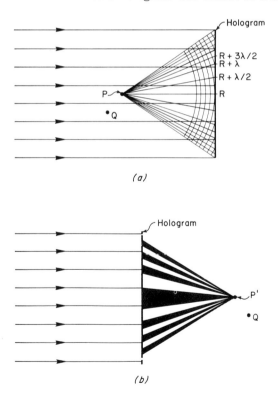

(a)

(b)

Fig. 2.3.24   Illustration of the construction of a hologram for a single point source.

and dark zones similar to the Fresnel zones discussed above. If the film is developed and a negative of the record is made into a transparency, it can be made to focus a parallel incident beam at P', as shown in Fig. 2.3.24(b). If a second point object had been present at Q, the resulting zone plate would have been more complicated, but could have been used to reproduce both points at P' and Q', in their correct mirrored relationship to each other. This process can be generalized to an arbitrary number of object points. The production of the resulting complex zone plates, or holograms, and their use in forming images are illustrated in Fig. 2.3.25. An ordinary photograph, a hologram, and an image reconstructed from the hologram are shown in Fig. 2.3.26.

Holography has already many technological applications, e.g., in pattern recognition and measurement of small geometrical deviations. There is a high probability that holography will have applications in three-dimen-

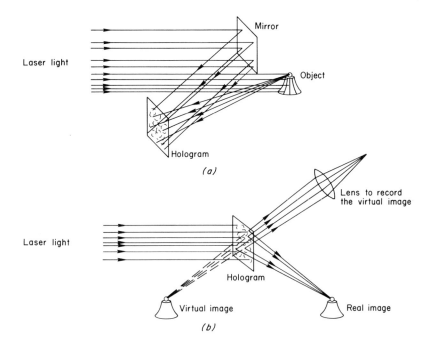

Fig. 2.3.25   (a) Formation of a hologram. A part of the coherent light from a laser illuminates the object, whereas another part serves as reference beam. The light which is scattered from the object and the reference beam (after reflection in a mirror) both impinge on a photographic plate. The resulting photograph of the interference pattern is the hologram. (b) Formation of a real and a virtual image from a hologram. The coherent light which emerges from the different parts of the illuminated hologram interferes in such a way in space to form a real image. Also a virtual image can be observed.

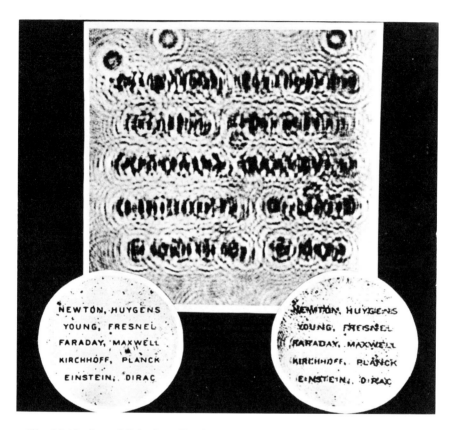

Fig. 2.3.26 One of Gabor's earliest holograms [Proc. Royal Soc. A **197**, 454 (1949)].
Left: Original, Center: Hologram, Right: Reconstruction (Courtesy of Dr. D. Gabor,
Staff scientist CBS Laboratories, Stamford, Conn.)

sional television and moving pictures, and also in x-ray (and electron)
microscopy. X-ray microscopes cannot be constructed like ordinary microscopes because the index of refraction for x-rays in glass is much too close
to 1. X-rays are essentially not refracted by any medium we know. If a
hologram is taken with coherent x-ray light and then viewed with visible
coherent light having some thousand times longer wavelengths, the image
would be magnified by this amount. However, the problem is that a strong
source of coherent x-radiation is not at present available. The principle of
holography is not limited to electromagnetic waves. Acoustical holography
with ultrasonic waves is already used on an experimental basis for the
detection of cancerous tumors.

Resolving Power

In a discussion of the formation of images from the point of view of geometrical optics, we find that a bundle of rays originating from some point on an object can be made to converge again in such a way as to form an image. The analysis involves the assumption of the rectilinear propagation of light rays in homogeneous media and of the laws of reflection and refraction applicable at the boundary between two media. The assumption of rays and sharp shadows is only an approximation to the truth. Light waves can interfere with each other under proper circumstances and, due to diffraction, can travel around corners, as sound waves or water waves do. These wave aspects of light also play a part in the formation of images.

To see how this comes about we must examine images in detail. How faithfully can we expect the object being examined to be reproduced? A pattern of waves can hardly be expected to reveal detail much smaller than the wavelength of the waves being used. Light, whose wavelength is thousands of times larger than an atom, can hardly be expected to show up atomic structure. We should not expect to form an image of a pebble on a beach by observing reflected ocean waves.

Actually the amount of detail to be found in an image depends on two characteristic lengths, one associated with the light and the other associated with the lens. Experimentally, we should find, if with some lens we produced an image of an object of variable size, that the size of the image was proportional to the size of the object down to some lower limit. If the size of the object is decreased beyond this limit, the "image" size remains constant. The size of the image of small, or "point," sources depends on the wavelength of the light being used and on the diameter of the lens. A large lens can produce a smaller image of a point source than can a small lens. A large lens produces a more perfect image than a small one because the "spots" on the image representing "points" on the object are smaller. Essentially, from each point of the object waves go out which produce a diffraction pattern of the aperture of the lens. Amplitude and wavelength depend on the brightness and color of the object point. The function of the lens itself is solely to bring this pattern from far away to a much closer distance. We saw in the previous section that the size of the diffraction pattern of a slit depends on its width and the wavelength of the light. Correspondingly, the diffraction pattern of a circular aperture depends on its diameter. Each element of a photograph can be considered as the diffraction pattern of the aperture produced by the light emerging from a corresponding point of the object. When we examine an object in great detail, for example, if we examine a living cell with a microscope, or a distant ship with binoculars, or the moon with a telescope, a convenient description

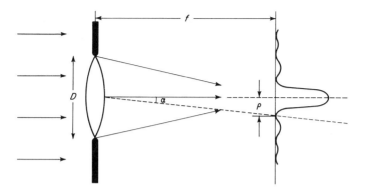

Fig. 2.3.27   The diffraction pattern produced by a lens using light from a distant point source.

of the amount of detail we can see is in terms of the linear or angular separation between points than can be seen separately, or "resolved" from each other.

It is useful, therefore, to know how large a spot is produced in the focal plane of a lens by a distant point source. This is determined by the ratio of the wavelength to the diameter of the lens, or aperture. The greater the wavelength and the smaller the aperture, the greater will be the angular diffraction and the greater the size of the spot. The symbols to be used are shown in Fig. 2.3.27. As in discussing interference, we find that the angular size of the interference pattern is determined by a relation of the form $\sin \alpha \sim \lambda/D$. For circular apertures[12] the angular distance from the central maximum to the center of the first minimum is given by

$$\sin \alpha = 1.22 \frac{\lambda}{D}. \qquad (2.3.23)$$

It is useful to express this in terms of the size of the spot. Since $\rho/f = \tan \alpha \simeq \sin \alpha$ for small angles, we may write

$$\rho = 1.22 \frac{\lambda}{D} f. \qquad (2.3.24)$$

We can understand intuitively that the numerical factor must be > 1 because, compared with a slit of width D, the width of a circular aperture of

---

[12] A more rigorous treatment of this circular problem would use polar coordinates, which would lead to a Bessel function, instead of the sine function which is appropriate for the slit problem. The first zero value of this Bessel function is reached for 0.61 (λ/a), a being the radius of the aperture. This leads to formulas 2.3.23 and 2.3.24.

diameter D is equal to the diameter only at mid-height but is smaller in general. Even the best corrected lens cannot reduce the size of the diffraction pattern. A poor lens might only blur this pattern into an even bigger spot.

The limit of resolution of a lens is reached when the images are a distance ρ apart, such that the central bright spot of one falls on the first dark ring of the second. In angular measure this limit of resolution, or resolving power, is given in Eq. 2.3.23. This is the smallest angular separation of two stars, for instance, that can be separated in the image formed by a perfect lens or parabolic mirror.

2.4 WAVES IN CRYSTALS

X-Ray Crystallography

A most important early landmark in the development of atomic physics was the recognition of the existence of electromagnetic waves having an appreciably shorter wavelength than that of light.

In 1895 W. C. Röntgen[13] discovered the x-rays. Very soon Röntgen himself suspected that these rays might be of electromagnetic nature, but had no proof of it. Later on, indications of diffraction patterns from narrow slits made it clear that x-rays were not beams of electrically neutral particles (magnetic fields did not deflect them!) but waves. The size of the diffraction patterns gave some indication of the order of magnitude of the wavelength. The combined results of a number of experiments made it at last virtually certain that x-rays are electromagnetic waves. For example, it was found that x-rays in passing through matter were scattered similar to the scattering of light in a cloudy medium. Furthermore, these scattered x-rays were polarized. Then an accurate method to determine the wavelength of x-rays was very helpful, and this measurement was accomplished by diffraction from a grating. The grating formula, giving the direction in which radiation from all apertures is in phase (Fig. 2.4.1), is

$$\sin \theta = n\lambda/d. \qquad (2.4.1)$$

For appreciable angular separation of the interference maxima, λ should be comparable to d. Hence, for wavelengths much shorter than that of light, gratings with much closer rulings than those of optical gratings

---

[13] W. C. Röntgen (1845–1923), professor of physics in Würzburg, Bavaria, later in Munich. Nobel prize in physics, 1901, for the discovery of x-rays.

Wilhelm Conrad Röntgen (1845–1923) (Courtesy of American Institute of Physics, Meggers Gallery of Nobel Laureates).

would be required. Such gratings are hard to make but are found to exist in nature.

In 1912 M. von Laue[14] got the idea that crystals could serve as gratings to produce diffraction patterns because it was estimated that the wavelength of the x-rays should be of the same order of magnitude as the spacings of the atoms in a crystal lattice. The experiment was performed with a positive result, proving that x-rays were indeed electromagnetic waves of short wavelengths. We now take up a review of these facts.

In gases atoms are arranged more or less at random and are far apart. In liquids the atoms are held close together by attractive forces, but thermal agitation is still sufficient to permit rapid diffusion of atoms among

---

[14] M. von Laue (1879–1960), professor of theoretical physics, at Swiss and German universities, in particular Berlin; Nobel prize in physics, 1914, for x-ray diffraction in crystals, which was done in Munich.

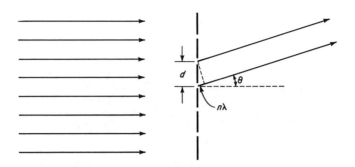

Fig. 2.4.1   Illustration of conditions for a maximum in intensity produced by a diffraction grating

each other. This fairly violent random thermal motion prevents the formation of any marked long-range regular arrangements of the atoms in a liquid. At sufficiently low temperatures the arrangement of the atoms is not determined by the thermal agitation, but by the interatomic forces, resulting in a solid.[15] The nature of these forces is such that some one particular form of clustering of the atoms in a crystalline array has a lower energy than other arrangements.[16] As the disturbing influence of thermal agitation decreases, the atoms of a substance will tend to arrange themselves in this particular way. Although atoms may still occasionally change places and diffuse through the body of the crystal (particularly near the surfaces, or if holes, impurities, or other crystallographic imperfections are present), the main form of thermal motion is vibration around some equilibrium position in the regular pattern established by the interatomic forces.

A regular arrangement of lines on a surface, in other words a diffraction grating, interacts in a very striking manner with waves having wavelengths comparable to the spacing between. It produces a spectrum of the incident radiation for each value of n in Eq. 2.4.1. The three-dimensional periodicities in the structure of crystals may likewise be expected to produce characteristic effects in the interaction with waves. Moreover, since the periodicities in crystals are of the order of atomic dimensions, or 10^{-10} m, we may expect to find the most interesting effects for wavelengths of this order, which are shorter than are encountered in the range of visible light, around 10^{-6} to 10^{-7} m.

In crystals the atoms are arranged in a regular pattern. This pattern can be thought to be generated by a translational repetition of small units

[15] However, the structure of a solid can depend also on the temperature.
[16] More precisely, it is the free energy which is minimum.

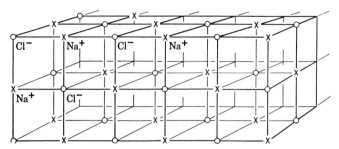

Fig. 2.4.2   The arrangement of sodium aud chlorine ions in a rock salt crystal.

of the crystal in three dimensions. Geometrically we can represent the locations of the atoms by points which also show this periodic sequence. Such an array of geometrical points is called a lattice. On the other hand, an array of atoms which are at the places of the lattice points is a crystal.

There are, in the main, four categories of crystals with regard to the binding forces between the atoms. However, the boundaries between these categories are not sharp. The first category is the *ionic crystals*, of which a simple example is rock salt, or NaCl, shown in Fig. 2.4.2. The sodium chloride molecule, when dissolved in water, breaks up into a positively charged sodium ion and a negatively charged chlorine ion. In the molecule, the two particles retain their charged character, the work required to pull them apart being very nearly that computed on the assumption that the attractive forces are electrostatic. In the crystal the particles are also ions. They are arranged at the corners of an imaginary pile of cubes. The atoms are of course large enough so that they fill in most of the volume of the crystal. We show here only the nuclear positions. Along any line of cube edges positive and negative charges alternate. Each positive ion has six nearest negatively charged neighbors one cube edge away. The NaCl molecule loses its identity in such a crystal. Large single crystals of rock salt are readily obtainable, and the distances between atoms may be accurately deduced from the molecular weights of the constituents and the density of the crystal.

A crystal is commonly described in terms of a *unit cell*, which is some convenient, often the smallest, block of the crystal which is repeated over and over unchanged along the three axes of the crystal. For NaCl, if the distance between adjacent Na^+ and Cl^- ions is d, the unit cell is a cube having an edge length $2d$, since this is the shortest distance between like particles along an edge. The smaller cell, having an edge d, is not exactly repeated in an adjacent cell, in which the Cl^- and Na^+ are interchanged.

The second class of crystal is the *molecular* crystal. Such a crystal is shown in Fig. 2.4.3. Molecules have a structure of their own which in some cases is preserved when they form crystals. Some molecular crystals may contain more than one kind of molecule, for example, potassium cobaltinitrite

$$6KNO_2 \cdot 2Co(NO_2)_3 \cdot 3H_2O.$$

The third type is typified by the pure *metals*. We shall consider in particular those which crystallize in the so-called "face-centered cubic" structure shown in Fig. 2.4.4. The simple cubic structure consists of an arrangement somewhat similar to that of a NaCl crystal, and with all the atoms of a single kind only. A unit cube of such a lattice

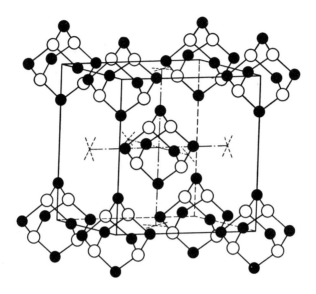

Fig. 2.4.3   A molecular crystal, hexamethylenetetramine, $C_6H_{12}N_4$. The unit of structure and the molecular configuration.

is shown in Fig. 2.4.4 (a). The length of each side is a. A face-centered lattice is arrived at through placing atoms not only at the corners but also at the centers of the faces of the cube, as shown in Fig. 2.4.4 (b). Each atom has twelve nearest neighbors, the distance between them being $a/\sqrt{2}$. Many metals crystallize in this form, for example, copper, silver, and gold.

A fourth type of crystals is the *covalent crystals*. To this category belong diamond, silicon, and germanium. The latter two have gained enormous importance because they constitute the basic material for transistors, and so on. In a covalent bond neighboring atoms share the valence electrons.

The aspect of crystallographic arrangements of atoms which we particularly wish to emphasize is the formation of plane layers of atoms. Understanding of the interaction

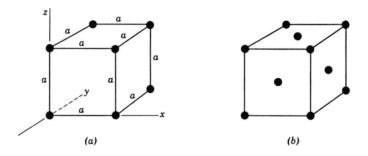

(a)   (b)

Fig. 2.4.4   Unit cell of a simple cubic unit and a face-centered cubic lattice.

of waves and crystals can be built up through considering the effects due to individual atoms, but the mathematical complications are considerable. By far the simplest statement of the results is given in terms of the crystallographic planes that characterize a lattice. We might consider that the simplest interaction between waves and obstacles is reflection at a plane surface. This should therefore be a fruitful starting point in considering waves in crystals.

Miller Indices

The conventional manner of designating a crystallographic plane is in terms of the "Miller indices" (hkl). Let us consider three axes x, y, z parallel to our unit cube and shown in Fig. 2.4.4 (b). Any plane may be defined by its intercepts p, q, r on these axes. It is convenient to measure the distance of these intercepts from the origin in units of the length of the cube edge. We now consider a plane which is situated in such a way that it includes many lattice points, for example, the plane labeled 1 in Fig. 2.4.5 (a). This plane cuts each of the three axes at one unit of length defined by the size of the unit cube. The reciprocals of these intercepts are 1/1, 1/1, 1/1, from which the Miller indices (hkl) are obtained by multiplication with the smallest common factor in order to eliminate fractional numbers, in our example therefore 1. The Miller indices for this plane are hence (111). Plane 2, which is parallel to plane 1, has the intercepts 2, 2, 2. The reciprocals are 1/2, 1/2, 1/2. Multiplication by 2 yields again the Miller indices (111). All planes parallel to planes 1 and 2 and containing lattice points are (111) planes. The arrangements of atoms in this plane is shown in Fig. 2.4.5 (b). Here the black dots represent atomic positions, and the circles around them represent approximate atomic sizes. This is the closest packing possible for spherical objects arranged in a plane. This close packing extends to the arrangement of layers with respect to each other. In the layer above the one shown, the atoms would be located at the points indicated by crosses or in the depressions between spheres arranged in a triangle. The face centered cubic lattice is characterized by close packing.

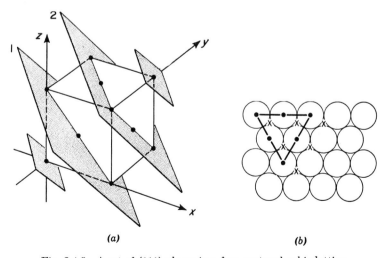

(a)   (b)

Fig. 2.4.5   A set of (111) planes in a face-centered cubic lattice.

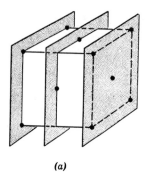 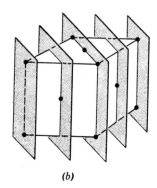

(a)   *(b)*

Fig. 2.4.6   The (200) and (220) planes of a cubic face-centered lattice.

Two other crystallographic sets of planes are shown in Fig. 2.4.6. They are the (200) and (220) planes, respectively. In Fig. 2.4.6 (a), the intercept on the x axis of the plane next to the one that passes through the origin is $1/2$. The planes are parallel to both the y and the z axes. The intercepts on these axes may be thought of as infinitely distant. The reciprocals of these numbers are 2, 0, and 0, which are the Miller indices. Two other sets of planes are equivalent to the (200) set. They are the (020) and (002) planes. The (220) planes shown in Fig. 2.4.6 (b) are parallel to a face diagonal and are crystallographically equivalent to the (202) and (022) planes.

X-Ray Diffraction

An electron in the path of an electromagnetic wave with which it interacts will be forced to oscillate as we have seen already in our discussion of polarization of light by scattering. Due to these oscillations the atom will emit wavelets according to classical electromagnetic theory. Therefore, in a crystal through which a beam of electromagnetic waves is passing, each atom will emit such wavelets, and the diffraction effects may be computed by adding these wavelets together. We have already treated the case of an incident plane wave and have found that Huygens' wavelets reinforce each other to produce a new reflected wave. Its direction of propagation is given by the law of reflection, namely, the angle of incidence equals the angle of reflection; furthermore, the incident and reflected rays and the normal to the surface at the point of incidence are all in the same plane. This reflected ray will contain all the wavelengths present in the incident light. It is true that if the reflecting surface contains periodicities, as in a grating, then additional diffracted rays will appear—that is, the first- and higher-order spectra—but in these diffracted rays at any particular angle θ^* only a certain particular wavelength λ^* will appear. We shall neglect these special rays[17] and consider only the more intense rays that are reflected from a single surface according to Snell's law, or specularly, with the angle of incidence equal to the angle reflection, regardless of wavelength. The incident ray, the reflected ray, and the normal to the surface at the point of incidence all are in the same plane.

If an x-ray beam falls on a crystallographic surface, the atoms in this surface will radiate secondary wavelets and these secondary wavelets will form a specularly reflected ray just as did the Huygens' wavelets. Let us now consider the effect of adding successive parallel atomic planes, separated by a distance d as shown in Fig. 2.4.7. We shall assume that the planes are highly transparent, and that the velocity of propagation of the wave between planes is the same as the velocity of the incident wave. This is justified because, as we shall see in later chapters, normal unexcited atoms have no natural frequencies in the x-ray region. The dielectric constant and permeability are therefore very close to ϵ_0 and μ_0. We seek the condition that the reflected rays, due to reflection at successive planes, shall add and therefore produce a maximum intensity.

Let the dashed line AB be a wave front, perpendicular to the outgoing rays. The condition that the rays reflected at B and O interfere constructively, or that their amplitudes add, is that the path difference be an integral number of wavelengths.

$$OB - OA = n\lambda \tag{2.4.2}$$

where n is an integer. From that the construction of the figure we see that

$$OB = CB$$

$$OA = MB$$

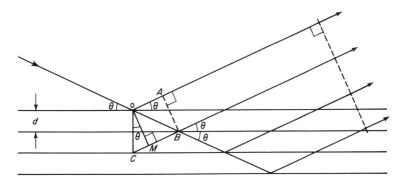

Fig. 2.4.7   The reflection of waves by parallel planes.

and therefore

$$OB - OA = CB - MB = CM = n\lambda.$$

The distance MC can be expressed in terms of the spacing of the planes d, and the angle θ which the incident rays make with the crystallographic planes:

$$\sin \theta = CM/2d.$$

Note that θ here is the complement of the angle of incidence which is used in optics to specify the direction of an incoming ray. Equation 2.4.2 may be rewritten

$$2d \sin \theta = n\lambda \tag{2.4.3}$$

which is called *Bragg's law*.[18] It says that, in general, rays of arbitrary wavelength incident at an arbitrary angle will not be reflected. Only if the

W. H. Bragg (1862–1942) (Courtesy of American Institute of Physics, Meggers Gallery of Nobel Laureates).

[18] W. L. Bragg (1890–1971), professor in Manchester and Cambridge; worked in x-ray diffraction and crystallography. His father, Sir W. H. Bragg (1862–1942), developed the x-ray diffraction method named after him. Father and son shared the Nobel prize in physics in 1915 for their work in x-ray crystallography.

W. L. Bragg (1890–1971) (Courtesy of Niels Bohr Library, American Institute of Physics).

relation in Eq. 2.4.3 is satisfied will reflection take place. Note that if $\lambda > 2d$, it is impossible to satisfy Bragg's law for these planes, or that waves will be diffracted from crystals only if their wavelengths are less than twice the distance between planes. Note also that Eq. 2.4.3 provides a means for producing monochromatic waves, or waves of a single wavelength. If we have a source of short waves of arbitrary spectral distribution, for example, an x-ray tube, we may selectively reflect those of a particular wavelength from a crystal at the Bragg angle specified by Eq. 2.4.3.

A most important practical modification of the above considerations involves the application of Bragg's law to a polycrystalline sample or to a powder in which individual crystal grains are randomly oriented. This is the powdered crystal method or, named after its inventors, the Debye-Scherrer[19] method. Let us assume that a ray is incident on such a powder,

[19] P. Debye (1884–1966), born in Holland. Physicist and chemist. Professor at many universities in Switzerland, Holland, Germany, and U.S.A. (Cornell). Investigations‎ in the fields of structure of molecules, liquids and solid state. Nobel prize in chemistry 1936. His theory of the specific heat of solids is discussed in Chapter 5.

P. Scherrer (1890–1969), Swiss physicist. Co-worker of Debye in Göttingen, Germany. Later professor at the Swiss Federal Institute of Technology in Zurich. Worked in solid-state and nuclear physics.

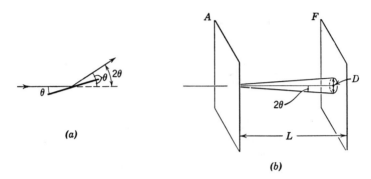

Fig. 2.4.8   The origin of Debye-Scherrer rings or powder pattern.

and that the wavelength λ is such that the Bragg relation is satisfied for some given value of n at the angle θ. The reflected ray will be deviated through an angle 2θ, shown in Fig. 2.4.8(a). All the crystals so oriented that their planes make an angle θ with the incoming ray will reflect. These reflected rays will form a cone whose half-angle is 2θ, as shown in Fig. 2.4.8(b), and the intersection of this cone with a plane perpendicular to the undeviated ray, at a distance L from the sample at A will produce a circle of diameter D, with

$$\tan 2\theta = \frac{D/2}{L}. \tag{2.4.4}$$

The wavelength of x-rays may be established through demonstrating the validity of Bragg's law, Eq. 2.4.3, for diffraction from a crystal with known lattice spacing. This can be done, for example, with a rock-salt crystal (NaCl). X-rays produced at the electrode of an x-ray tube analyzed in this way show first of all a continuous spectrum whose range depends primarily on the voltage applied to the tube. (We shall discuss this process in more detail later in this chapter.) On top of this continuous distribution certain wavelengths may appear with particular intensity. The wavelengths found in this line spectrum depend primarily on the material used as the target for the electrons. Such x-rays are therefore called characteristic x-rays. Radiations having wavelengths of the order of an angstrom unit, 10^{-10} m, or less are readily produced.

Monochromatic x-rays may be used in an arrangement such as is shown in Fig. 2.4.9(a) to produce ring-shaped patterns, called Debye-Scherrer rings. The rays are scattered from a polycrystalline sample at A placed at the center of a strip of film bent into a circle around the scatterer. The conical shape of the scattered rays leaves the traces on the film shown in Fig. 2.4.9(b), which is the pattern produced by scattering from copper. The observed pattern is indeed what would be expected on the basis of the Bragg law.

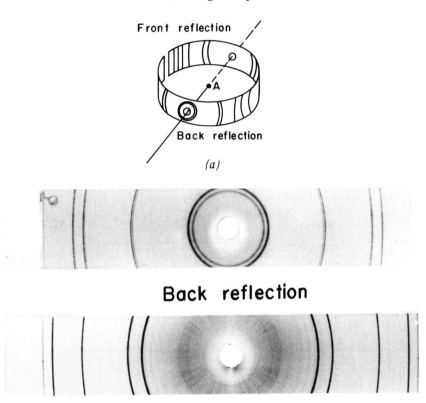

Fig. 2.4.9 A Debye-Scherrer diagram for copper. (Courtesy of Laboratory for Crystallographic Biophysics, R. P. I.)

The intensity of the individual lines depends on the density of atoms in the reflecting plane and on the number and distribution of electrons in the atom because x-rays are scattered chiefly by electrons rather than by the atoms as a whole. For this reason it is possible to construct "contour maps" of the electron density in a plane of a crystal. An example is shown in Fig. 2.4.10.

Electron and Neutron Diffraction

Not only do electromagnetic waves have particle aspects, but all particles—for instance electrons, protons, and neutrons—have wave aspects. Although this is not germane to a discussion of the electromagnetic spec-

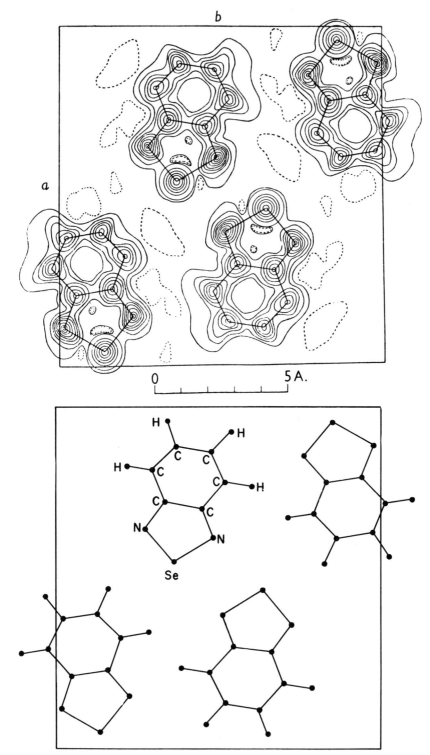

trum, the present discussion of waves in crystals will be briefly extended from the electromagnetic x-rays having wavelengths of the order of atomic dimensions to include also particle waves that are diffracted by crystals. To do this we must assign a wavelength to a moving particle. In our discussion of the momentum of quanta we came to the equation (see Eq. 2.1.9)

$$p = \frac{h}{\lambda}.$$

In 1924 L. de Broglie[20] suggested in his doctoral thesis,[21] in which he set out to unify the physics of particles and the physics of waves, that this relationship might also hold for particles, p now being their momentum mv. If we switch here to the low-energy relativistic limit m is the rest mass of the particle having the wavelength λ. This, thus, leads to the famous *de Broglie relation* for matter waves

$$\lambda = \frac{h}{mv}. \tag{2.4.5}$$

(Because de Broglie used relativistic mechanics nearly throughout, this simple formula does not appear in his treatise,—with one exception regarding the wavelength of molecules in a gas in order to deduce the distribution of the kinetic energy among the gas molecules!) The significance of the de Broglie relation for electron diffraction by crystals is shown by computing the magnitude of the wavelength of an electron with 100 eV of energy. If $eV = \frac{1}{2}mv^2$, we get $v = 5.9 \times 10^6$ m/sec and $\lambda = 1.23 \times 10^{-10}$ m $= 1.23 \times 10^{-8}$ cm. This is just in the range of interatomic spacing in crystals and therefore the right order of magnitude to produce diffraction effects.

Instead of being diffusely scattered by collisions with individual particles, electrons are "reflected" from crystallographic planes, much as x-rays are. A ring pattern formed by shooting a beam of electrons through a poly-

---

[20] Prince Louis de Broglie (1892–   ), professor of theoretical physics in Paris. Nobel prize in physics in 1929 for his hypothesis of the wave-particle duality.

[21] Also published in *Ann. Phys.* (*Paris*) **3**, 22 (1925). Translated excerpts in *Wave Mechanics* by G. Ludwig, Pergamon Press 1968. Preceding his thesis were short articles in *Comptes Rendus* **177**, 507, 548, 630 (1923) and (in English) in *Phil. Mag.* **47**, 446 (1924).

Fig. 2.4.10 (top) Projection on a plane of the electron density of 3-4 benzo 1-2-5 selenodiazol. The dotted lines in this electron-density contour map correspond to zero density. The equidistance of the curves is 1 $\AA^2$, with the exception of the selenium peaks where the equidistance is ten times bigger. The hydrogen atoms are not showing because of the too low electron density around them. (bottom) Projection of the unit cell.—[V. Luzzati, *Acta Crystallographica* **4**, 193 (1951)].

Louis de Broglie (born 1892) (Courtesy of American Institute of Physics, Meggers Gallery of Nobel Laureates).

crystalline sample of MgO is shown in Fig. 2.4.11. This is qualitatively similar to a Debye-Scherrer diagram with the rings quite close together as might be expected for short wavelengths.

If we consider the motion of a macroscopic object, say a bowling ball, the de Broglie wavelength becomes exceedingly small. We know from optics that in order to observe the wave nature of light the linear dimensions of the crucial parts of the apparatus, namely slit width and distance between the grooves in gratings, must be of comparable size with the wavelength of the light. For the same reasons the effects of matter waves of macroscopic objects cannot be observed.

The Experimental Evidence for $\lambda = h/mv$

Experimental evidence for the wave nature of electrons and the validity of the relation $\lambda = h/mv$ came in 1927. C. J. Davisson,[22] a physicist at the

[22] C. J. Davisson (1881–1958) and Sir G. P. Thomson (1892–   ), professor in Aberdeen, Scotland, later in London and Cambridge, shared the 1937 Nobel prize in physics for their discovery of electron diffraction.

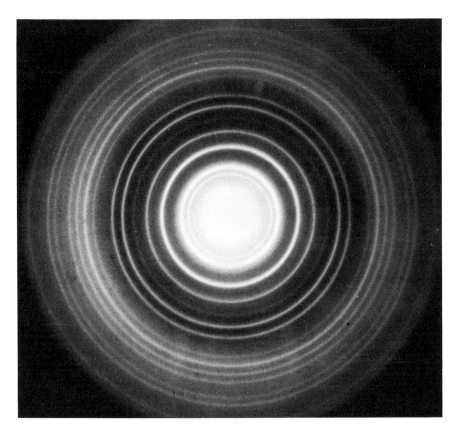

Fig. 2.4.11   Electron diffraction pattern obtained by transmission through poly-crystalline MgO. (Courtesy of H. F. Meiners, R. P. I.)

Bell Telephone Laboratories in New York, had investigated for several years the elastic scattering of electrons from metallic surfaces and in 1925, according to his own words, discovered "purely by accident, that the intensity of elastic scattering varies with the orientation of the scattering crystals." Theoretical physicists whom he asked for advice about the interpretation of this strange effect surmised that this was due to the wave character of the electrons. They suggested that Davisson undertake experiments specifically directed towards a verification of de Broglie's hypothesis. These experiments, in cooperation with Germer, led to success in 1927.

At the same time, G. P. Thomson and A. Reid in Scotland also investigated the diffraction of electrons to test de Broglie's hypothesis. Their experiments are most instructive. A beam of electrons accelerated with a known voltage is fired through various thin foils onto a photographic plate. The diameters of the rings obtained, like those in Fig. 2.4.11, are then measured and compared with theoretical predictions. Because electrons of this energy do not penetrate far, Davisson and Germer worked with electrons reflected at a surface whereas Thomson and Reid used thin films.

As a first step, let us compare the theoretical expression of Eq. 2.4.5 for the wavelength with the experimental result. From Eq. 2.4.4 we have for the diameter of any ring for small θ

$$D = 2\,L\tan 2\,\theta = 4\,L\,\theta$$

and from Bragg's law

$$\theta \simeq \sin\theta = \frac{n\lambda}{2d}$$

$$D = 2\,\frac{L}{d}\,n\lambda. \qquad (2.4.6)$$

But, if the electrons are accelerated by falling through a potential difference V, their kinetic energy E is

$$E = \tfrac{1}{2}mv^2 = e\,V$$

and their momentum therefore is

$$mv = \sqrt{2m\,(\tfrac{1}{2}mv^2)} = \sqrt{2mE} = \sqrt{2meV}. \qquad (2.4.7)$$

If relativistic mass changes are taken into account, the above result must be modified. The correct expression is

$$mv = \sqrt{2m_0eV}\left[1 + \frac{e\,V}{2m_0c^2}\right]^{1/2}. \qquad (2.4.8)$$

In the following the last factor in no instance amounts to more than 3%, but in other experiments in which energies of over 1 MeV were used, the agreement between theory and experiment is equally satisfactory. Substituting Eqs. 2.4.5 and 2.4.8 into Eq. 2.4.6, we have

$$D = 2\,\frac{L}{d}\,n\,\frac{h}{\sqrt{2m_0e\,V}\left[1 + \dfrac{e\,V}{2m_0c^2}\right]^{1/2}}$$

or

$$D\sqrt{V}\left[1 + \frac{e\,V}{2m_0c^2}\right]^{1/2} = \text{constant.} \qquad (2.4.9)$$

The extent to which this expression is satisfied is shown in Table 2.4.1. The variation of the diameter of a diffraction ring produced by aluminum and also gold with the accelerating voltage used in forming the electron beam, as well as the constancy of the left side of Eq. 2.4.9, are illustrated. Equally good results were obtained for all the metals investigated, including platinum, silver, copper, lead, iron, nickel, tin, and also for several

TABLE 2.4.1

A Check of Formula 2.4.9

	V	D	$D(V)^{1/2}[1 + (eV/2m_0c^2)]^{1/2}$
Aluminum	17,500	3.1	415
	30,500	2.45	434
	31,800	2.32	418
	40,000	2.12	430
	44,000	2.08	445
	48,600	1.90	430
	48,600	1.98	446
	56,500	1.83	446
	56,500	1.80	438
Gold	24,600	2.50	398
	31,800	2.15	390
	39,400	2.00	404
	45,600	1.86	405
	54,300	1.63	438
	61,200	1.61	410

compounds. We may conclude that the variation of the patterns with applied voltage is that required by Eq. 2.4.5.

We next inquire whether all the rings can be accounted for correctly by the known lattice structure of the diffracting substance. For this purpose a set of results on gold is to be examined in detail. We must find a convenient way of describing the various values of the spacing between planes, d, in the face-centered cubic lattice in which gold crystallizes

If a plane has the intercepts p, q, and r on the axes of a rectangular coordinate system, the normal distance from the origin to this plane is

$$[p^{-2} + q^{-2} + r^{-2}]^{-1/2}.$$

From the definition of the Miller indices as the reciprocals of the intercepts of the plane next to the one passing through the origin, measured on a scale in which the cube edge of length a is taken as unity, we have

$$\frac{d}{a} = \left[\frac{1}{p^2} + \frac{1}{q^2} + \frac{1}{r^2} \right]^{-1/2}$$

or, after simplification, since $h \equiv 1/p$, $k \equiv 1/q$, and $l \equiv 1/r$,

$$\frac{1}{d} = \frac{\sqrt{h^2 + k^2 + l^2}}{a}. \tag{2.4.10}$$

Substituting this into Eq. 2.4.6, we have for the diameter of the rings

$$D = \frac{2Ln\lambda}{a} \sqrt{h^2 + k^2 + l^2}$$

$$= \frac{2L\lambda}{a} \sqrt{(nh)^2 + (nk)^2 + (nl)^2}. \tag{2.4.11}$$

TABLE 2.4.2

Relative Diameters of Electron Diffraction Rings in Gold[a]

$(nh\ nk\ nl)$	(111)	(200)	(220)	(113) (222)	(400)	(331) (420)	(422)	(511) (333)	(440)	(531) (600)	(620)	(533) (622)
$\sqrt{(nh)^2 + (nk)^2 + (nl)^2}$	$\sqrt{3}$	$\sqrt{4}$	$\sqrt{8}$	$\sqrt{11.25}$	$\sqrt{16}$	$\sqrt{19.5}$	$\sqrt{24}$	$\sqrt{27}$	$\sqrt{32}$	$\sqrt{35.4}$	$\sqrt{40}$	$\sqrt{43.5}$
Observed values	$\sqrt{2.96}$	$\sqrt{4.08}$		$\sqrt{11.2}$	$\sqrt{15.7}$	$\sqrt{19.3}$	$\sqrt{22.7}$	$\sqrt{26.6}$		$\sqrt{35.4}$		$\sqrt{43.1}$
	$\sqrt{3.02}$	$\sqrt{4.25}$		$\sqrt{11.7}$		$\sqrt{19.9}$	$\sqrt{24.3}$	$\sqrt{27.8}$		$\sqrt{34.9}$		$\sqrt{42.6}$
	$\sqrt{2.95}$	$\sqrt{4.08}$		$\sqrt{11.2}$		$\sqrt{19.5}$	$\sqrt{24.1}$	$\sqrt{27.5}$		$\sqrt{35.0}$		$\sqrt{43.5}$
	$\sqrt{2.96}$	$\sqrt{3.98}$		$\sqrt{11.0}$		$\sqrt{19.5}$	$\sqrt{24.4}$	$\sqrt{26.7}$		$\sqrt{34.7}$		$\sqrt{43.5}$
	$\sqrt{3.06}$	$\sqrt{3.9}$		$\sqrt{11.0}$		$\sqrt{19.5}$						
				$\sqrt{11.25}$		$\sqrt{19.4}$						

[a] Where reflections from two sets of planes are unresolved, the average predicted diameter is listed.

TABLE 2.4.3

Size of the Unit Cube, a

	X-rays	Electrons
Aluminum	4.046×10^{-10} m	4.06×10^{-10} m
		4.00
Gold	4.06	4.18
		3.99
Platinum	3.91	3.88
		3.89
Lead	4.92	4.99
Iron	2.87	2.85
Silver	4.079	4.11
Copper	3.60	3.66
Tin (white), spacing of (200)	2.91	2.86

A comparison of this result with experiment is shown in Table 2.4.2, in which the quantity $2L\lambda/a$ is determined from the (220) ring; and then $Da/2L\lambda$, using this and the observed diameter, is tabulated for all the other rings. Some of the rings fall so closely together that their weighted average is taken for comparison with the single ring observed. We have shown that the three with the greatest spacings are (111), (200), and (220). A large number of other planes leading to reflections of varying intensity is listed in Table 2.4.2. The agreement is very satisfactory. The missing rings may be accounted for either by the weakness of the reflection from certain planes or by the absence of the required grain orientation as a result of the hammering process by which the gold foil was produced.

Finally it remains to be shown that the lattice parameter a obtained by electron diffraction is the same as that determined by x-rays. The results are shown in Table 2.4.3.

The evidence of the wave aspect of an electron beam and for de Broglie's specifications of its wavelength is complete and overwhelming. There can be no doubt of it. We might also just mention that electron diffraction in solids due to Bragg's law plays an important role in electric conductivity. This will be discussed in detail in Chapter 5.

Electrons are not the only particles which show diffraction effects; all particles show them in principle. The energy of a particle having a wavelength of 10^{-8} cm, using Eq. 2.4.5, is given by

$$\lambda = \frac{h}{mv} = \frac{h}{\sqrt{2mE}}$$

$$E = \left(\frac{h}{\lambda}\right)^2 \frac{1}{2m}.$$

For a proton, the required energy is about 0.08 eV, or the same order of magnitude as thermal energies of motion at room temperature. Protons with such energies cannot penetrate appreciably into crystals, and therefore in practice they cannot be diffracted. Slow neutrons, however, can penetrate into crystals and are diffracted.

Without going into detail at this point, we merely state that the nuclear reactions which proceed inside nuclear reactors liberate many neutrons. These particles are uninfluenced by the electric fields inside atoms and move through solids unimpeded until they collide with a nucleus. Because

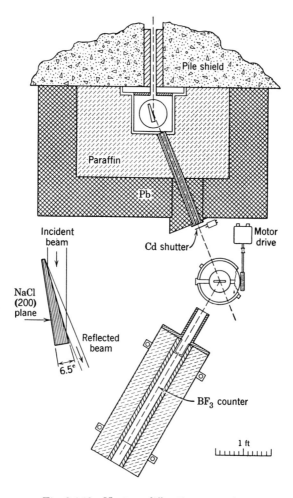

Fig. 2.4.12   Neutron diffraction apparatus.

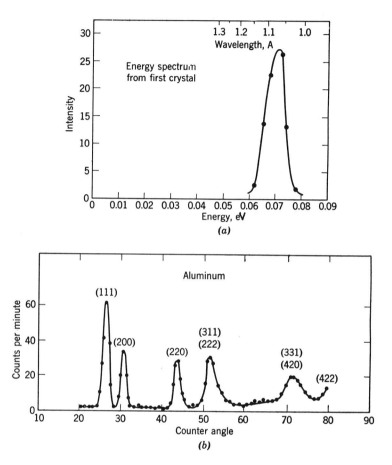

Fig. 2.4.13 (a) Energy distribution of neutron beam. (b) Diffraction pattern from neutrons by powdered aluminum.

of the small size of the nuclei, the mean free paths of neutrons are very large, even in solid matter. Fast neutrons, having energies of the order of MeV, such as are released in a nuclear reaction, may either be slowed down to thermal energies by successive collisions or be absorbed by nuclei and produce new nuclear reactions. Which of the two processes is more likely to occur depends on the kinds of nuclei with which the neutrons collide. Many thermal neutrons are present in a reactor and escape through ports. Here they may be collimated and reflected from crystallographic planes. This process selects a particular wavelength, according to the Bragg relation, and the monochromatic beam may then be used for further experimentation.

The experimental arrangement used by Wollan and Shull at the Oak Ridge National Laboratory in 1948 to demonstrate neutron diffraction is shown in Fig. 2.4.12. Neutrons are collimated and diffracted from a NaCl crystal. Cadmium is used as a shutter because cadmium nuclei are effective in absorbing slow neutrons. The neutron beam is not truly monoenergetic, but has the distribution shown in Fig. 2.4.13(a). The beam is diffracted from a polycrystalline sample $\frac{1}{2}$ in. thick. The beam is detected in a BF$_3$ counter, a device that makes use of nuclear reactions in the BF$_3$ gas induced by neutrons to measure the intensity of the neutron beam. The results obtained are shown in Fig. 2.4.13(b). The correspondence of this pattern to the electron diffraction pattern obtained for face-centered cubic crystals is apparent. This is an important further demonstration of the wave properties of matter.

Neutron diffraction is a particularly important method in investigation of structures containing hydrogen. The scattering of x-rays by atoms is

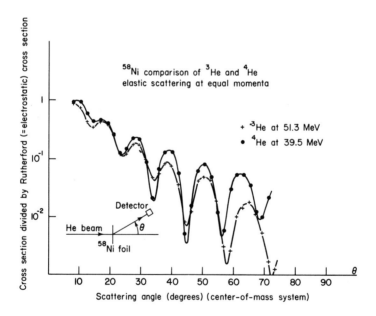

Fig. 2.4.14   Diffraction pattern in the elastic scattering of ³He and ⁴He by ⁵⁸Ni, measured by B. W. Ridley, T. H. Braid, and T. W. Conlon at the Atomic Energy Research Establishment, Harwell, England. The effects of the electrostatic repulsion between the positively charged He and Ni nuclei have been suppressed in this graph by plotting for each angle the *ratio* of the actual intensity to the intensity which one would expect if the scattering were of purely classical electrostatic nature. The scattering due to the latter interaction is a rapidly decreasing but smooth function of the angle. Note also that this is a semi-logarithmic plot.

caused by the electrons of the atoms. Since hydrogen contains only one electron, and even this may be removed from its proton in a solid, the x-ray reflections by hydrogen are very weak or even nonexistent. The positions of the hydrogen atoms can therefore not readily be determined from x-ray diffraction but must be deduced in other ways. Protons, that is hydrogen nuclei, however, are excellent scatterers for neutrons. Neutron diffraction therefore complements x-ray diffraction in a most useful way.

Another striking demonstration of wave aspects of particles is pictured in Fig. 2.4.14. ^{3}He and ^{4}He nuclei which have been accelerated in a cyclotron to energies of 51.3 MeV and 39.5 MeV, respectively, were elastically scattered on ^{58}Ni nuclei. ^{4}He nuclei have two protons and two neutrons, altogether four nucleons, whereas ^{3}He nuclei have only one neutron besides the two protons. Protons and neutrons have approximately equal mass. Thus the mass of the ^{3}He nuclei is approximately $\frac{3}{4}$ that of the ^{4}He nuclei. The ratio of the two particle energies was chosen such that the momenta were equal and hence also their de Broglie wavelengths. The angular distribution of the intensity of the scattered beams with regularly spaced maxima and minima is strongly reminiscent of the diffraction pattern of light produced by an opaque disk. Because the momenta are the same for both kinds of particles, the maxima and minima occur at the same angles. It is left as an exercise to compute the order of magnitude of the size of nickel nuclei from the data given in the figure. The differences in the shapes of the two curves are caused by the internal structure of the bombarding and target nuclei and are of no concern to us here.

2.5 QUANTA

Black-Body Radiation

The existence of quanta of energy was discussed by Max Planck[23] at the turn of the century. Today we think of the existence of quanta as being demonstrated primarily by atomic (or nuclear) radiation and collision phenomena. When quanta are absorbed from the electromagnetic field, their energy and momentum are transferred to the atomic system absorbing them. The experiments which demonstrate the quantum aspects of radiation most clearly are the photoelectric effect and Compton scattering of

[23] Max Planck (1858–1947), German theoretical physicist; worked principally in Berlin; one of the giants in physics; founder of the quantum theory; Nobel prize in physics 1918. Planck's profile is on the present 2-Deutsche-Mark coins.

Max Planck (1858–1947) (Courtesy of American Institute of Physics, Meggers Gallery of Nobel Laureates).

quanta by free electrons. However, Max Planck in 1900 used a much more subtle argument for the postulation of quanta of energy and the determination of the crucial quantity h. It was based on experimental data on radiation of heat that were well established long before the advent of the physics of this century.[24]

If we look into a small aperture in a closed furnace, into which no light can penetrate from outside, we see nothing if the temperature is much below 500°C. We may sense heat, and with suitable thermal measuring devices we may measure the thermal radiation as well as its spectral dis-

[24] An excellently written and highly recommended book on the history of quantum theory is *The Conceptual Development of Quantum Mechanics* by Max Jammer (McGraw-Hill, New York, 1966). Although addressed to scientists, the more technical passages can be omitted in reading without too much loss. Another excellent book, covering the period from 1899 to 1913 is *The Genesis of Quantum Theory* by Armin Hermann. MIT Press, Cambridge, 1971.

tribution, but it is not until the temperature gets higher than 500°C that we begin to see light. At first the color is red (600–1000°C), then, as the temperature rises, it changes to orange (1100°C), next to yellow (1200°C), and then to nearly white (1400°C). What we see in the furnace depends on the temperature and not on the materials of which the furnace is constructed.

The electromagnetic energy radiated from a small aperture in a furnace is usually called "black-body" radiation, because a "black" surface is one which absorbs all the energy which falls on it; somewhat more precise, but less frequently used, is the term "cavity radiation." A small opening in a large cavity may be thought of as a trap that lets in any energy which strikes it and, being small, makes it difficult for this energy to get out again. In other words, the hole of the cavity absorbs essentially all the energy that falls on it from the outside. That which does get out is then emitted as if by a "black body" and is representative for the properties of the radiation inside the cavity.

The amount of energy radiated per second per unit area is called the *radiant emittance*. We designate it by W and express it in watts/m². The fraction of this energy in the range of wavelengths between λ and $\lambda + d\lambda$ is proportional to $d\lambda$. We may write $dW = W_\lambda d\lambda$, where $W_\lambda = dW/d\lambda$ is called the *spectral emittance*, and is here measured in watts/meter³, or often watts/m² − mμ where mμ stands for millimicrons, or 10^{-9} m.[25]

The principle of such a measurement is given in Fig. 2.5.1. The radiation emerging from the furnace is collimated and falls on a rock-salt prism. A bolometer, which is a black (and therefore radiation absorbing) temperature-sensitive device, can be moved along the periphery of a circle. Hence the radiated energy can be measured as a function of the wavelength. Although in principle a regular blackened thermometer could be used, actual bolometers contain thermocouples which generate small amounts of thermoelectricity.

[25] The importance of specifying a wavelength interval $d\lambda$ (or later in our discussion, a frequency interval $d\nu$) may become clearer from the following analogy; If we are going to measure the heights of a group of people and plot a graph of the distribution of heights, we need to specify the magnitude of the height intervals or "bins." E.g., for 1-in. intervals we might have found 40 individuals in the interval between 5'9" and 5'10", in the next one 43, then 31, and 12. Had we chosen 2-in. intervals, the same 126 individuals would have been distributed between two bins, with 83 and 43 people, respectively. To ask how many people are accurately 5'11" tall is asking an improper question, because nobody could precisely qualify. It is also evident that the area under the curve in the graph represents the total number of people in our survey. Had we chosen, instead of their height, another criterion, for example, their weight, the distribution would have been different, but the area under this new curve would have represented the same number of people.

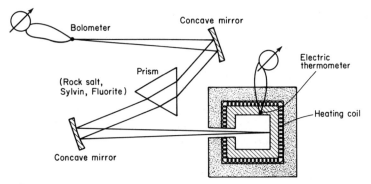

Fig. 2.5.1   Principle of a measurement of cavity (black-body) radiation.

The spectral emittance from a furnace at several temperatures is plotted in Fig. 2.5.2. Wavelengths are given in microns, 1 micron being designated by the symbol $\mu(= 10^{-6}\,\mathrm{m})$. Notice that at 1650 K the total energy radiated is much greater than at 1100 K and that at the higher temperature the maximum has shifted to shorter wavelengths. Finally, whereas there is only a small amount of energy in the visible region at 1100 K, there is very

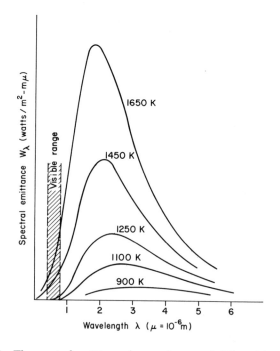

Fig. 2.5.2   The spectral emittance from a furnace at different temperatures.

much more at 1650 K. Quantitative measurements bear out the qualitative point already made. The curves in Fig. 2.5.2 depend only on the temperature and not on the material of which the furnace is constructed. The spectral distribution must therefore be explicable from relatively general arguments not involving the details of the interaction of the radiation with matter.

Inside the cavity the electromagnetic radiation is reflected back and forth between the walls. The situation is somewhat similar to that of the molecules of a gas at sufficiently low pressure such that collisions between gas molecules can be neglected. An equilibrium will be established between the energy of the gas and the energy of the wall (a hot wall heats the gas and vice versa!), and the speed distribution of the gas molecules at a given temperature can be computed with the methods of classical statistical mechanics, leading to the Maxwell-Boltzmann[26] distribution. In the theory of cavity radiation the electromagnetic waves now take the place of the gas molecules. There had been several theoretical attempts to explain the energy distribution inside the cavity. They were based on assumptions and methods of classical electromagnetic theory, thermodynamics, and statistical mechanics. For short wavelengths and high temperatures Wien's law[27] fitted the data reasonably well but failed for long wavelengths. Particularly, when data for the very long wavelengths of 24 μ, 32 μ, and 51 μ became available, the discrepancy from the predictions of Wien's law became very striking. For long wavelengths the experiments displayed a dependence of the emitted energy density as a function of their wavelength which could be described by a relatively simple empirical formula. Just about this time, but unknown to Planck, such a formula had been derived theoretically by Lord Rayleigh, using only classical physics; it is known today as the Rayleigh-Jeans[28] law. This law fails, however, at the

[26] Ludwig Boltzmann (1844–1906), Austrian physicist, mostly theoretical work, particularly thermodynamics. One of the founders of statistical mechanics. His experimental investigations of the optical index of refraction of gases were one of the earliest confirmations of Maxwell's electromagnetic theory.

[27] Wilhelm Wien (1864–1928), German physicist. Research with electron beams (cathode rays) and H-ion beams. He determined the energy of x-rays, and hence was able to estimate their wavelength. Nobel prize in physics in 1911 for his investigations in heat radiation. Wien's law is

$$W_\lambda = c_1 \lambda^{-5} e^{-c_2/\lambda T}$$

where the constants c_1 and c_2 are chosen to fit the experimental data.

[28] Lord Rayleigh (1842–1919), British physicist. Contributed to nearly all fields of classical physics. 1904 Nobel prize in physics for the discovery of argon. Sir James Jeans (1877–1946), British mathematical physicist and astrophysicist. His contribution to the Rayleigh-Jeans law is a factor 8 which Rayleigh had overlooked. Significant contributions particularly in thermodynamics and stellar dynamics.

other end of the spectrum because it indicates a continuously increasing energy density as the wavelength gets shorter, a trend to which physicists now refer as the "ultraviolet catastrophe."

Planck concluded that the correct radiation law had to reproduce Wien's law and the empirical formula in their respective domains of validity. He was able to interpolate between the two by use of a mathematical trick and arrived at a formula that fitted the data excellently in the whole range of the spectrum. It remained now for him to interpret the physical content of his formula.[29] He assumed that the walls of the cavity consisted of radiation-absorbing and emitting oscillators (we would today speak of oscillating electrons) through which the energy exchange with the electromagnetic field was made. He was forced thereby to stipulate that the oscillators could absorb or emit energy only in quanta of energy of magnitude $h\nu$. From the experimental data he determined the constant h with an accuracy of about 1% of today's accepted value of 6.62×10^{-34} joule-sec.

It should be pointed out that only the energies of the oscillators of the furnace wall were quantized according to Planck's opinion at this time, not the electromagnetic radiation in the cavity.

Planck found for the equilibrium distribution of the energy inside the furnace, as a function of the frequency of the radiation, the correct expression

$$dW = W_\nu d\nu = \frac{2\pi h}{c^2} \frac{\nu^3 d\nu}{e^{h\nu/kT} - 1} \text{ watts/meter}^2, \tag{2.5.1}$$

where h is Planck's constant, k is the Boltzmann's constant, and c is the velocity of light. Expressed per unit range of wavelength, we find, since

$$\lambda\nu = c,$$

$$\lambda d\nu + \nu d\lambda = 0,$$

$$d\nu = \frac{\nu}{\lambda} d\lambda = -\frac{c}{\lambda^2} d\lambda,$$

that

$$W_\lambda = \frac{c_1 \lambda^{-5}}{e^{c_2/\lambda T} - 1} \tag{2.5.2}$$

where $c_1 = 2\pi hc^2 = 3.740 \times 10^{-16}$ and $c_2 = hc/k = 1.438 \times 10^{-2}$ in mks units; $e = 2.71$. This is called *Planck's law* of the spectral emittance of an enclosed furnace or black body. It is in excellent agreement with all observations (Fig. 2.5.3).

For low frequencies, Planck's law as expressed in Eq. 2.5.1 may be simplified through putting

$$e^{h\nu/kT} - 1 = 1 + \frac{h\nu}{kT} + \cdots - 1 \simeq \frac{h\nu}{kT}$$

[29] *Verhandlungen der Deutschen Physikalischen Gesellschaft* **2**, 237 (1900).

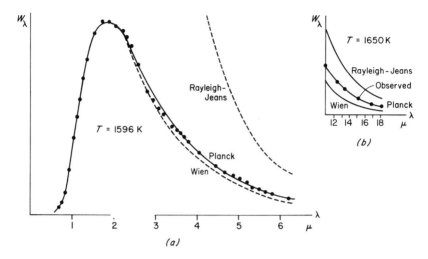

Fig. 2.5.3 Experimental data by W. W. Coblentz (Bull. of the Bureau of Standards *13*, 459, 1916) at 1596 K and of Lummer and Pringsheim (Verh. phys. Ges. Berlin *2*, 163, 1900) at 1650 K compared with Planck's, Wien's and Rayleigh-Jeans' law.

and we get

$$W_\nu = \frac{2\pi\nu^2}{c^2} kT \quad \text{for} \quad \frac{h\nu}{kT} \ll 1 \tag{2.5.3}$$

which is the *Rayleigh-Jeans' law*. Planck's constant has dropped out. The Rayleigh–Jeans' law, according to the foregoing, is valid only for long wavelengths.

Planck's radiation law also contains the Boltzmann constant k whose value had been known before only to an accuracy of about 30%. From the best fit through the experimental points Planck could calculate this constant too. But this was not all! The last section of Planck's paper is devoted to the numerical determination of no less than four constants. Apart from h and k he evaluated also Avogadro's number N from the relation $R = kN$, R being the gas constant. Finally, Planck computed the elementary charge e from N and the well-known amount of electric charge necessary to deposit one mole of a metal (e.g., silver) by electrolysis, the so-called Faraday's number.

About 30 years later, Planck explained in a private letter[30] the psychological aspects which led him to the quantum hypothesis:

"... shortly summarized, I may call the whole action an act of desperation, since by nature I am peaceful and opposed to doubt-

[30] to R. W. Wood, dated October 7, 1931, in German: deposited in the R. W. Wood collection, Center for History and Philosophy of Physics, American Institute of Physics.

ful adventures. But I had now already for six years (from 1894 on) wrestled with the problem of equilibrium between radiation and matter without having success; I knew that this problem is of fundamental importance for physics, I knew the formula which represents the energy distribution in a normal spectrum; a theoretical interpretation *had* to be found at any cost whatsoever. Classical physics was not sufficient, this was clear to me. . . . one can prevent the energy from converting into radiation by assuming that the energy, from the beginning, is forced to stay together in certain quanta. This was a purely formal assumption, and I did not give much thought about this. My only thought was that I had to arrive at a positive result, whatever it might cost. . . ."

It was Einstein who in 1905 extended the concept of quanta by showing that light itself consisted of quanta, using as an example the photoelectric effect described later. Planck, who was much more conservative in his opinions than Einstein, had not felt at ease when he was forced to introduce quanta to describe the interaction between radiation and matter. Even in 1909 he was not convinced that light consisted of quanta. In the discussion following a lecture by Einstein he said:

"... I, too, emphasize the necessity of the introduction of certain quanta. We do not make any progress in the theory of radiation without dividing up the energy in some sense into quanta which may be thought of as atoms of action. It is now the question where one should look for these quanta. According to the remarks of Mr. Einstein it might be necessary to assume that the free radiation in the vacuum, i.e., the light waves, have an atomistic constitution, hence to relinquish Maxwell's equations. This is a step which in my opinion seems not yet necessary."[31]

The foregoing shows that these ideas struck the leading physicists of those days, who had been brought up to think in classical concepts, as truly revolutionary. A great struggle was going on in their minds concerning the meaning of all this.

The Photoelectric Effect

According to Planck's theory of black-body radiation, the quantization was limited to the oscillators, but the electromagnetic radiation was not

---

[31] *Physikalische Zeitschrift* **10,** 777 (1909), reprinted in *Physikalische Blätter* **25,** 386 (1969) (in German).

quantized. Einstein, who became interested in Planck's work and also studied the problem of black-body radiation, went one step further and concluded that the electromagnetic radiation was also quantized. He was of the opinion that the wave theory and the "graininess" of electromagnetic radiation could coexist and wrote in his first paper about this topic[32]:

"The undulation theory of light which uses continuous space functions was eminently successful in representing the purely optical phenomena, and probably it will not be replaced by another theory. However, one should keep in mind that optical observations relate to average values with respect to time, not to instantaneous values. In spite of the full experimental confirmation of the theory of diffraction, reflection, refraction, dispersion, etc., one could well imagine that the theory of light which uses continuous space functions might lead to contradictions with the experimental evidence, when it is applied to the phenomena of the creation and conversion of light."

As corroborating evidence for the light quantum hypothesis, Einstein discussed the photoelectric effect in his paper. Its explanation in terms of quanta is very simple, but it cannot be understood on the basis of classical electromagnetic theory. The critical features of the photoelectric effect were discovered by Lenard[33] in 1902 (following work by Hertz and others) and were explained by Einstein in 1905, some years after Planck's introduction of the quantum concept in 1900.

The photoelectric effect consists of the emission of electrons from metallic surfaces when illuminated by light. That such an effect can exist is readily understandable in terms of electromagnetic theory. According to this theory light is an electromagnetic wave motion, and the electric vector in the wave may be expected to act on the electrons in a metal surface. Oscillations are produced, and energy is consequently absorbed, until the electron has sufficient kinetic energy to overcome the forces of attraction which bind it to the metal. One might expect, on the basis of electromagnetic theory, that the number and velocity of the ejected photoelectrons would depend on the amplitude of the electric vector and, therefore, on the intensity of the light, rather than critically on the wavelength.

The relevant experimental facts are that, for a particular surface, light

[32] *Annalen der Physik* **17**, 132 (1905). Einstein's Nobel prize in 1921 was particularly for his work on the photoelectric effect.

[33] Philipp Lenard (1862–1947), German experimental physicist, professor, primarily in Heidelberg. Nobel prize in physics 1905 for his investigations with cathode rays (i.e., electron beams). Although an excellent physicist he became a vehement opponent of Einstein's Theory of Relativity.

having a frequency below a certain critical frequency produces no photo-electrons, no matter what the incident intensity. Further, for frequencies above the critical frequency, photoelectrons are always produced, even for a very feeble intensity of the incident light, and their emission is immediate. These results are difficult to understand on the basis of a classical model for energy absorption, in which the electric vector produces a force acting on the electron proportional to E, or proportional to the square root of the intensity of light. No such dependence of the energy of the emitted electrons on the incident light intensity is found. Only the total current, or the number of photoelectrons emitted, is increased by increasing the light intensity.

The explanation in terms of the quantum theory is straightforward if we assume that the energy in a beam of monochromatic light is concentrated in energy quanta whose magnitude is determined by the frequency, and that all of the energy in a quantum is absorbed by a single electron. If the minimum work required to remove an electron from the metal being illuminated, the work function, is W_C, the following condition must be fulfilled if an electron is to escape:

$$h\nu \geq W_C. \tag{2.5.4}$$

If we define a frequency ν_0 by the relation

$$W_C = h\nu_0,$$

Eq. 2.5.4 may be rewritten in the form

$$\nu \geq \nu_0 = W_C/h. \tag{2.5.5}$$

Regardless of the intensity of the incident light, photoelectrons are to be expected if Eq. 2.5.5 is satisfied. A more detailed verification of the explanation advanced above is contained in the quantitative interpretation of the following experiment illustrated in Fig. 2.5.4. Light of variable frequency ν or intensity I from a spectrograph falls on a metal plate C, the cathode, in a vacuum tube. Electrons are ejected, some of which will travel to a second plate, the anode A, and thus produce a current i measured by the deflection of the galvanometer G. If the retarding potential is just sufficiently negative for no ejected electrons to have a kinetic energy great enough to reach A, the observed current will be stopped, and the condition satisfied by the stopping potential will be

$$eV = \tfrac{1}{2}mv_{\max}^2. \tag{2.5.6}$$

But the maximum kinetic energy of the emitted electrons will be the energy of a quantum less the minimum energy required to remove the

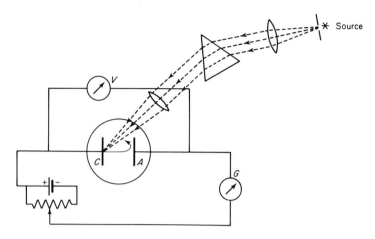

Fig. 2.5.4 Experimental arrangement for measuring the maximum kinetic energy of photoelectrons.

electron from the cathode C, or

$$\tfrac{1}{2}mv_{\text{max}}^2 = h\nu - W_C = h\nu - h\nu_0 = eV. \tag{2.5.7}$$

This may be put into the form

$$V = \frac{h}{e}(\nu - \nu_0). \tag{2.5.8}$$

Equation 2.5.8 is plotted in Fig. 2.5.5. The experimental results are in accordance with the above, not only to the extent of yielding points along a straight line with a positive slope and a positive intercept ν_0, but the slope of the line is just that computed with the value of e obtained from Millikan's oil drop experiment, and with the same value of Planck's constant used in describing the wavelength of a particle and in the Compton effect.

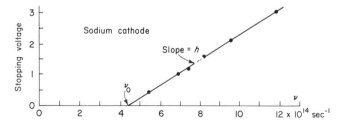

Fig. 2.5.5 Graph of Eq. 2.5.8 concerning the photoelectric effect. [After R. A. Millikan, *Phys. Rev.* **7**, 355 (1916).]

Work functions[34] for metals are in general a few electron volts in energy and are lowest for alkali metals. The frequencies of light used in such investigations correspond to the visible part of the spectrum and the near ultraviolet. The light quanta have therefore an energy of some electron volts. For example, the energy of quanta of yellow light

$$(\lambda = 6000 \text{ Å} = 6 \times 10^{-7} \text{ m}, \quad \nu = 5 \times 10^{14} \text{ sec}^{-1})$$

is

$$E = h\nu = 6.62 \times 10^{-34} \text{ joule-sec} \times 5 \times 10^{14} \text{ sec}^{-1} = 3.31 \times 10^{-19} \text{ joule}$$

or

$$(3.3 \times 10^{-19} \text{ joule})/(1.6 \times 10^{-19} \text{ joule/eV}) \approx 2 \text{ eV}.$$

The contradiction to the classically expected result, that the energy of the emitted electrons will be increased by the intensity of the illumination, is contained in Fig. 2.5.6. Here the potential of the emitting plate C is increased from some positive value at which no electrons escape and at which the galvanometer current $i = 0$, to a sufficiently large negative value so that all emitted electrons reach plate A. The current then has its saturation value i_s. The value of V_0, designating the stopping potential in this figure, is unaffected by the magnitude of I but the saturation current is proportional to I.

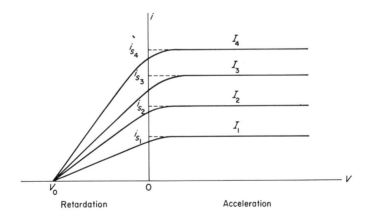

Fig. 2.5.6 The dependence of photocurrent on the potential difference for different intensities of illumination I and voltage. [Richardson and Compton, *Phil. Mag.* **24**, 575 (1912).]

[34] Work functions will be discussed in more detail in Chapter 5.

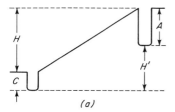 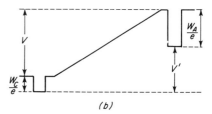

Fig. 2.5.7   Mechanical potential energy differences (a) as an analogy to work functions and electric potential differences in the photoelectric effect (b).

Although the slope of the straight line in an eV-vs.-ν diagram, as shown in Fig. 2.5.5, from which h is computed, is relatively easily determined in an actual experiment, the true value of the work function W_C cannot be measured in a straightforward way because also the work function W_A of the anode has to be considered. Perhaps this can best be visualized with the help of a mechanical analogy. An inclined plane (Fig. 2.5.7) has two holes of different depths, C and A, at each end. At the bottom of each hole are a number of balls of mass m. The minimum energy that is necessary to bring a ball from the lower hole to the rim of the upper hole (from where it can fall into the upper hole) is $mg(C + H)$. On the other hand, the difference in potential energy between the position of a ball in the lower and in the upper hole is $mg\,H'$. Some hypothetical measuring device for potential energy differences which works by sensing the location of the balls will therefore measure this latter quantity.

After this excursion into mechanical potential energy we revert to the discussion of the photoelectric effect. W_C and W_A are now the work functions of the cathode and anode, respectively, and V is the retarding potential. If $h\nu = W_C + eV$ the electrons will just reach the anode. However, a voltmeter connected to the two plates will measure the potential difference V' (not $V!$), which represents the potential difference between the least bound electrons of each plate. If V is the stopping potential, the energy of the incident quanta is, according to Eq. 2.5.7,

$$h\nu = W_C + eV,$$

but because

$$W_C/e + V = W_A/e + V'$$

$$h\nu = W_A + eV'.$$

Because the voltmeter across the cathode and anode measures V', the intercept of the straight line on the ν-axis is a measure of W_A, not of W_C, as one might first believe. Millikan[35] who investigated the photoelectric effect in great detail from 1912 on observed indeed that V' changed with the material of the anode, but not of the cathode for a given light frequency. It might be added that many elementary texts have the facts regarding the determination of W_C wrong.

---

[35] Robert A. Millikan (1868–1953), professor of physics at the University of Chicago. Since 1921 at the California Institute of Technology whose president he became and which he brought to fame. Nobel prize in physics 1923 for his work on the photoelectric effect and the determination of the electronic charge.

Robert A. Millikan (1868–1953) (left) and the astrophysicist Ira S. Bowen (Courtesy of Niels Bohr Library, American Institute of Physics).

It was partly due to Millikan's careful experimental investigations of the photoelectric effect that Einstein's explanation by postulating quanta of radiation found more acceptance. We mentioned in the preceding section Planck's opinion in 1909. Still in 1913, Planck and three other well known scientists wrote in a letter to the Prussian Ministry of Education in which they proposed Einstein for a vacant seat in the Prussian Academy of Sciences:

> "It should not be held too much against him that occasionally he may have overshot the target in his speculations, as for example in his hypothesis of light quanta, because even in the most exact science there can be no breakthrough without accepting once in a while a risk."

It may be added that the photoelectric effect, which releases free electrons (in contrast to electrons bound to atoms) from a metallic surface, is not the only kind of photoelectric effect. Quanta can also interact with atoms, ejecting tightly bound electrons. The energy necessary for such a process varies very much with the binding and in massive atoms, like lead, may surpass 100 keV. Photoelectric effects are also observed on nuclei. Protons or neutrons can be emitted from a nucleus by the interaction of a quantum with a nucleus. Because the energy to separate a proton or a neutron from a nucleus is approximately 8 MeV, the quanta that produce nuclear photoeffects must accordingly be very energetic.

The Compton Effect

What finally and completely convinced the community of physicists of the existence of light quanta was the discovery of the Compton effect in 1922 by A. H. Compton.[36]

In the discussion of the photoelectric effect we took into account only the conservation of energy, but did not invoke the principle of conservation of momentum. We tacitly assumed that the crystal lattice could easily take up any momentum from the small impact of the incident quantum or of the recoil of the emitted electron. The Compton effect, however, deals with the interaction between a quantum of electromagnetic radiation and an electron which is free. This means that interactions or forces between the electron and its environment are negligible. Hence the principles of conservation of momentum as well as of energy play a role.

Let us review qualitatively what we might expect of a collision between a quantum of frequency ν and a particle of mass m_0 initially at rest. If a collision occurs, the particle after the collision will no longer be at rest. It will have picked up energy and momentum. These must have come from the quantum whose energy and momentum have been decreased. But, if the energy of the quantum is decreased, its frequency, according to the equation $E = h\nu$, must be decreased. We should therefore expect to find, if the quantum concept is correct, that the frequency of the light scattered by a charged particle is decreased relative to the frequency of the incoming light.

Qualitatively, at least, we know that in the visible range this is not true. Scattered light appears to have the same frequency as the incident light. This, however, is no disproof of the idea. We must examine it more carefully and quantitatively. First, we should review what we know about the collision of two particles. When a golf ball strikes a large bowling ball, it

[36] A. H. Compton (1892–1962), American physicist, professor at the Washington University in St. Louis, and the University of Chicago. Research in x-rays and cosmic radiation. Nobel prize in physics 1927 for the discovery of the Compton effect.

Arthur H. Compton (1892–1962) (Courtesy of Niels Bohr Library, American Institute of Physics).

loses very little energy (apart from that lost in internal friction). Only when two more nearly equal particles collide, such as two billiard balls, will the moving one in general pass on a reasonable fraction of its energy to the one at rest. We should not, therefore, expect any appreciable change in wavelength unless the equivalent mass of the quantum $h\nu/c^2$ is somewhere near the rest mass m_0 of the particle. The condition for an appreciable change in frequency or wavelength on scattering is, hence,

$$h\nu = mc^2 \approx m_0 c^2$$

where m is the photon "mass" and m_0 the rest mass of the particle, or

$$\lambda = \frac{c}{\nu} = \frac{h}{m_0 c}. \qquad (2.5.9)$$

For a change of λ in a collision with a proton to occur, the critical electromagnetic wavelength is

$$\lambda = \frac{6.62 \times 10^{-34}}{1.67 \times 10^{-27} \times 3 \times 10^8} = 1.3 \times 10^{-15} \text{ m}.$$

This is the range of high-energy γ-rays, which we shall consider further in Chapter 7. However, if we consider the critical wavelength of collisions with electrons which are either free or so loosely bound that the binding energy can be neglected, we get

$$\lambda = \frac{h}{m_0 c} = \frac{6.62 \times 10^{-34}}{9.1 \times 10^{-31} \times 3 \times 10^8} = 2.4 \times 10^{-12} \text{ m} \qquad (2.5.10)$$

which is generally known as the *Compton wavelength of the electron*. This falls not too far from the range of x-rays whose wavelength can be accurately determined by diffraction from crystals, and it is therefore in the scattering of x-rays that we should expect to find accurately measurable effects. For visible light, on the other hand, whose wavelength is several hundred thousand times as great, $\sim 5 \times 10^{-7}$ m, the quanta have such small masses compared to electronic masses that no appreciable energy or frequency change is to be expected. It should be emphasized that the Compton wavelength of the electron does not represent the wavelength of the electron in the same sense as the charge e and the rest mass m_0 which are inherent properties of the electron. The Compton wavelength is primarily a quantity which is derived from the appropriate combination of the constants of nature h, m_0, and c.

In order to make quantitative predictions we must set up the equations of conservation of energy and momentum. Moreover, if we are to deal with quanta for which $h\nu \sim m_0 c^2$, we see that, if the quanta are to lose an appreciable portion of their energy, the electron must acquire a velocity comparable to that of light. We must therefore set up our conservation equations so that they are relativistically correct. In other words, the mass of the electron must be taken as

$$m = \frac{m_0}{\sqrt{1 - \beta^2}}$$

where $\beta = v/c$, the ratio of its velocity to that of light. The total energy of the electron is mc^2, and its kinetic energy is this quantity less the "rest energy," or $(m - m_0)c^2$. The momentum in the direction of motion is mv. Using the symbols shown in Fig. 2.5.8(a), we have for the statement that the energy before the collision is equal to that after the collision

$$h\nu_i = (m - m_0)c^2 + h\nu_s, \qquad (2.5.11)$$

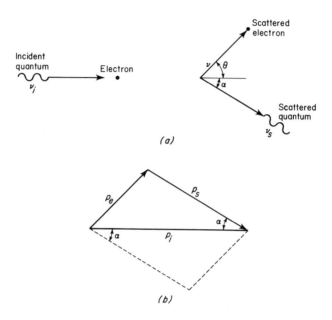

Fig. 2.5.8   The Compton effect. (a) Directions of the incident and the scattered quantum and the scattered electron. (b) Momentum triangle due to the conservation of momentum.

and for the statement that the initial and final momenta, in and perpendicular to the direction of the incident quanta, must be equal [Fig. 2.5.8(b)]

$$\frac{h\nu_i}{c} = mv \cos \theta + \frac{h\nu_s}{c} \cos \alpha \qquad (2.5.12)$$

$$0 = mv \sin \theta - \frac{h\nu_s}{c} \sin \alpha. \qquad (2.5.13)$$

From these three equations, two variables may be eliminated. Since we propose to make observations on the incident and scattered quanta, and not on the scattered electron, we shall eliminate the variables v and θ specifying the motion of the electron. We shall be left with a single equation containing, in addition to the constants h, m_0, and c, the incident and scattered frequencies or wavelengths and the scattering angle α. This relation will then specify, if an incident quantum of frequency ν_i and wavelength λ_i is scattered through an angle α, what the frequency or wavelength of the scattered quantum must be. The mathematical steps leading to the expected result are carried out below. The result is

$$\lambda_s = \lambda_i + \frac{2h}{m_0 c} \sin^2 \frac{\alpha}{2} \tag{2.5.14}$$

$$= \lambda_i + 0.05 \times 10^{-10} \sin^2 \frac{\alpha}{2} \text{ meter (approx.)}$$

for electrons.

Derivation of the Compton Shift in Wavelength

Referring to Fig. 2.5.8 (*b*) we can write the conservation of momentum

$$\mathbf{p}_i = \mathbf{p}_s + \mathbf{p}_e \tag{2.5.15}$$

and the conservation of energy, where E is the total, relativistic energy of the electron,

$$m_0 c^2 + h\nu = E + h\nu'. \tag{2.5.16}$$

We start from the relativistic relation (e.g., Eq. 2.1.6) for the electron

$$c^2 p_e^2 - E^2 + m_0^2 c^4 = 0 \tag{2.5.17}$$

from which we eliminate momentum and energy of the electron after the collision (in which we are here not interested) introducing quantities concerning the quanta. Thus we get

$$c^2 (\mathbf{p}_i - \mathbf{p}_s)^2 - [m_0 c^2 + h(\nu - \nu')]^2 + m_0^2 c^4 = 0. \tag{2.5.18}$$

Considering that the momentum of a quantum is $h\nu/c$,[37] applying the law of cosines and multiplying out the square of the expression in brackets we find

$$h^2 [\nu^2 + \nu'^2 - 2\nu\nu' \cos \alpha - (\nu - \nu')^2] = 2 m_0 c^2 h (\nu - \nu'). \tag{2.5.19}$$

We multiply out the expression $(\nu - \nu')^2$ and rearrange, which yields

$$h\nu\nu' (1 - \cos \alpha) = m_0 c^2 (\nu - \nu').$$

Since $\nu = c/\lambda$, we can write

$$\lambda' - \lambda = \Delta\lambda = \frac{h}{m_0 c} (1 - \cos \alpha) \tag{2.5.20}$$

or

$$\Delta\lambda = \frac{2h}{m_0 c} \sin^2 \frac{\alpha}{2} \approx 0.05 \times 10^{-10} \sin^2 \frac{\alpha}{2} \text{ m.} \tag{2.5.21}$$

Thus, quantum theory predicts that light scattered by an electron at

---

[37] This follows from the relativistic equation $E^2 = c^2 p^2 + m_0^2 c^4$ for zero rest mass and $E = h\nu$.

any given angle will have its wavelength increased by a few hundredths of an angstrom unit, regardless of the incident wavelength. If the incident wavelength is in the visible and several thousand angstrom units long in the first place, the addition of a few hundredths of an angstrom will be difficult to observe. We had already arrived at this conclusion on qualitative grounds. But when we come to the scattering of x-rays having wavelengths comparable to the calculated change, we may expect measurable effects.

On the basis of the classical scattering theory of light waves, one should have expected that the scattering electrons vibrate with the frequency of the incoming radiation, and therefore should reradiate the x-rays with the original frequency. It was this effect that was discovered by A. H. Compton in 1922. After a false start of trying to explain the observed shift in wavelength with classical theory, Compton (and, independently, P. Debye) was able to interpret the effect, using the above arguments, as an experimental demonstration of the existence of electromagnetic quanta. It is still one of the most convincing arguments for the corpuscular character of light.

Compton's measurements are shown in Fig. 2.5.9. The energy of the scattered x-ray quanta was measured by observing the Bragg-reflection angle from a calcite crystal. The incident x-ray is the so-called $K\alpha$ line of molybdenum, having a wavelength $\lambda = 0.708$ Å. The x-rays are scattered from graphite. A great percentage of the x-ray quanta are elastically scattered, that is without loss of energy, and give rise to the peak at 6° 43′. The greater the scattering angle α, the greater is the energy difference between the elastically scattered x-rays and the Compton scattered ones.

It may be added that the Compton effect represents one of the principal modes of interaction between electromagnetic quanta and matter. The attenuation of x-rays and γ-rays in their passage through matter is, to a great extent, due to the Compton scattering of the quanta by the electrons in the material.

Pair Production and Annihilation

A third way of interaction of electromagnetic quanta with electrons is to be found in the production of electron-positron[38] pairs. At high energies

[38] The terminology is not yet fully standardized. Some physicists prefer to reserve the term electron to include positive and negative particles of this mass, but to use the names positon (without r!) and negaton if the sign of the charge is to be specified. We adhere in this book to the more common, although not quite as consequent, usage by calling the negative particle electron and the positive particle positron, unless it is expressly stated that the term electrons includes also the positive variety.

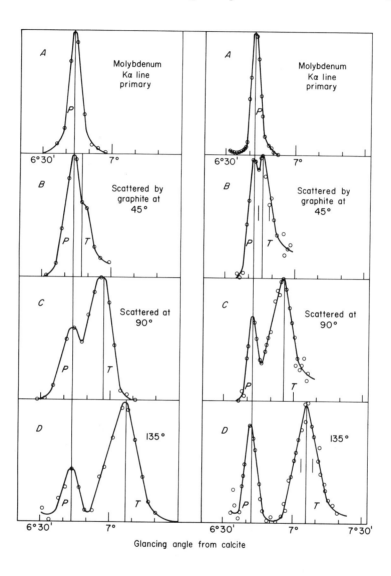

Fig. 2.5.9. Compton's measurements, using slits of two different widths. Curve A represents the spectrum of the K_α line of molybdenum and curves B, C, and D are the spectra of this line after being scattered at angles of 45°, 90°, and 135°, respectively, with the primary beam. The lines P and T are drawn at the expected positions for the primary and the scattered beam. [*Phys. Rev.* **22**, 409 (1923).]

(say beyond a few MeV quantum energy) this process is more probable than the Compton effect or particularly the photoelectric effect, which has only minimal importance at such energies. Nearly all the electrons and positrons in the cosmic radiation are the results of such pair-production processes.

Quanta may transform themselves into electron-positron pairs when they can do so subject to

(a) the conservation of charge
(b) the conservation of energy
(c) the conservation of momentum.

The disappearance of a quantum with the creation of an electron-posi-pair satisfies criterion (a). Criterion (b) is satisfied provided the energy of the quantum is greater than the rest energy of two electrons, or $2m_0c^2 = 1.02$ MeV. This is then the expected, and also the observed, minimum energy, or threshold, for pair production. The third criterion cannot be satisfied in free space. Conservation of energy would require that

$$h\nu = \frac{m_0c^2}{\sqrt{1 - v_e^2/c^2}} + \frac{m_0c^2}{\sqrt{1 - v_p^2/c^2}} \qquad (2.5.22)$$

which can always be satisfied provided $h\nu > 2m_0c^2$. The subscripts e and p stand here for electron and positron. Conservation of momentum would require that

$$\frac{h\nu}{c} = \frac{m_0v_e}{\sqrt{1 - v_e^2/c^2}} + \frac{m_0v_p}{\sqrt{1 - v_p^2/c^2}} \qquad (2.5.23)$$

which is obviously impossible, as can be seen by multiplying Eq. 2.5.23 by c and comparing the result with Eq. 2.5.22 because v_e and v_p cannot equal equal c. However, in the close vicinity of a nucleus, or when the nucleus is somehow coupled to the conversion process, we have another variable at our disposal, the final velocity v_n of the nucleus of mass M. Energy and momentum conservation can then both be satisfied. Moreover, in view of the large nuclear mass the fractional correction in the energy equation $Mv_n^2/h\nu$, is small compared to the fractional correction in the momentum equation $Mv/(h\nu/c) = Mv_n c/h\nu$, and the calculated threshold is not essentially changed.

Figure 2.5.10 shows the tracks of a positron-electron pair in a liquid-

---

Fig. 2.5.10 Tracks of an electron-positron pair in a bubble chamber, created by the decay of a neutral particle coming from the left (Brookhaven National Laboratory).

hydrogen bubble chamber, a detection device used in high-energy physics. In this case, however, the pair was not created by a quantum but by a spontaneously decaying neutral meson. This meson did not leave a visible track in the liquid hydrogen. Because the bubble chamber is in a magnetic field, the positron and electron tracks are curved in opposite directions.

The inverse process to pair production is the annihilation of such a pair. This process is subject to the same conservation principles as the pair production. Annihilation radiation is observed when positrons "come to rest" in a solid, or are sufficiently slowed down so that their kinetic energy is very small compared to their rest energy. A positron can then combine with an electron, thereby releasing the same amount of energy necessary for pair production discussed above, namely 1.02 MeV. Under these conditions the initial momentum is essentially zero, and it will be necessary for the conservation of momentum that two quanta of equal energy be emitted in opposite directions, Fig. 2.5.11. Their energy will be 0.51 MeV each, and their wavelength will be the Compton wavelength of the electron

$$\lambda = \frac{c}{\nu} = \frac{hc}{h\nu} = \frac{hc}{m_0 c^2} = \frac{h}{m_0 c},$$

as is actually observed.

These matters are further discussed in Section 3.8 in connection with Dirac's relativistic theory of the electron. Annihilation of positrons in flight also occurs, and was discussed in Section 1.7. The probability for this process, however, is very small.

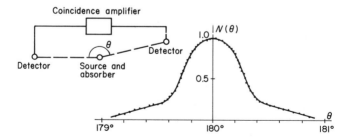

Fig. 2.5.11 (a) Arrangement for the measurement of the angular correlation of the two annihilation quanta. A positron-emitting radioactive source is surrounded by absorber material in which the positrons are stopped and where the annihilation takes place. Only when the two counters are in opposite places will both counters register the arrival of quanta at the same instant, a so-called coincidence. (b) Data of a coincidence measurement of annihilation radiation in brass. [F. Badoux and F. Heinrich, *Helvetica Physica Acta* **43**, 473 (1970).]

The Bremsstrahlung Spectrum

Fast electrons which may have gained their kinetic energy by acceleration through an electric potential will be stopped more or less suddenly when impinging on matter. From classical electromagnetic theory we know that the acceleration and deceleration of electric charges produces radiation of which an antenna is a good example. This deceleration when hitting matter takes place in the field of the nucleus or in the field of the electronic shell of the atoms. In most cases an individual electron undergoes several encounters until it has lost all its energy. Thus, each of the resulting quanta that are emitted each time have only a fraction of the original energy of the electron. In a few cases the electron, however, may lose all its energy in a single event. The quantum that is emitted has then an energy $E = h\nu$ corresponding to the kinetic energy of the electron. If, therefore, a monoenergetic beam of electrons hits a target, a continuous spectrum of quanta is emitted from that target. The maximum frequency of the quanta is given by $\nu_{max} = eV/h$, where eV is the kinetic energy of the electrons. This upper limit does not depend on the target material but only on the energy of the electrons. The emitted radiation has two names: bremsstrahlung (from the German *bremsen* = braking, *Strahlung* = radiation) and x-radiation.

The observed continuous x-ray spectrum often has certain spikes superimposed on it. These x-ray lines have a very different origin and will be discussed in Chapter 4. They are emitted from the atoms of the target material, and their energy depends therefore on the material being bombarded.

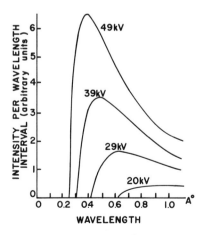

Fig. 2.5.12   X-ray spectra of tungsten for different accelerating voltages.

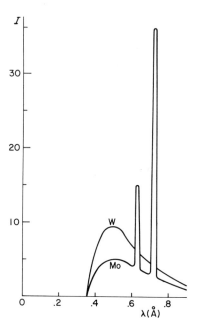

Fig. 2.5.13 X-ray spectra as a function of wavelength of tungsten (wolfram) and molybdenum for an accelerating potential of 35 kV.

Figure 2.5.12. gives x-ray spectra as a function of frequency for tungsten (correctly called wolfram, chemical symbol, W) for different electron energies. Figure 2.5.13 shows x-ray spectra for two different elements, tungsten ($Z = 74$) and molybdenum ($Z = 42$), for the same acceleration potential.

A cross section through a modern x-ray tube is given in Fig. 2.5.14. The tube is usually made of metal and is evacuated. Electrons are emitted by thermionic emission from the cathode which is heated by a filament. The

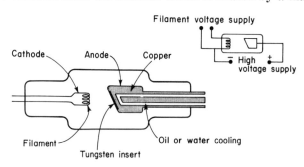

Fig. 2.5.14 Cross section through a modern x-ray tube.

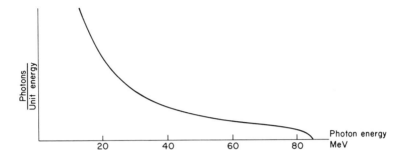

Fig. 2.5.15   Bremsstrahlung spectrum from 85-MeV electrons.

target, called an anode, is on a positive potential. This anode is usually cut at a slight angle so that the x-rays can emerge without being absorbed by the anode material. At lower acceleration energies, say below 100 keV, the emitted radiation is fairly isotropic. At higher energies, because of conservation of momentum, the radiation is peaked more forward, that is in the direction of the impinging electrons. For medical diagnostic purposes x-rays of the order of 60 keV energy are usual, for x-ray therapy often a higher energy is chosen. Inspection of metal castings is done with x-rays of 2 MeV to approximately 30 MeV. To obtain x-rays of such and even much higher energies the electrons are accelerated in betatrons or linear accelerators to the necessary energy. Bremsstrahlung is also used for inducing nuclear and particle reactions. A bremsstrahlung spectrum from 85-MeV electrons is shown in Fig. 2.5.15.

Optical Pumping and Lasers

The preceding sections described interactions between quanta and electrons in which the question of how the electrons are bound in the atoms played no particular role. However, the structure of atoms is one of the main fields of quantum mechanics, as we shall see in the following chapters. Before we go into detail we want to discuss here a beautiful example of the interaction of quanta with atoms, optical pumping and lasers, which have become very important in physics and technology.

Until 1960 the only way to produce coherent light beams had been to let the beams originate in one direction from the same small source. Each light beam then contained an identical ensemble of wave trains, but was necessarily very weak. It was then discovered that coherent light can be produced by an instrument called a "laser," an acronym for *Light Amplification by Stimulated Emission of Radiation*.

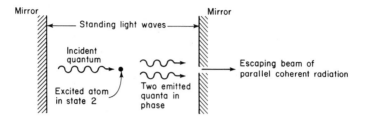

Fig. 2.5.16 Illustration of the operation of a laser.

We mentioned earlier that in a sodium vapor lamp, for example, atoms which are brought into excited states emit light quanta when returning to their ground state. We also pointed out that the lifetimes of these excited states are the order of 10^{-8} sec, and that we cannot predict at exactly what time any one atom will emit a quantum. In other words, their decay is a random process. This mode of emission of a quantum is called a spontaneous emission. On the other hand, we also mentioned that a collision can shorten the life of the excited state of an atom. There is still another possibility of de-excitation. In just the same way in which an atom can absorb energy from an electromagnetic wave or a quantum of the correct frequency, namely $\nu = \Delta E/h$, and thus be lifted into an excited state, so can an excited atom, interacting with an electromagnetic wave or quantum of the same frequency be triggered to fall back to its ground state. This is called stimulated emission of radiation. Such a forced emission of energy by an oscillating system occurs when the driving force is in phase. Moreover, in an electromagnetic wave, forced emission by excited atoms always occurs in the direction of propagation of the wave responsible for the forced emission. The functioning of the laser is illustrated in Fig. 2.5.16. The radiation to be amplified has the frequency of

$$\nu_{21} = \frac{E_2 - E_1}{h} \tag{2.5.24}$$

corresponding to the transition $2 \rightarrow 1$ shown in the energy level diagram in Fig. 2.5.17.

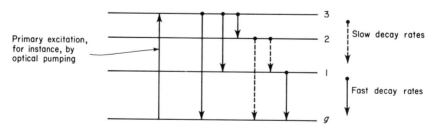

Fig. 2.5.17 Energy-level diagram of an atom suitable for a laser.

In thermal equilibrium between two states of an atom, the one having the lower energy is more populated, since according to the Boltzmann distribution law the population of a state i of energy E_i is given by

$$n_i = Ce^{-E_i/kT}. \tag{2.5.25}$$

The ratio of the numbers of atoms in a state x to the number in state y in equilibrium is, hence,

$$\frac{n_x}{n_y} = e^{-(E_x-E_y)/kT}. \tag{2.5.26}$$

If $E_x > E_y$, the ratio n_x/n_y can never be greater than unity in thermal equilibrium. A situation in which $n_x > n_y$ is called a population inversion and requires special conditions.

If two atoms, one in the lower state 1 and the other in the upper state 2, are exposed to the same electromagnetic wave field of frequency $\nu_{21} = (E_2 - E_1)/h$, the probabilities for stimulated transitions $1 \rightarrow 2$ and $2 \rightarrow 1$ turn out to be identical. (The spontaneous transitions $2 \rightarrow 1$ here may be neglected.) Since a laser is supposed to amplify light, that is, to increase the number of emitted quanta, a situation is required where the $2 \rightarrow 1$ transitions outnumber the $1 \rightarrow 2$ transitions. Obviously, the total number of transitions of one kind is proportional to the number of atoms in the state from where the transition starts. Hence, the higher state should be more populated or, in other words, a population inversion is a necessary condition to achieve laser action.

A way of producing this population inversion is shown schematically in Fig. 2.5.17 and is called optical pumping. Most of the atoms in a plasma are usually in the lowest or ground state, so that this is usually not suitable for the lower state in the laser process. If the population inversion is to be achieved in states 2 and 1, we would like state 2 to have a long lifetime, with a low probability of transition to any lower lying states, and state 1 to have a short lifetime, with a high probability of spontaneous decay. In our figure the optical pumping frequency is ν_{3g}. Radiation at this frequency, or other means of excitation such as collisions, are required in maximum available quantities. Excited atoms then decay spontaneously to states 2, 1, and g. Because of the assumed slow decay rate from state 2, and the high decay rate from state 1, the required population inversion can be produced.

Recent Experiments with Laser Beams

We now report some recent experiments which, although they do not involve new principles, are nevertheless beautiful modern extensions of the Compton effect and of electron diffraction.

In the ordinary Compton effect a quantum is scattered by an electron at rest. In this process the quantum loses, whereas the electron gains, energy. An effect going the opposite way, the inverse Compton effect, was first demonstrated in the U.S.S.R. and in the United States at the Cambridge Electron Accelerator.[39] A laser beam of visible light is directed against the beam of high-energy electrons. In the head-on collisions the back-scattered quanta have much more energy than the original quanta. Relativistic calculations show that for electrons of 6 GeV (1 GeV = 10^9 eV) and primary light quanta of 1.8 eV the energy of the back-scattered quanta is approximately 850 MeV. Because of the small collision probability for this process, only the availability of very intense laser beams made this experiment possible. There are indications that this inverse Compton effect is of some importance in the generation of high-energy photons in the cosmic radiation.

Another experiment which became feasible with the advent of lasers is the Bragg reflection of electrons from standing light waves. This effect, predicted in 1933 by Kapitza and Dirac,[40] was observed in 1965.[41] In the experiment a laser beam ($\lambda = 1.06 \times 10^{-6}$ m) was sent against a mirror and reflected back towards the laser. A standing light wave was therefore set up in front of the mirror. A very narrow beam of 10-eV electrons intercepted the light beam at a nearly right angle. When the laser beam was on, a great number of the electrons was slightly deflected in comparison to the position when the laser was shut off.

The standing light wave acts as a grating from which the matter waves of the electrons are diffracted. We might say that the two entities which we customarily consider as waves (the light) and particles (the electrons) have their roles reversed in the Kapitza-Dirac effect, because the more common case is that where the electromagnetic x-ray waves are diffracted by the electrons of the atoms in a crystal. In Schwarz's experiment the angle of deflection of the electron beam was of the expected magnitude for Bragg diffraction.

Kapitza and Dirac's (what they called simple) explanation goes somewhat deeper than necessary for our purpose, but is quite instructive (the quantitative calculation follows these remarks in their paper):

"A simple way of dealing with the problem theoretically is as follows. Instead of supposing the electron to pass through a field of stationary waves, we may suppose it to be acted on by two beams of progressive waves with the same frequency and moving in opposite directions. Each of these beams by itself would give rise to Compton transitions, in which a photon is absorbed from that beam and re-emitted in an arbitrary direction, the electron experiencing at the same time a recoil which deflects it out of its original path. With both beams acting together, however, a new effect must also occur, according to Einstein's laws of radiation, provided that the initial velocity and direction of motion of the electron are suitably adjusted. This is the effect of stimulated Compton scattering, in which a photon is absorbed from one beam and its re-emission is then stimulated by the existence of the other beam, the electron again experiencing a recoil. The frequency of the occurrence of this second

[39] R. H. Milburn, *Phys. Rev. Letters* **10**, 75 (1963): Bemporad, Milburn, Tanaka and Fotino, *Phys. Rev.* **138**, B1546 (1965).

[40] P. L. Kapitza and P. A. M. Dirac, *Proc. Cambridge Phil. Soc.* **29**, 297 (1933).

[41] Schwarz et al., *Phys. Letters* **19**, 202 (1965); H. Schwarz, *Zeitschrift für Physik* **204**, 276 (1967) (in English); see also L. S. Bartell et al., *Phys. Rev.* **166**, 1494 (1968).

process is proportional to the product of the intensities of the two beams, in contradistinction to that of the first process, which is of course proportional simply to one of the intensities. Thus when the field of radiation is weak, the ordinary Compton effect predominates, while when it is sufficiently strong the stimulated effect predominates."

Kapitza and Dirac when proposing this experiment, long before the invention of the laser, considered it "just on the verge of possibility, and would be very difficult to carry out."

Interference Effects with Single Photons

In the last sections we emphasized mainly those properties of quanta which we may summarize as particle aspects. The wave aspects were only somewhat indirectly taken into consideration by assigning to each quantum a certain frequency according to the relation $E = h\nu$. We know, however, from the study of optics that light, which we assume to be nothing but quanta en masse, will give rise to interference and diffraction phenomena which always have considered as the strongest evidence for its wave character. We may recall the interference fringes observed in a Michelson interferometer or in Young's double-slit arrangement. In such experiments light usually originates from a single small source (in order to insure coherence); it is then split into two (or more) beams which are afterwards recombined and cause interference phenomena.

We can now ask what will happen if we reduce the light intensity to such an extent that we can be certain that nearly always at most only one quantum at a time is in transit between light source and screen, or photographic plate or other light-sensitive detector. For example, if we use a photographic plate which we must obviously expose for a long time because of the low light intensity, will we observe interference fringes on it? Such experiments have been performed, the first one[42] as early as 1909 which, however, did not make a great impact on the physicists of those days. The first experiment that was carried out under good conditions was published in 1927.[43] Monochromatic light of very low intensity from a helium gas discharge passed through a certain type of interferometer and was registered on a film. It clearly produced interference fringes. Later experiments[44] also confirmed that single quanta ended up predominantly in those regions

---

[42] G. I. Taylor, *Proc. Cambridge Phil. Soc.* **15,** 114 (1909).

[43] A. J. Dempster and H. F. Batho, *Phys. Rev.* **30,** 644 (1927).

[44] L. Jánossy and Z. Náray, *Aca Phys. Acad. Sci. Hung.* **7,** 403 (1957); G. T. Reynolds et al., *Nuovo Cimento* **61B,** 355 (1969); J. King, Film "Interference of Photons," produced by the Physical Science Study Committee (PSSC). A nice account is given in "Take a Photon" by O. R. Frisch, *Contemporary Physics* **7,** 45 (1965).

of the detection device where one would expect interference maxima for high light intensities. If the reflecting mirror at the end of one of the interferometer arms is taken away, the interference pattern disappears. It is therefore important that both paths are available for the quantum in transit to enable it to contribute to the interference pattern.

It cannot be predicted where a certain quantum will hit the screen or plate, just as in general one cannot predict when a certain person will die. However, in the first case the physicist and in the second case the life insurance company can calculate the probability for a quantum to fall on a certain square millimeter of the plate or for an individual to pass away in a certain year. With many quanta and many insured persons this probability for a single event can be translated into a statement of how often certain events will occur in comparison to others. The statistical probability for a quantum to arrive at a certain location of the screen can be calculated from the laws of classical wave optics. We may therefore conclude that there is no difference between interference patterns that are produced by light of high intensity and by quanta which arrive one by one at the screen or photographic plate. We may further deduce that in interference experiments at normal light intensities (excepting perhaps those produced with laser light), hence involving a very great number of quanta, each individual quantum may be considered to interfere with itself and in this way to contribute to the resulting interference pattern.

Another closely related experiment[45] should also be mentioned (Fig. 2.5.18). Light, again from a source of such low intensity that the individual quanta are well separated in time, is falling on a half-reflecting mirror at an angle of 45°, as in a Michelson interferometer. However, instead of mirrors at the ends of the interferometer arms there are photomultipliers (which in essence are very sensitive photocells) responding to the arrival of single light quanta. The simultaneous arrival of signals (we deliberately avoid the

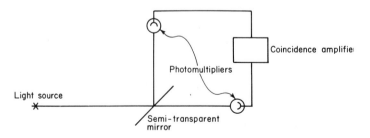

Fig. 2.5.18   Arrangement to check if a quantum is "split" by a half-transmitting mirror into two separate components.

[45] E. Brannen and H. I. S. Ferguson, *Nature* **178,** 481 (1956).

word quantum, because what we now might, or might not, detect is only one half of a quantum) at both photomultipliers, so-called coincidences, can be recorded by appropriate electronic devices. No coincidences beyond those expected and caused by accidental events were observed. (The possible objection can be ruled out that half the energy of the original quantum might not have been sufficient to bring the photomultipliers to a response.) The conclusion we can draw from this experiment is that a fraction of a quantum is not observed, but only whole quanta!

A quantum behaves very much like a particle, both when it is emitted and when it arrives at the location where it is detected as a very well localized event, much smaller in size than the whole interference pattern. In between, the quantum acts like a wave because it can produce interference phenomena. This complementarity of aspects, or particle-wave duality of the quantum (and also of the electron or other particles with a rest mass), cannot be explained with concepts that have evolved from our experience with classical physics. Therefore, physicists have worked very hard in order to arrive at a satisfactory interpretation of such experiments, and even today discussions among physicists about the correct, or at least best, interpretation have still not fully subsided.

The currently most popular standpoint is to say that quantum mechanics can only make statements about observable facts. We can observe where a quantum was emitted and where it hits the screen. Quantum mechanics can indeed predict the statistical probability for a quantum to strike a certain area. According to the second experiment we can also observe if a quantum was transmitted or reflected by the 45°-mirror of the apparatus, and quantum mechanics will again state the probability for each of the two possibilities. However, we know that if we locate the quantum along one of the possible ways we have destroyed its capability to contribute to the interference pattern and that we cannot observe a quantum on both paths at once. Hence, quantum mechanics cannot make a statement about the way being taken. Quantum mechanics will not give direct answers to such obvious and burning questions as "Is the quantum split and therefore takes several paths at once?" or "Is it so that although the quantum takes only one of the paths, it somehow (!) knows that another path would be available, and therefore it hits the screen preferentially at certain places?" A statement that goes as far as physicists are usually willing to go today is that for each point on the screen a wave amplitude can be calculated for each of the different paths. These amplitudes, when added up under consideration of their phase relationship, determine the probability for the quantum to arrive at the screen.[46]

[46] For readers interested in the fundamental problems of quantum mechanics (and also other fields of physics) the journal *Foundations of Physics* is highly recommended.

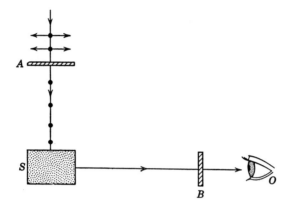

Figure P.2.1 (Problem 1)

PROBLEMS

1. Unpolarized light passes through a Polaroid A with its axis so oriented that, in the transmitted light, the electric vector is normal to the plane of the paper, as in the figure. This *light* falls on a soap solution S where it is *scattered* and viewed by an observer at O through a second Polaroid B. (*a*) Will the light intensity seen by the observer vary as the Polaroid B is rotated? (*b*) The Polaroid A is rotated through 90°. Does the light intensity now vary as B is rotated?

2. (*a*) Unpolarized light penetrates two *Polaroids* whose transmitting axes make an angle θ with each other. How does the intensity of the transmitted light depend on the angle θ? (*b*) The Polaroids are now crossed so that no light passes through the combination. A third Polaroid is introduced between the two crossed Polaroids. Its axis makes an angle ψ with that of the first. What fraction of the incident unpolarized light is transmitted by the first two Polaroids, and by all three?

3. Can you think of any evidence to show whether the electric field in a beam of visible light passing through a *transparent medium* produces primarily nuclear displacement, or acts primarily on individual electrons?

4. What are the first few *sinusoidal components* of the function shown in the figure?

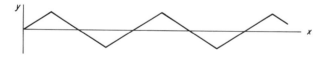

Figure P.2.2 (Problem 4)

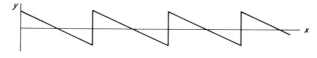

Figure P.2.3 (Problem 5)

5. What are the first few *sinusoidal components* of the function shown in the figure?

6. Sketch and sum the first three *Fourier components* for Fig. 2.1.12(a).

7. Sketch and sum the first three *Fourier components* for Fig. 2.1.12(b).

8. If the *oscillations* shown in Fig. 2.1.5 were *damped* more strongly, how would the frequency spectrum be changed?

9. Lifetimes of excited energy levels in atoms are in general between 10^{-11} and 10^{-7} sec. What is the *width* in Å of a *spectral line* of 6000 Å wavelength which is emitted from an atom in an excited state having a lifetime of 10^{-9} sec?

10. Nuclei can be in excited states from which transitions to lower-lying states are possible. For transition energies of 1 MeV the lifetimes of excited states may be as short as 10^{-15} sec. What is the frequency ν of the emitted quanta and the *width* $\Delta\nu$ of this transition?

11. Spectral lines are often produced by electric gas discharges. Due to the often high pressure in the discharge tubes the atoms collide frequently, thereby shortening the time during which atoms can radiate. This results in a *broadening of the spectral line*, the so-called pressure, or collision, broadening. The natural lifetime of a Hg atom from which the line of 254 mμ wavelength is emitted is of the order of 10^{-9} sec. In high-pressure mercury lamps this lifetime might be reduced to 10^{-13} sec. What is the natural width of this line? What is its pressure-broadened width?

12. The beam of a CO_2 laser has an average beam power of 100 watt and a cross section 1 cm². It strikes perpendicularly a reflecting aluminum foil of an area of 1 cm² and a thickness of 0.01 mm. The foil is suspended by a fine fiber of a length of 1 m and a mass of 10 mg. (a) What is the force exerted by the laser beam on the foil? (b) What is the deflection of the foil due to the *radiation pressure*? Density of aluminum: 2.7 g/cm³.

13. Show that light takes the shortest time to travel from A to B (a) when in a reflection at a surface the incident angle equals the reflected angle r', (b) when in passing from a medium of index of refraction n_i to one of index of refraction n_r Snell's law is satisfied. (These are examples of *Fermat's principle*.)

14. The mean flux of *radiation from the sun* at the top of the earth's atmosphere is 2.0 cal/cm²-min, or 1.42 kW/m², called the solar constant. (a) What is the mean value of the electric field intensity E of the sunlight

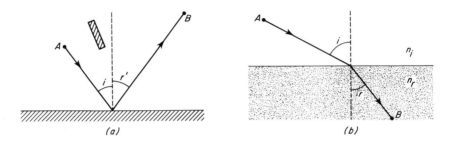

Figure P.2.4 (Problem 13)

at the top of the atmosphere? (b) How big is the solar radiation pressure there? (c) Find the force of the solar radiation on our planet. Assume that none of the incident energy is reflected back, $R_{\text{Earth}} = 6000$ km. (d) What is the radiation pressure at the surface of the sun? $R_{\text{Sun}} = 7.0 \times 10^8$ m, distance Sun-Earth 1.50×10^8 km.

15. Show that the deflection of a light beam by a *prism* is smallest when the angle of incidence at the surface where the beam enters is equal to the angle between the emerging ray and the normal to the surface from which the beam leaves the prism.

16. A horizontal beam of light is normally incident on the glass side of a tank containing a solution in which the concentration varies from top to bottom. The *index of refraction* is greater at the bottom than at the top. (a) Draw some Huygens' wavelets at the incident surface, and be prepared to discuss the path of the light in the solutions. (b) Explain the wet appearance of dry streets on a hot day.

17. The *index of refraction* at the surface of the Earth is $n_0 = 1.000293$. The quantity $(n - 1)$ decreases linearly with the density of the air. The light from a star having the true zenith angle α_1 will therefore arrive at the surface with an angle $\alpha_0 < \alpha_1$. Calculate the difference between α_0 and α_1 if a star appears to an observer at a zenith angle of $10°$.

18. A liquid has an *index of refraction* $n(z)$ which decreases linearly in the z direction, i.e., $dn/dz = $ const. (Such a situation might be realized by a sugar solution which is more concentrated on the bottom than on the top.) Show that a light beam entering the liquid horizontally is curved downwards by calculating the trajectory of the beam.

19. Prove that for normally incident light at the plane *interface between two dielectrics* the intensity of the incident beam is just equal to the sum of the intensities of the reflected and transmitted beams.

20. An air-core *coaxial cable* is connected to another having the same dimensions but having a dielectric between conductors. Show that the condition that V and i shall have the same values on both sides of the

junction is equivalent to the condition that the tangential components of E and H shall be the same on both sides of the junction. What fraction of the incident power is reflected?

21. Starting from Snell's law derive Eqs. 2.2.11 and 2.2.12 for the *reflecting power* for an arbitrary angle of incidence.

22. (a) What is the·value of *Brewster's angle* of light incident from air on the surface of water ($n = 1.33$)? (b) What is the value of Brewster's angle for light incident from water to air?

23. A beam of unpolarized light is incident at *Brewster's angle* at the surface of a dielectric whose index of refraction is 1.5. What fraction of the incident intensity is reflected?

24. A man 6 ft tall has a *mirror* just large enough so that he can see himself entirely in it. How tall is the mirror?

25. The south wall of a large dark room is a *mirror*. A man is seated facing south in this room on a platform capable of being moved east and west. The perpendicular distance from the man to the mirror is 10 ft. Near the center of the room, and 15 ft from the mirror, are two small lights, a red one and a blue one. The red one is to the east and the blue one is to the west. Considering that the man sees the lights in the direction in which rays from the lights reach him, show in a diagram where the man sees the lights. How far away will they appear? Which will be.on the man's left?

26. In the above room, the east, as well as the south, wall is covered with a *mirror*. The movable platform is reoriented so that the man looks southeast into the corner where the two plane mirrors meet, and the platform is capable of movement at right angles to this direction. The lights are rearranged so that when he is opposite the corner they are just behind him, with the blue to his left, and the red to his right. Be prepared to discuss what the man will see.

27. A 6-ft man stands on the edge of a circular *swimming pool* 12 ft in diameter, and everywhere 6 ft deep. (a) In what direction must he look to see the opposite bottom corner of the pool when it is filled with water? (b) Where is the image which the man is looking at? Graphical solutions are probably easiest for (a) and (b). (c) If he looks straight down, what will be the apparent depth of the pool?

28. A narrow pencil of parallel light rays is normally incident on a solid *glass sphere* of index of refraction n and radius R. Where are the rays brought to a focus?

29. Calculate the intensity resulting from the *superposition of two plane waves*

$$y_1 = A \cos(kx - \omega t + \alpha), \quad y_2 = B \cos(kx - \omega t + \beta)$$

(a) for the case that α and β at any time have a fixed value, the two waves thus being coherent, (b) for the case that the waves are incoherent, i.e., α and β can assume any possible value as a function of the time.

30. In *Young's double-slit experiment*, suppose that the two slits are separated by 10^{-4} m, the distance to the screen is 1 m, and the wavelength of light is 5461 Å. Find the distances from the central maximum to the first five bright maxima. Do the same for a slit separation of 10^{-5} m.

31. In the above problem, how many bright maxima are there in principle for each of the *two slit* separations?

32. In the same experiment, suppose that the single slit is placed 0.10 m from the *two slits*, which are 0.001 m apart and 1 m from the screen. How wide, approximately, can the single slit be before there is no interference pattern on the screen? How wide can it be if the two slits are separated by 0.001 m?

33. Light from a narrow slit passes through *two* parallel *slits* 3×10^{-4} m apart. The interference bands on a screen 2 m away are 4.47×10^{-3} m apart. What is the wavelength of the light? What is the order of the spectrum? Consider that visible light extends from 4 to 7×10^{-7} m in wavelength.

34. If a point source of *incoherent light* illuminates two small holes, as in a Young interference arrangement, these holes become coherent light sources. Show that if the holes are illuminated by an incoherent light source of length l, as shown in the figure, the light emerging from these two holes is coherent only if $l \sin \alpha \ll \lambda/2$.

35. The angular diameter of some of the closer stars has been measured with a *Michelson stellar interferometer*. Therefore, if the distance is known from parallax measurements, the true diameter of a star can be determined. This interferometer is based on the principle of Young's double-slit experiment. The salient features of the interferometer are shown in the figure. Assume first that light from a distant *point* source of incoherent light which

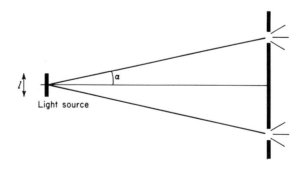

Figure P.2.5 (Problem 34)

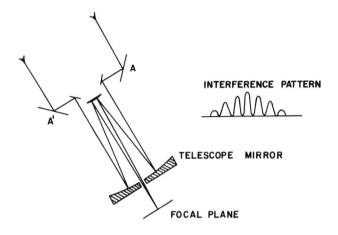

Figure P.2.6 (Problem 35)

lies on the axis of the instrument falls on two mirrors A and A' a distance d apart. The light is directed into a mirror telescope and finally impinges on a screen. Because the light arrives on the screen in two different ways, via A or A', an interference pattern will result. (a) If the distance traveled by the light from mirrors A or A' to the screen is 12 m, and the distance between these mirrors is 6 m, how far are the maxima apart on the screen? (b) By what angle must the light source be off the interferometer axis so that the new maxima coincide with the locations of the minima for an on-axis light source? (c) If a star has an angular diameter comparable or bigger than the angle calculated in (b), what kind of interference pattern will result? (d) The angular diameter of α Tauri, a giant star, was determined to be 2×10^{-2} sec of arc. How far would the maxima on the screen originating from opposite points of the star be apart, measured in terms of the distance between maxima originating from a point source?

36. Light composed of two wavelengths 6000 Å and 5000 Å falls at normal incidence on a *thin piece of glass* which has an index of refraction $n = 1.6$. What must be the thickness of the glass in order to produce maximum reflection for one of these wavelengths and maximum transmission for the other? Which is reflected?

37. Calculate thickness d and index of refraction n_1 of the *coating material for a lens* to obtain minimum reflection at normal incidence. Use the formula for the reflecting power given in Section 2.2. Assume light of a wavelength of $\lambda = 5300$ Å in vacuum and glass with an index of refraction $n_0 = 1.5$.

38. In a set of *Newton's rings* formed as in Fig. 2.3.10 the radius of the fiftieth ring is 10^{-2} m. Find the radius of the spherical glass surface. The

wavelength of light used is 5893 Å. What would be the pattern formed if white light instead of monochromatic light were used?

39. A planoconvex lens made of glass having an index of refraction $n = 1.5$ and having a radius of curvature $R = 0.1$ m is placed on a flat piece of glass having an index of refraction $n = 1.8$, as shown in Fig. 2.3.10. $\lambda_{air} = 6 \times 10^{-7}$ m, $R = 0.1$ m. (a) Is the central spot of the system of *Newton's rings* formed bright or dark as seen in reflected light? (b) Find the radius of the third dark ring if the wavelength of the light used is 6×10^{-7} m in air. (c) If the air film between the lens and the glass plate is replaced by a liquid having an index of refraction $n = 2$, what would be the radius of the third dark ring?

40. Light from a point light source S impinges on a *glass plate* of thickness d and index of refraction n. Light is reflected from both surfaces and falls on a screen. (a) For which angles i is the intensity on the screen a minimum? (b) How thick is the glass plate if for light of $\lambda = 5890$ Å the first minimum appears at an angle $i = 10°$ and if the index of refraction is $n = 1.5$?

41. An *air wedge* is formed between glass plates having an index of refraction $n = 1.5$ and is normally illuminated with light having a wavelength 5×10^{-7} m in air, as shown in the figure. (a) As seen by reflected light, will the tip (point) of the wedge look light or dark? (b) What is the spacing between adjacent bright bands? (c) What is the effect of replacing the upper plate by one having an index $n = 2$ and filling the air wedge with a liquid having an index of 1.8?

42. (a) Monochromatic light of wavelength 600 mμ originates at a distant point source and passes through a circular opening onto a screen 1 m away. Find the diameter of the circular opening if it exposes n *Fresnel zones*. (b) This same light passes through a circular opening 2 mm in diameter. Find the distances of the screen from the opening that are larger than 0.5 m for which there will be a central bright spot. (Give numerical answers.)

43. In an experiment designed to show *Fraunhofer diffraction* from a

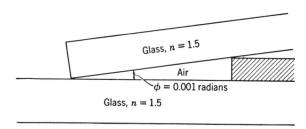

Figure P.2.7 (Problem 41)

single slit, parallel light strikes a slit 1 wavelength wide normally. A screen is placed 1 m away, and a lens of 1 m focal length is placed right at the slit. Find the positions of the first five maxima on the screen. Do the same for a slit 10 wavelengths wide. In principle, how many diffraction maxima are there?

44. (a) Using a *diffraction grating* with 8000 grooves per inch and light of wavelength 5500 Å incident normally, at what angles do maxima occur? (b) If the third-order maximum for red light 6500 Å coincides with the fourth-order maximum for violet light, what is the wavelength of the violet light?

45. The angular deviation of a third-order spectrum line produced by a transmission *grating* 2 cm wide with 110 lines per millimeter normally illuminated is 11°11'. What is the wavelength of the light? If another line can barely be resolved, in this order, from the one just mentioned, what is the difference between the wavelengths?

46. Parallel light falls normally on a plane reflection *grating* with 1000 lines per millimeter. In what direction is the first-order spectrum of sodium light reflected from the grating ($\lambda = 5890$ Å)? What is the answer if the angle of incidence is 30°?

47. An idealized *grating* with alternate perfectly clear and perfectly opaque spaces gives a spectrum in which all the even orders are missing. What is the ratio of the widths of the clear and opaque spaces?

48. Discuss the *intensity distribution* of monochromatic light transmitted by an idealized grating consisting of alternate clear and opaque strips.

49. According to Eq. 2.3.16, the intensity minima of the *diffraction pattern of a slit,*

$$I = I_0 \left(\frac{\sin z}{z} \right)^2$$

occur for $z = \pi, 2\pi, 3\pi, \ldots$. The intensity maxima will occur approximately halfway between these minima, or for $z = 3\pi/2, 5\pi/2, 7\pi/2, \ldots$, and the corresponding values of I/I_0 will be $(\frac{2}{3}\pi)^2$, $(\frac{2}{5}\pi)^2$, $(\frac{2}{7}\pi)^2$, $\ldots$. Compute the exact location of the subsidiary maxima, and compare the correct intensities with the above approximate values.

50. If yellow light is observed at an angle of 36° with a *grating* ruled with 5000 grooves per cm, what is the wavelength of the light?

51. The limits of the visible spectrum are nearly 4000 to 7000 Å. (a) Find the angular breadth of the first-order visible spectrum formed by a plane *grating* with 12,000 lines per inch. (b) Does the violet of the third-order visible spectrum overlap the red in the second-order spectrum? If so, by how much (approximately)?

52. Light containing two wavelengths of 5000 and 5200 Å is normally

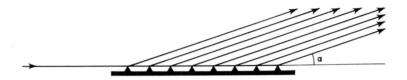

Figure P.2.8 (Problem 53)

incident on a plane *diffraction grating* having a grating spacing of 10^{-5} m. If a 2-m lens is used to focus the spectrum on a screen, find the distance between these two lines (in millimeters) on the screen: (*a*) For the first-order spectrum. (*b*) For the third-order spectrum.

53. Before crystals were used for the determination of the wavelength of x-rays, man-made *gratings* were used at a *grazing angle*. (*a*) Calculate the angle α for the first-order spectrum if a 78-rpm phonograph record is used for a grating (20 grooves per cm) for green light of 5000 Å. (*b*) Calculate the angle α for x-rays of the relatively long wavelength $\lambda = 4 \times 10^{-9}$ m and a grating with 500 grooves per mm?

54. Which of the following statements are true and which false? (*a*) Light from a distant point source falls normally on a small circular opening in a screen. Beyond the hole a second screen is placed at a distance x, and a *diffraction pattern* appears on it. The central spot of the diffraction pattern is always bright, regardless of the distance x. (*b*) A lens of focal length f is placed behind the above circular opening, and the second screen is placed at the focal point of the lens. The central spot of the diffraction pattern is bright.

The following statements refer to the figure. (*c*) If the incident light is unpolarized, no interference maxima or minima are formed. (*d*) There will always be an intensity minimum at P if $\sin \phi = \lambda/d$. (*e*) The third-order

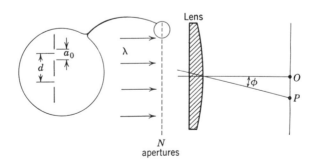

Figure P.2.9 (Problems 54 and 55)

spectrum will be found at P if $\sin \phi = 3\lambda/d$. (f) The first minimum next to the central image at O is at P if $\sin \phi = \lambda/Nd$.

55. Which of the following statements are true, and which false? (a) Light from a distant point source falls normally on a small circular opening in a screen. Beyond the hole, a second screen is placed at a distance x and a *diffraction pattern* appears on it. The central spot of the diffraction pattern may be bright or dark, depending on the distance x. (b) A lens of focal length f is placed behind the above circular opening, and the second screen is placed at the focal point of the lens. The central spot of the diffraction pattern is bright.

The following statements refer to the figure of the preceeding problem. The light incident on the grating is from a distant point source. (c) If the incident light is circularly polarized, no interference maxima or minima are formed. (d) There will always be an intensity minimum at P if $\sin \phi = \lambda/a_0$. (e) The third-order spectrum will be found at P if $\sin \phi = 3\lambda/a_0$. (f) The first minimum next to the central image at O is at P if $\sin \phi = \lambda/Nd$.

56. Two narrow slits 0.14 mm apart are illuminated by a flame giving sodium light ($\lambda = 5890$ Å). What must be the diameter of a lens 6 m away to *resolve* the *images* of the two slits?

57. In Problem 56 at what distance will the same lens *resolve* the *images* of the slits if they are illuminated with light of wavelength 4.86×10^{-7} m?

58. What is the *limit of resolution*, for $\lambda = 5.60 \times 10^{-7}$ m, of the large refracting telescope in the Yerkes observatory (diameter of objective 1.02 m)?

59. (a) Find the angular separation in seconds of arc of the closest double star which can be resolved by the 100-in. *Mt. Wilson telescope*, assuming a wavelength of 6000 Å. (b) Suppose such a binary star is found at a distance of 100 light-years from the earth. What is the distance between the two stars in this binary star?

60. What is the smallest separation of objects on the *planet Mars* that can be seen with a telescope having an objective 0.3 m in diameter? The radius of the earth's orbit about the sun is 150×10^6 km, and that of Mars' orbit is 225×10^6 km. Consider a wavelength of 5×10^{-7} m.

61. Compute the approximate radius of the *central diffraction disk* formed on the *retina of the eye* by a distant point object, assuming a pupillary diameter of 2.0 mm. The distance from the cornea to the retina is about 1 in., and the index of refraction of the vitreous humor, the medium in which the image is formed, is 1.33. Assume $\lambda = 5500$ Å. The so-called cones in the back of the eye are the sensitive elements for vision in bright light. There are about 14,000/square millimeter. Compare the diameter of the diffraction disk with the distance between the cones.

62. Two pinholes, 1 mm apart, are made in a screen and placed in front of a bright source of light. They are viewed through a *telescope* with its objective stopped down to a diameter of 1 cm. How far from the telescope may the screen be for the pinholes still to appear as separate sources for a wavelength of 5000 A?

63. The spacing between the (200) planes in a KF crystal, which crystallizes in cubic form, is 2.671 Å. This is also the distance between nearest K and F atoms. What are the *diffraction angles for x-rays* of a wavelength of 1.542 Å (the K_α lines of copper) for $n = 1$ and 2 in Bragg's law?

64. Analysis of x-ray data shows that *NaCl crystallizes* in the cubic form. How many atoms of Na and of Cl are there per unit cube? Compute the separation between nuclei in NaCl. Density = 2.16 g/cm³; molecular weight = 58.4; Avogadro's number = 6.02×10^{23}.

65. Analysis of x-ray data shows that *copper crystallizes* in the face-centered cubic form. How many atoms are there per unit cube? Find the dimensions of the unit cube and the distance between nearest neighbors in copper. Density = 8.9 g/cm³; molecular weight = 63.7.

66. Consider the *crystallographic planes* shown in Fig. 2.4.6 for the face-centered cubic lattice. Make drawings showing the arrangement of atoms in these planes. [See Fig. 2.4.5(b) for an example.] Make a drawing equivalent to Fig. 2.4.6 but showing the (200) and (202) planes.

67. Make three drawings showing the (111), (200), and (220) *planes* for a simple *cubic lattice*. Make a drawing showing the arrangement of atoms in each of these planes.

68. Using the result of Problem 64, find the distance between successive (111) and (220) *planes in NaCl*.

69. Using the result of Problem 65, find the distance between successive (111) and (220) *planes in copper*.

70. Using the results of Problem 68, compute the angle at which first-order *Bragg reflection* occurs for the (111) and (220) planes of NaCl for x-rays of the following wavelengths: 1 and 0.1 Å.

71. Using the results of Problem 69, compute the angle at which first-order *Bragg reflection* occurs for the (111) and (220) planes of copper for x-rays of the following wavelengths: 1 and 0.1 Å.

72. Compute the *wavelength of electrons* accelerated through the following potentials: 0.025 V, 10 V, 4 MeV, 100 MeV. What will be their velocities? What energies are suitable for demonstrating electron diffraction by crystals?

73. Determine the approximate energy and velocity a neutron should have for a demonstration of *neutron diffraction* in NaCl. Choose a reasonable value for the Bragg angle. If the neutrons in a beam do not all have the same energy, how will the spread of neutron energies affect the results of a diffraction experiment?

74. What is the least energy which an electron could have and still be *Bragg-reflected* from a face-centered cubic crystal whose unit cell has an edge length of 1.5 Å? From what planes, and at what angles, could this reflection take place?

75. At room temperature the average kinetic energy of translation of a gas molecule is $\frac{3}{2} kT$, k being the Boltzmann constant and T the absolute temperature; kT at room temperature is 0.025 eV. (*a*) What is the *wavelength* of an argon molecule, which is monatomic (mass number of argon = 40, Avogadro's number = 6×10^{23}/mole). (*b*) What are the wavelength and mass of a light quantum of this energy?

76. Show that for *nonrelativistic electrons* (<10 keV) the following useful relation holds: λ (in angstrom units) = $[150/E(\text{in electron volts})]^{1/2}$.

77. Compare the de Broglie wavelength of a *highly relativistic* 100-MeV *electron* with the wavelength of a 100-MeV quantum. Do the same for a nonrelativistic 1-keV electron and quantum.

78. (*a*) Check if the ³He and ⁴He ions used in the scattering experiment described in Fig. 2.4.14 have indeed *equal momenta*. Rest mass in mass units u ($1u = 1.66043 \times 10^{-27}$ kg, based on the mass of ¹²C = $12.000u$) of ³He atoms $3.016u$, of ⁴He atoms $4.003u$, of an electron $5.5 \times 10^{-4} u$. (*b*) What is the velocity of the ions? (*c*) What is their wavelength? (*d*) According to the laws of physical optics the diffraction pattern of an opaque disk is the same as that of an aperture of the same size. From the angular spacing of adjacent minima determine the radius of the ⁵⁸Ni nuclei.

79. The temperature of a *black body* is 3000 K. Compute the ratio of its spectral emittance at a wavelength 10,000 Å (infrared) to its spectral emittance at 5000 Å (visible).

80. At what wavelength is the spectral emittance of a *black body* a maximum if its temperature is (*a*) 500 K? (*b*) 5000 K? (*c*) At what temperature does the maximum spectral emittance lie at a wavelength of 5550 Å where the eye is most sensitive?

81. Show that the maximum of the *spectral emittance* W_λ at a given temperature does not coincide with the maximum for W_ν.

82. Plot a few points of the W_λ vs. ν curve for $T = 1600$ K. What is the wavelength where W_ν is a *maximum*?

83. What is the *radiant emittance* of a black body at a temperature of (*a*) 300 K? (*b*) 600 K? (*c*) 1200 K?

84. What is the average *density of quanta* in a radio wave having a wavelength of 100 m transmitting 1 microwatt/m²? What is the average number of quanta in a volume λ^3?

85. Assume that an x-ray tube generates x-rays having a wavelength of 1 Å at the rate of 1 mW. What is the *average number of quanta* in a volume λ^3 at a distance of 1 m from the anode of the tube?

86. *Wien's displacement law,* $\lambda_m T = c_2/4.965 = 2.897 \times 10^{-3}$, gives the

relation between the wavelength λ_m for which the spectral emittance has a maximum and the absolute temperature T. Prove that this law is a consequence of Planck's law, Eq. 2.5.2.

87. The *Stefan-Boltzmann law*,

$$W = \int_0^\infty W_\lambda d_\lambda = \frac{\pi^4}{15} \frac{c_1}{c_2^4} T^4 = 5.672 \times 10^{-8} T^4 \text{ watts/m}^2,$$

expresses the fact that the total energy radiated per second per unit of area from an opening in an enclosed surface is proportional to the fourth power of the absolute temperature. Prove that this law is a consequence of Planck's law, given the following integral:

$$\int_0^\infty \frac{x^3 dx}{e^x - 1} = \frac{\pi^4}{15}.$$

88. Show that, for *isotropic radiation*, if K is the energy flow per unit area per unit solid angle per second, u is the energy density, and W is the power transmitted per unit area, then $W = \pi K$, and $u = (4\pi/c)K = 4W/c$.

89. Prove that the T^4 *dependence* for the total radiation (see Problem 87) is a consequence of (a) the thermodynamic relation,

$$dQ = dU + pdV = d(uV) + pdV,$$

(b) the fact that

$$p = u/3,$$

(c) the second law of thermodynamics, according to which the change in entropy dS for reversible processes is

$$dS = dQ/T,$$

and is independent of the conditions under which the heat dQ is added, so that we may write

$$dS = \left(\frac{\partial S}{\partial T}\right)_V dT + \left(\frac{\partial S}{\partial V}\right)_T dV.$$

The desired result will then be found to follow from the fact that

$$\frac{\partial^2 S}{\partial T \partial V} = \frac{\partial^2 S}{\partial V \partial T}.$$

90. The work functions for particular samples of certain metals are as follows: nickel, 4.05 eV; lithium, 2.13 eV. Determine the respective *threshold wavelengths*.

91. Determine the *maximum velocity of the electrons ejected* from each of

the metals in Problem 90 when the metal is illuminated with light of wavelength 2530 Å.

92. The photoelectric thresholds ($\lambda_0 = c/\nu_0$) of particular samples of certain metals are as follows: aluminum, 4770 Å; copper, 3000 Å; potassium, 6000 Å; sodium, 6800 Å; tungsten, 2300 Å. Determine the *photoelectric work function* for each of these metals in electron volts.

93. Determine the *stopping potential* in volts for electrons from each of the metals in Problem 92 when the metal is illuminated (*a*) with light of wavelength 1849 Å and (*b*) 3500 Å, and the anode is of copper.

94. What is the maximum wavelength of light which can *dissociate* a HI molecule? The dissociation energy of HI is 3.06 eV.

95. Monochromatic *x-rays* of wavelength $\lambda = 0.708$ Å are *scattered* from a carbon block. Calculate the wavelength of the rays scattered by the electron in the block at 50°, 90°, 150°.

96. (*a*) Calculate the *angle* between the direction of motion of the *recoil electron and the incident quantum* in Problem 95 above. (*b*) Determine the energy of the recoil electron.

97. Monochromatic *x-rays* of wavelength $\lambda = 0.124$ Å are *scattered* from a carbon block. (*a*) Determine the wavelength of the x-rays scattered through 180°. (*b*) Determine the kinetic energy of the recoil electrons.

98. Show that the energy of a *photon scattered* by 180° approaches asymptotically 0.256 MeV as the incident photon energy increases.

99. A quantum of 1000 MeV (= 1 GeV) is *scattered on a proton*. The proton recoils at an angle of 10°. What energy does the proton have? The mass of a proton is approximately that of a hydrogen atom.

100. Show that the wavelength of a *quantum* and its *energy* are connected by the *relation*

$$\lambda \text{ (in angstrom units)} \cdot E \text{ (in electron volts)} = 12,400.$$

(This is a very useful relation, easily memorized if one cheats slightly by writing $\lambda \cdot E = 12,345$.)

101. A 5-MeV quantum *generates* a *positron-electron pair*, and these share the excess energy available equally. What is the kinetic energy of each particle? What is its velocity?

102. The annihilation of a positron-electron pair usually proceeds by the emission of two photons going in opposite directions. However, another mode of *annihilation*, by emission of *three photons*, also occurs. Is it necessary that these photons have equal energies in order to satisfy the conservation laws of energy and angular momentum?

103. The data of Badoux and Heinrich on positron-electron *annihilation* in brass, shown in Fig. 2.5.11, indicate that the pairs had not fully come to rest when annihilation took place. (The broadening of the angular dis-

tribution due to the finite size of source and counter has already been corrected for in this plot.) The curve appears to have two components. Estimate the velocities of the center of mass of pairs which result in deviations from 180° by 0.3° and 0.9°.

104. The π^0 *meson*, a chargeless π meson, has a mass of 264 electron masses. It has a lifetime of the order of 10^{-16} sec and decays into two *annihilation* quanta. (*a*) If the π^0 in the moment of decaying in flight has a kinetic energy of 50 MeV, what is the sum of the energies of the two quanta? (*b*) Do both quanta have the same energy when measured in the laboratory system? in the center of mass system? (*c*) Assuming that the two quanta are emitted symmetrically to the direction of flight of the π^0, what is the angle between them in the center-of-mass system? (*d*) in the laboratory system?

105. Energetic photons, through an interaction with a nucleus, can produce π-*meson pairs*, consisting of a positive (π^+) and negative (π^-) meson. The rest mass of both these mesons is 273 electron masses. If it is found that the kinetic energy of one of them is 30 MeV, of the other 50 MeV, what was the energy of the incoming quantum, if it is assumed that the nucleus does only acquire an insignificant amount of energy?

106. X-rays are produced in an evacuated tube in which electrons are emitted at a heated cathode, are accelerated by a difference of potential V between anode and cathode, and finally are stopped at the anode. What is the *shortest wavelength* to be expected in the x-rays produced in a tube in which the accelerating voltage V is (*a*) 10 kV? (*b*) 100 kV? (*c*) 1 MV?

107. What is the limit of the wavelength of *bremsstrahlung* produced by 60-keV electrons, as typically used for medical diagnostics?

108. *X-rays* of 100 MeV energy may be used for research in nuclear physics. Compare their wavelength with the diameter of a nucleus, which is approximately 10^{-14} m.

109. What is the energy of an x-ray of the wavelength equal to the *Compton wavelength* of the electron, 2.4×10^{-12} m?

110. A 100-MeV electron is stopped in a block of aluminum, and *bremsstrahlung* is emitted. In consecutive steps, by pair production, annihilation, Compton effect, and bremsstrahlung production more and more electrons, positrons and photons are produced, forming a cascade shower. Draw such a cascade shower and assign each particle a reasonable energy.

111. X-rays can be used to induce photoelectric effects, usually here called *photoeffects*, *on atoms and nuclei*. Instead of the work function in the photoelectric effect on metals we now have the binding energy to remove an electron from the atom, or the separation energy to remove a proton (or neutron) from the nucleus. (*a*) In a medium-heavy atom, e.g. silver, the

most tightly bound electrons have a binding energy of 25.5 keV. Calculate the maximum wavelength of the quanta which can eject these electrons from silver atoms. (*b*) The usual separation energies for separating a proton or a neutron from a nucleus are around 8 MeV. What is the maximum wavelength and minimum frequency for quanta which can eject such a particle bound by 8 MeV?

112. The beam power in the parallel light beam of a small *He-Ne laser* is 0.5 mW. The beam leaves the apparatus through a circular aperture of 2 mm diameter. The wavelength λ is 6328 Å. (*a*) How many photons are emitted per second? (*b*) What is the amplitude of the *E* vector of the emitted electromagnetic wave? (*c*) What is the theoretical beam diameter at a distance of 1 km?

113. The Stanford Linear Accelerator accelerates electrons to an energy of 20 GeV (= 20 $\times$ 10^9 eV). What is the energy of the 180° back-scattered photons by the *inverse Compton effect*, if the primary light quanta have an energy of 1.8 eV?

114. In the experiment to detect the *Kapitza-Dirac effect*, Schwarz used an electron beam of approximately 5 μm diameter. (*a*) What is the "grating constant" of the standing light waves? (*b*) What is the Bragg angle? (*c*) Design some detector device that permits us to observe the deflection of the electron beam.

115. *Two independent* identical and perfectly stable *lasers* are placed next to each other, which illuminate the same region of a screen. (a) Explain why there will be an interference pattern on the screen. (b) By means of filters the intensity of each of the laser beams is now so much reduced that most of the time no photon is in transit between lasers and screen. At the place of the screen a recording device is now set up that cumulates the arriving light over a time span, e.g. a photographic plate, or a number of detectors like photomultipliers connected to a register. Does one still expect an interference pattern to develop after an appropriately long time? (c) Design an experimental arrangement which takes account of the fact that actual lasers are never perfect and stable in their operation over time intervals longer than 10 to 100 microseconds. [Hint: See R. L. Pfleegor and L. Mandel, *J. Opt. Soc. Am.* **58**, 946 (1968).]

Chapter 3

Wave Mechanics

In classical mechanics there is never any doubt if in a certain situation we have to deal with waves or with particles. The trajectory of a baseball is fully described by assuming that the ball is a particle; there is no place in its description for specific wave properties, such as interference or diffraction. On the other hand, the study of the radiation of a radio antenna leaves us no chance to use a particle picture for the description of the radiation pattern or the outflow of energy.

When in the last chapter we discussed phenomena of atomic sizes we saw that the distinctions between waves and particles can be somewhat blurred. Electrons and neutrons, which undoubtedly are particles, also have the characteristics of waves, as we saw from the diffraction experiments performed on crystals. However, the Compton and the photoelectric effects both showed us that waves come in portions of quanta, each quantum carrying a definite amount of momentum and energy, like particles. We also recall that the wavelengths of the particle waves, $\lambda = h/mv$, were of the order of magnitude of the relevant linear dimensions of the system with which the particle interacted, namely the lattice constant of the crystal.

Let us now go back to the field of optics. Many phenomena in optics can be treated with the methods of geometrical optics, for instance, reflection and refraction of light rays, the formation of images, and so on. However, when it came to phenomena like those of passing a light ray through a slit (diffraction) or a great many narrow slits (interference), if the relevant dimensions were of the order of magnitude of the light waves, ordinary ray or geometrical optics was inadequate; we had to use wave optics. We also saw that wave optics can explain the behavior of rays although we usually prefer to treat situations by means of ray optics because the latter is much simpler to deal with. Ray optics turned out to be an adequate way to analyze optical phenomena provided the wavelength of

187

the light is negligibly small compared with the other important dimensions of the system.

On the one hand we have ray optics; on the other hand, we have wave optics. Do we perhaps have a similar division or relationship in mechanics, with ordinary particle mechanics corresponding to ray optics, being the mechanics of macroscopic objects, and wave mechanics, as the proper way to describe atomic systems?

We should be careful not to make statements that are too strong. One cannot say that electromagnetic radiation consists of particles, or that it consists of waves. It has both aspects. Similarly, a neutron or an electron is not a wave itself. There are certain wave-like aspects, and we have to investigate what these wave aspects are and how to treat them quantitatively.

3.1 TRAVELING WAVES. FREE PARTICLES

In order to describe wave phenomena in more detail we must assume something, perhaps analogous to a field with which we can associate a wavelength. This "something" we shall call a wave function, and shall designate it by Ψ. Traveling or standing Ψ waves may be described as functions of x, y, z, and t, just as we have described any other kind of wave.

So much is simply concerned with mathematical description. But what can we ask of this wave function in regard to physical properties? Will it have any other observable attribute than a wavelength?

The attributes to be expected of a wave function can perhaps best be understood through considering possible analogies with electromagnetic waves. We have found that the presence of electric and magnetic fields implies an energy density in space. If at some point in a traveling wave we have an electric field E and a magnetic field H, we then have an energy per unit volume

$$u = \frac{\epsilon_0}{2} E^2 + \frac{\mu_0}{2} H^2.$$

This function is a continuous function, but it does not necessarily imply that energy is really continuously distributed. It is perfectly consistent with a situation in which energy is distributed in quanta in such a way that $u =$ (number of quanta per unit volume) $\cdot (h\nu)$. This is the same situation we encounter in describing the density of air as being ρ kg/m³ under given conditions of temperature and pressure. The existence of such a density function in no way contradicts the further fact that air is made up of discrete molecules very far apart compared to their diameters. The density of air may be expressed as the average number of molecules per unit volume by the average mass of a molecule.

The concept of an "average number per unit volume" may be considered in greater detail. In air there are roughly 30×10^{18} molecules per cubic centimeter. This is the average number that one would find in any sample of air chosen at random. The average number in an element of volume 10^{-6} cm on a side would be $30 \times 10^{18} \times 10^{-18} = 30$. One might find 35, or 29, or other comparable numbers, but the average would be 30. How about an element of volume 10^{-7} cm on a side? The average number $\rho \, dv$ will be $30 \times 10^{18} \times 10^{-21} = 0.03$. What does it mean that the average number is 0.03 of a particle? It means that, if one were to examine a series of volume elements of this size, one would find either a molecule within or no molecule. The quantity $\rho \, dv$ must be interpreted not as the average number of particles in dv but as the *probability that a particle will be found in dv*. If $\rho \, dv = 0.03$, this means that the probability of finding a particle in a volume element of this size is 0.03, or that in 3% of a large number of tries one would find a particle. In this sense ρ is a *probability density*.

We return now to our wave function and assume that we are dealing with a plane wave which at some instant of time has the form $\Psi = A \sin 2\pi x/\lambda$. We shall interpret the square of this function as being proportional to the probability of finding the particle being described. Ψ^2 is a probability density, and $\Psi^2 \, dv$ is the probability of finding the particle in the volume element dv. In this sense the wave function plays a part similar to electromagnetic fields in determining the distribution of mass or energy in space.

Looking back to our analogy with the electromagnetic energy density, we see that this expression is made up of two terms, one proportional to E^2 and the other proportional to H^2. We also recall that in an oscillating system we have two terms, one for the potential and one for the kinetic energy. In order to have a similar situation with our Ψ-waves we replace Ψ^2 by $\Psi\Psi^*$, where Ψ and Ψ^* are both complex functions, $\Psi = a + ib$ and $\Psi^* = a - ib$, where a and b are real functions. Ψ^* is called the conjugate complex of Ψ, which means that each i in Ψ is replaced by $-i$ in Ψ^*. Although Ψ and Ψ^* are complex, $\Psi\Psi^*$ is real, because

$$(a + ib)(a - ib) = a^2 + b^2.$$

Through this procedure our product $\Psi\Psi^*$ represents the sum of the two terms a^2 and b^2. We need not have worried that Ψ is a complex number; the physical meaning is vested in $\Psi\Psi^*$, and this quantity is real, and measurable. In our elementary treatment of wave mechanics it would not have been absolutely necessary to introduce complex numbers. For many purposes it suffices to treat Ψ as real, and to write Ψ^2 instead of the more correct $\Psi\Psi^*$. Following mathematical custom we will use $|\Psi|^2$ and understand by it $\Psi\Psi^*$. $|\Psi|^2$ is therefore our probability density, and $|\Psi|^2 \, dv$ is the probability for finding a particle in the volume element dv.[1] The interpretation of $|\Psi|^2$ as a probability density is due to Max Born[2] and was published in 1926.

In the electromagnetic theory we described the flow of energy in terms of the Poynting vector. Similarly, we can use the Ψ-function to describe the flow of electrons, neutrons, or protons. Ψ is evidently a function of the space coordinates; however, it is in general also a function of the time. Often it is possible, and profitable, to separate the time variable from the space variable by writing, as for standing waves, for example

$$\Psi(x, y, z, t) = \psi(x, y, z) \, (\cos \omega t + i \sin \omega t)$$

where the small ψ is now only a function of the space coordinates. In other words, ψ is a time-independent function. This procedure is important, if we are interested in stationary or steady-state situations where ψ does not depend on the time. We shall see that such situations are very important in quantum physics.

Our first task in wave mechanics is to describe a freely moving particle by means of ψ-functions, or ψ-waves. However, before we do this, it is good to consider how we might describe a quantum emitted by an atom in terms of electromagnetic waves.

An atom does not radiate an infinitely long wave train. In making a transition from state 2 to state 1 it emits a quantum whose predominant frequency is $\nu_0 = (E_2 - E_1)/h$. But it takes a characteristic time τ to emit a quantum. The radiated energy is not monochromatic, but consists of a range of frequencies with an intensity distribution given by $1/[(\nu - \nu_0)^2 + (1/\tau^2)]$ as already indicated in Chapter 2, Section 2.1. This spectral distribution will give rise to a wave train in space illustrated in Fig. 3.1.1. Its length will be of the order of magnitude $c\tau$ and its amplitude such that the total energy contained is $h\nu_0$. Electromagnetic waves of all frequencies travel in vacuum with the same speed, that is, there is no dispersion, so

---

[1] If we have in a system, instead of one particle (as for example the electron in a hydrogen atom), several particles, e.g. the two electrons in a helium atom, the interpretation of the Ψ function becomes more complicated. This will be discussed in Chapter 4.

[2] Max Born (1882–1970), German theoretical physicist; Professor at German universities, particularly Göttingen, until 1933. Among his many co-workers were Heisenberg and Pauli. Later professor in Edinburgh. Nobel prize in physics 1954 for his work on the interpretation of $|\Psi|^2$ as a probability density.

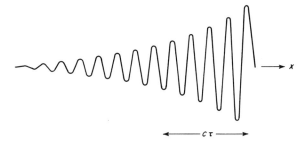

Fig. 3.1.1 A wave train describing a quantum.

that the wave "packet" shown in Fig. 3.1.1 moves as a whole, without change in shape, with the velocity c.

The description of a particle moving with an arbitrary velocity v is not possible until we know more about the velocity w with which ψ-waves move. We know how to specify the wavelength of the ψ-wave in terms of v, or the momentum of the particle

$$p = \frac{h}{\lambda} = mv. \qquad (3.1.1)$$

But we do not know its frequency ν, and therefore not the wave velocity w,

$$w = \lambda\nu. \qquad (3.1.2)$$

One point is clear: If we want to describe a particle moving with a velocity v by means of a packet of ψ-waves like that shown in Fig. 3.1.1, we should like the packet to move with this velocity v also, so that we may think of the wave packet as an aspect of the particle. This can be done by means of a well-known property of waves in dispersive media, that is, media in which the velocity of propagation w of a pure sinusoidal wave is a function of frequency, as for example, in the case of light in water or glass. We shall discuss first the propagation of a wave packet in dispersive media, introducing the concepts of the group velocity u and the phase velocity w and then apply this to ψ-waves describing the motion of a particle.

Phase and Group Velocity

If a stone is dropped into a pond, a group of rings can be seen expanding with a certain speed. In trying to follow a particular crest one will observe that the crest which at a given instant is at the tail end of the group creeps ahead and finally disappears at the leading edge. The group velocity u is

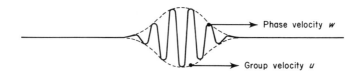

Fig. 3.1.2 Phase and group velocity of a wave packet.

the velocity with which the disturbance as a whole, or the wave packet, travels, whereas the phase velocity w represents the velocity of the individual crest or valley, as illustrated in Fig. 3.1.2. For water waves, it turns out that the group velocity is half the phase velocity.

Group and phase velocity can also be demonstrated by a simple experiment using Fig. 3.1.3. The reader is asked to cut into a sheet of paper of the size of half a page a slit about 3 inches long and 1/16 inch wide. Then place the paper such that the slit is horizontal at the upper end of Fig. 3.1.3. Now slowly move the paper downwards and note that the intersections between the diagonal lines and the slit move to the right. If the thickness of the lines is a measure for the amplitude of the wave, we observe that the individual crests move faster than the wave group.

We now begin our mathematical analysis by giving answers to the questions how we can represent wave packets mathematically and what their characteristics are. Figure 3.1.4 shows (a) a part of an infinitely long wave train, (b) a wave packet, and (c) the snapshot of a wave with a beat in it. There is no doubt that (b) and (c) have something in common, namely the increase and decrease in amplitude as a function of x at a given instant of time.

First, we want to show that a wave with a beat, as pictured in (c), can

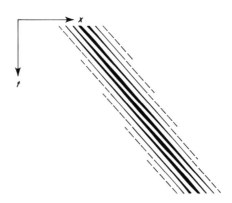

Fig. 3.1.3 A model for phase and group velocity.

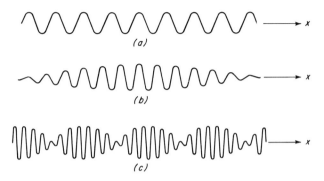

Fig. 3.1.4 Three important wave forms.

be represented by two waves of slightly different wavelengths. We shall do this only in a graphical way (Fig. 3.1.5). We match the crests of the two waves at a certain point 0. At distances a in front of and behind 0 the two waves are 180° out of step and therefore cancel. At twice the distance they add up again. We therefore have constructed a wave corresponding to Fig. 3.1.4 (c). Let us consider that this modulated wave is a sound wave and assume that it moves toward our ear. We will hear a succession of crescendos and diminuendos, a phenomenon familiar to us from pianos which are out of tune. In such instruments the two or three strings responding to the same key do not oscillate with exactly the same frequency and therefore cause these beats.

We can go further by adding a number of waves of different frequencies and amplitudes. In Fig. 3.1.6 three different frequency spectra and the

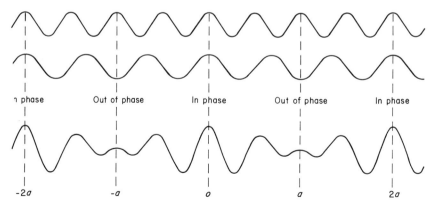

Fig. 3.1.5 The wave form due to two sinusoidal waves of slightly different frequencies. Plotted is the amplitude versus x.

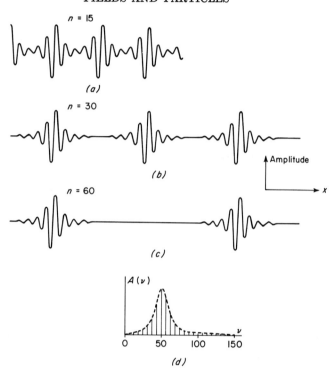

Fig. 3.1.6 Dependence of the spacing of wave packets on the number of waves with different frequencies. (*a*) 15 components. (*b*) 30 components. (*c*) 60 components. (*d*) Frequency spectrum for (*b*) with 30 frequencies. The spectra for (*a*) and (*c*) contain half as many and twice as many frequencies, respectively, below the same envelope.

resulting wave forms are plotted. The frequency spectra have in common the envelope describing the amplitude, but they differ in the number of individual frequencies. In each case the frequencies lie between 0 and 150 frequency units, and the maximum amplitude belongs to the frequency of 50 units. The resulting wave packets for the three frequency spectra are quite similar. The big difference is that the more frequencies are involved the farther apart are the individual wave packets. It is therefore plausible to assume that with an infinite number of frequencies the wave packets would be spaced infinitely far apart.

Let us now analyze mathematically what happens when two waves of slightly different wavelengths travel with slightly different velocities. The first wave traveling with the velocity $w = \nu\lambda$ shall be represented by

$$y_1 = A \sin(kx - \omega t)$$

where

$$k = 2\pi/\lambda \quad \text{and} \quad \omega = 2\pi\nu.$$

The other wave is

$$y_2 = A \sin[(k + dk)x - (\omega + d\omega)t].$$

The sum of the two waves, if we use the familiar addition theorem

$$\sin \alpha + \sin \beta = 2 \sin \frac{\alpha + \beta}{2} \cos \frac{\alpha - \beta}{2},$$

is

$$y_1 + y_2 = 2A \sin \left[\left(k + \frac{dk}{2}\right)x - \left(\omega + \frac{d\omega}{2}\right)t\right] \cos \left[\frac{(dk)x - (d\omega)t}{2}\right].$$

In the sine function we can neglect dk compared to k, and $d\omega$ compared to ω, since they are only small increments. We are, however, not allowed to do this with the argument of the cosine function, where k and ω cancel. We therefore can write

$$y = y_1 + y_2 = 2A \sin(kx - \omega t) \cos \left[\frac{(dk)}{2} x - \frac{(d\omega)}{2} t\right].$$

$2A \sin(kx - \omega t)$ represents the original wave y_1 with the double amplitude. This wave is, however, modulated by a term $\cos[(dk/2)x - (d\omega/2)t]$, which has also the characteristic of a wave that moves in space and time. This term can be considered as a change in amplitude of the original wave which proceeds slowly because dk and $d\omega$ are small. Let us now suppose that we want to keep up with a particular crest of the wave. In this case we must keep the value of $(kx - \omega t)$ constant. We want to find our velocity which is dx/dt. The expression $(kx - \omega t) = constant$ is equivalent to $kdx - \omega dt = 0$, which gives us the velocity

$$w = \frac{dx}{dt} = \frac{\omega}{k} = \frac{2\pi\nu}{(2\pi/\lambda)} = \nu\lambda.$$

We call this the *phase velocity*, as it is the velocity with which a particular crest, or a point of constant phase, moves.

If, instead of staying steadily with the same crest, we elect to stay always with the momentarily greatest crest or, more generally, with the crest that is closest to a certain amplitude $2A \cos[(dk/2)x - (d\omega/2)t]$, we have to keep $[(dk/2)x - (d\omega/2)t]$ constant. This, however, is equivalent to $dkdx - d\omega dt = 0$ which leads us to another velocity

$$u = \frac{dx}{dt} = \frac{d\omega}{dk}.$$

Therefore, u is the velocity of the whole group, or the velocity of the maximum amplitude, and is therefore called the *group velocity*. In order to determine u we must know the connection between $d\omega$ and dk.

$$u = \frac{d\omega}{dk} = \frac{d(2\pi\nu)}{d(2\pi/\lambda)} = \frac{d\nu}{d(1/\lambda)} = \frac{d\nu}{-(1/\lambda^2)d\lambda}$$

$$= \frac{d(w/\lambda)}{(-1/\lambda^2)d\lambda} = -\lambda^2 \frac{\lambda(dw/d\lambda) - w}{\lambda^2}$$

or (from the last expression)

$$u = w - \lambda \frac{dw}{d\lambda} \qquad (3.1.3)$$

or (from the third last expression)

$$u = -\lambda^2 \frac{d\nu}{d\lambda}.$$

If w is independent of λ, as for example in electromagnetic waves in vacuum, u will be equal to w. If w depends on λ, that is, if we have dispersion, phase and group velocity are different. Light waves in a transparent medium and also surface water waves show dispersion.

Conversely, if phase and group velocity are different there must be dispersion according to Eq. 3.1.4. That there is a difference in the phase velocity for long and short water waves can be deduced from Fig. 3.1.7. The interval between the two most advanced crests far behind the boat is greater than the distance between the following crests. Since the waves which started from the same location on the path of the boat were created simultaneously, it is obvious that in the same time interval the long waves did travel a greater distance than the short waves, and therefore had a greater velocity. Dispersion is also the reason that the crests of the waves are slightly curved and not straight lines.

It should be emphasized that the foregoing is in no way an explanation for the causes of dispersion in wave propagation, but merely a mathematical description of this phenomenon.

The example of water waves created by a falling stone makes it also evident that the velocity with which a signal or the energy associated with a wave travels is the group velocity and not the phase velocity. The phase velocity is often unobservable, and energy does not travel with this velocity. In some cases the phase velocity can be greater than the velocity of light in vacuum; but because no signal can be transmitted with this velocity,

Fig. 3.1.7   Waves behind a steamer on Lake Geneva showing the dispersion of water waves. (Courtesy of the Regional Tourist Office of Lake Geneva.)

this is not in contradiction with the concepts of the special theory of relativity.

The Propagation of ψ-Waves

We wish to compute the dispersion of ψ-waves which would bring about a group velocity u equal to the particle velocity v which the waves represent. By definition we have for the phase velocity w

$$w = \lambda \nu, \tag{3.1.4}$$

and according to the previous section we propose that

$$v = u = w - \lambda \frac{dw}{d\lambda} = -\lambda^2 \frac{d\nu}{d\lambda}. \tag{3.1.5}$$

The physics of the situation is introduced by the postulate that the total energy E of the particle represented be

$$E = mc^2 = \frac{m_0}{\sqrt{1 - v^2/c^2}} c^2 \qquad (3.1.6)$$

and that its momentum be

$$p = mv = h/\lambda. \qquad (3.1.7)$$

Substituting the values of v and λ in terms of p into 3.1.7 we get for the particle velocity

$$v = \frac{p}{m} = \frac{pc^2}{E} = -\lambda^2 \frac{d\nu}{d\lambda} = -\lambda^2 \frac{d\nu}{dp} \frac{dp}{d\lambda}. \qquad (3.1.8)$$

But from 3.1.7

$$\frac{dp}{d\lambda} = -\frac{h}{\lambda^2}$$

so that

$$\frac{pc^2}{E} = h \frac{d\nu}{dp}. \qquad (3.1.9)$$

Eliminating v from equations 3.1.6 and 3.1.7 results in the well-known relation

$$p^2 = \frac{E^2}{c^2} - m_0^2 c^2$$

from which follows after differentiation

$$2p \, dp = \frac{2E \, dE}{c^2}$$

or

$$\frac{pc^2}{E} = \frac{dE}{dp}.$$

Inserting this expression into Eq. 3.1.9 yields

$$\frac{dE}{dp} = h \frac{d\nu}{dp}$$

or

$$dE = h d\nu.$$

Except for an arbitrary constant of integration which we are at liberty to choose as zero, this relation for particles with a rest mass is formally equivalent to the condition for electromagnetic quanta

$$E = h\nu. \tag{3.1.10}$$

The dispersion formula for ψ-waves in free space follows from the above. From 3.1.8 and 3.1.10 we have, in the absence of potential energy,

$$E = h\nu = \sqrt{p^2 c^2 + m_0^2 c^4} \tag{3.1.11}$$

and using 3.1.4

$$w = \lambda\nu = \frac{\lambda}{h} \sqrt{p^2 c^2 + m_0^2 c^4}$$

or

$$w = c \left[1 + \frac{m_0^2 c^2}{h^2} \lambda^2 \right]^{1/2}. \tag{3.1.12}$$

The presence of potential energy V can be considered by way of the constant of integration mentioned in connection with Eq. 3.1.10. Equation 3.1.11 then becomes

$$E = h\nu = \sqrt{p^2 c^2 + m_0^2 c^4} + V. \tag{3.1.13}$$

The quantity h/mc we have found already in Section 2.5. It is the Compton wavelength, approximately 2.4×10^{-12} m, or of the order of magnitude of nuclear dimensions.

An important question is that of the spread of a wave packet in empty space with time. We have shown how to relate wavelength and velocity. It follows that a wave packet with a certain spread of wavelength, and therefore having a certain size, will also be characterized by a certain spread of wave velocities. It can be shown from these relationships that the size of a wave packet, or the uncertainty Δx in the location of the particle within it, grows with time in a manner dependent on the uncertainty in the velocity Δw. If Δw_0 is the size at the time $t = 0$, at the time t it will be

$$\Delta x \sim \Delta x_0 + \Delta w \cdot t.$$

If all wavelengths propagated with the same velocity, $\Delta w = 0$, and the packet would not change its dimensions with time, as in the electromagnetic case. But for particle waves, Δx increases as time goes on. However, as the packet gets larger, it requires a narrower frequency band for its description, and consequently a smaller Δw.

The Heisenberg Uncertainty Principle

The above discussions lead us also to the uncertainty principle which was discovered by Heisenberg[3] who published it in 1927[4] when he was a visitor at Niels Bohr's famous Institute for Theoretical Physics in Copenhagen. Classical Newtonian mechanics leads to the conclusion that from a knowledge of the condition of a mechanical system at some one time we

Enrico Fermi (1901–1954), left, Werner Heisenberg (born 1901), center, and Wolfgang Pauli (1900–1958) on Lake Como during an international physics conference at Como, Italy, in 1927. (Photo by Fermi's friend and colleague F. Rasetti; courtesy of Segrè Collection, Niels Bohr Library, A.I.P.).

[3] Werner Heisenberg (1901–   ), German theoretical physicist. At the age of 24 he was one of the founders of quantum mechanics by originating, together with Max Born, the matrix mechanics, an alternative form of wave mechanics (see Sect. 3.7). Nobel prize 1932 for the uncertainty principle.
[4] *Zeitschrift für Physik* **43**, 172 (1927).

can accurately predict its later behavior. The usefulness of this conclusion depends on our ability to observe the functioning of the system without disturbing it. Thus if we can determine the positions and velocities of two stars circling around each other at some one time, we can predict from Newton's laws of motion and gravitation their future motion.

When we come to objects too small for us to see, such as atoms and electrons, we must reconsider the above propositions. How shall we observe the position and velocity of such particles? If we shine a light on the particle, as we would on a macroscopic object to measure its position and velocity, we must remember that, in a collision between a light quantum and a particle, the motion of the particle is disturbed. We saw that quanta having short wavelengths will, in a collision, impart velocities comparable to the velocity of light to an electron. If we use long wavelengths, on the other hand, though we do not so violently disturb the motion of the particle we are observing, we are lessening the information we can acquire about its position. There seem to be definite limits to what we can measure concerning atomic systems, limits set not by the perfection of the instruments used but by the means available to us for making observations. Heisenberg in his paper, accordingly, concludes that "in the rigorous formulation of the law of causality 'If we know precisely the present, we can compute the future,' not the latter part of the sentence, but the premise is wrong. As a matter of principle, we *cannot* get to know the present in its exact condition."

Out of a study of this situation has come a new principle of physics, called the "uncertainty principle," or "principle of indeterminacy." It states that certain pairs of variables defining a mechanical system cannot simultaneously be measured with arbitrary accuracy. In fact, it goes farther and specifies the limit of the attainable accuracy. We shall discuss this principle for a particular pair of variables, the x coordinate and the momentum of a particle moving in the x direction and shall show that the product of the uncertainty Δx in the position of a particle and the uncertainty Δp_x of the x component of its momentum, when x and p_x are measured at the same time, must exceed a certain value, which turns out to be Planck's constant h.

We saw in Chapter 2 that the wave aspect of light set a limit to the detailed knowledge about external objects that could be acquired by studying their images. Since matter itself must be described in terms of waves, we may expect the wavelength involved to set a limit on our knowledge of the position of a particle. A wave packet of length Δx must contain waves whose wavelengths differ in such a way that there is cancellation of all its waves outside the interval Δx. We may simplify matters by considering only one of the shortest and one of the longest waves, λ_1 and λ_2, respectively.[5] The two waves are in phase, hence constructively interfering in the center of Δx, and they are out of phase by at least one half wavelength at the two ends of Δx in order to interfere destructively, as seen, for example in Fig. 3.1.5. The number of wavelengths λ_1 that fit into the interval Δx is $\Delta x/\lambda_1$, and the corresponding number for the longer wavelengths λ_2, that is $\Delta x/\lambda_2$, must be at least one less, or

$$\frac{\Delta x}{\lambda_1} \geq \frac{\Delta x}{\lambda_2} + 1.$$

Hence

$$\frac{\Delta x}{\lambda_1} - \frac{\Delta x}{\lambda_2} \geq 1.$$

The left side can be transformed into

$$\Delta x \frac{\lambda_2 - \lambda_1}{\lambda_1 \lambda_2} = \Delta x \frac{|\Delta\lambda|}{\lambda_2} = \Delta x \Delta \left(\frac{1}{\lambda}\right).$$

Therefore

$$\Delta x \Delta \left(\frac{1}{\lambda}\right) \geq 1.$$

Since according to de Broglie $1/\lambda = p/h$,

$$\Delta \left(\frac{1}{\lambda}\right) = \frac{\Delta p}{h}.$$

We obtain therefore

$$\Delta x \cdot \Delta p_x \geq h, \tag{3.1.14}$$

where the subscript x in Δp_x signifies that only the x component of the momentum is under consideration.[6] Equation 3.1.14 represents one of the

---

[5] We use only two wavelengths, although for total and continuous cancellation beyond the range Δx a continuous spectrum of waves between λ_1 and λ_2 is needed. However, this does not affect the result.

[6] A somewhat more rigorous derivation would have modified the relation by a factor $1/4\pi$, making the relation

$$\Delta x \cdot \Delta p_x \geq \frac{h}{4\pi}.$$

We omitted this factor because we arbitrarily identified the uncertainty in position Δx with the total length of the wave packet which corresponds to a maximum uncertainty in Δx rather than only the root-mean-square one. Often also the relation

$$\Delta x \cdot \Delta p_x \geq \frac{h}{2\pi}$$

is used.

formulations of the Heisenberg uncertainty principles. Analogous relationships hold for the y and z components. The Heisenberg relation tells us that if we try to reduce the uncertainty in Δx by measuring the position more and more accurately, we have to pay for it by increasing the uncertainty Δp_x in our knowledge of the momentum, and vice versa. It must be pointed out that the relation sets only a lower limit for this product. As long as this limit is not reached, the Heisenberg principle is of no significance.

Some examples might reveal the magnitude of the uncertainties involved. A dust particle of a mass of 10^{-6} g($= 10^{-9}$ kg) can be located under a good optical microscope with an uncertainty of 0.1 $\mu(= 10^{-7}$ m). The resulting theoretical uncertainty in a determination of its velocity is

$$\Delta v = \frac{h}{m\Delta x} = \frac{6.6 \times 10^{-34} \text{ joule-sec}}{10^{-9} \text{ kg} \cdot 10^{-7} \text{ m}} = 6.6 \times 10^{-18} \text{ m/sec.}$$

The experimental error would be far beyond the uncertainty imposed by the Heisenberg principle, because the optical wavelength is so much longer then the de Broglie wavelength.

If the particle is an electron, we might locate it within an accuracy of 10^{-6} m, by observing the trace it leaves in passing through a medium, for example, a photographic emulsion specially made to detect such tracks. The corresponding uncertainty in velocity is 7×10^2 m/sec. For comparison the speed of a 100-eV electron is 6×10^6 m/sec. This, on the other hand, is also very roughly the speed which an electron has inside an atom, but because of the small dimensions of an atom—10^{-10} m—the uncertainty in its velocity is about 10^6 m/sec.

The uncertainty relations do not limit the precision of a position measurement alone, or of a velocity (or momentum) measurement alone. This effect manifests itself in such a way that each experiment undertaken to determine the position of a particle disturbs its velocity to some degree, and vice versa.

We shall now discuss this point by describing Heisenberg's hypothetical experiment in which position and momentum of an electron are determined simultaneously. We shall see that the uncertainty principle sets fundamental limits.

For this *gedanken* (German for "thought") *experiment* Heisenberg imagines a γ-ray microscope. γ-rays are quanta of electromagnetic radiation of very short wavelength, thus allowing in principle precise position measurements, because as we have seen in Chapter 2, the resolving power of a microscope increases the shorter the wavelength of the illuminating light. The underlying idea of the experiment is as follows: If we shine "light," the γ-quanta, on the electron in order to observe the scattered light in our microscope, we must remember that in a collision between a light quantum

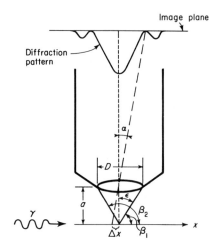

Fig. 3.1.8   Heisenberg's γ-ray microscope.

and the electron (i.e., the Compton effect), the latter will suffer a certain recoil in scattering the quantum; hence its momentum is disturbed. By improving the resolving power of the microscope and consequently the determination of its position, through the use of light of short wavelengths, we have to pay the price of an increased uncertainty in the motion of the particle.

Let us assume that the electron travels with known momentum p in the direction of the x axis under the microscope shown in Fig. 3.1.8. The resolving power of a lens of diameter D is given by Eq. 2.3.18

$$\sin \alpha = 1.22 \, \lambda/D.$$

We recall that the limitation of the resolving power is due to the width of the diffraction pattern which is indicated in the image plane of the microscope. Replacing the factor 1.22 in our rough calculation by unity, the position of an object a distance a in front of the lens can hence be determined to an accuracy

$$\Delta x = a \sin \alpha \approx a\lambda/D.$$

In our microscope the illuminating light quanta of frequency ν come from the left. In order that the electron can be seen, a light quantum has to be scattered by it into the microscope lens by an angle β, which is between β_1 and β_2, or $90° \pm \epsilon$. Through the Compton effect the quantum loses some momentum in the x direction which the electron gains, and which is according to Eq. 2.5.12

$$p_x = \frac{h}{c}\,(\nu - \nu_s \cos\beta) \simeq \frac{h\nu}{c}\,(1 - \cos\beta).$$

(The admittedly rough approximation is here being made that the frequency ν_s of the scattered quantum is the same as the initial one, ν.) However, because of the uncertainty 2ϵ of the scattering angle β, which can be anything between $90° - \epsilon$ and $90° + \epsilon$, the uncertainty in the momentum tranferred to the electron is

$$\Delta p_x = (h\nu/c)\{[1 - \cos(90° + \epsilon)] - [1 - \cos(90° - \epsilon)]\}$$

or

$$\Delta p_x = \left(\frac{h\nu}{c}\right)[-\sin(-\epsilon) + \sin\epsilon] = \left(\frac{h\nu}{c}\right)2\sin\epsilon \simeq \left(\frac{h\nu}{c}\right)2\left(\frac{D}{2}\,a\right)$$

$$= \left(\frac{h}{\lambda}\right)\left(\frac{D}{a}\right).$$

In this rough calculation we set boldly the sine equal to the tangent. The product $\Delta x \cdot \Delta p_x$ becomes therefore

$$\Delta x \cdot \Delta p_x \approx (a\lambda/D)(h/\lambda)(D/a) = h.$$

Hence we again have arrived at the uncertainty principle for position and momentum which tells us that nature sets us a limit regarding the degree of accuracy with which we can measure simultaneoulsy the momentum and the position of a particle. Obviously, human imperfection and stupidity set no limit how poorly such a measurement can be performed. The experiment with Heisenberg's imaginary microscope lets us therefore conclude that

$$\Delta x \cdot \Delta p_x \geq h.$$

Another pair of physical variables connected by an uncertainty relation is Δt and ΔE, which we already discussed briefly in Section 2.1 of Chapter 2. This uncertainty relation says that

$$\Delta t \cdot \Delta E \geq h \qquad (3.1.15)$$

meaning that, if we would measure the energy of a mechanical system within some interval of time Δt, then there is a limit ΔE to the exactness of the result, and the uncertainty in the energy ΔE may be computed by Eq. 3.1.15. The meaning of this relation is perhaps more understandable if we consider a measurement of the energy of light quanta whose energy is

$E = h\nu$. Equation 3.1.15 may be expressed in the form

$$\Delta\nu \, \Delta t \geq 1.$$

Planck's constant has been canceled out, and we may expect to be able to interpret this statement from a classical point of view if we apply it to a classical wave, where the frequency ν is measurable.

If we want to measure the frequency ν of a wave, we may do this by comparing it with a known frequency ν_0 of a frequency generator. We tune our frequency generator until the two frequencies ν and ν_0 are equal, deducing this equality from the absence of frequency beats. In order to be sure that there are no beats we must extend our observation over an infinite time. If we measure over a shorter time interval, the accuracy of our frequency determination will suffer. The number of beats per second is equal to the difference in frequency of the two waves, or $\Delta\nu = \nu_0 - \nu$. Figure 3.1.5 may illustrate this: If the interval between the two dotted lines labeled $2a$ represents now a time interval of 1 second, the upper wave has a frequency of 8 hertz, the lower one 6 hertz, and the beat frequency is 2 hertz. To observe at least one beat during the observation time Δt we must require that $\Delta t \geq (1/\Delta\nu)$, or

$$\Delta t \cdot \Delta\nu \geq 1.$$

Multiplying both sides with h, and remembering that $E = h\nu$ and therefore $\Delta E = h\Delta\nu$, we have

$$\Delta t \cdot \Delta E \geq h.$$

An important example of this formulation of the Heisenberg uncertainty principle is the sharpness of energy levels. Atomic, but particularly nuclear, excited states with very short lifetimes will have energies that are not sharply defined. The width of these levels can be calculated directly from the uncertainty principle. Excited nuclear states may have lifetimes as short as 10^{-15} sec. Consequently the energy uncertainty or width ΔE of such a short-lived level is $\Delta E \approx h/\Delta t = 6.62 \times 10^{-34}$ joule-sec/10^{-15} sec $\approx 7 \times 10^{-22}$ joule ≈ 4 eV.

Conversely, the experimentally determined width of an energy level may be used to deduce the lifetime of this state which is too short to be measured directly. In the discussion of optical pumping we had mentioned that a quantum which is emitted by an atom undergoing a transition from an excited to the ground state may be absorbed by another atom of the same species which then changes from its ground state to the corresponding excited state. If the lifetime of this excited state is short it will decay very soon with emission of a quantum. Assuming that this decay leads directly to the ground state the emitted quantum will have the energy and fre-

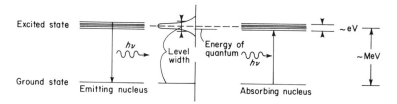

Fig. 3.1.9   Resonance absorption by a nucleus.

quency of the original absorbed one but it may be emitted in almost any direction. Such a process is therefore called *resonance scattering*.

This same process can also occur with nuclei and is illustrated in Fig. 3.1.9. However, because of the conservation of momentum the first emitted quantum will impart a recoil to the emitting nucleus. Consequently the energy of the quantum will be slightly less than the energy difference between the two levels; or in other words, due to the Doppler effect the frequency of the quantum and its energy will be somewhat lower. Similarly, the nucleus which absorbs the quantum will transform some of the energy of the incoming quantum into kinetic energy of translation.

Because the two nuclear recoil energies act at the expense of the quantum, the question arises if the quantum has still enough energy to bring the nucleus into the excited state. Quanta emitted by a nucleus, the γ-quanta, have energies in the order of MeV. The recoil energy, E_{recoil}, of a nucleus of mass M due to a γ-quantum of energy E_γ can be computed from conservation of energy and momentum principles (see problem 16) and is $E_{\text{recoil}} = E_\gamma^2/(2Mc^2)$. For $E_\gamma = 1$ MeV and a nucleus of mass number $A = 200$ (i.e., in the region of gold and lead of the table of nuclei), this recoil energy is therefore 2.5 eV. With the emitting and absorbing nucleus both taking up recoil energy the energy deficit of the quantum is thus 5 eV. This is therefore of the order of the width of a state having a lifetime of 10^{-15} sec which we computed above to be 4 eV. We can therefore expect that a certain percentage of the γ-quanta will be absorbed by the resonance process and re-emitted again. On the other hand, if the lifetime of the excited state is 10^{-12} sec, the probability for resonance absorption is near zero if the involved nuclei are both at rest before the quantum is emitted and if they are free to recoil.

Resonance scattering is also important in atomic systems but, because of the generally longer lifetimes of atomic states ($\sim 10^{-8}$ sec), the uncertainty principle usually does not play such an important role in atomic resonance scattering; broadening of the energy distribution of the emitted quanta by the Doppler effect due to the thermal motion of the atoms is as a rule much more important in transitions involving valence electrons only.

This formulation of the uncertainty relation is not only important in regard to the broadening of energy levels and therefore also of the emitted spectral lines. Physicists postulate that so-called virtual (because they cannot be observed) particles of mass m and hence of rest mass energy $E = mc^2 = \Delta E$ can be created and decay within the time Δt alloted by the Heisenberg principle. We may consider this way of describing nature as a very useful theoretical procedure and shall use it later in our discussions of nuclear forces and elementary particles.

It should not be overlooked that in the uncertainty relation $\Delta E\, \Delta t > h$ the meaning of Δt is somewhat ambiguous. In one example it was the duration of a measurement, in others the lifetime of a state. We have to accept the fact that the situation in regard to this uncertainty relation is not so clear cut as in the case of $\Delta p_x\, \Delta x > h$.

3.2 STANDING WAVES. CONFINED PARTICLES

The great importance of wave mechanics is in its description of the behavior and properties of bound particles, as in atoms, molecules, solids, and in nuclei. Particles are bound to each other by means of forces, forces that are usually a function of their distance apart. Thus in a hydrogen atom, the forces are Coulomb forces, varying inversely as the square of the distance between proton and electron. Schrödinger's wave equation, to be discussed Section 3.3, tells us how to approach problems of this kind. Hence we shall here confine ourselves to very short-range forces, such as are experienced by a ball bouncing around in a box. The particle moves as in free space inside the box, and it experiences restraining forces only when it bounces at the walls.

Let us begin by considering a particle in a long narrow tube of length L_x, with one end at the origin of a coordinate system, and the other end at a point $X = L_x$. This we shall presume to be a mechanical system like an atom, in which we cannot observe the motion of the particle as a function of time. We therefore cannot apply Newtonian mechanics as we would, for example, to the motion of the earth around the sun. In the case of large bodies, we can specify their position and velocities at some initial time and predict the future positions by applying Newton's laws of motion. For an atom we cannot do this, and attempts to build up hypothetical models along these lines did not prove useful. We shall now consider an entirely new approach involving wave functions. We shall make one assumption about these wave functions, namely, that they must be continuous. We shall assume that, like electric or magnetic fields, they vary smoothly from point to point.

We deal here with a steady-state condition because the particle will not leave the tube, but only oscillates back and forth. Hence we can use the time-independent function ψ which may be considered as the amplitude of Ψ, since $\Psi = \psi(\cos \omega t + i \sin \omega t)$.[7]

If we know that the particle is in our tube, and that the wave function ψ which we use to describe the particle must be zero wherever the particle cannot be, we must conclude that, outside of the tube, $\psi = 0$, as shown in Fig. 3.2.1 (a). If the wave function is to be continuous, then it must be zero for $X = 0$ and $X = L_x$. The simplest sort of non-zero function satisfying this condition would be a sine wave with $L_x = \lambda/2$. Other possible forms would be waves having shorter wavelengths. In (b) the length L_x is two half-wavelengths. In (c) and (d), L_x is three and four half-wavelengths. In general we may put

$$L_x = s_x \frac{\lambda}{2} \quad \text{or} \quad \lambda = \frac{2L_x}{s_x} \tag{3.2.1}$$

where s_x may be any integer but not zero. If s_x were zero, then ψ would have to be constant, and the only constant value of ψ consistent with our boundary condition is $\psi = 0$, which means that no particle is in the tube, and therefore this is not a relevant solution of our problem.

This sort of discussion of standing waves would hardly be worth repeating were it not for the fact that, when we are dealing with ψ waves, rather

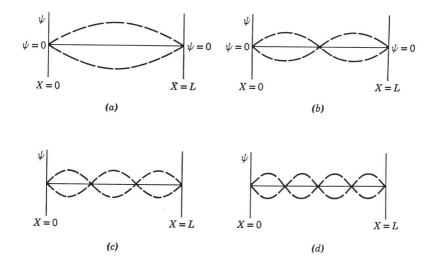

Fig. 3.2.1   Standing ψ waves.

[7] It should not be forgotten that Ψ is a complex quantity!

than electromagnetic or acoustic waves, some entirely new conclusions must be drawn. The ψ waves tell us something about a particle which we cannot see. First, they specify its energy. If $\lambda = h/mv$, then, since $mv = [2m(\frac{1}{2}mv^2)]^{1/2}$, or $mv = (2mE)^{1/2}$ in the nonrelativistic range of energies, we have

$$\lambda = \frac{h}{\sqrt{2mE}} \qquad (3.2.2)$$

Combining Eqs. 3.2.1 and 3.2.2, we have

$$\lambda = \frac{2L_x}{s_x} = \frac{h}{\sqrt{2mE}}$$

$$E = \frac{h^2}{8mL_x^2} s_x^2. \qquad (3.2.3)$$

The various possible waveforms shown in Fig. 3.2.1 are called states of the system. With each one is associated an energy. For these waves, in contrast to those we are used to, the energy is given not by their amplitude but by their wavelength. This is a very important point to remember. The meaning of the amplitude will be discussed later. The energies of the four states of the system shown in Fig. 3.2.1 may be computed from the mass of the particle and the length of the tube in which it is confined, and the values of s_x in Eq. 3.2.3 are equal to 1, 2, 3, and 4.

Notice that, according to wave mechanics, the particle we are discussing has only certain definite energies, and that zero kinetic energy is not one of these allowed energies. The particle cannot come to rest. There is a lowest possible energy and a lowest possible velocity. Since we think of atoms as small solar systems whose size is determined by the motion of the electrons, is there in this inability of the electron to come to rest a clue as to why atoms do not collapse as a result of the slowing down of the electrons in their orbital motions?

Before concluding this introductory discussion we shall make a few additional points concerning possible conclusions. The first of these deals with the magnitude of the parameter $h^2/8mL^2$ of Eq. 3.2.3, which we shall call E_0. This determines the order of magnitude of the energy intervals of our system. Expressed in electron volts, we have

$$E_0 = \frac{h^2}{8mL^2} \frac{1}{e} = \frac{3.4 \times 10^{-49}}{mL^2} \text{ eV}$$

For a particle having the mass of an electron, 9.1×10^{-31} kg, confined to a box of the order of atomic dimensions, or $L \simeq 2 \times 10^{-10}$ m, we get $E_0 \simeq 10$

eV. This is actually the order of magnitude of the energies involved in atomic interactions and is physically determined by these two parameters, m and L. For protons and neutrons confined to regions of nuclear dimensions, on the other hand, we find, for $m = M_p = 1.67 \times 10^{-27}$ kg and $L \simeq 4 \times 10^{-14}$ m, that $E_0 \simeq 2$ MeV. This again is just the order of magnitude of the energies involved in nuclear interactions and again is determined by the wave nature of particles, the mass of the particles, and the dimensions of the region to which they are confined. The size of the region to which a wave is confined determines the spacing of the energy levels, and the spacing predicted by these simple considerations is the spacing actually found in atoms and nuclei. Furthermore, if only certain definite energies of our system are possible, this fact must mean that the system cannot get rid of arbitrarily small amounts of energy. It must get rid of certain definite amounts or not change its state at all. If we anticipate what this must mean in connection with the process of radiation, is there here perhaps a first clue concerning the quanta of electromagnetic energy which we have had to postulate to explain many of the experimentally observed aspects of the interaction of light and matter?

It may be well to point out here that there is no crass violation of everyday experience in the above. The minimum possible velocity v_o of a mass $M = 0.1$ kg in a tube of length $L = 1$ m is given by

$$E_0 = \tfrac{1}{2}Mv_0^2 = \frac{h^2}{8ML^2} = \frac{5.5 \times 10^{-68}}{ML^2} \text{ joules}$$

$$v_0^2 = \frac{11 \times 10^{-68}}{10^{-2} \times 1}$$

$$v_0 = 3.3 \times 10^{-33} \text{ m/sec}$$

which is an acceptable approximation to zero.

One point which we have glossed over and should explain here relates to the amplitude of the ψ wave. If the energy is determined by the wavelength and not by the amplitude, what is the physical significance of the amplitude? To treat this question we return to our assumption that $\psi^2 \, dv$ or, in this case, if S is the area of the tube, $\psi^2 \, S \, dx$ represents the probability of finding the particle in a range between x and $x + dx$ of the tube. Then if we know that the particle is in the tube we must have the probability of finding the particle somewhere in the tube equal to unity, or

$$\int_0^{L_x} \psi^2 \, S \, dx = 1. \tag{3.2.4}$$

This determines the amplitude of ψ. If for example, $\psi = \psi_0 \sin(2\pi x/\lambda)$, and we are dealing with the state $s_x = 1$, so that $\lambda = 2L_x$, we have

$$\int_0^{L_x} S\psi_0^2 \sin^2 \frac{\pi x}{L_x} \, dx = 1.$$

The value of the left-hand side of this equation depends on the amplitude ψ_0 of the wave function. We must choose this amplitude so that the value of the integral is unity. Having done so, we can use the adjusted wave function to compute the probability of finding the particle in any part of the tube. The process of adjusting the amplitude of the wave function so that the probability of finding the particle being described somewhere in the allowed space in unity is called *normalizing* the wave function.

The straight tube we have discussed above becomes much like a circular orbit if we simply bend the tube into a circle of radius r. If the wave function is to fit into the circular orbit smoothly, we must demand that the circumference, $2\pi r$, should be some integral number of wavelengths. Half-integral numbers of wavelengths could be made to fit without producing a discontinuity in ψ but would give rise to a kink at the joining point, which must be excluded. In fact, even the sharp kinks which we are allowed at the boundaries $x = 0$ and $x = L_x$ in Fig. 3.2.1 are to be considered with a certain skepticism. We shall return to them in the next sections. We conclude then that for circular orbits we should expect that

$$j\lambda = 2\pi r.$$

where j must be some integer. If, now, we use the expression for the wavelength of the particle moving in the circular orbit as specified by previous diffraction experiments, we get, according to L. de Broglie,

$$\lambda = \frac{h}{mv} = \frac{2\pi r}{j}$$

$$(mv)r = j\frac{h}{2\pi}. \tag{3.2.5}$$

The left-hand side of our expression is, in fact, the angular momentum of our circulating particle. It is quantized and is always some integral multiple of $h/2\pi$. Because the constant h appears very often in the combination with $1/2\pi$, it is often convenient to use the new constant $\hbar$ (pronounced h-bar), which is simply $\hbar = h/2\pi$. Thus one may write, for example, $E = h\nu$ or $E = \hbar\omega$.

We pointed out above the necessity for an integer number of wavelengths around the circumference. This requirement can also be made plausible by considering that standing waves are superpositions of traveling waves. A

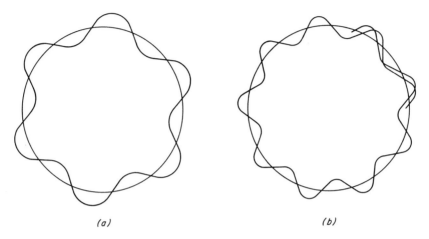

(a)   *(b)*

Fig. 3.2.2   (*a*) A plausible wavelength for a particle in a circular orbit.   (*b*) An impossible wavelength.

traveling wave of a wavelength that is not a simple fraction of the circumference of the circle would interfere destructively with itself as illustrated in Fig. 3.2.2. In further go-arounds the destructive effect of the interference of waves not fully in phase becomes complete. The amplitude of the ψ-function in this case would become zero along such an orbit. We must therefore conclude that this is not an allowed orbit for the particle under consideration.

A guess about the nature of the wave functions describing particles bound by a gradually varying attractive force is perhaps in order. As in the case of particles in a box, we may expect standing waves, but they will not be sinusoidal, because the velocity, and therefore also the wavelength, will change with position. We may expect the positions of greatest velocity to be near the attracting center, and therefore, because of the inverse relationship between velocity and wavelength, we should expect shorter wavelengths near the center rather than near the periphery. Also, since the particle is confined, we should expect the wave functions to approach zero at sufficiently great distances from the attracting center, and moreover this should occur gradually rather than discontinuously. Finally, we might expect the amplitude of the wave function to be greatest where the particle is most likely to be found, or where it spends most of its time. Near the attracting center it is moving with its greatest speed and therefore spends least time. The details will of course depend on the nature of the attractive forces, the total energy of the particle, and the ratio of wavelength to available volume. We shall find these predictions qualitatively borne out by the machinery which we now set up to solve our problems quantitatively.

3.3 THE SCHRÖDINGER EQUATION

Louis de Broglie had set up the wave theory of particles in the years 1923-24, specifying the wavelength in terms of momentum. At that time it was well known from Bohr's earlier work, to be discussed later, that atoms could exist only in certain discrete energy states. De Broglie realized that his assumption fitted a picture of standing electron waves, or characteristic modes of oscillation, in fact was "the first physically plausible explanation of the stability rules". Erwin Schrödinger,[8] at that time professor at the University of Zurich, extended this idea and developed the differential equation for these waves which is named after him.[9]

Before taking up the wave equation for particles, let us review the wave equation for a stretched string, with special reference to the description of standing waves. We had, for a plane wave, for example, with a displacement in the direction of the y axis and traveling in the direction of the x axis

$$\frac{\partial^2 Y(x, t)}{\partial x^2} = \frac{1}{w^2} \frac{\partial^2 Y(x, t)}{\partial t^2} \tag{3.3.1}$$

Erwin Schrödinger (1887–1961) during an international physics conference in Zurich, Switzerland 1934.

[8] Erwin Schrödinger (1887–1961), Austrian theoretical physicist. Originator of wave mechanics. Nobel prize 1933.

[9] Annalen der Physik **79**, 361, 489 (1926); **80**, 437 (1926); **81**, 109 (1926).

where w is the phase velocity of propagation of the wave along the string. The general solution of this equation may be expressed as the product of two functions, one containing the space variable x only and the other the time variable t only. For the periodic oscillations in which we are interested, the time variation may be written in the form $\sin(2\pi\nu t + \alpha)$. Thus if we substitute

$$Y(x, t) = U(x) \sin(2\pi\nu t + \alpha)$$

into Eq. 3.3.1, we get

$$\sin(2\pi\nu t + \alpha) \frac{d^2U(x)}{dx^2} = -\left[\frac{2\pi\nu}{w}\right]^2 U(x) \sin(2\pi\nu t + \alpha)$$

or simply

$$\frac{d^2U(x)}{dx^2} = -\left[\frac{2\pi\nu}{w}\right]^2 U(x)$$

$$= -\left[\frac{2\pi}{\lambda}\right]^2 U(x). \tag{3.3.2}$$

This is the equation whose solutions give the amplitude of the standing wave at any point along the string.

Similarly for any electromagnetic wave in space we might write an equation to be satisfied by the electric or the magnetic field. If we limit ourselves to a one-dimensional wave the formulas would be identical. For a three-dimensional field, the equation to be satisfied by a standing magnetic wave would be

$$\frac{\partial^2 H}{\partial x^2} + \frac{\partial^2 H}{\partial y^2} + \frac{\partial^2 H}{\partial z^2} = -\left[\frac{2\pi}{\lambda}\right]^2 H$$

or in the usual shorthand,

$$\nabla^2 H + \left[\frac{2\pi}{\lambda}\right]^2 H = 0. \tag{3.3.3}$$

The form of the solution to this equation depends on whether the medium is homogeneous and on the boundary conditions. If these boundary conditions are, for example, to have the field vanish, that is to make $H = 0$, on the surface of a homogeneous cube with sides perpendicular to the x, y, and z axes, the solutions will be simple periodic functions of these variables.

We now turn to the wave equation governing the standing waves of the ψ function. We may expect this to be of the form

$$\nabla^2\psi + \left[\frac{2\pi}{\lambda}\right]^2 \psi = 0. \tag{3.3.4}$$

This is a promising form for our wave equation since we have already learned how to specify the wavelength λ of the wave function describing a particle with given momentum. As an electron or other particle moves about in a field of force its velocity, and therefore also its momentum and wavelength, must be expected to change. The sort of problem which we shall want to solve is that of an electron moving about with some given total energy E in a field of force, for example, the Coulomb field of the nucleus. This field of force may be specified by the potential energy V of the electron at every point. For a Coulomb law of force we have, if the nucleus is a proton,

$$V = -\frac{1}{4\pi\epsilon_0}\frac{e^2}{r}.$$

For some other law of force we should have some other form for V. Notice that here V is not a potential, expressed in volts, but a potential energy, expressed in joules since our expression for V contains e^2 rather than e. The momentum, and consequently also the wavelength of the particle we are dealing with, can be described in terms of its total energy E and its potential energy V. In the range of velocities for which the Newtonian expression for the kinetic energy is valid, we have

$$\text{kinetic energy} = \tfrac{1}{2}mv^2 = E - V$$

and consequently the momentum is

$$mv = \sqrt{2m\cdot\tfrac{1}{2}mv^2} = \sqrt{2m(E - V)}$$

or

$$\lambda = \frac{h}{mv} = \frac{h}{\sqrt{2m(E - V)}}. \tag{3.3.5}$$

A possible form for the wave equation would therefore be obtained through substituting Eq. 3.3.5 into Eq. 3.3.4 giving

$$\nabla^2\psi + \frac{8\pi^2 m}{h^2}(E - V)\psi = 0. \tag{3.3.6}$$

This is, in fact, the famous *Schrödinger equation* for the standing waves, or the time-independent amplitude of the ψ functions describing a particle of mass m in a field of force defined by the potential energy function V.

The above discussion does not constitute a "derivation" of the Schrödinger equation. It merely shows that this wave equation is quite consistent with any wave equation in which the wavelength is specified by Eq. 3.3.5. In a more advanced presentation of the subject we might start by formulating certain basic general propositions from which the means of solving special problems can be derived. Thus, for Newtonian mechanics Newton's laws of motion constitute these basic propositions, or for electromagnetic theory, it is Maxwell's equations which must always be satisfied, and the electromagnetic wave equations may be derived from these. There are also certain fundamental well-established postulates of quantum mechanics from which the Schrödinger equation may be derived. At this point, however, we shall merely state that the Schrödinger equation is useful and correct, apart from relativistic effects which it does not take into account. In the following sections the Schrödinger equation will be applied to various physically different situations.

3.4 A PARTICLE IN A BOX

As we have already implied, one of the most important consequences of the adoption of a wave function in describing a particle is the insight which this gives us into the structure of atoms and nuclei. The particles confined in atoms and nuclei are described by particular wave functions describing characteristic modes of motion just as the harmonics of a stringed instrument describe it. The details of this description depend on precisely how the particles are held together just as the natural frequencies and tone quality of a horn, or violin, or double bass depend on its shape and construction.

One of the simplest problems occurring in nature which we might hope to solve using Eq. 3.3.6 is the hydrogen atom, consisting of a single electron held by the Coulomb attractive force of a proton. It turns out that even this simple problem involves mathematics with which the student at this stage is unfamiliar. We shall therefore take up an artificial problem whose solution is mathematically simple: that of a particle of mass m and total energy E in a box having the shape of a cube. Though we cannot expect the solution of this problem to reproduce atomic or nuclear properties in detail, we shall find certain general similarities. In particular we shall be able to understand the effect of the size of the box on the spacing of energy levels and, consequently, some of the differences to be expected between the properties of atoms and the properties of nuclei, already indicated by the discussion of Section 3.2.

The box within which we propose to confine our particle will have edges of length L_x, L_y, and L_z. Corners of the box are located at the origin, at the point $x = L_x, y = 0, z = 0; x = 0, y = L_y, z = 0$, etc. In the box the particle is subject to no force, and we may therefore choose the potential energy $V = 0$ inside the box. We shall specify that the particle is always necessarily inside the box by stipulating that its potential energy at all points outside the box is infinite. In other words, since an infinite amount of work must be done to remove the particle from the box, it must necessarily remain inside the box. This is graphically expressed in Fig. 3.4.1. We have then, within the box

$$0 < x < L_x$$

$$0 < y < L_y$$

$$0 < z < L_z$$

$$V = 0.$$

Because there is no potential energy inside the box, the Schrödinger equation for this region becomes

$$\nabla^2\psi = \frac{\partial^2\psi}{\partial x^2} + \frac{\partial^2\psi}{\partial y^2} + \frac{\partial^2\psi}{\partial z^2} = -\frac{8\pi^2 m}{h^2}E\psi \qquad (3.4.1)$$

and, for points on the surface and outside of the box, $V = \infty$ and therefore $\psi = 0$ in order to satisfy the Schrödinger equation in that region. This means that, from a wave mechanical point of view, the particle has zero probability of being outside of the box.

To some degree the situation is analogous to the particle in a tube, which we discussed in Section 3.2. We can consider the tube as a one-dimensional box. Just as in that case, we have to find functions that satisfy the boundary conditions. With regard to the tube a sine function was the appropriate function, yielding at both ends $\psi = 0$.

The solution to this problem requires us to find functions $\psi(x, y, z)$ which satisfy Eq. 3.4.1 for points within the box, and which satisfy the boundary conditions that $\psi = 0$ for $x = 0$ or L_x, for $y = 0$ or L_y, and for $z = 0$ or L_z. A graphical representation of the three-dimensional case is somewhat difficult, but the two-dimensional case can be adequately pictured. In the

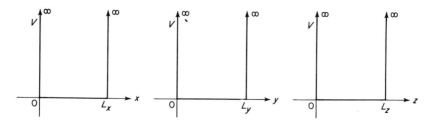

Fig. 3.4.1 Potential energy diagram for an impenetrable rectangular box with sides of length L_x, L_y, and L_z.

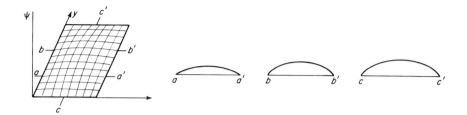

Fig. 3.4.2   A possible wave function for a particle in a two-dimensional square box.

simplest mode of oscillation, which corresponds to the ground state, the amplitude of ψ looks like a square pillow (Fig. 3.4.2). A cut through the pillow or the two-dimensional box parallel to the x axis is represented by a sine function. In the one-dimensional case (the particle in a tube) we had

$$\psi = A \sin \frac{\pi x}{L}$$

where A was a constant.[10] In the two-dimensional case A depends on the value of y. A is greatest if the cut is made halfway between $y = 0$ and $y = L_y$. It changes as the sine, being zero at $y = 0$ and $y = L_y$. We therefore write

$$\psi = B \sin \frac{\pi y}{L_y} \sin \frac{\pi x}{L_x}$$

whereby $B \sin(\pi y / L_y)$ must be considered as our y-dependent particle amplitude replacing the fixed amplitude A of the one-dimensional case.

The solutions of Eq. 3.4.1 are products of sine or cosine functions. If the functions are to vanish for $x = 0$, $y = 0$, or $z = 0$, we are restricted to sine functions. If they are also to vanish for $x = L_x$, $y = L_y$, or $z = L_z$, then they must have the form

$$\psi = A \sin \frac{s_x \pi x}{L_x} \sin \frac{s_y \pi y}{L_y} \sin \frac{s_z \pi z}{L_z} \tag{3.4.2}$$

where s_x, s_y, and s_z are any positive integers. By substituting Eq. 3.4.2 into Eq. 3.4.1 we find that these are in fact solutions if the energy E has certain special values. For other values of E, no solutions exist. We have, for

[10] Actually there we wrote ψ_0 instead of A, using S for the cross section of the tube. Here now A is the amplitude of the ψ wave.

example

$$\frac{\partial^2 \psi}{\partial x^2} = -A \left[\frac{s_x \pi}{L_x}\right]^2 \sin \frac{s_x \pi x}{L_x} \sin \frac{s_y \pi y}{L_y} \sin \frac{s_z \pi z}{L_z} = -\left[\frac{s_x \pi}{L_x}\right]^2 \psi.$$

Substituting this and corresponding expressions for the y and z coordinates and canceling ψ from both sides of the equation, we have

$$E = \frac{h^2}{8m} \left[\frac{s_x^2}{L_x^2} + \frac{s_y^2}{L_y^2} + \frac{s_z^2}{L_z^2}\right]. \tag{3.4.3}$$

If the box is cubic, $L_x = L_y = L_z$, and the energy has the simpler form

$$E = \frac{h^2}{8mL^2} (s_x^2 + s_y^2 + s_z^2). \tag{3.4.4}$$

The wave equation and the boundary conditions are satisfied by the functions in Eq. 3.4.2. The particle in the box can exist only in certain discrete states given by this function with positive integral values of the constants s_x, s_y, and s_z. The energy of the particle in any one of these states is given by Eq. 3.4.3. The arbitrary constant A is not important in this discussion. It may, however, be evaluated through integrating ψ^2 over the volume of the box. The first four x components of the wave function are those shown in Fig. 3.2.1. They vanish, as required, for $x = 0$ and $x = L$. As we shall see, the properties of the particle in the box are determined by

TABLE 3.4.1

The States and Energies of a Particle in a Cubical Box

s_x	s_y	s_z	E	s_x	s_y	s_z	E
1	1	1	$3E_0$	2	2	2	$12E_0$
2	1	1		3	2	1	
1	2	1	$6E_0$	3	1	2	
1	1	2		2	3	1	$14E_0$
				1	3	2	
2	2	1		2	1	3	
2	1	2	$9E_0$	1	2	3	
1	2	2					
3	1	1					
1	3	1	$11E_0$				
1	1	3					

the wave function. We shall concentrate first on a discussion of the allowed energies in Eq. 3.4.4 and return to a discussion of wave functions further on. The characteristic and qualitatively new result brought about by the wave mechanical description of a mechanical system is that it can exist in only certain discrete states. In the problem under discussion these states are given by the set of numbers s_x, s_y, and s_z. The various possible different sets of numbers, and the energy of the system for each such state, are listed in Table 3.4.1. For the sake of brevity the symbol E_0 is used to designate $h^2/8mL^2$ throughout. These energies are plotted in an energy level diagram in Fig. 3.4.3. Such diagrams are characteristic of atomic and nuclear systems. The detail of the diagram depends on the precise way that the particle is confined. For the cubical box under discussion, we see that certain groups of states have the same energy. Three different states, for example, have the energy $6E_0$. Such states are called "degenerate." It is easy to see that the degeneracy of these states is removed if the lengths L_x, L_y, and L_z of the sides of the box in the x, y, and z directions are not equal.

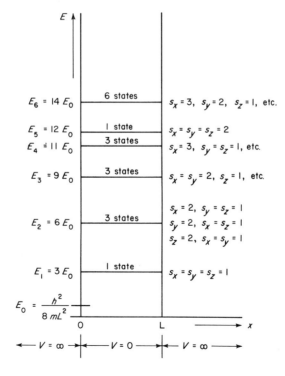

Fig. 3.4.3   The energy-level diagram for a particle in a cubical box.

An important point which we wish to make about the wave aspect of particles is illustrated by the change that is brought about in the previous problem if we stipulate that the potential outside of the box is not infinite but has some finite magnitude V_0. After reducing the height of the potential outside the box from the original value $V = \infty$ to $V = V_0$, the potential in the x-coordinate direction now has the form shown in Fig. 3.4.4. For the other coordinate directions the figure is identical.

Closely related to the cubical boxes, or potential wells, with infinite or finite walls, are spherical "boxes" with infinite or finite potential walls and flat potential bottoms. Examples are the atomic nuclei which are spherical, at least approximately. The nuclear potential in which a proton inside the nucleus moves can fairly well be represented by such a potential. Its level sequence is similar to that of cubical wells. Such geometrically spherical wells are called square wells. "Square" refers here to the right angle between the flat bottom and the vertical walls of the well, since wells of other shapes are also important in microscopic physics. Of all the different potential functions the square well is one of the simplest. It usually yields results that are qualitatively valid and often at least correct to an order of magnitude.

Classically a particle with a total energy $E < V_0$ is confined to the region within the potential well. We shall see that wave mechanics leads to slightly different conclusions. If the kinetic energy exceeds V_0, the particle can

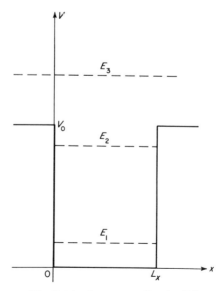

Fig. 3.4.4 A square-well potential.

leave the well. The box is transparent for particles with kinetic energies greater than V_0.

The general rule to be satisfied by the solutions of the wave equation is that, if we can solve it separately for two regions (in our specific case here inside and outside the well), then the solution of the complete problem is obtained through matching the wave functions in the two regions so that at the boundary the function and its first derivative (its slope) are continuous. We are already familiar with the first condition, but why should the first derivative be continuous? Let us look again at the Schrödinger equation. If the first derivative had a kink at the boundary as at P in Fig. 3.4.5, the second derivative would be infinite at that point. This would be a catastrophe because according to the Schrödinger equation this would mean that $(8\pi^2m/h^2)(E - V_0)\psi$ would also have to be infinite. Neither $(8\pi^2m/h^2)$ nor ψ can be infinite. We are therefore led to the conclusion that the first derivative of ψ at the boundary between two regions must in general be continuous. There are, however, some exceptions to this rule. In our first example in which the potential energy V outside the well (or box) was infinite, the kink in ψ was permitted.

We have shown that the solution of the wave equation in the well where $V = 0$ consists of periodic functions. In the region where $V = V_0$—that is, outside the well—the Schrödinger equation has the form

$$\frac{d^2\psi}{dx^2} = -\frac{8\pi^2m}{h^2}(E - V_0)\psi. \tag{3.4.5}$$

Solutions for which E is greater than V_0 are again periodic and represent states in which the particle can escape from the box. If, however, the total energy E is less than V_0, the right side of the equation will be positive and our equation has the form

$$\frac{d^2\psi}{dx^2} = + \text{constant } \psi.$$

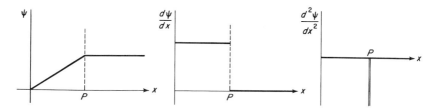

Fig. 3.4.5 A wave function with a discontinuous first derivative and an infinite second derivative at P.

This equation, because of the positive sign, is not satisfied by a periodic function, such as sine or cosine but, as is well known, by an exponential function of the form

$$\psi = A e^{\kappa x}.$$

Differentiating ψ twice yields

$$\frac{d^2 x}{dx^2} = \kappa^2 A e^{\kappa x}.$$

Inserting this value into Eq. 3.4.5 gives

$$\kappa^2 A e^{\kappa x} = \frac{8\pi^2 m}{h^2} (V_0 - E) A e^{\kappa x}.$$

Dividing both sides by $A e^{\kappa x}$ yields an equation for κ

$$\kappa = \pm \sqrt{\frac{8\pi^2 m}{h^2}} \sqrt{V_0 - E}.$$

We have to choose between the plus and minus sign. Of course ψ cannot increase exponentially as we go away from the boundary. In the region to the left of the boundary at $x = 0$ we therefore have to take the plus sign, whereas for values of $x > L_x$ the minus sign provides for an exponential decrease of ψ. The constant A must be chosen such that the two conditions mentioned above regarding ψ and $d\psi/dx$ are satisfied. The results are illustrated in Fig. 3.4.6. We do not want to go through the mathematical procedures but limit ourselves to a qualitative discussion. Inside the well, as stated before, the ψ-function is still represented by a sine or cosine function, but its value will not be zero at the boundaries. In the case of the

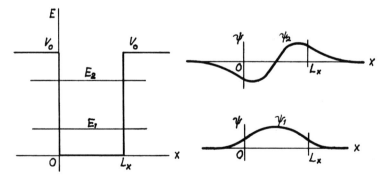

Fig. 3.4.6   Qualitative picture of ψ functions for the two lowest energy levels of a particle in a well.

lowest frequency the sine function does not extend over the whole 180° but only over a portion. This means that in comparison with an infinitely deep well of equal width the wavelength which the well can accommodate is somewhat longer, therefore the energy of the level is lower. The same holds for the higher levels; also they are slightly depressed in their energies, but it is important to note that the level sequence is not changed. The portions of the ψ function in the classically forbidden region are exponentially decaying. The distance within which this attenuation takes place is shorter the deeper the well is. In the limit of an infinitely deep well it becomes, as we already know, infinitely short.

Equation 3.4.5 and Fig. 3.4.6 show also that a curvature of ψ toward the abscissa, as in a sine or cosine function, implies that $E > V_0$. Conversely, a curving of ψ away from the abscissa, as in an exponential function, arises if $E < V_0$.

We here again remind the reader that we have discussed the ψ-function, but that the physical quantity to which we assign a distinct physical meaning is $|\psi|^2$. The function $|\psi|^2$ inside the well varies as $\sin^2$, and outside still as an exponential, decreasing however, more rapidly than ψ.

It is sometimes convenient to consider the mutual potential energy of infinitely separated particles as zero. A potential well is then characterized by a negative potential energy in the well. A particle trapped in the well must have a kinetic energy less than the depth of the well. Its total energy will then be negative, as for planets or satellites caught in orbits around the sun or the earth. The choice of the zero point of the potential energy scale does not affect the physics of the problem.

A few remarks should be added with regard to a particle with kinetic energy greater than $|V_0|$. Classically it will not be affected greatly by the existence of the well. If it had been in the potential well before and had in some way gained enough kinetic energy, it would inevitably leave the region of the well with only a change of velocity. Quantum mechanically this is no longer true. An analogy from wave optics will help us to understand this point. Although light penetrates window glass, some of the light is reflected by both surfaces, usually a few percent. The reason for this partial reflection, as we learned in Chapter 2, lies in the abrupt change of the index of refraction at the two boundaries. In wave mechanics we are faced with a similar situation. Here also we have an abrupt change in wavelength for a particle which, inside the well, has a greater kinetic energy and consequently a shorter wavelength than outside. The total energy, kinetic plus potential, of course remains constant. Therefore, because of the increased potential energy outside, less is available for the kinetic energy. The particle is slowed down as in the classical case. But, because there is some reflection standing waves will be possible. This will lead to levels above the rim of the well. From our picture, it is clear that these levels will not last for long if the reflection coefficient is small. The particle will soon escape. Such levels are called *virtual* levels. Particularly in nuclear physics where there is a fairly sharp discontinuity in the potential at the nuclear surface such virtual levels play an important role.

The standing acoustical waves in an open organ pipe are an analogy in classical physics to the virtual levels. Although there is no real barrier at the end of the pipe the abrupt change in environment gives rise to reflection and therefore standing waves. The behavior of traveling waves at an abrupt jump in potential will be discussed in the next section.

We will meet the finite square well again in our chapters on solid-state and nuclear physics, in which it plays an important role.

3.5. REFLECTION AND TRANSMISSION OF PARTICLES

In Chapters 1 and 2 we paid careful attention to the reflection and transmission of electromagnetic waves at the interface of two media. These discussions, for example, made it evident that a transparent sheet of glass will not transmit all the incident light, but will reflect a small portion of it. We learned that this is due to the difference of the index of refraction in air and in glass. Somewhat more to the point is the explanation that certain boundary conditions have to be satisfied at the interface. For electromagnetic waves, the normal components of the vectors D and B must be continuous at the boundary, that is, their respective values must be equal on both sides of it, and a similar condition holds for the tangential components of E and H. In view of this, it is not surprising that analogous boundary conditions exist for the Ψ-waves at discontinuities of the medium.

We shall first consider the behavior of a matter wave at a potential step, as shown in Fig. 3.5.1. We find such potential steps, although not quite so

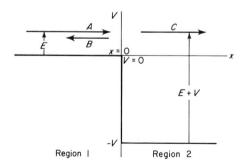

Fig. 3.5.1 Reflection and transmission of a matter wave at a potential step.

abrupt ones, for example, at the surface of nuclei which shall be discussed later. Here it suffices to know that the nuclear potential, as experienced by a neutron, can be approximated by a finite square well as illustrated in Fig. 3.4.4. A neutron which approaches the nucleus with a certain kinetic energy, $\frac{1}{2}mv^2$, will suddenly possess much more kinetic energy upon penetrating the nuclear surface because the nuclear potential well has a depth of several tens of MeV. If, for example, the neutron had a kinetic energy of 1 MeV outside of the nucleus, the kinetic energy increase is considerable, as is the corresponding change in the de Broglie wavelength. In the language of wave optics, this corresponds to a change in the index of refraction. The treatment of the reflection and transmission of particle waves is very similar to that of electromagnetic waves. Referring again to Fig. 3.5.1, we shall use the subscript 1 for the region to the left of the discontinuity in the potential and the subscript 2 for the other side. Furthermore, we assume that the particle approaches the potential step from the left, traveling in the positive x direction. Its velocity is $v_1 = (2E/m)^{1/2}$ from which follows its wavelength $\lambda_1 = h/(2mE)^{1/2}$. If the particle is reflected at the boundary, it returns with the same speed, hence its wavelength is not changed. If, however, it transits into the other region, its kinetic energy will increase to $E + V$, and its wavelength becomes $\lambda_2 = h/[2m(E + V)]^{1/2}$. Therefore, on the left-hand side we have the incident and the reflected wave, and on the right-hand side the transmitted wave. The incoming traveling wave Ψ_i can be written as

$$\Psi_i = A \cos(k_1 x - \omega t)$$

where A is the amplitude of the wave with $k_1 = (2\pi/\lambda_1)$. The reflected wave Ψ_r has the amplitude B which we shall determine, and can be written

$$\Psi_r = B \cos(k_1 x + \omega t).$$

The transmitted wave Ψ_t is written as

$$\Psi_2 = C \cos(k_2 x - \omega t)$$

where the wave number k_2 corresponds to the wavelength λ_2. As with the optical analogy the frequency ω is the same on both sides of the boundary. This is so because the total energy of the electron, E, does not change. (See Eq. 3.1.13.) The Schrödinger equation demands that the wave function at the boundary must be continuous, which implies that

$$A \cos(k_1 x - \omega t) + B \cos(k_1 x + \omega t) = C \cos(k_2 x - \omega t). \qquad (3.5.1)$$

Since for convenience we assume the boundary to be at $x = 0$, $k_1 x$ and $k_2 x$ at the boundary are also zero, and we can write

$$A \cos(-\omega t) + B \cos(\omega t) = C \cos(-\omega t).$$

But $\cos(-\omega t) = \cos(\omega t)$. Hence,

$$A + B = C. \tag{3.5.2}$$

A second boundary condition for the Schrödinger equation requires that the first derivatives of the wave function on both sides of the step have to match, because the wave function is not allowed to have a kink. This means that

$$\frac{d\Psi_1}{dx} = \frac{d\Psi_2}{dx} \quad \text{at the boundary } x = 0.$$

Differentiating, Eq. 3.5.1 yields

$$-Ak_1 \sin(k_1 x - \omega t) - Bk_1 \sin(k_1 x + \omega t) = -Ck_2 \sin(k_2 x - \omega t).$$

At $x = 0$ this reduces to

$$-Ak_1 \sin(-\omega t) - Bk_1 \sin(\omega t) = -Ck_2 \sin(-\omega t).$$

Because $\sin(-\omega t) = -\sin(\omega t)$, we get

$$Ak_1 - Bk_1 = Ck_2$$

or

$$(A - B)k_1 = Ck_2. \tag{3.5.3}$$

Adding or subtracting Eq. 3.5.2 and Eq. 3.5.3, which are the results of the two boundary conditions, yields

$$2A = C\left(1 + \frac{k_2}{k_1}\right)$$

$$\tag{3.5.4}$$

$$2B = C\left(1 - \frac{k_2}{k_1}\right)$$

and hence

$$\left|\frac{B}{A}\right| = \frac{k_1 - k_2}{k_1 + k_2}.$$

Since the particle density is expressed by the square of the amplitude, the reflection coefficient becomes

$$R = \left|\frac{B}{A}\right|^2 = \left(\frac{k_1 - k_2}{k_1 + k_2}\right)^2 \tag{3.5.5}$$

and the transmission coefficient which is $T = 1 - R$ is

$$T = 1 - \left(\frac{k_1 - k_2}{k_1 + k_2}\right)^2. \tag{3.5.6}$$

One might be tempted to assume that the transmission coefficient T is equal to $|C/A|^2$, but this is not true. Because the particles travel faster in the region to the right, due to their greater kinetic energy, their density (i.e., their number per unit volume), is smaller here than on the left-hand side. The situation is similar to the density of cars in a construction zone of a highway, where the automobiles follow each other closer than on the open road before and after the reduced-speed zone. The quantity which we have computed above is $|\Psi|^2$, the density of particles. However, we are right now more interested in knowing what fraction of the particles cross the boundary. Hence, we have to compute the flow of particles through a cross section of unit area, or the particle flux, on both sides of the boundary. This flux is given by $|\Psi|^2 v$, that is, the particle density times their velocity. The transmission coefficient then becomes

$$T = \frac{|C|^2 v_2}{|A|^2 v_1}$$

where v_1 and v_2 are the particle velocities in the two regions. C/A can easily be calculated from Eq. 3.5.4, which finally yields for the transmission coefficients at a potential step

$$T = \left(\frac{2k_1}{k_1 + k_2}\right)^2 \frac{v_2}{v_1}. \tag{3.5.7}$$

Since $v_2/v_1 = k_2/k_1$, it is easy to show that Eq. 3.5.7 is equivalent to Eq. 3.5.6 (see problem 34).

The expressions for the reflection and transmission coefficients for particles, which are very similar to the coefficients for electromagnetic waves, play an important role in atomic and nuclear physics. It is left as an exercise to show that these coefficients are the same when a particle approaches the boundary from the right-hand side in our figure. In nuclear physics the probability for the escape of a neutron of sufficient excitation energy from a nucleus is essentially determined by such an expression. (For protons, because of the Coulomb forces between the proton and the nucleus, the penetrability of the nuclear surface depends upon additional factors.) In the previous section we discussed the existence of virtual energy levels in nuclei and pointed out that such states can decay by the escape of a nucleon. The lifetime of such states can be estimated by assuming that the nucleon bounces back and forth inside the nucleus with a velocity corresponding to the kinetic energy it has inside the nucleus. Each time it hits the wall of the nucleus it has an escape probability which is given chiefly by a transmission coefficient similar to the one above.[11]

---

[11] In a more rigorous treatment we would have to consider the true shape of the nuclear potential. Furthermore, this formula needs some extension if angular momentum effects must be considered.

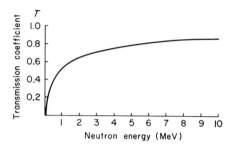

Fig. 3.5.2　The transmission coefficient for neutrons incident on a nucleus assuming a square-well potential depth of 50 MeV.

Figure 3.5.2 shows the calculated transmission coefficient for neutrons (of zero orbital angular momentum) incident on a nucleus with a potential well of 50 MeV depth. It is left as an exercise to check how well Eq. 3.5.6 agrees with the more correct formula used for this figure.

We now extend the problem of the potential step by considering a potential well being approached by a beam of particles, as shown in Fig. 3.5.3. Some of the particles are reflected at the first boundary at $x = a$, and the remainder proceed toward the second boundary at $x = b$. Here again the remaining beam is partly reflected and partly transmitted. The situation has an obvious analogy in the reflection and transmission of light in thin films. When discussing this optical problem previously, we saw that the reflected wave outside the thin film can be suppressed by destructive interference of the two components which are reflected at the two surfaces. For total destructive interference the thickness of the film

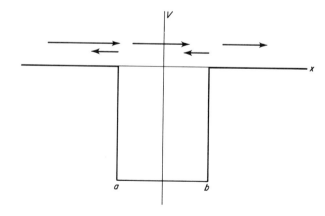

Fig. 3.5.3　Transmission and reflection at a square-well potential.

must be $n\lambda/2$, where λ is the wavelength of the light inside the film. This takes into account the reversal of phase at one of the boundaries. If, on the other hand, the thickness is $(n + \frac{1}{2})\lambda/2$, maximum reflection occurs. The same considerations also hold in wave mechanics, including the necessity of a phase change at one of the boundaries. It is left as an exercise to calculate the reflection and transmission coefficients of a Ψ-wave for such a square well.

Although one-dimensional potential wells for which the thin film is the optical counterpart do not occur in nature, related phenomena due to three-dimensional potentials can be observed in atoms and nuclei. Before physicists knew about matter waves, Ramsauer[12] observed such an effect in atoms between 1919 and 1921. When an electron beam passes through a gas, collisions between electrons and gas molecules scatter some of the electrons out of the beam. The collision probability depends, among other factors, on the size of the molecules, which can be expressed in terms of a cross section. This is the effective target area πR^2, where R is the effective radius of the molecule, and it is not necessarily the geometric area. The geometric cross section is found from gas-kinetic investigations, for example, the study of collisions between molecules. As is well known, noble gases are monatomic. Ramsauer found, surprisingly, that the medium and heavy noble gas molecules were, so to speak, transparent for very slow

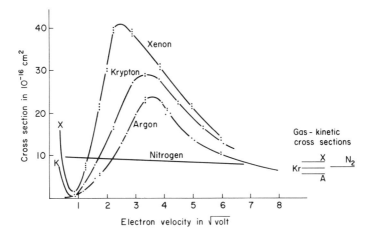

Fig. 3.5.4 The Ramsauer effect in argon, krypton, and xenon. Data points between 1 and 8 $\sqrt{\text{volt}}$ from C. Ramsauer [*Ann. Physik* **72**, 345 (1923)]. For comparison are also given the cross section for N_2 for electrons and gas-kinetic cross sections for these gases.

[12] Carl W. Ramsauer (1879–1955), German experimental physicist. Worked in industry and at universities.

electrons with energies of the order of half an electron volt. Their cross-section, as determined from these experiments, with slow electrons was only between 2% and 8% of the one determined from gas kinetic experiments, as seen from Fig. 3.5.4.

The explanation of this Ramsauer effect, as it is called, is as follows: The molecules of the noble gases are monatomic. Because of the tight binding of all their electrons, the electric potential, which arises from the charge of the nucleus and the surrounding electrons, undergoes a relatively abrupt change at the surface of the atom. In a very rough approximation the electrostatic potential may be considered, therefore, as a square-well potential. If, now, the wavelength of an impinging electron is $n\lambda/2$ inside the potential well, this electron should pass through the atom without being reflected. This explanation is not the full story, because the atom represents a three-dimensional well, and not a one-dimensional one. In the one-dimensional case, every particle that was transmitted had to pass through the potential well. Here, however, we also have to consider that the wave can be diffracted around the atom, similar to the light which is diffracted by a small object. The interference between the waves passing through and those being diffracted around the atom must be considered for a more rigorous explanation of the Ramsauer effect.

A similar phenomenon has also been observed in nuclei. The nuclear potential experienced by neutrons is, as mentioned earlier, roughly a square-well potential. If an incoming neutron has an energy corresponding to such a de Broglie wavelength inside the nucleus that the condition $D = \lambda(n + \frac{1}{2})$ is satisfied, where D is the diameter of the nucleus, maximum reflection is expected. This appears as a broad hump in the cross-section curve for the interaction of neutrons with a nucleus as a function of the neutron energy. Three examples are given in Fig. 3.5.5 for nuclei of different radii.

To avoid misconceptions, it should be emphasized that other, much

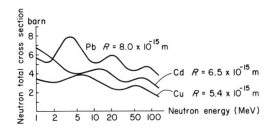

Fig. 3.5.5   Total cross section for neutrons from 1 to 100 MeV (1 barn $= 10^{-28}$ m²). [From J. M. Peterson, *Phys. Rev.* **125**, 955 (1962).]

sharper, peaks referred to as resonances, appear in nuclei which cannot be explained by an interaction of a single incoming particle with the nuclear potential.

In all the situations discussed in this section, the kinetic energy of the particle has been greater than its potential energy. From the standpoint of classical physics there was never any doubt that the particle could not pass the boundary. It remains for us to investigate what will happen to a particle that classically has not enough energy to pass a potential barrier, as shown in Fig. 3.5.6.

From the discussion of the wave function in a square well of finite depth in the previous section, where we saw that the ψ-function extends beyond the range of the well, we might guess that there is a finite probability for a particle to leak through the barrier. This is indeed the case. This phenomenon is called tunneling or barrier penetration, and it plays an enormously important role in nuclear and solid-state physics. We shall defer the mathematical treatment of barrier penetration to a later discussion of such physical phenomena.

A few historical remarks might be inserted here. In Chapter 2 we mentioned that Louis de Broglie in his dissertation in 1924 proposed the matter waves. In essence he adapted Einstein's equation for light quanta $E = h\nu$ to particles with a rest mass. His hypothesis had little impact on the community of physicists, until Einstein in 1925 took it up in a paper[13] on the quantum theory of the monatomic ideal gas. This paper substantially motivated Schrödinger to set up his wave mechanics.

The experimental aspects of matter waves first came to light in the experiments of C. J. Davisson in New York and his co-worker C. H. Kunsman, who in 1921[14] had seen and published observations of maxima and minima as function of angle in the reflections of electrons from metal surfaces, without realizing what had caused this effect. The two investigators

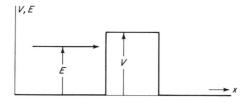

Fig. 3.5.6   A particle approaching a barrier of height greater than the kinetic energy of the particle.

[13] *Sitzungsberichte der Preussischen Akademie der Wissenschaften, Phys.-Math. Klasse,* p. 3 (1925).

[14] *Science* **54,** 522 (1924).

rather believed that they had found a method to probe the different atomic shells using electrons as projectiles. In 1923 they published a longer article[15] about their research, which contained graphs showing the dependence of the angle for maximum reflection on the velocity of the bombarding electrons. A 21-year-old student at Göttingen, Elsasser,[16] who read this paper, was also familiar with Ramsauer's puzzling results of the much smaller than expected electron cross sections of rare-gas atoms at certain velocities. Now in 1925, having studied Einstein's paper, which induced him to read de Broglie's thesis, it occurred to Elsasser that both experiments might be explained if one took the wave nature of electrons literally. He published a short article[17] on the interpretation of both experiments in terms of matter waves. Davisson held on to his interpretation until some mishap with his apparatus caused a crucial change in his setup, yielding experimental results which put him and his new co-worker, Germer, on the right track.[18]

3.6 THE HARMONIC OSCILLATOR

Other examples of the application of the Schrödinger equation, which are important in atomic and nuclear physics, are the harmonic oscillator and the rotator which will be taken up in the next section. A diatomic molecule behaves rather like a harmonic oscillator, because the two atoms are bound by forces which for small displacements are approximately proportional to the displacement from the equilibrium position. The vibration of the two atoms of the molecule against each other can be more or less violent. The total energy, which is the sum of the kinetic and potential energy must remain constant during the motion of an isolated oscillator, but can have a range of values, depending on the violence or amplitude of the motion. We shall show that only certain energy values are permitted, as in the case of the particle in a box. We shall meet the harmonic oscillator again later when we discuss molecules and nuclei.

For the sake of simplicity, we shall treat first the one-dimensional case, and we shall assume that a mass point, of mass m, is connected elastically to the origin of coordinates with a restoring force kx.[19] Using a classical treatment, we should find that at an elongation x the potential energy is $V = \frac{1}{2}kx^2$, that the characteristic frequency is $\omega_0 = 2\pi\nu_0 = \sqrt{k/m}$, and

---

[15] *Phys. Rev.* **22**, 242 (1923).

[16] Walter Elsasser (1904–   ), taught physics at several American universities, now at the University of Maryland.

[17] *Naturwissenschaften* **13**, 711 (1925).

[18] We thank Dr. Elsasser for valuable information and for checking the correctness of this account.

[19] Here k is the spring constant, not the wave number; and λ, introduced below, is an abbreviation, not a wavelength.

therefore that $V = \frac{1}{2}m\,\omega_0^2 x^2$. To prevent any misconception, ω_0 is the frequency of the oscillator, *not* of the de Broglie wave. We have to insert this value of the potential energy into the one-dimensional Schrödinger equation, 3.3.6,

$$\frac{d^2\psi}{dx^2} + \frac{8\pi^2 m}{h^2}(E - V)\psi = 0$$

which becomes in our case

$$\frac{d^2\psi}{dx^2} + \frac{8\pi^2 m}{h^2}\left(E - \frac{m}{2}\,\omega_0^2 x^2\right)\psi = 0. \tag{3.6.1}$$

Since we are interested in physically realizable bound states, we seek solutions subject to the condition that ψ must go to zero as $x \to \pm\infty$. Let us first introduce the abbreviations: $\lambda = (8\pi^2 m/h^2)E$ and $\alpha = 2\pi m\omega_0/h$. The Schrödinger equation can be written

$$\frac{d^2\psi}{dx^2} + (\lambda - \alpha^2 x^2)\psi = 0. \tag{3.6.2}$$

The behavior for large values of x can be inferred by neglecting λ compared to $\alpha^2 x^2$. This leads to the simple differential equation

$$\frac{d^2\psi}{dx^2} - \alpha^2 x^2\psi = 0, \tag{3.6.3}$$

whose solution is approximately

$$\psi = e^{\pm(\alpha/2)x^2}. \tag{3.6.4}$$

Since we want ψ to become zero for big values of x, only the minus sign can be used, and this is called the *asymptotic* solution, $\psi = e^{-(\alpha/2)x^2}$. We shall assume that the complete solution has the form

$$\psi = e^{-(\alpha/2)x^2}v(x) \tag{3.6.5}$$

where $v(x)$ is to be determined. The mathematical steps required to find $v(x)$ and the allowed values of λ, or E, are given below.

Derivation of the Solutions

We substitute the assumed form of ψ, Eq. 3.6.5, and its second derivative $d^2\psi/dx^2$ into the Schrödinger equation, 3.6.2. Since

$$\frac{d\psi}{dx} = e^{-(\alpha/2)x^2}\left[\frac{dv}{dx} - \alpha x v\right]$$

$$\frac{d^2\psi}{dx^2} = e^{-(\alpha/2)x^2}\left[\frac{d^2v}{dx^2} - 2\alpha x\frac{dv}{dx} - \alpha v + \alpha^2 x^2 v\right]$$

we get

$$\frac{d^2v}{dx^2} - 2\alpha x \frac{dv}{dx} + (\lambda - \alpha)v = 0. \tag{3.6.6}$$

This equation can be solved with the following power series:

$$v = \sum c_l x^l = c_0 x^0 + c_1 x^1 + c_2 x^2 + c_3 x^3 + c_4 x^4 + c_5 x^5 + c_6 x^6 \ldots \tag{3.6.7}$$

from which it follows that

$$\frac{dv}{dx} = 0 + c_1 + 2c_2 x + 3c_3 x^2 + 4c_4 x^3 + 5c_5 x^4 + 6c_6 x^5 + \cdots$$

$$\frac{d^2v}{dx^2} = 0 + 0 + 1 \cdot 2c_2 + 2 \cdot 3c_3 x + 3 \cdot 4c_4 x^2 + 4 \cdot 5c_5 x^3 + 5 \cdot 6c_6 x^4 + \cdots.$$

If we insert these values into Eq. 3.6.6 we get a somewhat lengthy expression

$$1 \cdot 2c_2 + 2 \cdot 3c_3 x + 3 \cdot 4c_4 x^2 \quad + 4 \cdot 5c_5 x^3 \quad + 5 \cdot 6c_6 x^4 \quad + \ldots$$
$$- 2\alpha c_1 x \quad - 2 \cdot 2\alpha c_2 x^2 - 2 \cdot 3\alpha c_3 x^3 - 2 \cdot 4\alpha c_4 x^4 + \ldots$$
$$+ \lambda c_0 + \lambda c_1 x \quad + \lambda c_2 x^2 \quad + \lambda c_3 x^3 \quad + \lambda c_4 x^4 \quad + \ldots$$
$$- \alpha c_0 - \alpha c_1 x \quad - \alpha c_2 x^2 \quad - \alpha c_3 x^3 \quad - \alpha c_4 x^4 \quad - \ldots = 0.$$

This equation must be satisfied for any value of x. This is possible only if the sum of the coefficients for each power of x is independently equal to zero. For example, the coefficients of the x^4 terms must fulfill the equation

$$5 \cdot 6c_6 - [2 \cdot 4\alpha - \lambda + \alpha]c_4 = 0.$$

We can generalize this by replacing 4 with n:

$$(n + 1)(n + 2)c_{n+2} - [(2n + 1)\alpha - \lambda]c_n = 0. \tag{3.6.8}$$

If in our assumed solution

$$\psi = e^{-(\alpha/2)x^2}v(x)$$

the asymptotic behavior for large x is not to be dominated by

$$v = \sum c_l x^l,$$

the coefficients c_l for large l must be very small, or vanish. The relationship 3.6.8 makes this possible. This is a recursion formula which connects the coefficient c_n with the coefficient c_{n+2}. If we can make a coefficient c_{n+2} zero, all higher coefficients will also be zero and our power series will terminate with x^n. But c_{n+2} will be zero if the expression in the square brackets of 3.6.8

$$[(2n + 1)\alpha - \lambda] = 0,$$

or if

$$\lambda = (2n + 1)\alpha.$$

Because the recursion relation is between c_n and c_{n+2}, we must at the beginning set either $c_0 = 0$, which eliminates all the even polynomials, leaving only odd ones, or set $c_1 = 0$, which has the opposite effect. Since λ and α are only abbreviations, the last equation can be written as

$$\frac{8\pi^2 mE}{h^2} = (2n + 1)\frac{2\pi m\omega_0}{h} \tag{3.6.10}$$

which leads to an expression for the energy E.

The allowed values of the energy are

$$E = (n + \tfrac{1}{2})\frac{h}{2\pi}\,\omega_0 = (n + \tfrac{1}{2})h\nu_0 \tag{3.6.11}$$

where n is the vibrational quantum number which can assume the values
0, 1, 2, 3 .... This is a very important relationship. The only permitted
energy values of the one-dimensional linear harmonic oscillator are

$$\tfrac{1}{2}h\nu_0, \tfrac{3}{2}h\nu_0, \tfrac{5}{2}h\nu_0, \tfrac{7}{2}h\nu_0, \text{ etc.}$$

The lowest value is not zero, but $\tfrac{1}{2}h\nu_0$. Like a particle in a box, a harmonic
oscillator cannot come fully to rest, but always has some minimum *zero-
point energy*. An important aspect of the energy levels of the harmonic
oscillator is that they are equally spaced, a feature found in molecules and
certain nuclei.

The functions $v(x)$ in Eq. 3.6.5 corresponding to the above energy levels
are usually written as $H_0, H_1, H_2, H_3 \ldots$.[20] They are

$$H_0 = 1, \quad H_1 = 2\sqrt{\alpha}x, \quad H_2 = 4\alpha x^2 - 2, \quad H_3 = 8\alpha^{3/2}x^3 - 12\sqrt{\alpha}x, \ldots$$

Figure 3.6.1 gives a graphic representation of the wave functions for $n = 0$
to $n = 4$. For $n = 0, 2, 4 \ldots$ the wave functions are symmetric with respect
to the ψ axis and thus are even wave functions; the ones for odd n, on the
other hand, are odd wave functions. More important than ψ is ψ^2 which

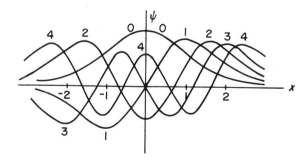

Fig. 3.6.1   Harmonic oscillator wave functions.

[20] In mathematics these functions are known as Hermite polynomials.

represents the probability of finding the oscillating particle at the location x. This is shown for $n = 0$, 2, and 4 in Fig. 3.6.2. One sees that with increasing energy the probability for finding the particle further away from the origin increases. Furthermore, this probability is greatest at the ends of the swing, or at the velocity reversal points. Here the velocity is smallest and therefore the time of its stay is longest. We see an analogous behavior in the quantum mechanical system. For $n \geq 2$ the biggest humps are the extreme ones, whereas the smallest one is at the center. For $n = 0$ it is reasonable to expect that the maximum is at the center. However, due to the zero-point energy and the motion associated with it there is a finite probability of finding the particle away from the origin. Looking at the wave function for $n = 4$ and comparing it with the behavior of a classical oscillator we see that at certain values of x the probability density goes to zero. This does not happen in the classical case where the corresponding probability w is a smooth function going abruptly to zero at the two reversal points, as in Fig. 3.6.3. Note also that the higher the energy, the more maxima we get, and the closer they lie together. A macroscopic oscillator will obey the laws of quantum mechanics, but because of the great energy in terms of the $h\nu$ unit, the quantum number n will be very great and the peaks and valleys of the probability ψ^2 are unobservable. This is an example of the so-called *correspondence principle* stated by Niels Bohr. It says that it is a general property of quantum-theoretical results that for very high quantum numbers the results are in quantitative agreement with the results obtained by classical theory.

In retrospect we might ask ourselves how we were led to the result that only certain discrete energies are permitted. We also want to compare the procedure here with that of the particle in a box. In both cases we required for physical reasons that ψ go to zero at the boundaries, either $\pm \infty$ for the oscillator or the particle in a finite well, or at the walls of the box if

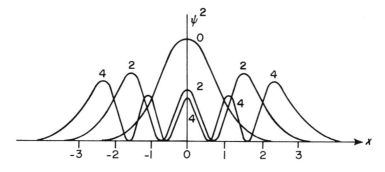

Fig. 3.6.2   The squares of the harmonic oscillator wave functions.

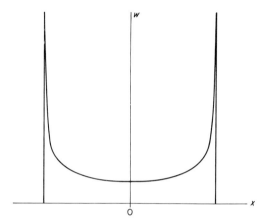

Fig. 3.6.3 The classical probability distribution corresponding to the quantum mechanical states shown in Fig. 3.6.2.

these were impenetrable. These boundary conditions were responsible for the existence of only certain energy levels, or certain forms of the wave functions. The situation is very reminiscent of the possible standing wave-forms in an organ pipe, or in a given length of cable.

The extension from the linear, or one-dimensional harmonic oscillator, as for example realized in a diatomic molecule or nucleus, to the three-dimensional oscillator is fairly straightforward when separated in Cartesian coordinates. The energy levels in this case are

$$E = (n_1 + n_2 + n_3 + \tfrac{3}{2})h\nu_0 = (N + \tfrac{3}{2})h\nu_0 \qquad (3.6.12)$$

where $N = n_1 + n_2 + n_3$, the n's representing the vibrational quantum numbers in the three coordinate directions. N evidently can assume the values

$$N = 0, 1, 2, 3, \ldots$$

Degeneracy of energy levels, which we observed in the case of the particle in a box, also happens here. This means that the same N, and therefore the same energy E, can be arrived at by different combinations of n.

It should also be pointed out that although the energy of the quantum mechanical oscillator can assume the values $(N + \tfrac{3}{2})h\nu_0$, its frequency ν_0 remains constant, just as for the classical harmonic oscillator. However, the frequency plays a lesser role, in that it cannot be observed directly. Only when the quantum-mechanical oscillator loses or gains energy, that is, when it undergoes a transition from one state to another, does it emit or absorb a quantum of frequency ν_0 which is observable. Consequently, only

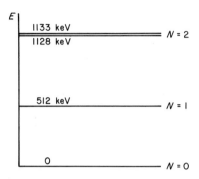

Fig. 3.6.4   Energy levels in $^{106}_{46}$Pd.

transitions between neighboring states should occur. Other transitions are relatively rare. They often may be explained by the fact that the oscillator is not perfectly harmonic.

Figure 3.6.4 shows the lowest energy levels of a nucleus, $^{106}_{46}$Pd, which clearly displays vibrational character. The zero-point energy is omitted in the diagram. The $N = 2$ level which should be degenerate in a harmonic oscillator is slightly split; furthermore, the energies of these two states are somewhat more than double the energy of the $N = 1$ state. This indicates that this nucleus is more complex than an ideal harmonic oscillator.

Quantum theory had its origin in 1900 with the postulation of quantized oscillators in the walls of the cavity to explain black-body radiation. However, it took a quarter of a century to understand the quantum-mechanical oscillator.

3.7   THE ROTATOR

A diatomic molecule may be imagined as a dumbbell. The two atoms can oscillate with respect to each other, a case we have just treated. However, they can also rotate around each other. The mathematical treatment of the general case of a free rotation in three-dimensional space shown in Fig. 3.7.1 (a) is quite a bit more complicated than the rotation in a plane, around a rigid axis, as shown in Fig. 3.7.1 (b). In the latter case we need only the circular functions, sine and cosine, which depend on one angle, ϕ. We shall treat only the simpler situation of rotation in a plane and state at the end the slightly different result for the general case.

We start again with the Schrödinger equation

$$\nabla^2 \psi + \frac{8\pi^2 m}{h^2} (E - V)\psi = 0.$$

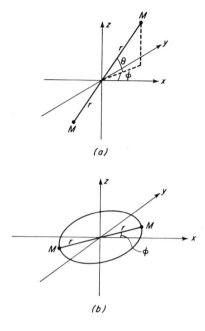

Fig. 3.7.1   The rotator; (a) free rotation, (b) rotation in a plane.

Since there is no potential energy involved, $V = 0$. The geometry of the problem suggests choosing polar coordinates for the motion in the x–y plane by introducing the angle ϕ. Because we limit ourselves to motion in a plane, z is always zero. The rotator is rigid, and therefore r is constant. However, instead of continuing with the three-dimensional Schrödinger equation we can make use of the fact that in many problems of mechanics the equations for one-dimensional, linear motion transform into those for rotational motion if x is replaced by ϕ and m by the moment of inertia I. The latter in our case is $2Mr^2$, or if we call the sum of both masses m, mr^2.[21] We therefore perform those substitutions in the one-dimensional Schrö-

[21] Problems involving two masses without external constraints are often easier solved by use of the concept of the reduced mass μ, whereby $1/\mu = 1/M_1 + 1/M_2$. One then assumes that one body is fixed in space. The other body, assumed to have the reduced mass μ, is rotating around the fixed body at a distance a, the separation distance between the two, instead of the two bodies rotating about their center of mass. The moment of inertia, calculated this way for two equal masses, has the same magnitude as computed in the conventional way: $I = \mu a^2 = (M/2)(2r)^2 = 2Mr^2 = mr^2$. Likewise the kinetic energy, angular momentum, and so on, can be calculated using the reduced mass. We can therefore redefine our quantities m and r by saying that m represents the reduced mass and r the distance between the mass points.

dinger equation. Obviously this procedure does not constitute a derivation of the Schrödinger equation in polar coordinates, but is only a plausibility argument, justifiable by the fact that it yields the correct result. We therefore obtain the Schrödinger equation in polar coordinates:

$$\frac{d^2\psi}{d\phi^2} + \frac{8\pi^2 I}{h^2} E\psi = 0.$$

The solutions are

$$\cos \sqrt{\frac{8\pi^2 E I}{h^2}} \phi \quad \text{and} \quad \sin \sqrt{\frac{8\pi^2 E I}{h^2}} \phi$$

(and also their linear combinations). Just as in the cases of the particle in a box or the harmonic oscillator, we must satisfy certain conditions in order to have a physically meaningful solution. Here, we must require that ψ has the same value after each full rotation, that is

$$\psi(\phi + 2\pi) = \psi(\phi).$$

This can only be achieved, if $\sqrt{8\pi^2 E I/h^2}$ is an integer. In this case not only $\cos(\phi + 2\pi) = \cos \phi$, but also $\cos n(\phi + 2\pi) = \cos n\phi$. We therefore arrive at the quantum condition

$$\frac{8\pi^2 E I}{h^2} = n^2$$

or

$$E_n = \frac{h^2}{8\pi^2 I} n^2 \qquad n = 0, 1, 2, 3, \ldots. \qquad (3.7.1)$$

This is the expression for the possible energy values of the rotator in a plane. The energy eigenvalues of a rigid rotator with a free axis, for example, a mass point moving on the surface of a sphere or two mass points which are rigidly connected, are slightly different. These values are

$$E_l = \frac{h^2}{8\pi^2 I} l(l + 1); \qquad (3.7.2)$$

l is called the rotational quantum number. Since $l(l + 1)$ for $l = 0, 1, 2, 3, 4, \ldots$ has the values $0, 2, 6, 12, 20, \ldots$, the energy levels are not equally spaced. Writing the energy interval between the states $l = 0$ and $l = 1$ as E_1, the other levels are at $E_2 = 3E_1$, $E_3 = 6E_1$, $E_4 = 10E_1$, $\ldots$, as shown in Fig. 3.7.2.

We required above that the wave function for the rigid rotator after a

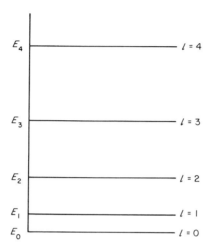

Fig. 3.7.2 Level diagram of a three-dimensional rotator.

full rotation should be the same as before. However, if the two masses of the rotator in our example are completely identical, this condition must be modified because a rotation by 180° will bring the rotator into a position which cannot be distinguished from the original one. Therefore also, the wave function must be the same. This has the effect, as can easily be shown, that the states with $n = 1, 3, 5, \ldots$ do no longer correspond to a solution of the Schrödinger equation. These considerations are also valid for the free rotator. One finds indeed that an H_2 molecule has rotational levels only for $l = 0, 2, 4, 6, \ldots$, whereas an HCl molecule has $l = 0, 1, 2, 3, \ldots$ rotational levels. This reduction of the number of levels, which is a consequence of the symmetry of the system, can also be found in the rotational states of symmetrically rotating spheroidal nuclei. Such an example is given in Fig. 3.7.3 with the rotational spectrum of ^{180}Hf.

It is also instructive to consider the angular momentum of the rotator. In the classical case it is $L = I\omega$, whereas the kinetic energy is $E = \frac{1}{2}I\omega^2 = L^2/2I$. The angular momentum is therefore $L = (2IE)^{1/2}$. This relationship is the same for the quantum-mechanical rigid rotator; hence, from Eq. 3.7.1 follows

$$L = n\frac{h}{2\pi} = n\hbar, \qquad (3.7.3)$$

and for the free rotator

$$L = \hbar\sqrt{l(l+1)}. \qquad (3.7.4)$$

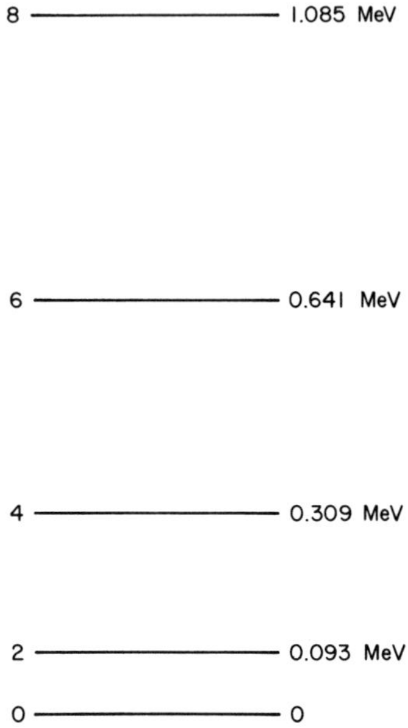

8 ——————————— 1.085 MeV

6 ——————————— 0.641 MeV

4 ——————————— 0.309 MeV

2 ——————————— 0.093 MeV
0 ——————— 0

Fig. 3.7.3   Rotational levels of the ^{180}Hf nucleus. Indicated on the left is the angular-momentum quantum number, on the right the energy.

We may surmise from the simplicity of these formulas that the angular momentum is primarily the physical quantity which is quantized, and the quantization of the energy is merely its consequence.

3.8   COMMENTS

Before closing this chapter it may be well to review our very elementary approach to wave mechanics, and the results achieved. The ingredients have been

1. The nonrelativistic statements of Newtonian mechanics,

$$E_{kin} = \tfrac{1}{2}mv^2, \quad \text{and} \quad p = mv.$$

2. The de Broglie wavelength $\lambda = h/p$.
3. The assumption of the standard wave equation which has the form

$$\nabla^2 Y(x, y, z, t) = \frac{1}{w^2} \frac{\partial^2 Y(x, y, z, t)}{\partial t^2}$$

and which with the assumption that the time can be separated from the space coordinates

$$Y(x, y, z, t) = \psi(x, y, z)e^{i\omega t}$$

reduces to the time-independent Schrödinger equation, 3.3.6

$$\nabla^2\psi + \frac{2m}{\hbar^2}(E - V)\psi = 0.$$

4. The assumption that if the wave function is normalized, or has its amplitude suitably adjusted so that

$$\int_{-\infty}^{\infty} \psi\psi^* dv = 1$$

then $\psi\psi^*$ is the probability density, or that $\psi\psi^* dv$ is the probability of finding the particle represented in dv. For a confined particle, $\psi \to 0$ far from the region of confinement.

The physics of atoms, nuclei, and solids requires a far deeper and more subtle foundation than this, as well as a mathematical treatment going beyond the elementary level adopted in this book. It is true that we have been able to calculate wave functions and energy levels for simple one-particle mechanical systems defined by suitable potential energy functions. But they have been specially selected because of their simplicity. The next chapter is devoted to atoms, of which the simplest is the one-electron hydrogen atom held to its nucleus by Coulomb attraction. Even this we shall be able to treat in only a very superficial way, partly because of our limitation to the solution of the Schrödinger equation in rectangular coordinates. For particles with rotational motion in which angular momentum is most important, the use of angular coordinates, r, θ, ϕ, is essential. We shall clearly have to gloss over many points in order to say anything at all about real physical structures. It is the purpose of the following discussion to mention other concepts than those outlined in the previous sections, so that the reader may have some inkling of the supporting structures that hold up the small corner of material science under consideration here. An understanding of these matters requires a deeper study than we can undertake. We shall simply state a few accepted assumptions relevant to our discussion, and the results that flow from them without attempting derivations or justifications. Reference to other texts is required to bridge the gaps left here.

The Time-Dependent Schrödinger Equation

Earlier in this chapter we saw that the time-independent Schrödinger equation is a powerful means for determining the energies of the stationary states of a system.

However, many interesting problems in physics involve nonstationary situations. An example is the calculation of the rates of transition from one state of a system to another. In such cases, the time-independent Schrödinger equation is of no use, and we require a wave equation containing the time as a variable.

About half a year after he had published the time-independent equation, Schrödinger advanced his time-dependent wave equation.

Let us consider a wave described by a wave function

$$\Psi(x, t) = A e^{i(kx - \omega t)} \tag{3.8.1}$$

where $\omega = 2\pi\nu = (1/\hbar)E$, and $k = 2\pi/\lambda = p/\hbar$. $\tag{3.8.2}$

Our goal is now to find a differential equation for which the above function 3.8.1 is a solution. Differentiation of Eq. 3.8.1 with respect to x yields

$$\frac{\partial \Psi}{\partial x} = ik\Psi = i\frac{p}{\hbar}\Psi.$$

Hence,

$$p\Psi(x, t) = \frac{\hbar}{i}\frac{\partial}{\partial x}[\Psi(x, t)]. \tag{3.8.3}$$

This relation leads us to the concept of mathematical *operators*, which play an important role in quantum mechanics. Such an operator A_{op} turns a function $f(x)$ into another function $u(x)$. In general this operation is written symbolically as a product of A_{op} and f, therefore

$$A_{op}f = u.$$

For example, one operator is the square root sign, $A_{op} = \sqrt{}$ When applied to f, this operator prescribes taking the square root of f, to get u. The differential operator d/dx to the left of $f(x)$ is the prescription to differentiate f with respect to x. In the same way we can interpret $(\hbar/i)(\partial/\partial x)$ in Eq. 3.8.3 as an operator operating on $\Psi(x, t)$. On the left-hand side of this equation, p may be regarded as an operator operating on $\Psi(x, t)$, too. Hence,

$$p_x = \frac{\hbar}{i}\frac{\partial}{\partial x} \tag{3.8.4}$$

and similarly for the y and z coordinates. We may alternatively say that the differential operator associated with p_x, the x component of momentum, is $(\hbar/i)(\partial/\partial x)$. Thus we have arrived at the plausible prescription that we may substitute this differential operator for p in a quantum mechanical equation.

The operator for the energy can be found in a similar manner from Eq. 3.8.1:

$$\frac{\partial \Psi}{\partial t} = -i\omega\Psi = i\frac{E}{\hbar}\Psi$$

which yields

$$E\Psi(x, t) = -\frac{\hbar}{i}\frac{\partial}{\partial t}[\Psi(x, t)].$$

Hence the operator for the energy is

$$E = -\frac{\hbar}{i}\frac{\partial}{\partial t}. \tag{3.8.5}$$

These two operators for p_x and E enable us to set up the time-dependent Schrödinger equation, by replacing E and p in the expression for the total energy,

$$E = \frac{p^2}{2m} + V(x, y, z, t), \tag{3.8.6}$$

by their corresponding operators. The operator p^2 is obtained by allowing the operator for p to operate a second time, hence

$$p_x{}^2 = \frac{\hbar}{i}\frac{\partial}{\partial x}\cdot\frac{\hbar}{i}\frac{\partial}{\partial x} = -\hbar^2\frac{\partial^2}{\partial x^2}.$$

Similar expressions hold for the y and z components.

After the substitution we let these operators and also V (which we may also consider as an operator), operate on Ψ on both sides of the equation to obtain the *time-dependent Schrödinger wave equation*

$$\frac{\hbar}{i}\frac{\partial\Psi}{\partial t} - \frac{\hbar^2}{2m}\nabla^2\Psi + V(x, y, z, t)\Psi = 0. \tag{3.8.7}$$

For a free particle not subject to a potential V this equation reduces to

$$\frac{\hbar}{i}\frac{\partial\Psi}{\partial t} - \frac{\hbar^2}{2m}\nabla^2\Psi = 0. \tag{3.8.8}$$

It is easy to show that this is the required wave equation. For the sake of simplicity we limit our discussion to one dimension. Starting with the wave function for a free particle wave

$$\Psi(x, t) = Ae^{i(kx-\omega t)}, \tag{3.8.9}$$

we take the second derivative with respect to the x coordinate, $-k^2\Psi$, and the first derivative with respect to the time, $-i\omega\Psi$. By substituting these derivatives into Eq. 3.8.8 we readily verify that this is indeed a wave equation for which Eq. 3.8.9 is a solution.

If the potential V in Eq. 3.8.7 is only a function of the space coordinates, thus independent of the time, we should expect that the time-dependent Schrödinger equation reduces to the time-independent equation.

In such cases the time-dependent function $\Psi(x, t)$—we again limit ourselves to the x coordinate—can be expressed as a product of the time-independent function $\psi(x)$ and a time-dependent function $\varphi(t)$. It is then mathematically possible to separate the partial-differential equation 3.8.7 into two ordinary differential equations

$$\frac{d\varphi(t)}{dt} + \frac{i}{\hbar}E\varphi(t) = 0$$

with the solution $e^{-i(E/\hbar)t}$, and

$$\frac{d^2\psi(x)}{dx^2} + \frac{2m}{\hbar^2}[E - V(x)]\psi(x) = 0$$

with a solution for $\psi(x)$, as we know it from earlier discussions of the time-independent Schrödinger equation. The complete solution is then

$$\Psi(x, t) = \psi(x)e - i(E/\hbar)t.$$

Inserting the appropriate derivatives into Eq. 3.8.7 will give proof that this is indeed a solution of the time-dependent Schrödinger equation.

Although we may now have convinced ourselves that the time-dependent Schrödinger equation is indeed a wave equation, it may be somewhat surprising to the reader that it does not have much formal similarity with the wave equation of electromagnetic waves or elastic waves, for example, waves on a stretched string. These equations are of the type

$$\frac{1}{w^2}\frac{\partial^2 Y}{\partial t^2} - \nabla^2 Y = 0$$

where w is the phase velocity. In electromagnetic waves in vacuum and in elastic waves on a string this velocity was tacitly assumed to be identical with the group velocity. In electromagnetic waves, energy and momentum of a photon are proportional. In matter waves, due to the rest-mass energy of the particles, this relationship is no longer linear. Matter waves have to satisfy the de Broglie conditions, hence dispersion plays a principal part in the propagation of these waves. For this reason a wave equation of the above form is not suitable. We do not want to investigate this point further, other than to mention that under such conditions, a wave equation can be set up only with a wave function Ψ which is complex, that is, having a real and an imaginary part.

The first one to feel uneasy about this state of affairs was Schrödinger himself, who wrote in the closing paragraph of the paper containing the time-dependent equation:

> "Without doubt, a certain harshness still remains at the present time by using a *complex* wave function. If it should turn out that this is fundamentally inevitable and not merely a computational tool, this would mean that fundamentally there exist *two* wave functions which only *together* yield the information about the state of the system. This not so pleasant conclusion permits, in my opinion, the much more pleasant interpretation, that the state of a system is given by a real function . . . ." [22]

Due to the complex character of Ψ, the imaginary quantity $i = \sqrt{-1}$ in the wave equation does not cause a problem.

In classical physics, the complex representation of a wave, $Ae^{i(kx-\omega t)}$, is only a mathematical convenience, and in general either the real or the imaginary part is used. For wave mechanics, on the other hand, both parts are necessary for the description of a Ψ wave. Hence, this complex representation is ideally suited for wave-mechanical problems.

Time-Dependent Wave Functions

We saw earlier that $|\Psi|^2 dv = \Psi\Psi^* \, dv$ is the probability for finding a particle in the volume element dv, and that $\Psi\Psi^*$ represents a probability density. If the particle has a charge q, we can hence define a charge density $q\Psi\Psi^*$.

[22] *Annalen der Physik* **81**, 109 (1926) (in German).

If the time-dependent wave function can be separated into a periodic term having a frequency ν and a time-independent term, we may write the charge density as

$$q\Psi\Psi^* = q\psi_n\exp(i2\pi\nu_nt)\cdot\psi_n^*\exp(-i2\pi\nu_nt) = q\psi_n\psi_n^* \tag{3.8.10}$$

where ψ is the steady-state solution of the time-independent Schrödinger equation, a function of the space coordinates only, and characterized by certain quantum numbers n, and corresponding energy levels $E_n = h\nu_n$. The charge density $q\psi\psi^*$ is stationary and does not fluctuate in time, although ψ itself does. Since radiation results from the acceleration of electric charge, and there is no such acceleration in the steady-state solutions of the Schrödinger equation, it is clear why they are in fact constant.

While the wave function gives us the complete charge distribution in any state n, it is often convenient to use the mean value of some function of the variables, say r, or somewhat more general r^j, which can readily be calculated

$$\langle r_n^j\rangle_{av} = \int_{-\infty}^{\infty} \Psi_n r^j\Psi^*dv = \int_{-\infty}^{\infty} \psi_n r^j\psi_n^*dv \tag{3.8.11}$$

which is a function of the quantum numbers n only, and is independent of the time.

Electromagnetic radiation that is emitted or absorbed in a transition between two states n and m, requires an oscillating electric charge. This is introduced by involving the wave functions Ψ_n and Ψ_m^* of the two states. There will clearly be a time-dependent term in their product.

$$\exp(i2\pi\nu_nt)\exp(-i2\pi\nu_mt) = \exp(i\frac{E_n-E_m}{\hbar}t) = \exp(i2\pi\nu_{nm}t), \tag{3.8.12}$$

where the frequency of the oscillation is the difference frequency of the two wave functions, and is in fact given by the Bohr condition $h\nu_{nm} = E_n - E_m$. By analogy with classical physics we should expect the rate of radiation, or the transition probability between two states, to be dependent on the magnitude of the oscillating electric or magnetic moment. (See Eq. 1.3.1 for instance.) By far the most important of these is the electric dipole moment ex due to an oscillating charge e where the dipole is pointing along the x axis. This, for example, we can calculate

$$\langle(ex)_{nm}\rangle_{av} = \int_{-\infty}^{\infty} \psi_n(ex)\psi_m\,dv. \tag{3.8.13}$$

If this expression turns out to be zero, the transition is called forbidden. The analysis of allowed and forbidden transitions leads to *selection rules*, which govern the selection of those transitions that lead to observed spectral lines.

The Dirac Equation

Since the Schrödinger equations are nonrelativistic, it was obvious for theoretical physicists to seek for ways to obtain a relativistically invariant wave equation for the electron. Dirac[23] was particularly successful in this

---

[23] Paul A. M. Dirac (1902–   ), English theoretical physicist. Professor at the University of Cambridge, now at Florida State University. Nobel prize 1933 for the relativistic theory of the electron.

Paul A. M. Dirac (born 1902) (Courtesy of Niels Bohr Library, American Institute of Physics).

endeavor. In 1928 he published a paper containing the famous Dirac equation for the electron. A few years before, the spin of the electron had been discovered. This spin corresponds, in macroscopic physics, to the angular momentum of a sphere revolving about its own axis. In Dirac's theory, the spin enters automatically. The electron spin will be discussed further in Chapter 4.

The actual Dirac equation need not concern us here; we shall consider only the results of its formulation. Besides the explanation of the electron spin, another of Dirac's results is the expression for the total energy of a free electron which is formally equivalent to that given in Appendix II

$$E^2 = p^2c^2 + m_0^2c^4$$

$$E = \pm (p^2c^2 + m_0^2c^4)^{1/2}.$$

In classical relativistic mechanics, the negative values of the energy are discarded as physically meaningless. On the basis of his quantum-mechanical treatment, Dirac proposed retaining them. This leads to Dirac's positron theory, which we have already discussed in Chapter 2.

Matrix Mechanics

It should be pointed out in closing this discussion of wave mechanics that an entirely different approach to the quantum theory of matter is possible. In this book, waves, unobservable ψ waves, and their associated de Broglie wavelengths are taken as fundamental. From the equations governing their behavior the observable properties of matter are derived.

In 1925 Born and Heisenberg set up a completely different, but as it turned out, a completely equivalent formalism. The unobservable ψ functions are dispensed with. The theory deals exclusively with arrays of observable numbers, called matrices, for example, the frequencies radiated or absorbed by an atom in making transitions from a state n to a state m.

$$
\begin{array}{ccccccc}
\nu_{11} & \nu_{12} & \nu_{13} & \cdot & \cdot & \cdot \\[2ex]
\nu_{21} & \nu_{22} & \nu_{23} & \cdot & \cdot & \cdot \\[2ex]
\nu_{31} & \nu_{32} & \nu_{33} & \cdot & \cdot & \cdot \\[2ex]
\cdot & \cdot & \cdot & \cdot & \cdot & \cdot \\[2ex]
\cdot & \cdot & \cdot & \cdot & \cdot & \cdot
\end{array}
$$

In addition, matrix operators are introduced, specifying how to manipulate matrices in order to produce conclusions from initial postulates. In this way an equation corresponding to the Schrödinger equation may be set up, but instead of differential operators we have now matrix operators, and instead of the wave function we have a matrix.

While the mathematical procedures involved in matrix algebra are completely different from those involved in the solution of differential equations, the final results may be shown to be necessarily equivalent. The choice of which to use is entirely one of convenience.

PROBLEMS

1. An electron beam of 10-keV electrons has a beam current of 0.1 μA and a cross section of 10 mm^2. (*a*) What is the velocity of the electrons? (*b*) How many electrons are passing by at a given point? (*c*) What is the number of electrons/m^3, or number density of electrons? (*d*) How small must one choose a volume in the beam that the probability to have one electron in this volume at any instant is approximately 0.5?

2. Electrons are emitted with constant speed v and isotropically from a point source at a rate of n electrons/second. (a) How will, for an individual electron, $|\Psi|^2$ vary with the distance from the source? Lump all necessary constants into one constant C. (b) Calculate the number of electrons located at any instant in a spherical shell of thickness dr and radius r.

3. A parallel beam of electrons travels from left to right. At the left the electrons have a velocity v_1, at the right $v_2 < v_1$. (In the transition region the velocity changes gradually so that none of the electrons are reflected back.) (a) What is the ratio of the number densities of electrons, $n_1 : n_2$, for the two regions? (b) What is, for an individual electron, the ratio of the quantities $|\Psi|^2$ for these regions?

4. The phase velocity of water waves of relatively long wavelength on the surface of deep water, so-called gravity waves, is given by $w = [(g\lambda)/(2\pi)]^{1/2}$, as dimensional analysis makes plausible. What is the group velocity of such waves? Compare your result with Fig. 3.1.7.

5. The phase velocity w of water waves due to surface tension T and to gravity is given by

$$w = \sqrt{\frac{g\lambda}{2\pi} + \frac{T}{\rho}\frac{2\pi}{\lambda}}$$

where ρ is the density of water, 10^3 kg/m^3. (a) Show that the phase velocity has a minimum. With $T = 0.72$ newton/m for water, calculate w_{minimum} and calculate the corresponding wavelength, λ_{minimum}. (b) What is the corresponding group velocity u? (c) For $\lambda < \lambda_{\text{minimum}}$, is w greater or smaller than u? For $\lambda > \lambda_{\text{minimum}}$?

6. Using the data on the index of refraction for dense flint glass between 3000 and 4000 Å (Fig. 2.1.8), calculate the phase and group velocity for light which in vacuum has a wavelength $\lambda = 3500$ Å.

7. (a) What are group and phase velocities of the de Broglie wave of a a 10-eV electron? (b) Compute the product $v \cdot w$.

8. Light waves may be considered as matter waves of particles of zero rest mass, the photons. Show that these waves have no dispersion in vacuum.

9. Express the phase velocity of matter waves in terms of the particle ($=$ group) velocity u and the velocity of light c.

10. An electron travels across a potential step. Although the potential energy and the kinetic energy of the electron change, the total energy remains constant. (a) Does the wavelength of the electron change? (b) Does the frequency of the matter wave which is associated with the electron change?

11. Taking one of the wave packets of Fig. 3.1.6 (c) as an example, plot the function $|\Psi|^2$ for such a wave packet.

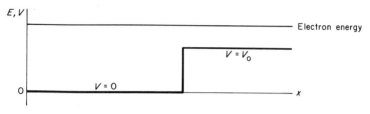

Figure P.3.1 (Problem 10)

12. If the abscissa in Fig. 3.1.6 is considered a time axis, relate the time interval between wave packets to the frequency spectrum (d). Do the same with the time interval between adjacent maxima within a wave packet.

13. Nuclei have diameters in the neighborhood of 10^{-14} m. Invoking the uncertainty relation, what would have to be the momentum and kinetic energy of the electrons inside such nuclei if, as one had seriously considered before the discovery of the neutron, they were constituents of nuclei, together with the protons?

14. Deduce for a free particle the uncertainty relation $\Delta E \Delta t \geq h$ from the relation $\Delta p \Delta x \geq h$.

15. Consider the ground state of a nucleus, 0, an excited state, 1, of energy E_1, and a second, higher excited state, 2, with energy E_2. State 2 has a lifetime of the order of 10^{-12} sec, whereas state 1 has one of the order of 10^{-15} sec. The ground state is stable. Assume that state 2 is fed by the decay of some higher-lying levels. Transitions by emission of quanta are possible from 2 to 0 directly and also via state 1.

Draw a level diagram and calculate the approximate widths of the levels and the approximate widths of the spectral distributions of the quanta emitted in the transitions $2 \to 0$, $2 \to 1$, and $1 \to 0$.

16. Verify that the recoil energy of a nucleus of mass M due to the emission of a γ quantum is $E_{\text{recoil}} = E_\gamma^2/(2Mc^2)$.

17. How short should the lifetime of a state of 0.5 MeV excitation energy in a nucleus of mass number A $=$ 200 (lead region) be, so that there is a reasonable probability for resonance fluorescence? Consider the emitting and the absorbing nucleus free to recoil.

18. A 60-hertz voltage is applied to the vertical deflector plates of an oscilloscope for 0.1 sec. The horizontal plates are connected to a linear sweep having a repetition rate of five sweeps per second. Make a sketch of what a photograph of the resulting trace would look like. Assuming that you can measure the location of a peak to approximately ±0.1 of the distance between peaks, what is the fractional uncertainty in your measurement of the applied frequency? What is the magnitude of the uncertainty $\Delta \nu$ of your determination of ν? If the frequency ν had been applied for 10

sec and a moving picture of the trace had been provided for detailed examination, what then would have been the uncertainty in the measurement of ν?

19. What is the complete normalized wave function for the particle moving in a tube of length L discussed in Section 3.2?

20. Modify Fig. 3.4.5 by removing the sharp kink in ψ at $x = P$ and by drawing accordingly the functions $(d\psi/dx)$ and $(d^2\psi/dx^2)$.

21. A particle of mass m is confined to a tube of length L. (a) What is the uncertainty in position, Δx? (b) Express the energy of the particle in its ground state in terms of its momentum. (c) Considering that momentum is a vector quantity, what is the uncertainty in momentum, Δp? (d) Find the product $(\Delta p) \cdot (\Delta x)$ using the results from parts (a) and (c). Compare this with the order of magnitude given by the Heisenberg principle. (e) Does the answer to part (d) depend on the mass m or dimension L?

22. A particle of mass m in a one-dimensional box extending from $-L/2$ to $+L/2$ is in its ground state. Find the average values of x, x^2, and p. (Such average values, usually called expectation values, play a considerable role in quantum mechanics.)

23. A particle is in a long narrow tube. What is the probability for it to be in the region between the end of the tube and one-quarter down? (a) Assume that the particle is in its ground state. (b) In its first-excited state [Fig. 3.2.1 (b)]. (c) In its second-excited state [Fig. 3.2.1 (c)]. (d) In its third-excited state [Fig. 3.2.1 (d)].

24. Find the solutions of Schrödinger's equation for a particle in a cubical box having an edge length L if the box has its center at the origin of coordinates.

25. What are the lowest three energy levels for a particle of mass m in an impenetrable cubical box whose side is L for the following cases: (a) A neutron for $L = 10^{-13}$ cm. (b) A neutron for $L = 10^{-12}$ cm. (c) An electron for $L = 10^{-12}$ cm. (d) An electron for $L = 10^{-8}$ cm. (e) An electron for $L = 10^{-2}$ cm.
Give your answers in electron volts.

26. Compare the variation of the spacing of adjacent energy levels in a three-dimensional box and a long narrow tube like the one discussed in Section 3.2, sometimes also called a one-dimensional "box," and a two-dimensional box.

27. Solve the problem of a particle in a rectangular box whose sides have the different lengths L_x, L_y, L_z. What are the degeneracies of the lowest six energy levels if $L_x = L_0$, $L_y = 2L_0$, and $L_z = 3L_0$?

28. (a) A particle of mass m is confined in a cubical box of length L whose sides are perpendicular to the axes of a rectangular coordinate system. Make a table of λ_x, λ_y, and λ_z, the wavelengths associated with the

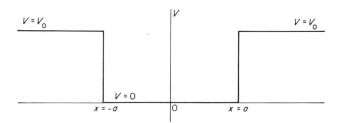

Figure P.3.2 (Problem 29)

motion of the particle in the x, y, and z directions, for the four different stationary states of motion having the least energy. (b) Show how, starting from the experimentally established relation between wavelength and momentum, $\lambda = h/mv$, the energy of the four states in part (a) may be computed, and compute the above energies in electron volts for a particle of mass $m = 9.1 \times 10^{-31}$ kg in a box for which $L = 2 \times 10^{-10}$ m.

29. A particle of mass m is confined to a square potential energy well illustrated in the figure. Its total energy E is therefore less than V_0. Find solutions of the wave equation which are continuous, and have continuous derivatives, at the boundaries $x = a$ and $x = -a$ for the following values of the depth of the well:

$$V_0 = \frac{h^2}{8\pi^2 ma^2}, \quad 4\,\frac{h^2}{8\pi^2 ma^2}, \quad \text{and} \quad 12\,\frac{h^2}{8\pi^2 ma^2}.$$

The solutions for the three regions of space are, for $-a < x < a$,

$$\psi(x) = A \sin \alpha x + B \cos \alpha x \quad \text{where } \alpha = \sqrt{\frac{8\pi^2 mE}{h^2}}$$

for $x > a$,

$$\psi(x) = Ce^{-\beta x}$$

and for $x < -a$,

$$\psi(x) = De^{\beta x} \quad \text{where } \beta = \sqrt{\frac{8\pi^3 m(V_0 - E)}{h^2}}$$

A, B, C, and D are arbitrary constants. Solutions will be found to be of two kinds:

$$A = 0, C = D, \text{ and then } \alpha \tan \alpha a = \beta \tag{1}$$

$$B = 0, C = -D, \text{ and then } \alpha \cot \alpha a = -\beta. \tag{2}$$

Numerical values are best found graphically. L. I. Schiff [*Quantum*

Mechanics, 3rd ed., McGraw-Hill, 1968, p. 41] suggests changing variables to $\xi = \alpha a$, $\eta = \beta a$, and plotting ξ as a function of η in accordance with Eqs. 1 and 2 above, and finding the intersections of these curves with

$$\xi^2 + \eta^2 = \frac{8\pi^2 m V_0 a^2}{h^2}$$

which satisfy the definitions of α and β above.

30. Given a one-dimensional potential of the form

$$V = +\infty \qquad \text{in the range} \quad -\infty < x < 0$$

$$V = V_0 > 0 \qquad \text{in the range} \quad 0 < x < a$$

$$V = V_0 + (x - a)(V_0/a) \quad \text{in the range} \quad a < x$$

(a) Sketch the wave functions for the ground state and the first excited state for a particle of mass m which moves in this potential. (b) Write the Schröd'nger equations for the different regions of this potential.

31. In the one-dimensional potential drawn in the figure a few levels are indicated. They are neither the lowest ones nor do they follow each other directly. Draw a reasonable wave function for each level.

32. Prove that for normally incident light at the plane surface between the two dielectrics the intensity of the incident beams is just equal to the sum of the intensities of the reflected and transmitted beams.

33. A beam of protons with a kinetic energy of 10 eV approaches a potential step of +9 eV. What is the percentage of the reflected and transmitted protons?

34. Show that Eq. 3.5.7 is equivalent to Eq. 3.5.6.

35. How well does Eq. 3.5.6 agree with the curve of Fig. 3.5.2?

36. With regard to Fig. 3.5.6, since there is indeed some leakage, can you guess how the ψ function might look to the left, within, and to the right of the barrier?

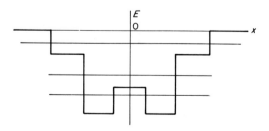

Figure P.3.3 (Problem 31)

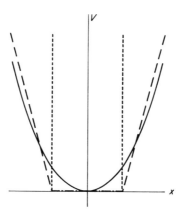

Figure P.3.4 (Problem 38)

37. Calculate the reflection and transmission coefficients for a square well as pictured in Fig. 3.5.3.

38. Draw qualitatively the four lowest energy levels for a particle for the three one-dimensional potentials in the figure which all are drawn to the same scale.

39. Sketch the squares of the harmonic oscillator wave functions for $n = 1, 3, 5$.

40. Sketch ψ^2 of the harmonic oscillator for $n = 20$.

41. What is the approximate oscillator quantum number of a mass of 1 gram oscillating with a frequency of 100 hertz and an amplitude of 1 mm?

42. Discuss the zero-point energy in the harmonic oscillator from the standpoint of the Heisenberg uncertainty relation.

43. Find the degrees of degeneracy of the first four energy levels of a three-dimensional harmonic oscillator.

44. When is Eq. 3.6.4 a good approximation?

45. The wave functions for the one-dimensional harmonic oscillator as given in Section 3.6 are not normalized. In order to normalize the one of the ground state, determine the value of the constant A for the ground-state wave function $\psi = Ae^{-(\alpha/2)x^2}$.

46. Show that $\psi_0 = e^{-(\alpha/2)x^2}H_0$ is a solution of the Schrödinger equation for the harmonic oscillator. Do the same for $\psi_2 = e^{-(\alpha/2)x^2}H_2$.

47. A particle of mass m, which can move along the x axis only, is attracted to the origin by a force such that the potential energy of the particle is $V = \frac{1}{2}kx^2$. If the motion of the particle is calculated according to Newton's laws, one finds that the particle is subject to a force $F = -kx$, and that it performs simple harmonic oscillations about the origin. (a) If the

total energy of the particle is E, what is the maximum possible distance X_0 of the particle from the origin?

If the motion of the above particle is calculated by use of Schrödinger's equation

$$\frac{d^2\psi}{dx^2} + \frac{8\pi^2 m}{h^2} (E - V)\psi = 0, \tag{1}$$

its wave function in the ground state is

$$\psi = Ae^{-(x/\alpha_0)^2}. \tag{2}$$

(b) For what value of α_0 is Eq. 2 a solution of Eq. 1?

(c) What is the value of the normalizing constant A?

(d) What is the energy E of the particle when it is in the state shown in Eq. 2?

According to Eq. 2, the wave function approaches zero rapidly when x/α_0 is greater than 1, and α_0 therefore plays a part in wave mechanics comparable to X_0 in classical Newtonian mechanics.

(e) Express both X_0 and a_0 as functions of E and k only, and show that the ratio $X_0/\alpha_0 = 1/(2)^{1/2}$.

48. Consider the potential given in the figure (which is in essence just one side of a harmonic oscillator potential). What are the energies of the possible levels? No calculation is necessary. Think about the boundary conditions of the wave functions.

49. Compare the level spacing in the one-dimensional square well with that of a rigid rotator. Discuss the zero-point energy.

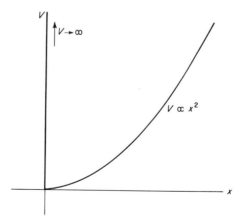

Figure P.3.5 (Problem 48)

50. Besides the Heisenberg uncertainty relations for energy and momentum there is one for rotational motion. What might it be?

51. In some rotating systems (e.g., diatomic molecules or nuclei) there is a tendency that the system stretches under the influence of the centrifugal forces. What consequences does this have with respect to the spacing of the energy levels?

52. A spherical dust particle of 2×10^{-3} mm diameter and a density of 2 g/cm^3 rotates about its axis with a period of 10 seconds. What is the approximate quantum number of this rotational state?

Chapter 4

Atoms and Molecules

4.1 THE HYDROGEN ATOM AND ITS RADIATIONS

Just as classical Newtonian mechanics provides us with rules for handling macroscopic mechanical problems, so quantum or wave mechanics provides us with rules for handling submicroscopic mechanical problems. Let us once more briefly review the formulation of classical mechanics. This will clarify the modifications that are required when we proceed to a system for describing invisible atomic particles, in particular, the electron and its motion around the hydrogen nucleus.

Classical mechanics is summarized in Newton's "laws of motion." These laws have certain consequences that are generally applicable and that may be very simply expressed. Such consequences are often called principles and may be thought of as underlying the more complex formulation of the laws themselves. These principles in turn could be used as the foundation for the laws. The example of classical mechanics may make this clear: In mechanics we can start out from Newton's laws of motion and derive from them the principles of conservation of momentum, angular momentum, and energy. But we just as well may start with the conservation principles and derive Newton's laws from them. Indeed, the conservation principles survived the impact of the theory of relativity no doubt much better than Newtonian mechanics!

Newton's laws of motion are used as follows: given certain material objects having prescribed properties, such as shape, density, or elasticity, with given initial positions and velocities, and subjected to given forces, one can compute their motion. This motion is observable, and the interest and importance of the procedure are that it relates observable quantities, namely the initial conditions and the subsequent motion. Important aspects of Newton's laws of motion are the principles of conservation of energy and momentum.

What may we expect of atomic mechanics? Fundamentally, to be useful, it must provide us with relationships between observable quantities, but these cannot be "laws of motion" in the Newtonian sense, since these motions are not observable.

To begin with, just as Newtonian mechanics deals with the interaction of objects that are postulated, so quantum mechanics deals with the interaction of particles whose attributes must be postulated. In atomic theory these particles are electrons and nuclei, characterized in our previous discussions by mass and charge. We shall see that they have other important attributes.

If the energy and momentum of atomic systems are observable, then we should certainly expect the laws of conservation of energy and momentum to hold, but further details about atomic structure must involve a new analysis of the motion of charged particles. This motion must somehow be described in terms of wave functions derived from Schrödinger's equation. An atom will be capable of existing in a series of "states." Each such state will be characterized by a wave function. From the wave functions we may expect to calculate the properties of the atom in this state. Particularly, we should be able to compute the energy and the angular momentum.

A most important way of observing the properties of atoms in the various states in which they can exist is to analyze the radiations which they emit. Our first problem in atomic theory will be to account for the spectrum of the radiation of hydrogen atoms. Having done this, we shall have produced an example of what we set out to do, namely, to derive or predict observable effects in terms of other observable effects. We shall also discuss qualitatively models and spectra of atoms with more than one electron, and some of the properties of diatomic molecules. The starting point of our theory involves electrostatic forces and the wave properties of the electron. These are based on many observations which we have described in detail. The result of our calculations will be the prediction of the optical and other observable properties of matter.

The simplest atom is that of hydrogen. It consists of a proton and an electron. The quantum mechanical treatment is relatively simple because we have here only one interaction, the electrostatic force, between these two particles. The proton has a large mass compared to the electron. The center of mass of the atom may therefore be considered to a good approximation at the center of the nucleus. If, then, we put the nucleus at the origin of a coordinate system, and the electron at some distance r from the origin, the force F on the electron will be

$$F = \frac{1}{4\pi\epsilon_0} Z \frac{e^2}{r^2} \qquad (4.1.1)$$

where Z is the number of protons in the nucleus, which for hydrogen is 1, and the potential energy V of the system will be

$$V = \frac{-1}{4\pi\epsilon_0} Z \frac{e^2}{r}. \tag{4.1.2}$$

Since the force between proton and electron is attractive, work must be done in separating them. Therefore, if we agree to designate the potential energy for infinite separation as zero, we must have negative potential energies for finite separations.

To this, we must add the fact that the wave function of the electron must satisfy Schrödinger's wave equation, which for a hydrogen atom (with $Z = 1$) with the potential energy function of Eq. 4.1.2 is

$$\nabla^2\psi + \frac{8\pi^2 m}{h^2}\left(E + \frac{1}{4\pi\epsilon_0}\frac{e^2}{r}\right)\psi = 0. \tag{4.1.3}$$

The usual analysis of this equation is beyond the scope of our present discussion. However, the most important results can be discussed in very simple terms. First, we must demand of a solution of Eq. 4.1.3 describing a hydrogen atom that the wave function be significantly different from zero only in the vicinity of the origin, where the attracting proton is located. Wave functions having finite values at remote points must be representations of an ionized hydrogen atom, or a free electron far from the proton. Further, the wave function must be such that the probability of finding the electron in the atom is unity,

$$\int_{\text{atom}} \psi^2 dv = 1 \tag{4.1.4a}$$

where dv represents a volume element.

However, we may also extend the limits of the integral beyond the volume of the atom over all space and have then

$$\int \psi^2 dv = 1. \tag{4.1.4b}$$

We recall that the simplest wave-mechanical solution of a particle contained in a box (Fig. 3.4.6) involved a wave function that had a hump in the middle of the box and tapered off toward the sides. By analogy we might expect something similar for the electron confined by the field of a proton. The corresponding solution in fact is

$$\psi_1 = Ae^{-r/a_0}. \tag{4.1.5}$$

This function has a maximum at the origin and tapers off as the distance r from the proton at the origin increases. The constant A must be chosen so that the integral of Eq. 4.1.4 is satisfied. Its value is therefore

$$A = \frac{1}{\sqrt{\pi a_0^3}}. \tag{4.1.6}$$

Finally, as may be shown by substitution into Eq. 4.1.3, the Schrödinger wave equation is satisfied if

$$a_0 = \frac{\epsilon_0 h^2}{\pi m e^2} \tag{4.1.7}$$

and if the energy E of the system has a particular value, which we call E_1, where

$$E_1 = -\frac{m e^4}{8\epsilon_0^2 h^2}. \tag{4.1.8}$$

The detailed calculation of these quantities is given at the end of this section. The wave function ψ_1, and its square, are plotted at the top left and center of Fig. 4.1.1. The abscissae are in units of the length a_0, and the ordinates give ψ and ψ^2, multiplied by $a_0^{3/2}$, and a_0^3, respectively. If the nucleus has a charge Ze, the factor e^4 in Eq. 4.1.8 has to be replaced by $(Ze)^2 e^2 = Z^2 e^4$.

There are various points of interest about this solution. The first is that the size of the atom is here specified by the constant a_0. The probability of finding the electron in a small volume element at a distance greater than $2a_0$ is quite negligible. The probability density of the electron in this ground state of hydrogen may be represented by a spherically symmetrical cloud tapering off from a maximum density at the proton and falling off to zero rapidly at distances greater than a few times a_0. The magnitude of a_0 may be found by substituting the known constants into Eq. 4.1.7. We find

$$a_0 = 0.528 \times 10^{-10}\,\text{m} = 0.528\,\text{Å} \tag{4.1.9}$$

The size of the hydrogen atom is difficult to determine experimentally, but atoms in general are of this magnitude.

Even more instructive is the representation of the function $4\pi r^2 \psi^2 dr$, which expresses the probability that the electron is somewhere in the spherical shell having a radius r and a thickness dr or, in short, the radial probability density. Since in this case we are not asking *where* in the shell the electron might be, only *that* it is in the shell, the probability is proportional to the volume of the shell, or $4\pi r^2 dr$. The further out we go the greater this volume becomes. This is related to something every rifleman knows,

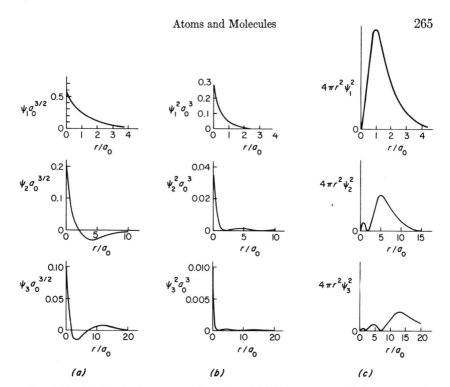

Fig. 4.1.1 (a) The hydrogen wave functions. (b) Their squares, which represent the probability density of the electron. (c) The radial probability densities, of the ground state of the hydrogen atom (top row) and of two excited states with $n = 2$ and $n = 3$ (second and third rows).

that it is easier to hit a ring outside the center than a bull's-eye on a target of concentric evenly spaced rings, although the density of impacts on the target after a great number of shots tends to have its maximum at the center. The function $4\pi r^2 \psi^2 dr$ is plotted at the top on the right-hand side of Fig. 4.1.1. It has a maximum at the distance a_0 from the origin. This distance of the electron from the nucleus therefore has the greatest probability.

Next we come to the energy E_1. If we stipulate that the potential energy of electron and proton, an infinite distance apart, will be called zero, then it follows that the magnitude of E_1 is just the work required to ionize the hydrogen atom from its ground state. In electron volts, we find upon substituting into Eq. 4.1.8

$$E_1 = -13.5 \text{ eV}, \qquad (4.1.10)$$

which is the experimental value for this quantity.

In addition to the solution ψ_1 for the ground state of hydrogen, there are many more. Two other particular solutions which depend only on r, and are therefore spherically symmetrical, are

$$\psi_2 = \frac{1}{4} \frac{1}{\sqrt{2\pi a_0{}^3}} \left(2 - \frac{r}{a_0}\right) e^{-r/2a_0} \tag{4.1.11}$$

$$\psi_3 = \frac{1}{81} \frac{1}{\sqrt{3\pi a_0{}^3}} \left(27 - 18\frac{r}{a_0} + 2\frac{r^2}{a_0{}^2}\right) e^{-r/3a_0}. \tag{4.1.12}$$

These wave functions, their squares, and $4\pi r^2 \psi^2 dr$ are also plotted in Fig. 4.1.1. Like ψ_1 these ψ's have maxima at the origin, but they change sign. They have additional nodes, just as the wave functions for a particle in a box had additional nodes at higher energies. Notice that, in these states of higher energy, the atom is expanded. There are additional maxima of ψ^2 for larger values of r/a_0.

The value which the energy E must have for these states may be found through substituting into Eq. 4.1.3. The values are

$$E_2 = -\frac{1}{4} \frac{me^4}{8\epsilon_0{}^2 h^2} \tag{4.1.13}$$

and

$$E_3 = -\frac{1}{9} \frac{me^4}{8\epsilon_0{}^2 h^2}. \tag{4.1.14}$$

A complete analysis of the wave equations shows that there are infinitely many solutions, and that they can all be classified according to the corresponding allowed energy of the atom

$$E_n = -\frac{1}{n^2} \frac{me^4}{8\epsilon_0{}^2 h^2} \tag{4.1.15}$$

where n is any integer greater than or equal to unity and is called the *principal quantum number*.

The potential energy of an electron in the field of a proton is plotted in Fig. 4.1.2. Since the potential energy for infinite separation is taken as zero, the attractive forces give rise to negative values at finite separations. This may be thought of as a potential energy well which confines the electron, much as the walls of the box did in the previous chapter. We should expect the solutions of the Schrödinger equation to establish certain possible energy levels for the electrons, with one or more wave functions corresponding to each. The allowed energy levels actually found are given by Eq. 4.1.15. Four of these energy levels are indicated by dashed lines in Fig. 4.1.2. The energy required to remove an electron from the lowest, or

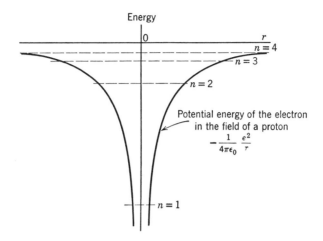

Fig. 4.1.2 The energy levels of the hydrogen atom.

ground state of a hydrogen atom, that is, to ionize it, is E_1, as given in Eq. 4.1.8. The size of the atom in excited states is greater than in the ground state. It is shown below that, for the spherically symmetrical states described above, the average value of r is given by the expression

$$\bar{r}_n = \frac{3a_0}{2} n^2. \tag{4.1.16}$$

We have considered only the solutions of the Schrödinger equation which are spherically symmetric. For these solutions ψ is a function only of the distance r from the origin and does not depend on the polar and azimuthal angles θ and ϕ of the spherical polar coordinates. However, solutions to the Schrödinger equation also exist which do depend on these angles, that is, where ψ is not spherically symmetric.

Although the experimental confirmation of the wave mechanical results obtained above is satisfactory, the overwhelming evidence for the correctness of our procedures comes from optical considerations. An atom can exist in any one of many stationary states. We have calculated the energies of these states for the hydrogen atom. In addition, however, an atom can spontaneously make a transition from some initial excited state to some final state having a lower energy. If the numbers n corresponding to these states are n_i and n_f, the energy lost by the atom in this transition is $E_{ni} - E_{nf}$, and this energy is radiated into space as electromagnetic radiation. Since the frequency of an electromagnetic quantum having an energy E is $\nu = E/h$, we must expect the frequency radiated by an atom in a transition from an initial state designated by n_i to a final state designated by n_f to be given by

$$\nu = \frac{E_{ni} - E_{nf}}{h}$$

or, for the hydrogen atom, using Eq. 4.1.15,

$$\nu = \frac{me^4}{8\epsilon_0^2 h^3}\left(\frac{1}{n_f^2} - \frac{1}{n_i^2}\right). \tag{4.1.17}$$

The coefficient above is often written as

$$\frac{me^4}{8\epsilon_0^2 h^3} = Rc \tag{4.1.18}$$

where R is called Rydberg's constant and c is the velocity of light. The value of the Rydberg constant may be found through substituting the known natural constants. It is

$$R = 1.097 \times 10^7 \text{ m}^{-1}. \tag{4.1.19}$$

The wavelengths which the hydrogen atom can radiate are then given by

$$\frac{1}{\lambda} = R\left(\frac{1}{n_f^2} - \frac{1}{n_i^2}\right).$$

These wavelengths are grouped in series, depending on the value of n_f. The various possible transitions are shown in Fig. 4.1.3. All the transitions from excited states to the ground state lead to radiation in the ultraviolet. This series of spectral lines is called the Lyman[1] series, and the radiated wavelengths are given by

$$\text{Lyman series:} \quad \frac{1}{\lambda} = R\left(1 - \frac{1}{n^2}\right) \quad n = 2, 3, 4, \dots. \tag{4.1.20}$$

Transitions terminating on the first excited level lead to radiation in the visible and ultraviolet. This series of spectral lines is called the Balmer[2] series. The radiated wavelengths are given by

$$\text{Balmer series:} \quad \frac{1}{\lambda} = R\left(\frac{1}{4} - \frac{1}{n^2}\right) \quad n = 3, 4, 5, \dots. \tag{4.1.21}$$

This part of the spectrum of hydrogen is shown in Fig. 4.1.3(b).

[1] Theodore Lyman (1887–1954), professor of physics at Harvard University; discovered the Lyman series 1906.

[2] Johann Jakob Balmer (1825–1898). Teacher of mathematics and penmanship at the high school for girls in Basle, Switzerland, also part-time lecturer of geometry at the university. Fascinated by the regularity of the visible lines in the hydrogen spectrum, he succeeded in describing their wavelengths by a series formula, published in 1885.

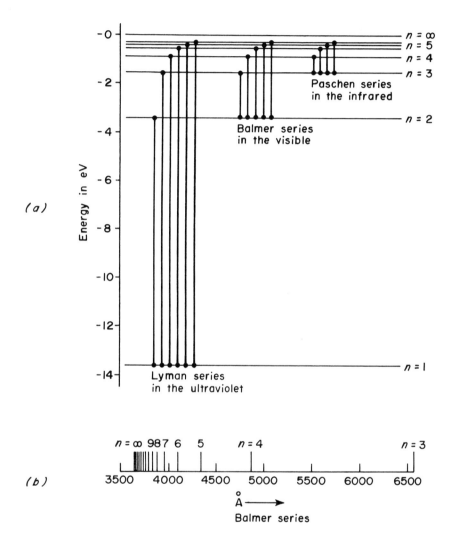

Fig. 4.1.3   (a) Radiative transitions in the hydrogen atom. (b) The Balmer series.

Three other series, terminating at the next higher levels, have also been observed. They are in the infrared. All the observed wavelengths radiated by atomic hydrogen fit into the above description. For each series the wavelength approaches for high values of n a limit which is called the series limit.

The Schrödinger Equation for the Hydrogen Atom

We wish to show that the function Ae^{-r/a_0}, where A and a_0 are constants, is a possible solution of the Schrödinger equation for an electron in the Coulomb field of force of a proton at the origin, as given in Eq. 4.1.3.

$$\frac{\partial^2\psi}{\partial x^2} + \frac{\partial^2\psi}{\partial y^2} + \frac{\partial^2\psi}{\partial z^2} + \frac{8\pi^2 m}{h^2}\left(E + \frac{1}{4\pi\epsilon_0}\frac{e^2}{r}\right)\psi = 0.$$

We have, by simple differentiation of our function $\psi = Ae^{-r/a_0}$,

$$\frac{\partial\psi}{\partial x} = -\frac{1}{a_0}\psi\frac{\partial r}{\partial x}$$

$$\frac{\partial^2\psi}{\partial x^2} = -\frac{1}{a_0}\psi\frac{\partial^2 r}{\partial x^2} + \frac{1}{a_0^2}\psi\left(\frac{\partial r}{\partial x}\right)^2$$

$\partial r/\partial x$ follows from $r = (x^2 + y^2 + z^2)^{1/2}$ (see Fig. 4.1.4), keeping y and z constant, as

$$\frac{\partial r}{\partial x} = \frac{1}{2}\frac{2x}{\sqrt{x^2 + y^2 + z^2}} = \frac{x}{r}.$$

Differentiating once more with respect to x yields

$$\frac{\partial^2 r}{\partial x^2} = \frac{1}{r}\left(1 - \frac{x^2}{r^2}\right).$$

Therefore,

$$\frac{\partial^2\psi}{\partial x^2} = -\frac{1}{a_0}\frac{1}{r}\left(1 - \frac{x^2}{r^2}\right)\psi + \frac{1}{a_0^2}\frac{x^2}{r^2}\psi$$

$$\frac{\partial^2\psi}{\partial x^2} + \frac{\partial^2\psi}{\partial y^2} + \frac{\partial^2\psi}{\partial z^2} = -\frac{2}{a_0 r}\psi + \frac{1}{a_0^2}\psi.$$

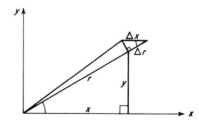

Fig. 4.1.4   Illustration of the relation $\partial r/\partial x = x/r$ for two dimensions.

On substituting, and combining, we get

$$\left(\frac{8\pi^2 m}{h^2} E + \frac{1}{a_0^2}\right)\psi + \left(-\frac{2}{a_0} + \frac{8\pi^2 m}{h^2}\frac{e^2}{4\pi\epsilon_0}\right)\frac{\psi}{r} = 0.$$

Since the equation must be valid for all values of r, we must demand that the constant term and the coefficient of $1/r$ be each equal to zero. From the first, we find that the energy of the system, E, must have the value

$$E = -\frac{h^2}{8\pi^2 m a_0^2}. \tag{4.1.22}$$

From the second, we find that the constant a_0 must satisfy the relation

$$a_0 = \frac{\epsilon_0 h^2}{\pi m e^2}. \tag{4.1.23}$$

Substituting this value of a_0 into Eq. 4.1.22, the energy must have the value

$$E = -\frac{m e^4}{8\epsilon_0^2 h^2} \tag{4.1.24}$$

as stated in Eq. 4.1.18.

The magnitude of the constant A in the above expression for the wave function ψ is obtained through "normalizing" the function, or ensuring that

$$\int \psi^2 dv$$

over all space is unity. To carry out this integration, we use for dv, our element of volume, the volume of a spherical shell of radius r and thickness dr.

$$dv = 4\pi r^2 dr.$$

This is acceptable since the wave function we are concerned with is a function of r only and is therefore spherically symmetrical. We have

$$\int \psi^2 dv = \int_0^\infty A^2 e^{-2r/a_0} 4\pi r^2 dr$$

$$= 4\pi A^2 \int_0^\infty r^2 e^{-2r/a_0} dr = 1. \tag{4.1.25}$$

If we substitute $x = 2r/a_0$ in the expression for $\psi^2 dv$, the integral becomes

$$\tfrac{1}{2}\pi a_0^3 A^2 \int_0^\infty x^2 e^{-x} dx = 1.$$

This may be evaluated using the general mathematical relation

$$\int_0^\infty x^b e^{-x} dx = b!$$

(4.1.26)

where b is an integer number. (To avoid confusion with the principal quantum number n we use here the letter b, not the customary n.) In our case above, $b = 2$, and we get

$$\tfrac{1}{2}\pi a_0^3 A^2 \cdot 2 = 1$$

$$A = (\pi a_0^3)^{-1/2}$$

(4.1.27)

in agreement with Eq. 4.1.6.

The average value of r for the ground state may be computed from Eq. 4.1.16 putting $n = 1$. This result follows from the definition of the mean value of r,

$$\bar{r} = \frac{\int r\psi^2 \, dv}{\int \psi^2 \, dv} = \frac{\int r\psi^2 \, dv}{1} = \int r\psi^2 \, dv$$

$$= \frac{1}{\pi a_0^3} \int_0^\infty r e^{-2r/a_0} 4\pi r^2 \, dr$$

$$= \frac{a_0}{4} \int_0^\infty x^3 e^{-x} \, dx$$

where again $x = 2r/a_0$. The definite integral may be evaluated using Eq. 4.1.26 with $b = 3$, or $b! = 3 \cdot 2 = 6$. Thus we get for the average value of r

$$\bar{r} \frac{a_0}{4} \cdot 6 = \tfrac{3}{2} a_0.$$

(4.1.28)

Such average values, here usually called *expectation values*, play a considerable role in quantum theory. Expectation values may also be calculated for, besides the position of a particle, other physical quantities, as the momentum or a component of the angular momentum.

4.2   THE QUANTIZATION OF ANGULAR MOMENTUM

A beam of electrons moving in a straight line carries not only kinetic energy but also momentum. Similarly, the electron cloud around an atomic nucleus may carry orbital angular momentum. In the semi-classical model of the atom where the electrons are thought to move in miniature planetary orbits, this fact is obvious. In the wave-mechanical picture, however, the appearance of angular momentum is much less obvious and is, in fact, hidden behind much mathematical formalism. It turns out that wave functions describe not only the probability density, but also motion within this cloud of probability density. The situation is quite analogous to that which one encounters in describing energy in electric and magnetic fields. The fields determine the energy density in space, but in addition one can specify the Poynting vector defining certain aspects of the motion of energy in space. Similarly, it is possible to compute not only a probability density from a known wave function but also a flow. In particular, by means which we shall not go into, it is possible to compute the angular momentum associated with a stationary state.

Some states of an atom contain no angular momentum. These are the states that have a spherically symmetric probability distribution. The states of the hydrogen atom which we discussed in some detail had this property. However, we had mentioned there that, in addition, other solutions of the Schrödinger equation exist which correspond to a non-spherical probability distribution. They describe the states of the atom with angular momentum. Angular momentum is quantized, both in magnitude and direction. We have already given an elementary and simplified account of this feature in Section 3.2. The simplification is due mainly to the fact that we considered a wave in a plane only, and not in three-dimensional space. On a macroscopic scale angular momentum appears to be continuously variable because the units by which it can change are small compared to the total angular momentum of objects that can be directly observed. On an atomic scale the effects of the quantization of angular momentum are tremendous. The angular momentum is usually expressed in units of $\hbar$. Planck's constant has the dimensions of energy $\times$ time, or $M(L/T)^2T$, which can also be written as $ML^2\omega$, or angular momentum.

We have to discriminate between different kinds of angular momentum in atomic, and also nuclear, systems which conveniently can be explained by the analogy of the Earth-Sun system. The *orbital angular momentum* in the planetary system is connected with the motion of the Earth around the Sun; the *spin* or *intrinsic angular momentum* is due to the rotation of the Earth about its own axis. The *total angular momentum* is the vector sum of the orbital angular momentum and the spin.

The value of the orbital angular momentum **L** of the electron in a hydrogen atom is given by

$$\mathbf{L} = \hbar\sqrt{l(l+1)}$$

where $l = 0, 1, 2, 3, \ldots$, is an integer and is called the *orbital quantum number*.

The product under the square-root sign, $l(l + 1)$, is reminiscent of the product $n(n + 1)$ of the energy levels of the quantum-mechanical free rotator (Sect. 3.7), which replaced the simpler n^2 of the rigid rotator rotating in a plane. A two-dimensional atom with its plane fixed in space also would have a simpler expression for its angular momentum, namely $\mathbf{L} = \hbar l$.

The intrinsic angular momentum of the electron, its spin, has only one possible value,

$$\mathbf{S} = \hbar \sqrt{\tfrac{1}{2}(\tfrac{1}{2} + 1)},$$

the *spin quantum number* s for one electron being $\tfrac{1}{2}$.

The total angular momentum $\mathbf{J}$ is the vector sum of both kinds of angular momentum, and it is also quantized. For this quantity we have

$$\mathbf{J} = \hbar \sqrt{j(j + 1)}$$

with j being the *total angular momentum quantum number*. Experimentally it is found for the one electron of the hydrogen atom that the quantum number j is a half-integer, that is, $j = \tfrac{1}{2}, \tfrac{3}{2}, \tfrac{5}{2}, \tfrac{7}{2}, \ldots$ This implies the rule for a single electron

$$j = l \pm s.$$

Examples for this rule are the following: Assume that the electron of the hydrogen atom has an orbital quantum number $l = 2$. The spin quantum number is in any case $s = \tfrac{1}{2}$. This can result in a total angular momentum quantum number $j = \tfrac{5}{2}$ or $j = \tfrac{3}{2}$. However, it cannot yield $j = 2$. The magnitude of the total angular momentum is, therefore, $\mathbf{J} = \hbar(\tfrac{5}{2} \cdot \tfrac{7}{2})^{1/2} = 2.96\,\hbar$ or $\mathbf{J} = \hbar(\tfrac{3}{2} \cdot \tfrac{5}{2})^{1/2} = 1.93$. Note also that a value of $j = \tfrac{5}{2}$ might be the consequence either of the addition of $s = \tfrac{1}{2}$ and $l = 2$, as above, or of the subtraction of $s = \tfrac{1}{2}$ from $l = 3$.

In general, if physicists say that an electron has an orbital angular momentum $l = 2$, they are referring to its quantum number. This implies a magnitude of the orbital angular momentum $\mathbf{L} = \hbar[2(2 + 1)]^{1/2} = \hbar(6)^{1/2}$. The same usage holds for the spin and the total angular momentum.

We might mention at this point that the energy of the atom depends mainly on the principal quantum number n and only to a secondary, although in certain respects important, degree on the spin and orbital angular momentum.

Fundamentally, space is isotropic, that is, all directions in space are equivalent. However, space can become anisotropic if, for example, an electric, magnetic, or gravitational field permeates it. In such an instance some directions in space become distinguishable from some other ones. It came as a surprising discovery—we shall discuss it below—that the angular momentum vector of a quantum-mechanical system (e.g., an atom) can assume only certain directions in a space in which one direction is specified. This singled-out direction might be that of a magnetic field, an electric field, or the direction of emission of a light quantum. The facts which are borne out by experiments show that the component of the angular momentum vector in the specified direction, which is usually designated as the z axis, must also be quantized. Disregarding for the present the spin and considering only the orbital angular momentum, the z component of $\mathbf{L} = \hbar[l(l + 1)]^{1/2}$ can have the following values: $l\hbar$, $(l - 1)\hbar$, $(l - 2)\hbar$, ..., $-l\hbar$. Note that this magnitude is an integer of $\hbar$, and does *not* have the form $\hbar[m_l(m_l + 1)]^{1/2}$. The component of $\mathbf{L}$ in the z direction can therefore also be described by a quantum number which is called the *magnetic quantum number* and has the symbol m_l. Its name is a reminder that the specified direction is most often realized by a magnetic field, but otherwise it has little to do with magnetism. To define a specific direction, an electric field, for instance, could also be used. For m_l the following relation holds with regard to l

$$l \geq m_l \geq -l,$$

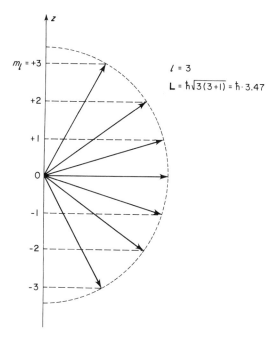

Fig. 4.2.1   Possible orientations of the angular momentum vector **L** with quantum number $l = 3$.

where m_l is an integer number. Figure 4.2.1 shows the different possible orientations of an angular momentum vector of three units of angular momentum. There are seven different possibilities, or in the general case $2l + 1$ possibilities. We might think of the angular momentum vector as precessing around the z axis, conserving hereby the angle it makes with this axis. Figure 4.2.2 depicts this precession for the case $l = 2$ and $m_l = +1$. However, such a representation should not be taken too literally, because it is basically a classical picture that is modified by quantum-theoretical rules, but it is not a genuinely quantum-mechanical picture.

Many of the above and the following rules were discovered before their origin was understood. The reader learning then finds himself therefore in a similar intellectual situation as the physicists in the years before 1925 or 1926, when Heisenberg and Schrödinger found the clue to a deeper insight into the structure of the atoms.

We remarked earlier that the wave functions for the hydrogen atom which belong to states having an angular momentum different from zero are not spherically symmetric. In these cases the nodes of the ψ function do not only lie on concentric spheres as was the case for zero angular momentum states, but their arrangement is much more complicated. States with orbital angular momentum zero are called s states. The states with $l = 1, 2, 3, 4$, etc. are called p, d, f, g, etc. states for historical reasons—namely the

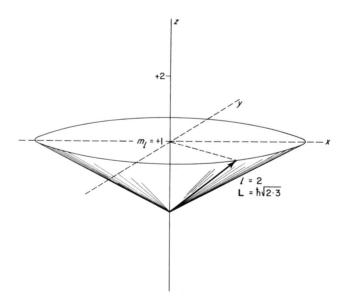

Fig. 4.2.2   Precession of the angular momentum vector with quantum numbers $l = 2$ and $m_l = 1$.

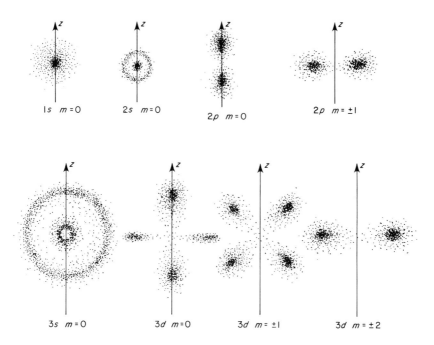

Fig. 4.2.3   The electron probability density of different atomic states. These figures represent cuts along the z axis, and in each case the density distribution is rotationally symmetric about this axis.

appearance of the lines in certain spectral series, sharp, principal, diffuse, fundamental, and then quite arbitrarily g, h, ... These designations have since acquired quite different, precise meanings. Figure 4.2.3 represents the spatial electron probability distributions for different states. These pictures show clearly the notches that correspond in two dimensions to nodal lines. However, these representations do not convey a particularly intuitive impression of the angular momentum of a state.

The rules governing the spin $\mathbf{S}$ and the total angular momentum $\mathbf{J}$ are analogous to the one for the orbital angular momentum $\mathbf{L}$. In the direction of a magnetic field or some other specified direction, the spin $\mathbf{S}$ can have only the components $m_s = +\frac{1}{2}$ or $-\frac{1}{2}$, whereas the z component of $\mathbf{J}$ can be expressed by the magnetic quantum number m_j which can assume the values

$$j \geq m_j \geq -j.$$

Figure 4.2.4 illustrates the situations for the spin $\frac{1}{2}$ and for $j = \frac{5}{2}$. It is important to note that in all three cases, m_l, m_s, and m_j, the possible values differ by one unit.

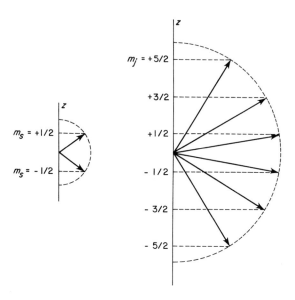

Fig. 4.2.4   Possible orientations of the spin $\frac{1}{2}$ and the total angular momentum $\frac{5}{2}$.

Although the quantization of angular momentum has here been illustrated only on the hydrogen atom, it may be pointed out that in atoms with several electrons, and also in molecules, the angular momentum is similarly quantized. However, the rules for adding angular momenta are more complicated, as will be seen later in this chapter.

The quantum numbers l, j, s, m_l, m_j, and m_s are not independent of each other. Only three of those, in addition to the principal quantum number n, are necessary to describe a state of an electron in an atom, for example, the set n, l, m_l, and m_s. Depending on the problem the most suitable combination may be chosen.

The presence of an angular momentum implies that the electron is moving around the nucleus. A single electron moving on a closed trajectory is sufficient to establish a current on this trajectory. According to electromagnetic theory a current loop has associated with it a magnetic dipole moment (or in short, magnetic moment)

$$\mathbf{\mu} = i\mathbf{A}$$

where i is the current and $\mathbf{A}$ is the area of the loop. Therefore the circulating electron of the hydrogen atom must produce a magnetic moment. The magnitudes of the mechanical angular momentum and of the magnetic moment are proportional to each other. We calculate this relation for the special case of a charged mass point of mass m and charge q orbiting with the frequency ν and leave it as an exercise to prove that the relationship so found holds for any distribution of a circulating charged mass as long as the mass-to-charge ratio for each volume element of the system is the same. The equivalent current, or the number of coulombs passing any point in the orbit in 1 second, is the magnitude of the charge multiplied by the number of times it passes around the orbit per second, or

$$i = q\nu.$$

Since the area is πr^2, we have

$$\mathbf{\mu} = i\mathbf{A} = q\nu\pi r^2 = \tfrac{1}{2}qr^2\omega.$$

The angular momentum $\mathbf{L}$ of the system is

$$\mathbf{L} = mr^2\omega.$$

The ratio of the magnetic moment to the angular momentum of an atomic system is called its *gyromagnetic ratio* γ and is

$$\gamma = \frac{\mathbf{\mu}}{\mathbf{L}} = \frac{q}{2m}.$$

A quantum-mechanical calculation yields the same result as the above classical treatment. However, only with respect to the *orbital* angular momentum does the gyromagnetic ratio have this value. For the spin, against all classical expectations, this ratio is q/m, or twice as big. It turns out that the spin is fundamentally a relativistic effect. Therefore even the Schrödinger equation, which is nonrelativistic, is of no help in explaining the gyromagnetic ratio for the electron spin; on the other hand, the Dirac equation provides for its understanding, as already pointed out at the end of Chapter 3.

Because the electronic charge is negative, the vectors μ and $\mathbf{L}$ are anti-parallel to each other. The angular momentum vector can assume only certain directions in space which has the consequence that also the magnetic moment vector, which is coupled to the former, is restricted to certain directions in space.

The first clear indication of space quantization, which is just another name for the property that only certain directions in space are permitted for the angular momentum, was achieved by the experiments of Stern and Gerlach[3] on a beam of atoms in 1921. The basic idea of the Stern-Gerlach

---

[3] Otto Stern (1888–1969). Professor at the University of Rostock, Germany where this experiment was first done, later at the University of Hamburg. From 1933 on at the Carnegie Institute of Technology in Pittsburgh, Pa. 1943 Nobel prize in physics for developing the molecular beam method and the measurement of the magnetic moment of the proton. Walter Gerlach (1889–   ). Professor at German universities, from 1929 on in Munich.

experiment is the following: Atoms that possess a magnetic dipole moment behave like small magnets in a magnetic field. If such atoms are traveling through an inhomogeneous magnetic field whose lines are perpendicular to the trajectory, the atoms will either be drawn into the regions of greater field strength or pushed away, depending on the orientation of the atomic dipoles with respect to the external field. This can be understood qualitatively by analogy with the force acting on a bar magnet in an inhomogeneous magnetic field as illustrated in Fig. 4.2.5, but a more quantitative analysis may easier be carried out for the analogous electric case which follows.

The forces which a field exerts on a dipole are most readily visualized in the electric case, in which the dipole consists of two equal poles of opposite sign a fixed distance apart. In a uniform field, the forces on the two poles are equal and oppositely directed. This condition may give rise to a torque that might turn the dipole, but not to a resultant force that could move it or change the motion of its center of mass. In an inhomogeneous field, there may be a resultant force on the dipole, as illustrated in Fig. 4.2.6(a). Here the dipole is so oriented that its moment is in the direction of the field, and in the direction of increasing field strength, since the field strength is greater when the lines are closer together. In this condition the force on the positive pole will be greater than the force on the negative pole, and there will consequently be a resultant downward force, as shown. When the dipole is at right angles to the field and the direction of increase, the

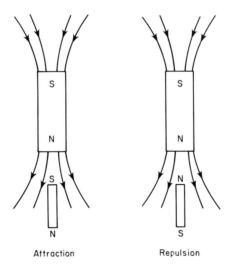

Attraction   Repulsion

Fig. 4.2.5 Forces on a small bar magnet in an inhomogeneous magnetic field.

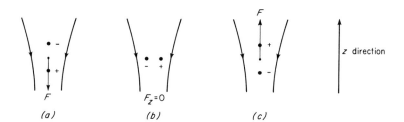

Fig. 4.2.6 The force on a dipole in an inhomogeneous field.

magnitude of the z components of the force on the two poles is equal and the resultant vanishes. (The resulting force in the x direction does not concern us.) For orientations between that shown in (a) and (b), the force is intermediate in magnitude but in the direction shown in (a). If now the dipole is turned so that it is pointing in a direction opposite to the field and to the direction of increase, the force on the negative pole will be greater, and the resultant force on the dipole will be upward, as shown in Fig. $4.2.6(c)$.

A general expression for the force on a dipole, applicable to the magnetic case in which we have a current loop rather than two poles, is easily derived from the expression for the energy of orientation of a dipole μ in a field B, which is

$$E = -\mu B \cos \theta,$$

where θ is the angle between B and μ. If we choose an axis, say the z axis, in the direction of B and assume that B varies from point to point along it, we get by differentiation

$$\frac{dE}{dz} = -\mu \frac{dB}{dz} \cos \theta. \tag{4.2.1}$$

But there must be a force F exerted by the field on the dipole opposite to the direction of increase of potential energy,

$$F_z = -\frac{dE}{dz} \tag{4.2.2}$$

and therefore, upon combining Eqs. 4.2.1 and 4.2.2, we find for the magnetic force

$$F_z = \mu \cos \theta \frac{dB}{dz}. \tag{4.2.3}$$

In one of their first experiments Stern and Gerlach investigated silver atoms. In the ground state of this atom the orbital angular momenta of the individual 47 electrons add up to zero. Of the 47 electron spins, 46 cancel mutually, but one spin remains uncanceled. The total angular momentum of the silver atom is due solely to this one spin and, hence, the spin quantum number is $\frac{1}{2}$. The gyromagnetic ratio is consequently e/m, the same as for the hydrogen atom.

A beam of atoms originating in a furnace O and moving through a vacuum is defined by a slit system S_1, S_2, as shown in Fig. 4.2.7(a). The beam traverses a region between the specially shaped poles of a magnet in which there is a nonuniform, or inhomogeneous field. A cross section of the poles is shown in Fig. 4.2.7(b). Here the beam is moving into the paper midway between the poles. In this field the atoms are deflected by a force perpendicular to the direction of motion in a manner further discussed below. After leaving the field, the atoms travel in straight lines to a photographic plate or other detector where the amount of the deflection is observed.[4]

The magnetic force acting on the atoms as they fly through the magnetic field is either up or down in Fig. 4.2.7(a), depending on their orientation. If, in the beam, all orientations are present, we should expect to find at the

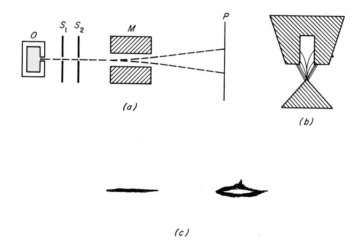

Fig. 4.2.7 The Stern-Gerlach experiment. The apparatus used (a,b). Magnetic splitting of a beam of silver atoms (c) at left without magnetic field, at right, with magnetic field. [after O. Stern and W. Gerlach, *Annalen der Physik* **74**, 673 (1924).]

[4] In the first experiments the silver beam impinged on a glass plate, but the trace was too faint to be visible. The plate was then treated with some kind of photographic developer and with silver nitrate whose silver precipitated at the places of the invisible silver.

detecting plate P all deflections between zero and some maximum deflection obtained for those atoms whose magnetic moment was more parallel or more antiparallel to the field. Actually, in the experiments with silver atoms, it was found that, upon application of the field, the central line obtained with no field was split into two (Fig. 4.2.7c), just as though in the field the magnetic momenta of all the atoms could assume only two orientations with respect to the direction of the field, but never an intermediate one.

Later observations on other atoms showed that more complex conditions can exist. The beam is always split up into several parts by the magnetic field, as though only certain orientations in the field are possible, but sometimes instead of splitting into just two beams, as in the case of silver, it splits into three, or four, or more components.

The discovery of the simple physical laws behind these observations required the correlation of many observations. First, it was necessary to consider not only the magnetic moments of the atoms used but also their angular momenta. It turned out that, whereas the magnitude of the deflection in an atomic beam experiment is determined by the magnetic moment, the number of beams into which the incident beam is split is determined by the possible number of orientations of the angular momentum. When all the facts were collected, the following very simple pattern in nature appeared.

1. The total angular momentum quantum number of an atom or molecule is always some integral multiple of $\frac{1}{2}$, including zero.

2. In the presence of a magnetic field, an atom can have only certain discrete orientations. The difference in the component of the angular momentum in the direction of the field for adjacent orientations is always $h/2\pi$, never $\frac{1}{2}(h/2\pi)$.

Returning now to the Stern-Gerlach experiment, we see that, if the beam is split into two components, as for silver, we should expect to be dealing with a case of $j = \frac{1}{2}$ which has two allowed orientations in the field. But, since the magnetic moment of a silver atom is a consequence of the angular momentum of the charged electronic shell, we should expect the silver atom to be oriented in the field so that not only its angular momentum, but also its magnetic moment has this orientation. The splitting into two beams is determined by the fact that $j = \frac{1}{2}$, but the magnitude of splitting is determined by the magnitude of the magnetic moment.

Not all atoms with $j = \frac{1}{2}$ have the same magnetic moment. The reason is in the following: As mentioned earlier, the gyromagnetic ratios for the orbital and for the spin angular momenta are different. The magnitude of the magnetic moment of the atom depends therefore on the relative contributions of spin and orbital angular momentum to the total angular momentum of quantum number j. The beautiful regularity and order which we have found in the description of angular momentum do not extend to magnetic moments. But for any given atom having angular momentum we shall always find some definite magnetic moment, although this will not always be along the direction of the angular momentum. However, the component of the magnetic moment vector in the direction of the angular momentum may always be calculated from the angular momentum $\mathbf{J}$ by means of an equation of the form

$$\mathbf{\mu} = \gamma \mathbf{J}$$

where to gyromagnetic ratio γ is a constant characteristic of an atom and may be positive or negative.

An atomic beam experiment on atoms having some arbitrary angular momentum given by j will involve a beam that splits into $2j + 1$ components, one for each possible orientation. By simply counting the number of traces on the plate P it is possible to specify the j value for the atom being investigated. From the magnitude of the splitting and the constants of the apparatus it is, in addition, possible to specify the magnitude of μ.

4.3 ORBITAL ANGULAR MOMENTUM AND SPIN IN THE HYDROGEN ATOM

The classification of the wave functions of the hydrogen atom proceeds as follows. We first make use of the principal quantum number n appearing in the energy expression, Eq. 4.1.15:

$$E_n = -\frac{1}{n^2} \frac{me^4}{8\epsilon_0^2 h^2}.$$

For $n = 1$ there is only one possible wave function. It is that given in Eq. 4.1.5 and has zero angular momentum or, in other words, is characterized by the orbital angular momentum quantum number $l = 0$. For $n = 2$, that is, for the next higher energy level, there are wave functions with two possible values of l, namely, 0 or 1. Thus there is one solution for $n = 1$, $l = 0$, and then three solutions with $n = 2$, $l = 1$, the three corresponding to different magnetic quantum numbers $m_l = \pm 1, 0$. This first excited state, therefore, has a fourfold degeneracy, with four possible different wave functions having the same energy. The next energy level, with $n = 3$, has solutions with $l = 0$, 1, or 2 or, as shown in Fig. 4.3.1, a total of nine different possible wave functions. In general it can be shown from the solution of the Schrödinger equation that all positive values of l are possible up to $n - 1$.

	s-states $l = 0$	p-states $l = 1$	d-states $l = 2$	f-states $l = 3$
$n = 4$	1 state $m_l = 0$	3 states $m_l = \pm1, 0$	5 states $m_l = \pm2,$ $\pm1, 0$	7 states $m_l = \pm3,$ $\pm2, \pm1, 0$
$n = 3$	1 state $m_l = 0$	3 states $m_l = \pm1, 0$	5 states $m_l = \pm2,$ $\pm1, 0$	
$n = 2$	1 state $m_l = 0$	3 states $m_l = \pm1, 0$		
$n = 1$	1 state $m_l = 0$			

Fig. 4.3.1   The classification of possible states of the hydrogen atom according to the Schrödinger wave equation.

We must now also consider the other component of the total angular momentum, namely the intrinsic angular momentum of the electron, the spin[5] which is characterized by the quantum number $s = \frac{1}{2}$. The spin has only two possible orientations: one in a positive direction and one in a negative direction, often expressed as spin up or spin down. At this stage in our study of atoms we must simply accept this as an experimental fact. In any state of motion of the electron in the hydrogen atom, the quantum number of the total angular momentum will be that of the orbital angular momentum, plus or minus the spin angular momentum.

The inclusion of the spin in the description of the degeneracy of the energy levels of the hydrogen atom results in our multiplying the previously obtained degeneracy, shown in Fig. 4.3.1, by two. The final result is shown in Fig. 4.3.2. The lowest level is doubly degenerate. The first excited state has eight different wave functions. The next 18, and so on. These results are confirmed by experiments described in the next section.

[5] The concept of spin was introduced in 1925 by the young Dutch physicists G. E. Uhlenbeck and S. Goudsmith to explain the doublet structure of certain spectral lines [*Naturwissenschaften* **13,** 953 (1925)].

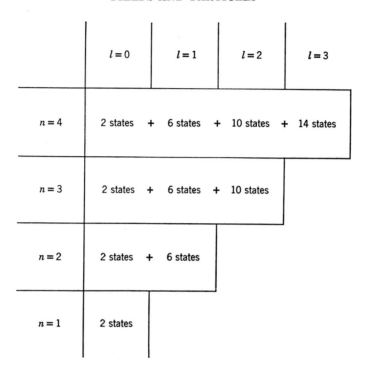

Fig. 4.3.2   The actual degeneracy of the energy levels of the hydrogen atom.

However, it must be pointed out that the degeneracy is not an absolute; some of these states are only to a certain, although very high degree, degenerate. Very often the slight energy difference between the levels, which results from the relative orientation of spin and orbital angular momentum, can be neglected. It is interesting to note that the Schrödinger equation makes the levels appear strictly degenerate, because it is based on a nonrelativistic theory and does not take account of the spin. A relativistic theory removes this degeneracy.

We shall now estimate the order of magnitude of the energy difference between two levels both of orbital quantum number $l = 1$, one with the electron spin more or less parallel to the orbital angular momentum, therefore $j = \frac{3}{2}$, and the other having the spin more or less antiparallel, resulting in $j = \frac{1}{2}$. Let us recall from the Stern-Gerlach experiment that there is a magnetic moment associated with the orbital angular momentum and likewise one with the spin angular momentum. These two magnetic dipoles interact with each other in about the same way as do two compass needles close to each other. We can also use the picture of one magnet needle in a magnetic field without asking how that magnetic field originated.

Such a system has its minimum energy when the magnet needle is aligned with the external field. In order to turn the needle by 180°, we have to feed energy into the system.

If μ is the magnetic moment of the compass needle, the torque τ exerted on it by the field B is

$$\boldsymbol{\tau} = \boldsymbol{\mu} \times \mathbf{B} = \mu B \sin \theta$$

where θ is the angle between $\boldsymbol{\mu}$ and $\mathbf{B}$. The work W necessary to turn the needle from the "downstream" direction to the "upstream" direction is therefore

$$W = \int_0^\pi \tau d\theta = \mu B \int_0^\pi \sin \theta d\theta = 2\mu B.$$

Hence, the energy difference between the two positions is

$$\Delta E = 2\mu B.$$

Returning now to our hydrogen atom we have a similar difference in energy depending on the relative orientation of the magnetic moment. Let us again assume for our rough calculation that the electron circles the nucleus at a radius r (Fig. 4.3.3). It is, however, in no way obvious how the magnetic moment of the orbital motion of the electron can act on the electron itself. A way to avoid this bootstrap process is by changing the frame of reference: We consider the electron fixed and the nucleus circulating around it (Fig. 4.3.4). The charge of the nucleus will produce, according to Biot-Savart's law, at the center of the circle, which is now the location of the electron, a magnetic induction $B = (\mu_0 i/2r)$. If we take the values for i and ω which we used in Section 4.2 in the discussion of the gyromagnetic ratio, namely $i = e(\omega/2\pi)$ and $\omega = (h/2\pi)(1/mr^2)$, we get the following value for B:

$$B = \frac{\mu_0}{2r} \frac{e}{2\pi} \frac{h}{2\pi} \frac{1}{mr^2} = \frac{\mu_0}{8\pi^2} \frac{eh}{mr^3}.$$

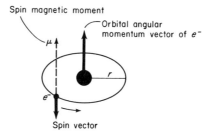

Fig. 4.3.3   An electron orbiting around a nucleus.

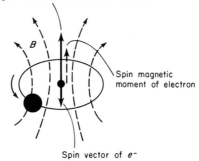

Fig. 4.3.4   A nucleus orbiting around an electron.

The magnetic moment associated with the orbital angular momentum $l = 1$ is $\mu = (e/2m)(h/2\pi)$,[6] and the one associated with the spin $s = \frac{1}{2}$ is of the same size. Therefore, if we take for r the value $4a_0$, which corresponds to the radius with maximum electron density for $n = 2$ and $l = 1$, the energy difference between the two $l = 1$ states is

$$\Delta E \approx 2\mu B \approx \frac{\mu_0 e^2 h^2}{16\pi^3 m^2 r^3} = 3.67 \times 10^{-24} \text{ joules} = 2.3 \times 10^{-5} \text{ eV}.$$

The actual difference ΔE is 4.5×10^{-5} eV, which is also the value deduced from more rigorous theory. It is rather surprising that with our crude assumptions we make an error of less than a factor 2 compared to the actual value. The only variable in our approximation is the radius r which enters into the calculation with the third power. The result depends therefore very sensitively on the chosen radius. Certainly it was a great oversimplification to assume a unique value for r as if the electron were going around the nucleus in a circle. First, the electron cloud is distributed over wide ranges of r, and second, the distribution is not spherically symmetric for electrons with angular momentum $l = 1$ as may be seen from Fig. 2.2.3. At least these features should be taken into account for a somewhat better theory. In addition, in a relativistic treatment a factor $\frac{1}{2}$ (the so-called Thomas factor) is introduced, which has its source in the change of the reference system.

If the two magnetic moments are parallel the system has the lowest energy. This is plausible if one considers the analogy of a magnet needle in a magnetic field. The needle will orient itself in such a way that the energy of the system is a minimum. This is achieved when the fields are

----

[6] This quantity is known as the Bohr magneton, μ_B.

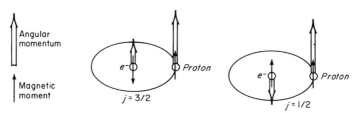

Fig. 4.3.5   Relative orientations of the mechanical and magnetic vectors for $j = \frac{1}{2}$ and $j = \frac{3}{2}$.

parallel. Because of the negative charge of the electron its spin vector and magnetic moment vector are opposite. Hence the level with the lower energy is the one in which spin and angular momentum are pointing in opposite directions, as illustrated in Fig. 4.3.5. The $j = \frac{1}{2}$ state is therefore lower than the $j = \frac{3}{2}$ state.

The Bohr Model of the Hydrogen Atom

Before the advent of wave mechanics, Niels Bohr[7] in 1913 derived an expression for the energy levels of the hydrogen atom in a different way. He assumed that the electron moved around the nucleus in elliptical orbits. In order to restrict the motion of the electron to a few possible orbits he applied certain quantum conditions which yielded the same expression for the energy levels found in the treatment of Section 4.1. The discussion of these elliptic orbits is not simple, especially if we try to obtain an insight into the degeneracy of the various possible energy levels. Some authors of physics texts have attempted to present the Bohr theory in a considerably oversimplified form. A brief review of this kind of discussion is included here for the benefit of those students who may look up the treatment of the hydrogen atom in other texts.

The assumption is made that we may consider only circular orbits of the electron around the nucleus. In a circular orbit, we must equate the centripetal force required for circular motion of the electrostatic force between proton and electron, where v is the velocity of the electron:

$$\frac{mv^2}{r} = \frac{1}{4\pi\epsilon_0}\frac{e^2}{r^2}.$$

[7] Niels Bohr (1885–1962), Danish theoretical physicist; Nobel prize 1922 for his atomic model. Important contributions also in nuclear physics. One of the most influential physicists during the first half of this century.

Niels Bohr (1885–1962) and Wolfgang Pauli (1900–1958) during a discussion period at Niels Bohr's Institute in Copenhagen in 1929 (Courtesy of Niels Bohr Library, American Institute of Physics. Photograph by S. Goudsmith).

If now we make with Bohr an additional assumption, that the angular momentum of the electron in its circular orbit must be some integral number times $h/2\pi$, and if we write for this integer the quantity n (in our previous discussion this was called l), we have

$$mvr = n\frac{h}{2\pi}.$$

These equations may be solved for r and v. The results are

$$r = \epsilon_0 \frac{n^2h^2}{\pi me^2} = n^2a_0 \qquad (4.3.1)$$

$$v = \frac{1}{\epsilon_0}\frac{e^2}{2nh}. \qquad (4.3.2)$$

Here, as above, $a_0 = \epsilon_0 h^2/\pi me^2$. The radii of the circular orbits are nearly the same as the mean value of r for the spherically symmetrical wave functions. The energy of the system may be computed from the radius and the velocity of the electron.

$$E_{\text{total}} = E_{\text{kinetic}} + E_{\text{potential}}$$

$$= \tfrac{1}{2}mv^2 - \frac{1}{4\pi\epsilon_0}\frac{e^2}{r}. \qquad (4.3.3)$$

On substituting values of v and r from Eqs. 4.3.1 and 4.3.2 into Eq. 4.3.3 we get the following values for possible energy levels,

$$E_n = -\frac{1}{n^2}\frac{me^4}{8\epsilon_0^2 h^2}$$

in complete agreement with the previously obtained result in Eq. 4.1.15. Although this treatment gives the correct levels, it gives wrong results for the angular momentum. In fact, we have seen that, if n is the quantum number specifying the energy, the maximum possible angular momentum in this state is $(n-1)h/2\pi$. The treatment of the Bohr atom assuming circular orbits therefore leads to conclusions at variance with the facts. We must conclude that circular orbits are inadmissible.

If we drop circular orbits and treat only elliptic orbits using Bohr's methods, we obtain essentially correct results with regard to energy and angular momentum but, in spite of this, such a representation of electron orbits will not convey even an approximately correct picture of the structure of atoms.

4.4   ANGULAR MOMENTUM IN MANY-ELECTRON ATOMS

We have seen that in the hydrogen atom the orbital angular momentum with quantum number l and the spin with quantum number s combine to a total angular momentum with quantum number j which is either $l + \tfrac{1}{2}$ or $l - \tfrac{1}{2}$. We shall now discuss the angular momentum of an atom containing several electrons.

It may be taken for granted that the total angular momentum of the atom is quantized. In analogy to the total angular momentum of one electron, whose magnitude is $\hbar[\,j(j+1)\,]^{1/2}$, the corresponding magnitude is $\hbar[\,J(J+1)\,]^{1/2}$, J being, hence, the quantum number corresponding to j. Similarly, components along a given direction are here now M_J for the atom, instead of m_j for the single electron. In other words: capital letters for the angular momentum quantum numbers refer to the atom and small letters to individual electrons.

We now want to discuss how the angular momenta of the electrons add to the total angular momentum J. It is found that in the cases where the interaction among the spins of all electrons is strong these spins will combine to a total spin S. For an even number of electrons in the atom, the quantum number S will be an integer; for an odd number it will be a half-integer. The individual orbital angular momenta of the electrons, on the other hand, will combine to give the orbital angular momentum, quantum number L of the atom, which is always an integer. L and S finally will combine to give the total angular momentum quantum number J which is, depending on the number of electrons, an integer (for an even number) or half-integer (for an odd number). This can be visualized in the so-called *vector model*.

A few examples illustrate the addition of the individual l's to L, and afterwards we shall do the same for S. Let us assume that an atom has two electrons with $l = 4$ and $l = 3$, respectively. The following values for L are possible: $L = 7, 6, \ldots, 2, 1$, as seen in Fig. 4.4.1. Generally, L can assume all integer values between $l_1 + l_2$ and $|\, l_1 - l_2\,|$. Because the magnitude of the individual angular momentum vectors is $\hbar[l(l + 1)]^{1/2}$, and that of their sum is $\hbar[L(L + 1)]^{1/2}$, we have again the somewhat strange

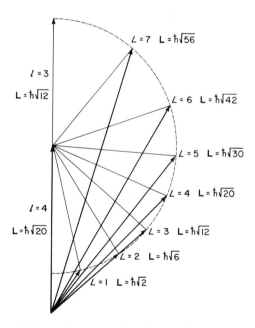

Fig. 4.4.1   Two orbital angular momenta with quantum numbers $l = 4$ and $l = 3$ combining to an orbital angular momentum with quantum number L, where $1 \leq L \leq 7$.

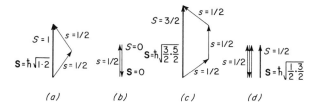

Fig. 4.4.2 The addition of the spins of two (a and b) and three electrons (c and d). The fat arrows represent the resultant spin S.

situation that the two angular momenta cannot exactly line up in the same direction. For three and more electrons the procedure for finding the possible L-values is similar. By analogy to the relationship between l and m_l, the component of the angular momentum L in a given direction has the values $\hbar M_L$, where M_L can assume the values L, $L - 1, \ldots, 0, \ldots,$ $-L + 1$, $-L$. The spins of the electrons, s_1, $s_2, \ldots$, are summed in a similar way with the restriction that for an even number of electrons the quantum number S for the sum of all the spins must be an integer (including zero), and for an odd number of electrons a half-integer. The situation for the spins of two and three electrons is shown in Fig. 4.4.2.

Our next step will combine L and S to give J. As pointed out above, the quantum number J must be an integer or an half-integer, depending on the number of electrons. We show this in Fig. 4.4.3 for three examples: $L = 3$ and $S = 2$, $L = 3$ and $S = \frac{3}{2}$, and $L = 3$ and $S = \frac{1}{2}$. In the first example L and S can combine to values of a total angular momentum of $J = \frac{7}{2}$ and $\frac{5}{2}$; in the second example they combine to $J = 4$, 3, and 2, and in the last one to $J = \frac{9}{2}, \frac{7}{2}, \frac{5}{2}$, and $\frac{3}{2}$.

The component of J in a specified direction, such as the direction of a

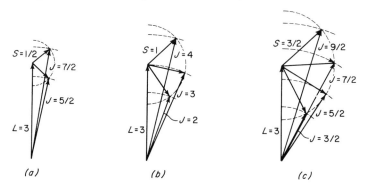

Fig. 4.4.3 The addition of the orbital angular momentum L and the spin S. a) L = 3, S = $\frac{1}{2}$, b) L = 3, S = 1, c) L = 3, S = $\frac{3}{2}$.

magnetic field, has the values $M_J = (h/2\pi)$, with M_J either an integer or a half-integer, according to the number of electrons, as before.

The same L and S can hence combine to a multiplicity of states. The ensemble of such states is called a *multiplet*. The degree of multiplicity depends usually only on S. Doublets appear for $S = \frac{1}{2}$, triplets for $S = 1$, quartets for $S = \frac{3}{2}$, and so forth. The term multiplet is not only used to describe the splitting of states; because spectral lines emitted in a transition to and from such a multiplet are also split because of the slightly different transition energies, one speaks here of doublet lines or simply doublets. Levels and lines that are not split are called singlets. The splitting of levels and lines due to the interaction of orbital and spin angular momentum is called *fine-structure splitting*.

The spectroscopical notation to describe states can best be made clear by an example: 2^3P_0 is the designation of an atomic state with principal quantum number 2, orbital angular momentum $L = 1$, total angular momentum $J = 0$, and which belongs to a triplet (see Fig. 4.4.4). Obviously the other two members of the triplet are 2^3P_1 and 2^3P_2. The latter abbreviation is pronounced "two triplet pee two." The state of a single electron is described similarly, using a small letter instead of the capital letter.[8]

An example of how configurations of several electrons are written is the following: $3s^2 2p$ means: Two s-electrons have the principal quantum number 3 and one p-electron has the principal quantum number 2.

Summarizing the situation we can say that in lieu of l, s, j, m_l, and m_j for the one-electron system, we have for the many-electron system the quantum numbers L, S, J, M_L, and M_J. As we emphasized at the beginning, the spins were assumed to interact strongly with each other in our model, and the orbital angular momenta were also assumed to interact strongly. The electrons behave like one single coherent blob with orbital angular

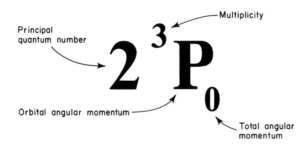

Fig. 4.4.4   The spectroscopical terminology.

---

[8] A transition between two levels, which gives rise to the emission or absorption of a spectral line, is written accordingly, for example, as $5p_{3/2} - 4s_{1/2}$.

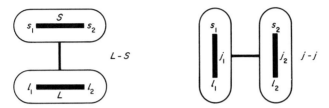

Fig. 4.4.5 The L-S and j-j coupling schemes. Thick lines represent stronger interactions than the thin lines.

momentum L and spin angular momentum S, hence a total angular
momentum J. This implies that the interaction between the spin and the
orbital angular momentum of the individual electrons is secondary; thus it
makes little sense to ascribe a quantum number j to a single electron. We
might even say that energies and angular momenta of the single electrons
have lost their importance in this scheme, which is called *Russell-Saunders*
or *L-S coupling*. The above description of the addition of angular momenta
of electrons is valid for the majority of the energy levels of the atoms.
Particularly the light atoms follow this rule, but the states with smaller
quantum numbers n of the medium and heavy elements also obey it.

However, nature also realizes another way of adding angular momenta
within an atom. If the interaction between orbital angular momentum and
spin of the *same* electron is strong, the two will combine to give a j of the
electron. Finally, the different j's of the electrons add to a total J. This
scheme goes under the name *j-j coupling*. Cases of pure j-j coupling are
relatively rare. However, in the medium and heavier elements the energy
terms with higher quantum number n are mixtures of L-S and j-j coupling.
In j-j coupling the quantum numbers L and S obviously have no meaning.

Figure 4.4.5 gives a schematic presentation of the difference between the
two coupling schemes that play a role not only in atoms but also in nuclei.
The thick lines in each case represent a strong electromagnetic interaction
between two angular momenta, and the thin lines represent the weaker
coupling between two pairs of angular momentum. The following analogy
might help to visualize what is meant by the relative strength of two interactions: Two magnet needles relatively far apart will align with the Earth's
magnetic field (Fig. 4.4.6(a)). If we bring them side by side close together
there will be some alignment between the needles (Fig. 4.4.6(b)), because
the interaction between them is now stronger than between a needle and
the terrestrial field.

A decision whether in a particular case the coupling is more along the
L-S or more along the j-j scheme depends mostly on the observed energy
differences between various levels. If L-S coupling predominates, the

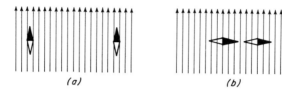

Fig. 4.4.6   The relative interaction strength between two magnet needles and the magnetic field of the earth.

energy differences of levels of different J, but of equal L and equal S are relatively small, because the magnetic forces between the orbit and the spin current are relatively weak. On the other hand, if the value of S or of L is changed, although the value of J might remain the same, the energy difference will be appreciable due to the strong interaction between the spins or between the orbital angular momenta. If j-j coupling dominates, the energy changes greatly between $j = l + \frac{1}{2}$ and $l - \frac{1}{2}$ for an electron. On the other hand, the energy does not depend much on how the different j's are combined because the interaction forces are strong between spin and orbit of the single electron, but relatively weak among the different electrons.

We shall contrast L-S and j-j coupling in the example of a system with two electrons with $l_1 = 0$ and $l_2 = 1$. L-S coupling will result in $L = 1$, $S = \frac{1}{2} \pm \frac{1}{2} = 1$ or 0. For $S = 1$ we get $J = 2, 1, 0$. The energy levels are relatively close together and form a triplet. For $S = 0$ we have only one value, namely $J = 1$, a singlet. In comparison with the energy intervals between any two members of the triplet, the energy interval between this triplet as a whole and the singlet state is relatively great. The situation is illustrated in Fig. 4.4.7 on the left-hand side. In j-j coupling the same two electrons couple in the following ways: the first electron can assume only the value $j_1 = 0 + \frac{1}{2} = \frac{1}{2}$, whereas the second electron can assume two

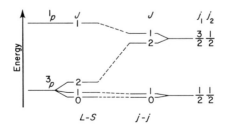

Fig. 4.4.7   Energy differences in L-S and j-j coupling for two electrons with orbital angular momentum 0 and 1, respectively. Corresponding levels are joined by dashed lines.

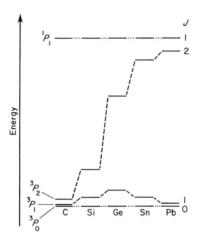

Fig. 4.4.8 Transition from L-S to j-j coupling in elements of group IV. The energy scale for each element is chosen such that the distance between the lowest and the highest level is equal in each case. The scales differ therefore greatly.

different j-values: $j_2 = 1 + \frac{1}{2} = \frac{3}{2}$ and $j_2 = 1 - \frac{1}{2} = \frac{1}{2}$. With $j_2 = \frac{3}{2}$ and $j_1 = \frac{1}{2}$ the following possibilities for J exist: $j_1 + j_2 = 2$ and $j_1 - j_2 = 1$. These two energy levels lie relatively close together, as illustrated on the right-hand side of the figure. With $j_2 = \frac{1}{2}$ and $j_1 = \frac{1}{2}$ the two possibilities are 1 and 0. These levels again are close together. Both coupling schemes yield four levels and both have the same quantum numbers for J.

Figure 4.4.8 illustrates the transition from L-S to j-j coupling in certain levels of the elements of the IV group of the periodic system. It shows that in the lighter elements L-S coupling predominates, in the heavier ones j-j coupling. The energy scale in the figure is different for each element and is chosen such that the distance between the lowest and the highest level is in each case the same.

4.5 THE PAULI EXCLUSION PRINCIPLE;
SYMMETRIC AND ANTISYMMETRIC WAVE FUNCTIONS

In Newtonian mechanics it is axiomatic that two objects cannot exist at the same place at the same time. We describe the contact force which we use to move objects from one point to another simply as a consequence of this fundamental postulate. An incautious observer might even conclude that this is "an established fact." It would be more correct to state that, as we bring microscopic objects closer and closer together, a greater and greater repulsive force is brought into play. This force is more or less what one might expect if a material object were to exclude other material objects from the space it occupies. But in point of fact, when we examine the situation in detail, from an atomic point of view, we find that there is no such exclusion. We cannot even specify exactly where a particle is at any given time. Our knowledge covers the statistical, or average, aspects of the motion of electrons within atoms, and statistically they move as though collisions did not take place.

From the quantum mechanical point of view, an electron or other similar particle must be described in terms of a wave function. For the problems of interest in connection with the present discussion, the particle is restrained by attractive forces, so that the motion of the particle is characterized by a number of stationary states. The wave functions of the particle in these states are localized. If the particle is in a potential energy box, the wave functions are predominantly within the box, though they may penetrate the walls to some extent. If the wave functions describe an electron in the field force of an atom, they are localized within a volume having linear dimensions of the order of a few times 10^{-10} m. If the wave functions describe the motions of a proton inside a nucleus, they are localized within a

Wolfgang Pauli with Albert Einstein in Leiden 1926 (Photograph by Paul Ehrenfest, professor of theoretical physics at Leiden, Courtesy of American Institute of Physics).

much smaller volume. We can, in each of these cases, specify that the particle is in the region occupied by the wave functions, but we cannot specify where, within such a region, the particle is at any one instant.

What, now, is characteristically different or new about the problem if we have present two or more identical particles in the same system at the same time? Without specifying here how the result is arrived at, we may summarize its significance in the *exclusion principle* of quantum mechanics. The physicist Wolfgang Pauli[9] stated this principle in 1925 on the basis of spectroscopic data even before the advent of wave mechanics. Often called Pauli principle, it can be formulated in the following way: *Two or more identical particles with half-integer spin, such as electrons (or protons, or neutrons), cannot exist in the same state at the same time.* The state of any one of these particles is entirely specified by the wave function, which we have discussed and from here on will call somewhat more precisely spatial wave function, and by one more item, the orientation of its intrinsic angular momentum, or spin. There are always two different possible orientations, namely "spin up" and "spin down," of the $\frac{1}{2}(h/2\pi)$ spin angular momentum of electrons, protons, or neutrons. Consequently for every spatial wave function, which depends on n, l and m_l, there are two possible states with different energies in general.

If in the box problem discussed in Chapter 3 we have one wave function corresponding to the lowest energy, then we may put two particles in the box. They can both exist in stationary states having this lowest energy as long as they differ by their spin direction, thus fulfilling the Pauli principle. If, however, we put a third particle in the box, all three particles cannot get into states having this energy. One of them must occupy a higher energy level. In this particular problem there are three different wave functions due to the threefold degeneracy that characterizes a particle with the next higher energy. If we put more particles into the lowest possible states, we can add six more before this energy level is "filled," and so on. The exclusion principle, as we shall see, is most important to our understanding of the properties of matter.

We should emphasize that the exclusion principle holds only for particles of half-integer spin, such as electrons, protons, or neutrons, all having spin $\frac{1}{2}$. On the other hand, pions (also called π-mesons) have spin 0 and do not obey the exclusion principle. Photons, that is quanta, which can be considered as particles of rest mass zero, carry a spin of one unit of $\hbar$. Consequently they do not observe the Pauli principle either; the same holds for

[9] Wolfgang Pauli (1900–1959), theoretical physicist. In 1925, professor in Hamburg, later at the Swiss Federal Institute of Technology in Zurich. Wrote at the age of 21 one of today's standard works on the theory of relativity. 1945 Nobel prize in physics for the exclusion principle.

deuterons, the nuclei of the heavy hydrogen isotope, which are particles consisting of a proton and neutron held together by nuclear forces. Since proton and neutron both have spin $\frac{1}{2}$, the spin of the deuteron must be either zero or one. (In fact, it is unity.) Particles with half-integer spin are called fermions (after the physicist Enrico Fermi) and obey the exclusion principle; particles with integer spin are called bosons (named for the Indian physicist Bose) and do not obey the exclusion principle.

We shall now discuss the Pauli principle in the more mathematical way of theoretical physics.

In our earlier discussions on wave functions, such as those of the hydrogen atom, we had neglected the spin without harmful effects. Obviously we cannot do this here anymore where the exclusion principle and therefore also the spin quantum number play a role. Inclusion of the spin can be accomplished by multiplying our old wave function, the spatial wave function $\psi_{spatial}$, with the spin wave function ψ_{spin}. The name "spin wave function" is somewhat misleading, because there is no wave associated with it. It has merely been chosen in analogy to the spatial wave function. In calculations like that of the hydrogen atom we may consider ψ_{spin} as a constant factor. The total wave function will then be a solution of the Schrödinger equation just as the spatial wave function has been. The total wave function can therefore be written

$$\psi_{total} = \psi_{spatial} \cdot \psi_{spin}.$$

In the following we drop the subscript "total" for simplicity.

Let us assume that we have two identical, undistinguishable, particles, say two electrons, labeled 1 and 2, in the same atom. The ψ function for the two particles together can symbolically be written as $\psi(1, 2)$, and therefore the probability density as $|\psi(1, 2)|^2$. The wave function $\psi(1, 2)$ could also have been written as $\psi(\mathbf{r}_1, \mathbf{r}_2)$, meaning that particle 1 is at a distance $\mathbf{r}_1$ from the origin, and particle 2 at a distance $\mathbf{r}_2$. ψ is therefore a function of two variables. With this probability density $|\psi(1, 2)|^2$ we can express the probability that one particle is in the volume element dv_1 and the other particle in the volume element dv_2 by writing $|\psi(1, 2)|^2 dv_1 dv_2$. If we exchange the positions of our two identical particles, that is, if we put particle 1 at the place of particle 2 and vice versa, nothing changes physically, therefore

$$|\psi(2, 1)|^2 = |\psi(1, 2)|^2,$$

where the change of place of particles 1 and 2 is symbolically expressed through the interchange of their position within the parentheses. This equality holds when

$$\psi(2, 1) = +\psi(1, 2),$$

but it also holds if

$$\psi(2, 1) = -\psi(1, 2).$$

If we know that one (but not which one!) of the two particles is in a state described by a certain set[10] of quantum numbers a, the other one in a state with quantum numbers b, we might be tempted to write $\psi(1, 2)$ in the following form:

$$\psi(1, 2) = \psi_a(1)\psi_b(2).$$

However, such a formulation would imply that we know that it is particle 1 which is in the state with quantum numbers a and similarly particle 2 in the state with quantum numbers b. Since the electrons are to us like identical twins without name tags, we do not have that much detailed knowledge. The only fact we know is that one of the electrons is in this state, the other one in that state. Hence, we have to erase the individuality of the particles in our wave function. This can be accomplished by the following two forms of wave functions; the first one is called symmetric, the second one antisymmetric:

symmetric: $$\psi_+(1, 2) = \frac{1}{\sqrt{2}} \left[\psi_a(1)\psi_b(2) + \psi_a(2)\psi_b(1)\right] \quad (4.5.1)$$

antisymmetric: $$\psi_-(1, 2) = \frac{1}{\sqrt{2}} \left[\psi_a(1)\psi_b(2) - \psi_a(2)\psi_b(1)\right]. \quad (4.5.2)$$

The factor $2^{-1/2}$ is of no importance for our discussion. It only takes care of the normalization of the wave function. Why these wave functions are called symmetric and antisymmetric can best be seen if we look at the spatial part of the wave functions. The total wave function will be symmetric if the spatial and the spin parts are both symmetric or both antisymmetric, and it will be antisymmetric if only one (in the general case an odd number) of the parts is antisymmetric. Spatial wave functions are pictured in Fig. 4.5.1. The abscissa in each graph represents the distance between the two electrons.

Clearly, the spin wave functions of a two-electron system with both spins up or down are symmetric against the exchange of the two spins. If, however, the spins are in opposite directions, we have again the two possibilities of a symmetric and an antisymmetric spin wave function, just as in the case of the total wave functions of Eq. 4.5.1 and 4.5.2.

A pictorial representation of the orientations of the individual spins of

---

[10] Such a set might consist, for example, of the quantum numbers n, l, m_l, m_s.

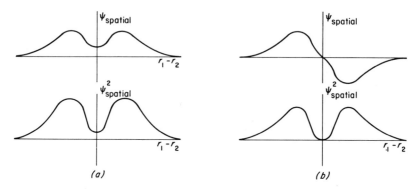

Fig. 4.5.1   Symmetric (a) and antisymmetric (b) spatial wave functions and their squares.

two electrons and their sum is given in Fig. 4.5.2. The vertical axis is the z axis around which the spins precess. The magnitude of the spin vectors is $(\frac{1}{2} \cdot \frac{3}{2})^{1/2} \hbar$ and the z component is $\frac{1}{2} \hbar$. The situations (a), (b), and (c) compose the triplet, and (d) is the singlet. Whereas the individual vectors in (d) are antiparallel and add up to zero, the vectors in (c) combine to a resultant rotating vector which has no z component, and whose x and y components averaged over several rotations are also zero.

If we exchange in the total wave functions particles 1 and 2, we get from

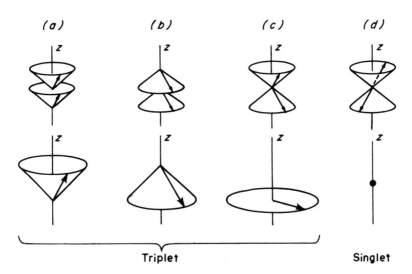

Fig. 4.5.2   The combination of two spins to a triplet (a), (b), (c), and a singlet (d).

Eq. 4.5.1

$$\psi_+(2, 1) = +\psi_+(1, 2).$$

From Eq. 4.5.2 follows

$$\psi_-(2, 1) = -\psi_1(1, 2).$$

These two wave functions have just the properties which we had required at the beginning. If we postulate that the wave function describing two electrons must be antisymmetric, we immediately see the following: In the case where both electrons are in the same state (which means that they have the same set of quantum numbers, that is, $a = b$), the antisymmetric wave function $\psi_-(1, 2)$ becomes zero, and obviously $|\psi|^2 = 0$. This result can also be considered as the consequence of an alternate and more general form of the Pauli exclusion principle: Assemblies of identical particles with half-integer spin must be described by an antisymmetric total wave function. Conversely, assemblies of identical particles for which the Pauli principle does not apply must have symmetric wave functions.

Why particles with half-integer spin behave differently from particles with integer spin was understood only many years after the Pauli principle had been stated, in its original pre-wave-mechanical, and alternate form. However, the reasons for this go far beyond the scope of this book. The Pauli principle solved at once the question why not all the electrons of an atom in its ground state occupy its lowest energy level, a question which Niels Bohr already had raised much earlier. If the electrons were particles that did not obey the exclusion principle, the whole physical world would look completely different. This principle not only plays an all-important role in the structure of atoms, but also in that of nuclei and in the structure of matter. Without the exclusion principle, the whole field of chemistry would be completely different from what it is.

4.6 THE PERIODIC TABLE OF ELEMENTS

A good deal about the structure of atoms in general may be inferred from the hydrogen atom and the exclusion principle. For example, if we have an atom consisting of a nucleus with a double proton charge and a single electron, this single electron will have hydrogen-like states, but the potential-energy well will be deeper and narrower, the energy levels will be lower and farther apart, and the wave functions will cover a smaller volume. If now we add a second electron, the problem is much more complicated electrostatically. However, it turns out that the hydrogen energy-level scheme is still approximately applicable. The electrons tend to keep out of each other's way. The second electron, if its spin is oppositely oriented to that of the first, may have the same spatial wave function as the first and may therefore also occupy the lowest energy level. This results in a particularly stable atom that is hard to excite. The ground state is separated from the next higher level by a greater gap than in any other atom. This atom is the helium atom, with $Z = 2$. It is chemically very inert. Helium atoms interact with each other so little that helium gas at a pressure of one atmosphere must be cooled to within a few degrees of the absolute zero before the very slight attractive forces between them will cause the gas to condense.

The degeneracy of the hydrogen energy levels is shown in Fig. 4.6.1. With a nuclear charge $Z = 2$, and two electrons, the lowest level is filled. The corresponding substances are hydrogen and helium.

If now we consider atoms with more and more electrons, we may think of the energy level with $n = 2$ being filled. Since there are four spatial wave functions and each may contain two electrons with oppositely oriented spins, we may expect to find another stable helium-like atom with eight more, or altogether ten, electrons. From the periodic table we find the

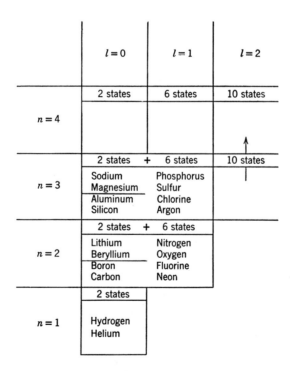

Fig. 4.6.1   The degeneracy of the hydrogen energy levels and the periodic table.

following:

$$Z = 3 \quad 4 \quad 5 \quad 6 \quad 7 \quad 8 \quad 9 \quad 10$$

Element   Li   Be   B   C   N   O   F   Ne

The element whose atomic number is 10, neon, is indeed a helium-like gas. All the levels whose energies are relatively close together, for example, the levels with the same value of n, comprise a shell, and subgroups of it are often called subshells. The $n = 2$ shell for example contains the $l = 0$ and the $l = 1$ subshells. This pictorial name comes from the old picture of the Bohr atom model which represented the atom as some sort of onion, each onion shell having a different quantum number n. The filling of the third shell proceeds in like manner. However, the energy levels are now closer together, as shown in Fig. 4.6.1, and the interaction of the electrons with each other is no longer negligible. As a result the addition of only eight more electrons, to give a total of 18, produces the next noble gas, argon, with $Z = 18$. The energy of the ten states with $n = 3$ and $l = 2$ is raised, and the corresponding substances occur in the next period of the periodic table. The further details of the periodic table become much more difficult to understand because of the greater influence of electron-electron interactions, and we shall not pursue them in detail.

Figure 4.6.2 contains the periodic table in a representation that should convey the sequence in which it is built up. At a few places an electron located in an already completed s or d subshell has moved to the subshell being filled because the resulting configuration is the more stable one. Such cases are indicated by -s or -d underneath the chemical symbol; for example, in $_{24}$Cr one of the two s electrons which were the valence electrons of $_{20}$Ca has been replaced by a fifth d electron.

Some assignments, which concern mostly d and f subshells, in the region of rare earths, the lanthanides ($Z = 57$–71) and actinides ($Z = 89$–103), are somewhat uncertain. It is worth emphasizing that the noble gases, with the exception of helium and neon, do not complete a shell, characterized by a principal quantum number n, but only a p subshell.

It is well known that Mendeléev[11] discovered the periodic table. He published it in 1869, preceding by a few months the German chemist Lothar Meyer who had discovered it a bit earlier but had delayed its publication. Mendeléev observed that certain elements had similar characteristics. For each element he had prepared a small card listing its atomic weight and its chemical properties, and he tried to arrange these cards in the most sensible way. After having worked again on this problem for an

---

[11] Dmitri Ivanovich Mendeléev (1834–1907), professor of chemistry in St. Petersburg, Russia.

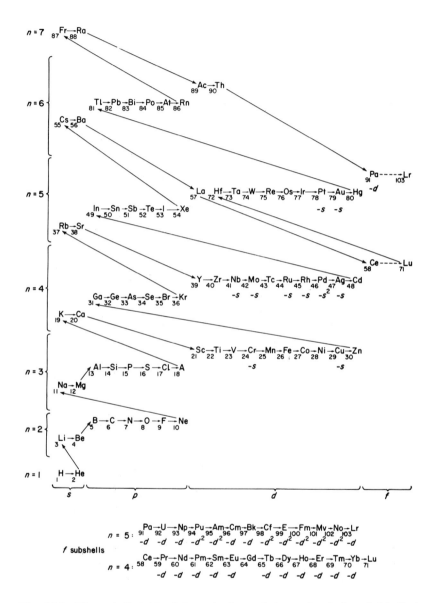

Fig. 4.6.2   The periodic table of elements. An $-s$ below a chemical symbol indicates that an electron has left the s shell and has moved to the new subshell. For example, Cr has only one $4s$ electron, but five $3d$ electrons. A $-d^2$ indicates movement of two d electrons.

evening without much success, the periodic table appeared to him in a dream, whereupon he woke up and immediately put it down on paper!

4.7 THE HELIUM ATOM; EXCHANGE ENERGY

After having treated the hydrogen atom in some detail we want to sketch how theoretical physics proceeds in the calculation of more complicated cases. We choose as an example the helium atom, which has two electrons in its shell.

The theoretical treatment of the binding forces in the hydrogen molecule later in this chapter is to some degree a variation of the ideas developed here. The main difference is that the hydrogen molecule has two nuclei which are separated by a distance of atomic dimensions, and the principal similarity is that both have two electrons. The wave mechanics of the helium atom and the hydrogen molecule brings to light a kind of interaction that has no counterpart in classical physics, namely the so-called exchange interaction. This interaction plays a great role in atomic, molecular, nuclear, and solid-state physics.

Some features of the helium atom have already been mentioned in connection with the periodic system. Here we want to add some further remarks regarding the energy level diagram of helium, referring to Fig. 4.7.1. In the ground state of the atom the two electrons must have opposite spin according to the exclusion principle. Thus the spin wave function of the two spins is antisymmetric. Because the total wave function of the two electrons in the ground state must be antisymmetric, as required by the Pauli principle, the spatial wave function must be symmetric. Since the two spins cancel, the total spin of the atom in the ground state is zero. In the first excited state, in which one electron may be thought to remain in the ground state while the other is excited, the spins can be either antiparallel or parallel, because the two electrons are now in different shells. The same holds also for the higher excited states. Parallel spins of the electrons add to a total spin of the atom of $S = 1$. This spin can, according to the L-S coupling scheme, combine with L in three ways to form a triplet of states with different values of J. The levels with antiparallel electron spins are not split and hence are singlets. The energy level scheme of helium, accordingly, consists of a singlet system and a triplet system. Transitions between the two systems are very rare, which is obviously due to certain rules that make such transitions forbidden. The lowest state in the triplet system is a metastable state. This state can only be de-excited by collisions of the atom with other atoms or with the walls of the container, whereby the

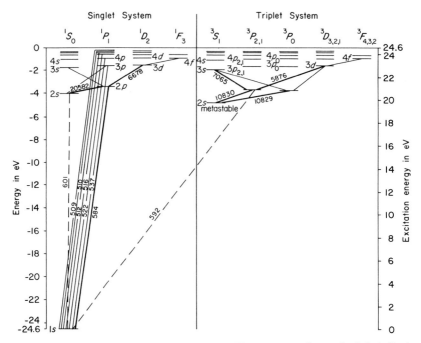

Fig. 4.7.1   Energy level diagram of helium. The energy scale on the left indicates the energy missing to singly ionize the atom, that is, to remove one of its electrons while the second electron remains in its 1s ground state. The scale on the right gives the excitation energy of the atom, with the ground state at zero. The diagonal lines joining two levels represent observed transitions. The predominent ones are drawn with bold lines. Transitions shown by dashed lines do not follow the selection rules discussed in Sect. 4.8 and are therefore called forbidden transitions. For some transitions the wavelength is given in Å.

excitation energy may be transferred to the collision partner. The energies of the singlet states are consistently higher than the corresponding energies of the triplet states. This might seem an unimportant detail, but it contains the clue for what is discussed on the following pages.

For the study of the helium atom it is worthwhile to investigate how this atom differs from the hydrogen atom. In the latter we had to deal only with the interaction between the nucleus and the electron. Here we have, if we designate the two electrons by 1 and 2 and the nucleus by n, the interaction potentials, V_{n1}, V_{n2}, V_{12}, where the first two represent the interaction between the nucleus and each of the electrons, and the last one the interaction between the two electrons which is

$$V_{12} = \frac{1}{4\pi\epsilon_0} \frac{e^2}{r_{12}}.$$

The position of the two particles in space clearly must be described with six coordinates x_1, y_1, z_1, x_2, y_2, and z_2, and the ψ function becomes a function of these six coordinates. According to the theory of probability, the probability P that event a *and* event b will happen is the product of the single probabilities P_a and P_b,

$$P = P_a \cdot P_b.$$

Therefore, we might be tempted also to consider ψ_{spat}, the spatial part of the ψ function of the He atom as the product of the spatial ψ functions for each of the electrons as follows,

$$\psi_{\text{spat}} = \psi_{a,\text{spat}}(1)\psi_{b,\text{spat}}(2) \tag{4.7.1}$$

where a stands for the set of quantum numbers for the first electron, and b is the analog for the second factor. However, we encounter here the same difficulties we faced when discussing the Pauli principle: The two electrons are undistinguishable from each other. Therefore,

$$\psi_{\text{spat}} = \psi_{a,\text{spat}}(2)\psi_{b,\text{spat}}(1) \tag{4.7.2}$$

is physically not different and leads to the same energy eigenvalue as Eq. 4.7.1. On the same grounds that were given in the discussion of the Pauli principle, the linear combinations

$$\psi_{\text{spat},+} = 2^{-1/2}[\psi_{a,\text{spat}}(1)\psi_{b,\text{spat}}(2) + \psi_{a,\text{spat}}(2)\psi_{b,\text{spat}}(1)]$$

$$\psi_{\text{spat},-} = 2^{-1/2}[\psi_{a,\text{spat}}(1)\psi_{b,\text{spat}}(2) - \psi_{a,\text{spat}}(2)\psi_{b,\text{spat}}(1)]$$

are therefore the appropriate solutions. $\psi_{\text{spat},+}$ is clearly a symmetric wave function and $\psi_{\text{spat},-}$ an antisymmetric wave function.

We now can set up the Schrödinger equation for the helium atom

$$\nabla_1^2\psi_{\text{spat}} + \nabla_2^2\psi_{\text{spat}} + \frac{2m}{\hbar^2}(E - V_{n1} - V_{n2} - V_{12})\psi_{\text{spat}} = 0$$

where

$$\nabla_1^2\psi_{\text{spat}} + \nabla_2^2\psi_{\text{spat}}$$

$$\equiv \frac{\partial^2\psi_{\text{spat}}}{\partial x_1^2} + \frac{\partial^2\psi_{\text{spat}}}{\partial y_1^2} + \frac{\partial^2\psi_{\text{spat}}}{\partial z_1^2} + \frac{\partial^2\psi_{\text{spat}}}{\partial x_2^2} + \frac{\partial^2\psi_{\text{spat}}}{\partial y_2^2} + \frac{\partial^2\psi_{\text{spat}}}{\partial z_2^2},$$

and ψ_{spat} is either $\psi_{\text{spat},+}$ or $\psi_{\text{spat},-}$ from above.

The solution of this problem follows lines of reasoning which had been developed in the last century for celestial mechanics, the so-called *perturbation theory*. The classical example is the computation of planetary orbits by taking into account the gravitational attraction between planets. In a first approximation, that is by neglecting this interaction, the planetary orbits are ellipses. Perturbation theory calculates the *small* perturbations originating from the interactions between planets. The details of the calculation are beyond the scope of this book, but it should be plausible that the average interaction energy may be calculated by an integration taking into account all possible configurations of the planets.

The quantum-mechanical calculations for the helium atom follow similar lines. The energy of an atomic state is in first approximation simply the sum of the energies of the single electrons. If electron 1 is in state E_1 and electron 2 in state E_2, the energy E of the atom is therefore in first approximation

$$E = E_1 + E_2.$$

To this we now have to add the interaction energy ΔE, which is

$$\Delta E = \int \psi^2{}_{\text{spat}}(a, b) V_{12} \, dv_a \, dv_b \qquad (4.7.3)$$

where $\psi^2{}_{\text{spat}}(a, b) dv_a \, dv_b$ describes the probability that one electron is in the volume element dv_a at the position a and the other in the volume element dv_b at b. V_{12} is the interaction potential energy $(1/4\pi\epsilon_0)(e^2/r_{12})$ between the two.

We found above that the wave functions for the two electrons have the symmetric and antisymmetric forms

$$\psi_{\text{spat}}(a, b) = 2^{-1/2}[\psi_{\text{spat},a}(1)\psi_{\text{spat},b}(2) \pm \psi_{\text{spat},a}(2)\psi_{\text{spat},b}(1)] \quad (4.7.4)$$

with the plus sign for the symmetric and the minus sign for the antisymmetric form. This yields for their squares

$$\psi^2{}_{\text{spat}}(a, b) = \tfrac{1}{2}[\psi^2{}_{\text{spat},a}(1)\psi^2{}_{\text{spat},b}(2) + \psi^2{}_{\text{spat},a}(2)\psi^2{}_{\text{spat},b}(1)$$
$$\pm 2\psi_{\text{spat},a}(1)\psi_{\text{spat},b}(1)\psi_{\text{spat},a}(2)\psi_{\text{spat},b}(2)]. \quad (4.7.5)$$

Inserting this expression into Eq. 4.7.3, one can calculate ΔE. The first two terms under the integral, which are equal in magnitude and can be lumped together, represent the Coulomb energy which is already expected on the basis of classical considerations. The third term, however, does not have a classical counterpart. Depending on the symmetric or antisymmetric character of the wave function, this term changes its sign. Inspection of the term reveals that the states of the two electrons are here completely mixed up, or exchanged. The energy associated with this term is called exchange energy. And just as the Coulomb energy is due to Coulomb forces, here one has to deal with exchange forces.

The two components of the perturbation energy, namely the Coulomb energy C and the exchange energy A are shown in Fig. 4.7.2. To the left are

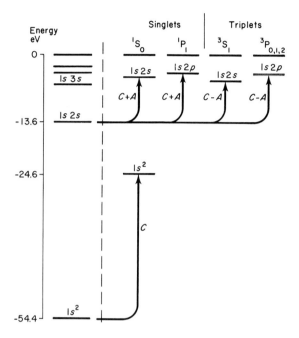

Fig. 4.7.2 The lowest levels of helium. Left: Neglecting interaction between elec-trons. Right: Taking into account Coulomb (C) and exchange (A) energies. The arrows indicate the shift of the levels. (The fine-structure splitting of the 3p state is greatly exaggerated.) The energy zero corresponds to the situation where one electron is lifted to the ionization limit, whereas the other one is still in the ground state.

the energy levels calculated like those of the hydrogen atom. One of the electrons remains in its ground state, whereas the other one can be in different excited states. At the energy zero in the scale of the figure this electron is no more bound to the atom. In the ground state of the atom, both electrons are 1s electrons. This state is therefore labeled $1s^2$. For the first excited state, labeled 1s2s, one electron has changed to the 2s level, whereas the other remains in the 1s level. In the rough approximation which completely neglects the interaction between the two electrons, the ground-state binding energy of one electron is four times that in a hydrogen atom, because the energy is proportional to Z^2. On the right-hand side of Fig. 4.7.2, the position of the same energy levels is given when the inter-action between the two electrons is taken into account, as sketched above. Because of the Coulomb interaction between the two electrons, the ground state has moved up. The Coulomb repulsion has lifted the level closer to the ionization energy, so to speak. In the ground state both electrons have the same spatial ψ function, $\psi_{\text{spat},a}(1) = \psi_{\text{spat},a}(2)$; therefore, there is no place for an exchange term.[12] In the excited levels the electrons are in different states. We find therefore Coulomb and exchange terms. The exchange energy is positive for the singlet states and negative for the triplet states. The reason for this is that singlet states must have symmetric spatial wave functions, because their spin wave function is antisymmetric (the two spins are opposite) and, according to the Pauli principle, the total wave function (spatial wave function times spin wave function) must be antisymmetric. The opposite holds for the triplet states regarding the spatial wave function because the spin wave function is symmetric. The exchange energy is negative because the spatial wave function must now be antisymmetric. The splitting between triplet and singlet terms is much greater than the fine-structure splitting within the triplets which is due, as we have seen in Section 4.2, to a magnetic interaction between orbital magnetic moment and spin magnetic moment. However, the exchange-energy term is not so great as the Coulomb term, although in general still of the same order of magnitude. This is not surprising since both have the same origin.

The concept of exchange energy is purely quantum mechanical. It has no direct classical counterpart. There is however a classical analog in the behavior of two coupled pendulums. Two pendulums (Fig. 4.7.3) can

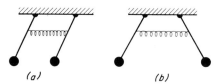

(a)   (b)

Fig. 4.7.3   The symmetric (a) and the antisymmetric (b) mode of oscillation of two coupled pendulums.

[12] This is seen more clearly from the following argument: For particles in the same state a, instead of Eq. 4.7.4 we have now simply

$$\psi_{spat}(a, a) = \psi_{spat,a}(1)\psi_{spat,a}(2)$$

or

$$\psi^2_{spat}(a, a) = \psi^2_{spat,a}(1)\psi^2_{spat,a}(2) \tag{4.7.6}$$

which already satisfies the requirement that the particles are indistinguishable. However, we might expect to arrive at the same result when starting from Eq. 4.7.4 by replacing each subscript b by a subscript a. This will give us instead of Eq. 4.7.5 the equation

$$\psi^2_{spat}(a, a) = \tfrac{1}{2}[\psi^2_{spat,a}(1)\psi^2_{spat,a}(2) + \psi^2_{spat,a}(1)\psi^2_{spat,a}(2) + 2\psi^2_{spat,a}(1)\psi^2_{spat,a}(2)]$$

$$= 2\psi^2_{spat,a}(1)\psi^2_{spat,a}(2).$$

Comparison of this equation with Eq. 4.7.6. shows that the last result is two times too big because of the superfluous "exchange term," where nothing is to be exchanged.

oscillate with two different frequencies, one belonging to the symmetric mode, and the other to the antisymmetric mode. Furthermore, if one pendulum is first at rest, and only the other oscillates, soon some, and at a later moment all, energy from the first pendulum is transferred to the second one; thereafter the energy is shifted back again to the first pendulum and so on. There is a steady exchange of energy. This analogy should not be taken too literally; it is not the same, but only a related physical phenomenon.

Even more important than in atoms is the exchange energy in molecules. The forces that hold a hydrogen molecule together are the exchange forces. In other words, exchange forces are the cause of the homopolar chemical bond.

4.8 THE ATOMIC STRUCTURE OF MANY-ELECTRON ATOMS

We do not intend to discuss in great detail energy levels and spectra of the atoms which are more complicated than the hydrogen and helium atoms. However, we want to give the reader some idea how different factors influence their atomic structure.

The third element in the periodic system is lithium. The two levels with $n = 1$ are filled with two electrons, and the third electron is alone in the $n = 2$ shell. We may expect that this least-bound electron might display a spectrum similar to the hydrogen spectrum because the two inner electrons neutralize two of the three positive charges of the nucleus as seen from the third electron, which (averaged over the time) is farther away from the nucleus than the other two. Inspection of the level diagram of Li (Fig. 4.8.1) shows that this is roughly so indeed, with certain exceptions.

The ground state of the atom is evidently the $2S$ level. (The $1S$ level is fully occupied by the two inner electrons.) The principal quantum number $n = 3$ has two levels that are relatively far apart; in hydrogen these levels were practically degenerate. Here the degeneracy is removed. The higher the orbital angular momentum l, the less the electron is bound. The screening, or neutralizing, of the central charge of the nucleus by the two inner electrons is more effective for a third electron of higher values of l because such an electron spends more of its time farther away from the nucleus than an electron with little angular momentum. The potential in which the third electron moves is no longer the Coulomb potential of a point charge which goes with $-1/r$, but a potential that approaches zero more rapidly as the screening becomes more effective with increasing r. This effect is also noticeable in the level diagram of the helium atom.

The spectrum of the next higher alkali atom, Na (Fig. 4.8.2) looks very

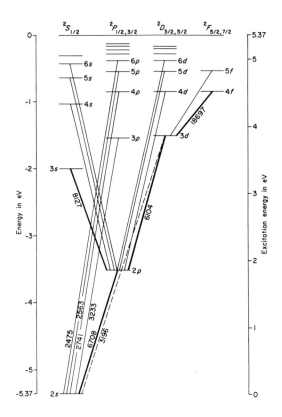

Fig. 4.8.1 Energy level diagram of lithium. The energy scale on the left indicates the energy missing to ionize the atom, the energy scale on the right gives the excitation energy of the atom, with the ground state at zero. The diagonal lines joining two levels represent observed transitions. The predominent ones are drawn with bold lines. The transition shown by a dashed line does not follow the selection rule $\Delta l = 1$; it is a so-called forbidden transition with $\Delta l = 2$. For some transitions the wavelength is given in Å.

similar, but the ground state is now the $3S$ state. In the level diagram of Li (and also of He) we neglected the splitting of the levels due to the different orientations of the spin in relation to the orbital angular momentum vector. We therefore want to make up this deficiency in the example of this element.

The levels for which electron spin and orbital angular momentum are antiparallel (and therefore have the magnetic moments parallel as seen in Fig. 4.3.5) are slightly depressed and the other levels raised. The two levels therefore form a fine-structure doublet. The S-levels are obviously not split because there is no orbital angular momentum present which could add in

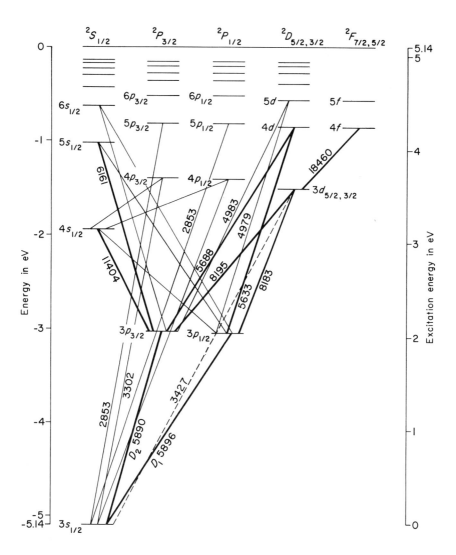

Fig. 4.8.2   Energy level diagram of sodium. The transitions $3p_{1/2} - 3s_{1/2}$ and $3p_{3/2} - 3s_{1/2}$ compose the doublet of the yellow sodium D spectral lines.

two different ways with the spin. Transitions to or from split levels, as mentioned earlier, show slightly different wavelengths and frequencies. A famous example is the doublet of the yellow sodium D lines[13] which are emitted in transitions from the states $3^2P_{3/2}$ and $3^2P_{1/2}$. The wavelength of one member of this Na doublet is 5890 Å and that of the other 6 Å more.

Our last example is carbon; its level diagram (Fig. 4.8.3) is representative for the somewhat more complicated atoms. Of the four valence electrons two are in the $2s$ subshell and hence contribute nothing to the angular momentum. The two electrons in the $2p$ subshell can combine their angular momenta in different ways, which results in three different terms having energies that are not far apart, namely ^3P, ^1D, and ^1S. If one of the p-electrons is excited, a number of configurations is possible. Following the

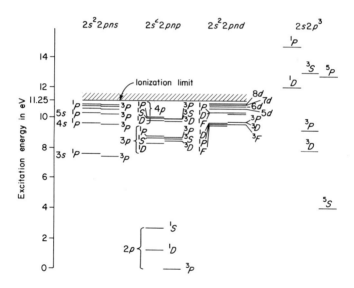

Fig. 4.8.3   Energy level diagram of carbon. In the three double ladders on the left the two $2s$ electrons pair off to zero angular momentum, and the fifth electron is in a $2p$ state. The sixth electron of carbon can be in either an s, p, or d state. Depending on the relative spin orientation of the fifth and sixth electron, either singlets or triplets are formed. In the ground state two $2p$ electrons add to a ^3P state. Excitation of one electron by more than 11.25 eV leads to ionization. In the triple ladder on the right one of the $2s$ electrons has changed into another $3p$ electron. The three $3p$ electrons and the unpaired $2s$ electron can combine to various states, some of them lying higher than 11.25 eV, without leading to ionization.

[13] The name D line has nothing to do with the spectroscopical D terms. Fraunhofer labeled the prominent absorption lines in the spectrum of the sun which he discovered (and which are now named after him) with letters.

practice of the spectroscopists, the level diagram contains, besides the value of the resulting angular momentum in capital letters, the electron configurations for these levels. $2s^2 2pnp$ signifies the four valence electrons, two (hence the superscript) of them in the $2s$ subshell, one in the $2p$ state and the last one in the np state ($n = 3, 4, 5, \ldots$). The spins of the two last electrons can combine either to a singlet or to a triplet system.

Having discussed energy levels, we shall now take up as our next topic the transitions between the levels. Certain so-called *selection rules* have to be followed. The physical basis of the selection rules was discussed briefly in Section 3.8. Although some of these rules are not strictly obeyed in certain cases, they influence at least the intensity ratio of spectral lines of competing transitions departing from the same level to two or more different levels.

One of the most striking features of these diagrams is that all the transitions are represented by diagonal, not by vertical, lines. This comes from the selection rule that the orbital angular momentum must change by an amount

$$\Delta L = \pm 1.$$

Since the total angular momentum of a closed system is one of the quantities which must always be conserved, in classical as well as in quantum physics, the emitted or absorbed light quantum carries angular momentum in addition to its energy.

From inspection, particularly of the helium diagram, another selection rule can be deduced:

$$\Delta S = 0.$$

Transitions between the triplet states of helium, which all have $S = 1$, and the states of the singlet system with $S = 0$ are not allowed. In heavier elements, such as mercury, where the coupling is not pure L-S, the existence of a total S is slightly questionable, and therefore we find some transitions that involve the spin flip of an electron.

By the same token there are also some lines in this spectrum which are associated with a $\Delta L = 0$, which is against the orthodox rules for L-S coupling. Another, and this time very liberal, rule is also easy to deduce from the diagram: Δn can assume any (of course, integer) value.

For M the selection rule is

$$\Delta M = 0, \pm 1.$$

Furthermore, there is a selection rule for J, which holds for L-S and j-j coupling

$$\Delta J = 0, \pm 1.$$

Transitions that should not appear according to the selection rules but in fact may be observed are called *forbidden* transitions. Much of the light of auroras comes from such forbidden transitions. Under the usual laboratory conditions an atom which is in a metastable state can get rid of its energy by collision with other atoms or with the walls of the apparatus. In the low pressure of the upper atmosphere the frequency of collisions is much reduced. The atom will therefore stay for a long time in its metastable state. Since the transition probability for a forbidden line is usually not strictly zero, but only very small, the forbidden transition will finally take place.

The Zeeman Effect

We have seen that the magnetic interaction between the magnetic moments associated with electron spin and orbital angular momentum plays an important role in the structure of atoms. Because of this interaction the energy levels of most atoms display a fine structure which is

Pieter Zeeman (1865–1943) (Courtesy of Niels Bohr Library, W. F. Meggers Collection, American Institute of Physics).

observable in a corresponding splitting of spectral lines radiated in transitions to or from these levels.

Our attention will now be focused on the interaction between an external magnetic field and an atom at a particular energy, as represented by a single atomic level. The upper state involved in a radiative transition will have some definite total angular momentum, specified by the quantum number J. Similarly, the lower level will also be characterized by some particular value of the resultant angular momentum. We proceed to describe the effect of an externally applied magnetic field on the single spectral line being considered. We shall see that it splits into several components. This splitting is accurately described by the quantum theory and is called the Zeeman effect in honor of its discoverer.[14]

By way of illustrating the Zeeman effect, let us consider a transition from an excited level with $J = 1$ to a ground state with $J = 0$. Furthermore, we will assume that the spin $S = 0$ for both levels, that is, that the atom is in singlet states. The spectroscopic notations of these levels are hence $^1P_1$ and $^1S_0$. The angular momentum is therefore only due to L. This will lead to the *normal* Zeeman effect. In the absence of a magnetic field, the atom will radiate a single line whose frequency is ν. In the presence of a magnetic field, the ground state will be unaltered, and in the excited state the atom can have any one of three orientations, with the z component of

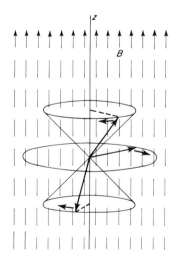

Fig. 4.8.4   The three orientations of a $^1P_1$ atom in an external magnetic field.

its angular momentum parallel or antiparallel to the applied field, or zero, as in Fig. 4.8.4. Because the magnetic moment μ of the atom in our specific case is in the direction of the angular momentum vector, the atom will therefore also have three different energies, corresponding to the three different orientations of μ with respect to the magnetic field B. These energies will be equal to the unperturbed energy E (the energy in the absence of a magnetic field) plus ΔE, where in our example

$$\Delta E = \pm\mu B \text{ or } 0.$$

The excited state is therefore split into three states, as shown in Fig. 4.8.5(a). Further, the single frequency radiated in the absence of a field and giving rise to a single spectral line will be modified to include three frequencies and three spectral lines having the frequencies ν_1, $\nu_1 + \mu B/h$, and $\nu_1 - \mu B/h$.

Spectral lines may split up in more complex ways. The Zeeman effect of a line involving a transition from an excited level with $J = \frac{1}{2}$ to a ground state with $J = \frac{1}{2}$ is shown in Fig. 4.8.5(b). In the presence of a magnetic field each level will split into two, corresponding to the two possible

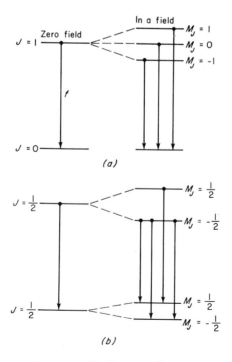

(a)

(b)

Fig. 4.8.5   The Zeeman effect.

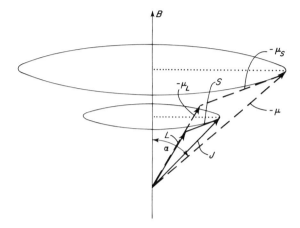

Fig. 4.8.6   Illustration of a case where J and μ are not parallel to each other, leading to the anomalous Zeeman effect.

orientations of J. If the magnetic moments of the atom in the ground and excited states are different, the amount of the splitting will be different, and we may expect to find the single line of frequency ν without a field split into four components by a magnetic field.

Although the splitting of an energy level in the general case is given by the equation

$$\Delta E = \mu B \cos \alpha$$

where α is the angle between μ and B, the calculation is usually not simple. μ is in general not in the direction of the total angular momentum J. This arises from the fact that the magnetic moment μ_S associated with a spin $S = \frac{1}{2}\hbar$ has the same magnitude as the magnetic moment μ_L which goes with an orbital angular momentum of $L = 1\hbar$; μ_S is therefore twice as great as the nonrelativistic theory predicts. Consequently, the direction of the resultant magnetic moment vector will in general not coincide with the direction of the total angular momentum vector. The result is that the angle α is not equal to the angle between J and B (Fig. 4.8.6). The corresponding level splitting leads to the *anomalous* Zeeman effect, in contrast to the earlier discussed normal Zeeman effect.

We had tacitly assumed that the external magnetic field did not alter the coupling between the orbital magnetic moment and the spin magnetic moment. This assumption is correct as long as the field is weak, and the foregoing discussion holds. If, however, the field is strong enough, the orbital and spin magnetic moments may be "decoupled" and through them also the corresponding angular momenta. If this happens, L and S sepa-

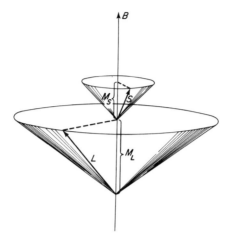

Fig. 4.8.7   Decoupling of L and S in a strong magnetic field (Paschen-Back effect).

rately will orient themselves with respect to the external field so that the z components of each satisfy the quantum conditions. J in this case has lost its importance. As a result the splitting of the levels is therefore different from the splitting caused by weak fields. Also the splitting of the spectral lines is different. This effect is known as the Paschen-Back effect. Figure 4.8.7 gives an example of the decoupling of the L and S vectors and their individual precession in the external magnetic field.

4.9   X-RAY SPECTRA

Let us consider the energy levels of a single electron in the field of a nucleus having a charge Ze. The expression for the potential energy becomes $-(Ze^2)/4\pi\epsilon_0 r$, and the energy levels of the atoms may easily be shown (see Problem 1) to be

$$E = -\frac{m(Ze^2)^2}{8\epsilon_0^2 h^2}\frac{1}{n^2} \tag{4.9.1}$$

or just Z^2 times the energy values obtained for the hydrogen atom. The frequency radiated in a transition from the second to the first level is then

$$\nu = \frac{E_2 - E_1}{h} = \frac{mZ^2 e^4}{8\epsilon_0^2 h^3}\left(\tfrac{1}{1} - \tfrac{1}{4}\right). \tag{4.9.2}$$

It will be seen that as Z increases, ν increases, and upon substituting numbers into Eq. 4.9.2 one finds frequencies in the x-ray region for not very great values of Z.

Highly ionized atoms to which Eq. 4.9.2 is applicable are difficult to produce. However, such transitions can also be generated in neutral atoms. In a heavy atom with large Z, the electrons in the lowest level are held in a small shell close to the nucleus. The larger the atomic number, the smaller the shell. This inner shell is called the K shell. Outside this inner K shell, with two electrons, is a larger shell, called the L shell, with eight electrons. Outside this, in turn, are other shells, the $M, N, \ldots$, shells; the outermost, and unfilled, shell containing the valence electrons.

Figure 4.9.1 illustrates the occupied levels for a series of neutral atoms. Note that the energy scales had to be chosen differently for different elements. The scales are labeled in such a way that they show the amount of energy necessary to remove an electron from a specific shell. The energy associated with the top level is therefore the energy necessary to singly ionize the atom. It is easily seen that with increasing charge Z of the nucleus the electrons of corresponding shells are more and more tightly bound, and that more and more electron shells are filled.

In a normal atom shells are filled from the bottom up. Because of the exclusion principle, transitions from one to another of these low-lying levels are not possible *unless a vacancy in some state is created by the removal of an electron.* If a K shell electron, for example, is removed from an atom, say by a collision with a fast-moving electron, then an electron in any one of the shells with higher energy may "drop" into the K shell. In doing so, it will emit a quantum, which may be in the x-ray region. X-ray spectra may be computed by using Eq. 4.9.2 with one modification, for reasons that may be understood on the basis of the following considerations. The field within a spherically symmetrical shell of charge is zero. The outer electrons

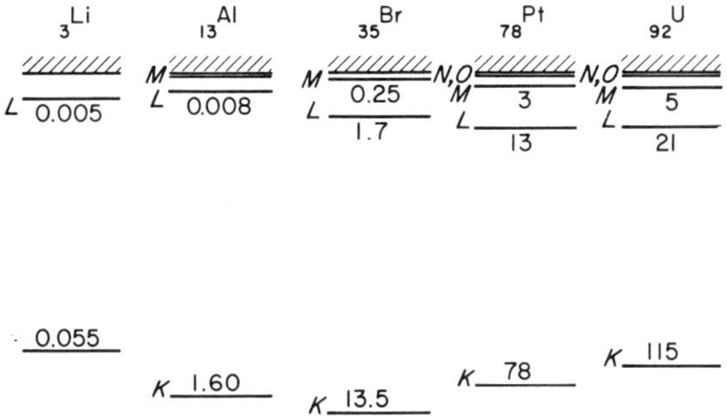

Fig. 4.9.1 Energies of occupied shells of different elements (in keV). (Values are approximate only, because different subshells have different energies.)

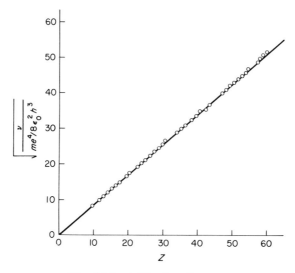

Fig. 4.9.2   A Moseley diagram.

contribute nothing to the field of which an inner electron in an atom is aware. In fact, we might estimate that an electron in the L shell of an atom from which one innermost K electron was missing would be moving in the attractive field of force of $Z - 1$ protons, the -1 being due to the one remaining K electron down nearer the nucleus than the L-shell electron. In general, we might expect to use a formula like Eq. 4.9.2 for the combination of x-ray frequencies and wavelengths if we replace the atomic number Z by some smaller number Z^*, the actual value of Z^* depending on which electron is missing and which transitions we are considering.

The dependence of the frequency of x-rays for this $L \rightarrow K$ transition as a function of the atomic number Z should then be given by the expression

$$\sqrt{\nu} = \sqrt{\frac{me^4}{8\epsilon_0^2 h^3}} \cdot 0.865 \, (Z^*) \qquad (4.9.3)$$

where Z^* is the atomic number Z less some constant of the order of unity and $0.865 = (\frac{1}{1} - \frac{1}{4})^{1/2}$. The degree to which this expression is satisfied is shown in Fig. 4.9.2, in which

$$\frac{\sqrt{\nu}}{\sqrt{\dfrac{me^4}{8\epsilon_0^2 h^3}}}$$

is plotted as a function of the atomic number Z, ν being the experimentally observed frequency. The predicted line according to Eq. 4.9.3 is shown as well as the experimental points. The agreement between theory and experiment is seen to be excellent. A plot of this kind is called a Moseley diagram in honor of the scientist who was killed during the First World War, and who first discovered the linear relationship between the $\nu^{1/2}$ and Z for corresponding x-ray lines of the elements.

Not only are transitions from the L shell to the K shell possible, which emit the so-called K_α lines, but also transitions from the M shell. These give rise to the K_β lines which are somewhat more energetic than the K_α lines. Furthermore, a vacancy in the L shell can be filled by an electron from the M shell, which leads to the emission of L lines.

X-ray spectra have found many applications as analytical tools. The basic principle is to bombard the material to be investigated with some radiation which knocks out electrons from the inner shells of the atoms. The vacancies will then be filled and x-rays emitted in this process. Often one refers to this as x-ray fluorescence. X-ray spectra are relatively simple, and the x-rays can penetrate layers of condensed matter easier than quanta in the visible range (with the exception of the few substances which are transparent). The quantitative determination of trace elements (e.g., traces of lead in blood) can easily be performed with this method, down to fractions of one part per million (ppm). Figure 4.9.3 shows a fluorescent

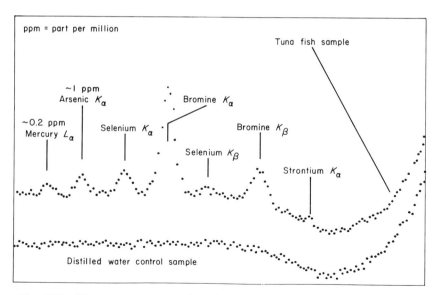

Fig. 4.9.3 Fluorescence x-ray analysis from a sample of tuna fish. K_α lines correspond to transitions from the L to the K shell, K_β lines from the M to the K shell, L_α lines from the M to the L shell. (Courtesy of Dr. R. Woldseth, Kevex Corporation, Burlingame, California.)

x-ray spectrum taken during the great mercury-in-tuna-fish scare around 1970. Not only the L lines of mercury, but also the K lines of other appetizing elements were found in this sample!

Another example[15] comes from the Apollo 15 moon flight mission. The x-rays from the sun which are not filtered out by an atmosphere have enough energy to eject electrons from the lighter elements up to silicon ($Z = 14$). The Command Service Module had an x-ray detector and also a monitor of the solar radiation. In flying over the lunar surface the fluorescent x-rays from aluminum ($Z = 13$) and silicon were monitored for about 100 hours. It was found that the Al/Si intensity ratios and therefore also the Al/Si concentrations over the maria (the dark regions of the moon, or the "seas") was in general around 0.35, whereas over the highlands, it was, in general, in the neighborhood of 0.60, proving that maria and highlands have different chemical and mineralogical compositions. More details about this experiment may be found in the article.

Spectra in the visible range (often called optical spectra) can be observed not only in emission, but also in absorption. In these cases an electron in the outermost shell is lifted to a higher, unoccupied level by selective absorption of radiation. Absorption of a K or L x-ray line cannot arise because there would have to be a vacancy in an inner shell into which the K or L electron could be lifted. The only possibility is to eject electrons from inner shells, say the K or L shell, into the continuum. The situation is therefore comparable to the photoelectric effect by visible light on bulk matter. For this reason one also speaks here about a photoeffect and photoelectrons. Instead of an absorption line an absorption edge is observed in such a process. Incoming x-ray quanta with energies below a certain amount cannot lift a K electron out of the atom and will thus not be much absorbed; they may, however, have enough energy to remove an L or M electron. As the energy of the incident x-ray quanta is raised, as soon as the threshold is reached, appreciable absorption suddenly takes place. Obviously the energy of the absorption edge depends on the atomic number Z of the absorbing material. The absorption coefficient μ is defined by the equation

$$I(x) = I_0 e^{-\mu x}$$

where I_0 is the intensity of the incident x-ray beam, $I(x)$ the intensity after having passed through a layer of thickness x (customarily in cm) of absorbing material; μ obviously has the dimension of a reciprocal length. The absorption of x-rays in general increases strongly with the binding of the electrons and therefore with the atomic number Z. Per unit thickness,

---

[15] I. Adler et al., "Apollo 15 Geochemical X-ray Fluorescence Experiment: Preliminary Report," *Science* **175**, 436 (1972).

lead is thus a much stronger absorber for x-radiation than iron or aluminum. Mass absorption coefficients, which are the absorption coefficients μ (in cm^{-1}) divided by the density ρ (in g/cm^3) of the material, are plotted in Fig. 4.9.4 for these three elements. In aluminum the K-absorption edge lies at 1.6 keV, in lead at 88 keV.

In addition to the discrete x-ray line spectra discussed above, there exists, as we have seen already in Chapter 2, a continuous x-ray spectrum whose origin is quite different, the bremsstrahlung spectrum. In an x-ray tube usually both types of x-radiation are produced simultaneously. Superimposed on the continuous spectrum appear the discrete lines emitted from the atoms of the anode material which were excited by the impact of the fast electrons. Figure 4.9.5 shows such a spectrum.

4.10 HYPERFINE STRUCTURE

The discussion of atomic structure has shown that the fine structure of atomic spectra is due to the coupling between the magnetic moments due to electron orbital angular momentum and electron spin. We shall now go one step further. Atomic nuclei too have angular momentum.[16] The nuclear

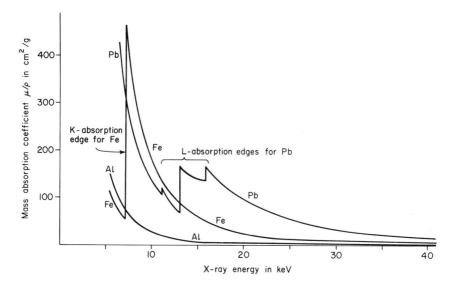

Fig. 4.9.4   The mass absorption coefficient μ/ρ for three different elements as a function of the x-ray energy.

[16] That nuclei have angular momentum that should give raise to hyperfine structure splitting was predicted by W. Pauli in 1924 [*Naturwissenschaften* **12**, 741].

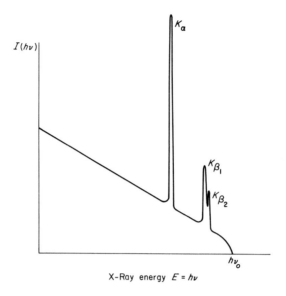

Fig. 4.9.5 Discrete x-ray lines superimposed on a continuous bremsstrahlung spectrum.

angular momentum quantum number I is, like the extranuclear angular momentum, a multiple of $\frac{1}{2}$ and is due to the spin angular momentum of the nucleons (the protons and neutrons) of $(\frac{1}{2} \cdot \frac{3}{2})^{1/2}\hbar$ and to their orbital angular momentum. This I of the nucleus and the corresponding J of the electrons combine to a grand total angular momentum with quantum number F according to the L-S coupling scheme (Fig. 4.10.1(a). Associated with the mechanical angular momentum of the nucleus is a magnetic moment. Whereas the magnetic moment of the electrons is expressed in Bohr magnetons, the magnetic moment of the nucleus is given in nuclear magnetons

$$\mu_N = e\hbar/2M$$

where M is the mass of a proton. The formula, hence, is the same as for the Bohr magneton except that the mass of the electron is now replaced by the 1836 times greater mass of the proton. A nuclear magneton is consequently 1836 times smaller than a Bohr magneton. Nuclear magnetic moments are in the order of a few nuclear magnetons and may be positive or negative. Because of the smallness of the nuclear magnetic moments, the difference in energies between the configurations in which nuclear and electron magnetic moments are parallel and those in which they are antiparallel is therefore very small and only observable with high resolution optical instruments. This splitting of atomic levels and of the observed transitions is called *hyperfine structure splitting*, often abbreviated HFS splitting (Fig. 4.10.1(b)).

The ground state for the hydrogen atom, which is an $1^2S_{1/2}$ state, shows a HFS splitting of 6×10^{-6} eV. This state must be considered as a doublet because of its spin $\frac{1}{2}$. However, the magnetic interaction is here not with the orbital moment, because $L = 0$, but with the nuclear moment. In one of the two substates the angular momentum vectors of electron and nucleon are parallel, in the other antiparallel. A flip of the electron spin from one position to the other is associated with the emission or absorption of a quantum of 6×10^{-6} eV, corresponding to a frequency ν of 1420 MHz and a wavelength $\lambda = 21$ cm. This transition is of greatest importance in radio astronomy, because in interstellar space hydrogen is the most abundant element. Although the probability of a spontaneous spin flip is very small for an atom (it happens on the average once every 11×10^6 years), the signals can be detected due to the large number of hydrogen atoms. A Dutch astronomer, Van de Hulst, predicted this line in 1944, and in 1951 the physicist E. M. Purcell at Harvard University, together with H. I. Ewen, discovered it with a radiotelescope. Fig. 4.10.2 shows some observations of this line taken in a direction in or near the plane of our galaxy. Because different arms of the galaxy, in which the hydrogen is concentrated, move with different velocities with respect to the earth, the Doppler effect splits the hydrogen line into several components.

Levels of atoms other than hydrogen also show hyperfine splitting. It

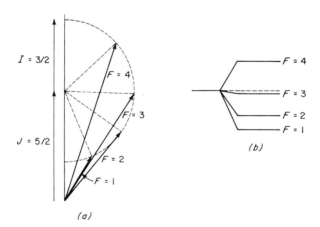

Fig. 4.10.1   (a) The combination of $J = \frac{5}{2}$ and $I = \frac{3}{2}$ to values of $F = 1, 2, 3, 4$. (b) The resulting HFS multiplet resulting from the magnetic interaction between J and I.

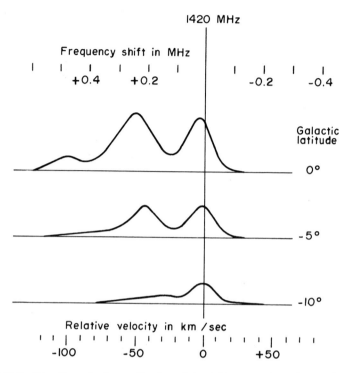

Fig. 4.10.2   The 21-cm hydrogen line from interstellar space in and near the galaxy at the galactic longitude of 77.5°.

should be pointed out that it is not only the magnetic interaction which causes this splitting. Another contributing factor is that nuclei quite often are not spherical but either flattened or elongated, and hence have a non-spherical charge distribution. Such nuclei are then said to have an electrical quadrupole moment. If, in addition, the charge distribution of the atomic shell is not spherically symmetric, the two electric quadrupole moments (the nuclear and electronic) couple in a similar way as the magnetic dipole moments. This quadrupole interaction causes slight energy shifts of the HFS levels. A study of the hyperfine structure therefore can reveal the following characteristics of the nucleus: nuclear angular momentum, nuclear magnetic moment, and nuclear electric quadrupole moment.

Because the hyperfine structure splitting is very small, it is usually not studied with grating or prism spectrometers but, if optical methods are used, with devices which allow still higher resolutions, such as interferometers. Completely different methods of studying the hyperfine structure exploit the circumstances that the energy differences between the states are such that the frequencies of the quanta emitted or absorbed are in the microwave and radio frequency ranges.

4.11 MOLECULES

Molecules offer a good opportunity to apply our modest quantum-mechanical skills, and here we will discuss and limit ourselves to diatomic molecules. First we will answer the question of what holds a hydrogen molecule together. We shall see that exchange forces which we have met in our discussion of the helium atom are responsible for this bond. Thereupon we will study the motion of atoms within a molecule and find that the energy levels of diatomic molecules can be explained with the aid of harmonic oscillator and free rotator models. Finally we will discuss the importance of the exclusion principle with regard to molecules.

The Chemical Bond

In many diatomic molecules the bond between the atoms comes about because the two atoms are essentially ionized. In the case of a NaCl molecule in vapor form the sodium atom gave its electron to the chlorine atom. The electrostatic forces of the ions formed this way hold the two atoms together. This is the *ionic* or *heteropolar bond* which can well be explained by classical physics if one takes the distance between the centers of the atoms as given. From the quantum-theoretical standpoint, the *covalent* or *homopolar bond* of like atoms, as for example in H_2, is more interesting. It was already pointed out above that this bond is due to the exchange energy. We recall that the exchange energy can be positive or negative depending on whether the wave function is symmetric or antisymmetric. We will not attempt to calculate the binding energy in this manner, but will only sketch how this calculation proceeds, stressing very much the analogy with the helium atom. The basic difference between the helium atom and the hydrogen molecule is that the former has one nucleus, but the latter has two nuclei, a distance x_{12} apart. The spatial wave function has therefore to take into account all the distances between the four particles of the hydrogen molecule, that is, the two protons and the two electrons. Again, as in the case of the helium atom, the spatial wave functions of the two electrons combine to a symmetric and an antisymmetric wave function, and again the interaction energy contains, besides the regular Coulomb terms C, cross-terms A which have a positive or negative sign. A detailed calculation reveals that the exchange terms are here of much greater

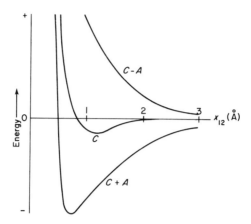

Fig. 4.11.1   The interaction energy between two H atoms as function of their distance.

magnitude than the regular Coulomb terms, as seen from Fig. 4.11.1. This is because the overlap of the spatial wave functions of the two electrons over wide regions of space is very great, hence also the corresponding interaction energy. The integrals for the Coulomb and for the exchange terms have to be computed for every distance between the two nuclei. It turns out that both integrals yield negative values over some range of the distance x_{12} between nuclei. Since the total interaction energy ΔE expresses the energy by which the molecule is held together and is

$$\Delta E = C \pm |A|, \tag{4.11.1}$$

the positive sign for A, corresponding to the symmetric wave functions, represents binding. The Pauli exclusion principle now requires that the total wave function $\psi = \psi_{\text{spat}} \cdot \psi_{\text{spin}}$ where ψ_{spat} stands for the spatial wave function and ψ_{spin} for the spin wave function, must be antisymmetric. Since for the bound state the spatial wave function must be symmetric, the spin wave function of the two electrons must be antisymmetric with regard to their interchange; in other words, the spins must be opposite, which makes the ground state of the molecule a singlet state.

Conversely, the triplet state of the hydrogen molecule would require an antisymmetric spatial wave function. Hence, the minus sign has to be taken in this case in Eq. 4.11.1. This leads however to an unstable configuration, and no binding becomes effective. We can therefore conclude that the hydrogen molecule is stable only in the singlet state. The occurrence of the exchange energy is based on the circumstance that the two electrons of opposite spin are shared by both atoms of the molecule which results in a stable configuration. It should be evident that the distance between the atoms is given by the location of the minimum in the potential curve, since any displacement of the atoms from this most stable configuration involves an increase in potential energy.

The Binding Energy of the Hydrogen Molecule

The above considerations regarding the molecular bond are quite elegant but only qualitative. Exact calculations are difficult, since for close distances between the hydrogen atoms their wave functions greatly distort one another and consequently introduce complications and inaccuracies.

Using a different approach which is due to the physicist Weisskopf[17] (and which we herewith shall follow closely), we shall semi-quantitatively calculate the binding energy of the hydrogen molecule. Despite some very crude simplifications, the result deviates from the actual value by less than 30%. This use of approximations serves as a good example of how a complicated problem often can be reduced to manageable dimensions.

We start our calculations by considering the hydrogen atom. The correct ground state wave function for the hydrogen atom is, as discussed in Section 4.1,

$$\psi_1 = A e^{-r/a_0} \tag{4.1.5}$$

with

$$a_0 = \frac{\epsilon_0 h^2}{\pi m e^2}, \tag{4.1.7}$$

a value which corresponds in the old Bohr theory of the hydrogen atom to the radius of the electron orbit of the ground state (Eq. 4.3.1). Retaining for the moment the old Bohr picture (which, in spite of its limitations, is frequently very useful) the total energy E_H, that is the sum of the potential energy E_p and the kinetic energy E_k, becomes

$$E_H = E_p + E_k = -\frac{e^2}{4\pi\epsilon_0 a_0} + \frac{e^2}{8\pi\epsilon_0 a_0} = -27.2 + 13.6 = -13.6 \text{ eV}.$$

$$\tag{4.11.1}$$

For the kinetic energy $\frac{1}{2}mv^2$ we inserted the velocity from Eq. 4.3.2 in conjunction with Eq. 4.1.7. Transforming the second term by substituting

[17] Victor F. Weisskopf (1908–   ), professor of theoretical physics at M.I.T., *Lectures on Theoretical Physics*, Vol. 3, Brittin, Downs, and Downs, eds. Interscience Publishers, New York, 1961.

for e^2 with the aid of Eq. 4.1.7 we have

$$E_H = E_p + E_k = - \frac{e^2}{4\pi\epsilon_0 a_0} + \frac{h^2}{8\pi^2 m a_0^2}. \tag{4.11.2}$$

Unfortunately, for our molecular problem the wave function of Eq. 4.1.5 is already too complicated. Weisskopf replaces it therefore with a much simpler one which, as shown in Fig. 4.11.2, is constant from the center to a radius R, and from there outward is zero. The electron cloud is thus considered as a uniformly charged sphere of radius R. This simplification basically reduces our problem to one of elementary electrostatics. The potential energy of a positive charge, equal to that of a proton, located at the center of such a sphere, is[18]

$$E_p = - \frac{3}{2} \frac{1}{4\pi\epsilon_0} \frac{e^2}{R}. \tag{4.11.3}$$

This expression can also be considered as the potential energy of the proton-electron cloud system. We must merely choose the radius R such that the value of the potential energy will be equal to the actual value given in Eq. 4.11.2. R is therefore $\frac{3}{2}a_0$. (This is, according to Eq. 4.1.28, just the average value of r.)

The actual kinetic energy, as seen in Eq. 4.11.2 is $(h^2/8\pi^2 m a_0^2)$. If a_0 is replaced by $\frac{2}{3}R$ in this expression, we can write for the total energy of the simplified H-atom

$$E_H = - \frac{3}{2} \frac{1}{4\pi\epsilon_0} \frac{e^2}{R} + \frac{9}{4} \frac{h^2}{8\pi^2 m R^2}. \tag{4.11.4}$$

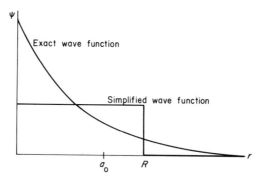

Fig. 4.11.2   Exact and simplified ground state wave function of the H atom.

[18] This can be found by calculating first $_\infty\!\int^R E_{\text{out}}(r)\,dr$, where $E_{\text{out}}(r) = (e/4\pi\epsilon_0 r)$, and $_R\!\int^0 E_{\text{in}}(r)\,dr$ where, as determined from Gauss's law, $E_{\text{in}}(r) = (er^2/4\pi\epsilon_0 R^3)$. The sum of the two potentials gives the potential at the center.

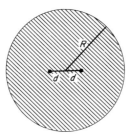

Fig. 4.11.3   The simplified hydrogen molecule.

Let us remind ourselves that the factors $\frac{3}{2}$ and $\frac{9}{4}$ account for the fact that the total energy of our simplified H-atom must be the same as that of the actual one, namely -13.6 eV.

We now are ready to discuss the hydrogen molecule. Although we should assume that its electron cloud is ellipsoidal, a reasonable approximation is that it is spherical (Fig. 4.11.3). Embedded in this spherical homogeneous electron cloud are the two protons, both displaced from the center by the distance d, which may be expressed in terms of a fraction f of the electron-cloud radius R, so that $d = fR$. Because we are no longer dealing with a hydrogen atom, but with a molecule, R is not more $\frac{3}{2}a_0$; its value will be determined later. It is a problem of electrostatics to calculate the potential energy of a single positive point charge $+e$ which is located inside a homogeneously charged sphere of radius R and total charge $-e$, but is displaced by the fraction f of the radius from the center of the sphere. The result is

$$E_p(f) = -\frac{3}{2}\frac{1}{4\pi\epsilon_0}\frac{e^2}{R}\left(1 - \frac{f^2}{3}\right) \tag{4.11.5}$$

according to the laws of electrostatics. For the extreme cases of $f = 0$ and $f = 1$ (that is, for the positive charge either at the center or at the surface), this formula reduces to familiar expressions.

The hydrogen molecule has two protons and two overlapping clouds of electrons. To compute the potential energy we must therefore multiply the above value by a factor of 2 due to the two protons and a factor of 2 due to the two electrons. In addition, the repulsion of both protons contributes to the potential energy. Finally, the superposition of the two electron charge clouds which tend to repel each other must be taken into account. The potential energy of the hydrogen molecule is therefore

$$E_p = \frac{1}{4\pi\epsilon_0}\frac{e^2}{R}\left[(-6 + 2f^2) + \frac{1}{2f} + \frac{6}{5}\right]. \tag{4.11.6}$$

The kinetic energy of the two electrons is, as can immediately be seen from Eq. 4.11.4,

$$E_k = \frac{9}{2} \frac{h^2}{8\pi^2 m R^2}. \tag{4.11.7}$$

Next we must find the value of f. The most stable configuration is obviously the one which has the lowest energy. On one hand the two protons tend to repel each other, on the other hand, as seen from Eq. 4.11.5, the potential energy for one proton only would be smallest if this proton were in the center. The minimum value of the total energy $E = E_p + E_k$ can be found by the usual method of differentiation of Eqs. 4.11.6 and 4.11.7 with respect to f. This yields $f = \frac{1}{2}$, and E thus becomes

$$E_{H_2} = -\frac{33}{10} \frac{1}{4\pi\epsilon_0} \frac{e^2}{R} + \frac{9}{2} \frac{h^2}{8\pi^2 m R^2}. \tag{4.11.8}$$

We must also investigate the energetically most favorable value of the radius R of the molecule. We shall see that this radius is not identical with the radius of the atom, although it is nearly the same. For this purpose, as above with respect to f, we minimize Eq. 4.11.8 with respect to R. The result is

$$R_{H_2} = \frac{15}{11} \frac{\epsilon_0 h^2}{\pi m e^2} = \frac{15}{11} a_0. \tag{4.11.9}$$

Recalling that we found for the radius of our simplified H atom the value $R = \frac{3}{2}(\epsilon_0 h^2/\pi m e^2) = \frac{3}{2}a_0$, we must conclude that the radius of the H_2 molecule is slightly smaller than that of the H atom.

We are finally approaching our goal, the calculation of the binding energy of the H_2 molecule. This quantity is the difference between the sum of the energies of two separated H atoms and the energy of the H_2 molecule. The latter is obviously the smaller one because energy has to be fed into the molecule in order to dissociate it, that is to separate it into two atoms.

By inserting the radius R_{H_2} of Eq. 4.11.9 into the energy expression for the H molecule (Eq. 4.11.8), and subtracting twice the energy of the H atom (Eq. 4.11.4), we arrive at the desired binding energy. The energy of the H_2 molecule is

$$E_{H_2} = -\frac{363}{150} \frac{1}{4\pi\epsilon_0} \frac{e^2}{a_0} + \frac{1089}{450} \frac{h^2}{8\pi^2 m} \frac{1}{a_0^2}. \tag{4.11.10}$$

The binding energy therefore is given by

$$E_{H_2} - 2E_H = -\frac{63}{150}\frac{1}{4\pi\epsilon_0}\frac{e^2}{a_0} + \frac{189}{450}\frac{h^2}{8\pi^2 m}\frac{1}{a_0^2}$$

$$= -0.42\frac{1}{4\pi\epsilon_0}\frac{e^2}{a_0} + 0.42\frac{h^2}{8\pi^2 m}\frac{1}{a_0^2}$$

$$= 0.42\left(-\frac{e^2}{4\pi\epsilon_0 a_0} + \frac{h^2}{8\pi\epsilon_0 a_0}\right). \qquad (4.11.11)$$

This energy is hence, as comparison with Eq. 4.11.2 shows, 0.42 times the binding energy of an electron in the hydrogen atom. The calculated molecular binding energy is thus $0.42 \cdot 13.6$ eV $= 5.7$ eV. The experimental value is 4.5 eV. Our crude theory led us to a value which is not very far away from the correct one!

This calculation shows us that the principal factor which is responsible for the molecular bond is the great negative potential energy which holds each of the two electrons bound to both protons. Two contributions to the total energy are counteracting this negative potential energy. First, the mutual repulsion of the protons is a source of positive potential energy, and so is that of the two electron clouds. Second, the kinetic energy of the electrons is also a positive contribution to the total energy of the molecule. Due to the smaller radius of the molecule in comparison with that of the atom the kinetic energy is somewhat greater in the molecular case. However, the sum of these positive energy components is not sufficient to overcome the negative potential energy and thus to prevent binding.

One might be tempted to use the same reasoning for calculating the possibility of a stable molecule which consists of three hydrogen atoms. However, in this case the Pauli exclusion principle makes such a simple calculation invalid. As is well known, an H_3 molecule does not exist in nature.

Oscillations and Rotations of Diatomic Molecules

Just as atoms have excited states, so molecules have also such states. Whereas in atoms only the electron configuration could change, which resulted in states of differing degree of excitation, molecules have additional degrees of freedom: The atoms of an H_2 molecule can oscillate against each other, but they can also rotate around their common center of mass. This is all in addition to the change in the electronic configuration.

Already rough general considerations can tell us the order of magnitude of the energies involved for these three different modes of excitation. We expect electronic transitions in molecules to be in the same energy range as in atoms since the electronic binding is due to the same force. The frequency of the vibrations of the nuclei against each other is determined, as with all vibrational frequencies, by a mass and a spring constant. The forces holding the two nuclei in place are of the same order of magnitude as the forces holding the electrons together. Since the masses to be set in motion in case of nuclei are usually ten to a hundred thousand times greater than in case of the electrons, we expect the oscillating frequencies and therefore also the energies for the nuclei to be in the order of a hundred times smaller, because the frequency is proportional to the square root of the reciprocal mass. Vibrational quantum jumps are therefore expected to be of the order of tenths of an electron volt. Similar considerations can be made for the rotational energy levels. Angular momentum is quantized and is of the order of $h/2\pi$. Because $mr^2\omega \approx \hbar$ and because the circular motions of the electrons in an atom and of the nuclei in a molecule have the same radius, the rotational energy differences of a molecule are some ten thousand times smaller than the energy differences between electronic levels. Summarizing, we may expect to find transitions with the greatest energy differences associated with changes in the electron configuration. The energy jumps arising from vibrational oscillations are smaller by a factor in order of magnitude of 100 and the rotational transitions are smaller by another factor of that magnitude. The actual situation is indeed very much like the one described. We find electronic transitions in the range of 0.1 to 1 μ, vibrational transitions in the order of 10 μ, and rotational transitions in the range of 100 to 1000 μ. Figure 4.11.4 shows schematically the spectrum of the HCl molecule with the different regions.

The differences in order of magnitude between the different processes simplify the theoretical treatment greatly because each mode can be treated separately. A simple superposition of different modes does not destroy the character of each. The situation is just as with the modulation of radio waves. A radiowave of, for instance, a frequency of 80 kHz, which is modulated by an audio frequency of 5 kHz, will be measured with a fre-

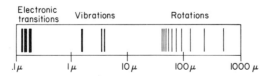

Fig. 4.11.4   The spectrum of the HCl molecule.

quency meter as two waves of 75 and 85 kHz. In the molecular spectra the vibrational transitions are "modulated" by the rotational transitions, giving rise to the rotational-vibrational spectra. The rotational-vibrational spectra in turn can be superimposed on the electron spectra.

The energy of the emitted quanta is therefore

$$h\nu = \Delta E_e + \Delta E_v + \Delta E_r$$

where ΔE_e is the energy difference due to the change in the electron configuration, ΔE_v the energy difference due to the change in the vibration of the atoms against each other, and ΔE_r the energy difference due to a change in the rotation frequency. As mentioned before, in general

$$\Delta E_e \gg \Delta E_v \gg \Delta E_r$$

for molecules. It might be added here that we will meet rotational and vibrational excitation modes again in nuclei, because nuclei are not completely rigid structures and can rotate.

We shall first take up the discussion of rotational spectra. In Chapter 3 we derived the energy levels for the rotator in a plane and remarked that the energy levels for the free rotator followed a similar regularity, namely

$$E_l = \frac{h^2}{8\pi^2 I} l(l+1) \tag{4.11.12}$$

where I is the moment of inertia. Let us calculate the rotational energy levels of the HCl molecule with this formula. With a distance d between the atoms of 1.29×10^{-10} m, the mass m_H for the H atom of 1.67×10^{-27} kg, and the mass m_{Cl} for the chlorine atom of 58.9×10^{-27} kg and using the reduced mass $\mu = (m_H \cdot m_{Cl})/(m_H + m_{Cl})$ for the moment of inertia $I = \mu d^2$ we get a value of $I = 2.70 \times 10^{-47}$ kg m². Since the quantum-mechanical selection rule for a pure rotator requires $\Delta l = \pm 1$, transitions can arise only between adjacent levels. The energy differences between these levels are represented by the series . . . , $10(\hbar^2/2I)$, $12(\hbar^2/2I)$, $14(\hbar^2/2I)$, . . . , and are given in Table 4.11.1. This table also contains the corresponding calculated frequencies and the actually observed ones. The very good agreement between theoretical and experimental data is obvious. A slight but systematic trend in the discrepancy between the two sets is due to some stretching of the molecule because of the growing rotational speed with higher values of l. It should be pointed out that this calculation was done, so to speak, backwards. In actuality the observed spectrum has been used in order to calculate the moment of inertia and from that the distance between the H and Cl atoms.

The two atoms of a diatomic molecule cannot only rotate around each

TABLE 4.11.1

The Rotational Spectrum of HCl

Lower State		Upper State		$l'(l'+1) -$ $l(l+1) = D$	$\Delta E = (\hbar^2/2I) D$ joules	$\nu = \Delta E/h$ sec^{-1}	$\nu_{observed}$ sec^{-1}
Rotational Quantum Number l	$l(l+1)$	Rotational Quantum Number l'	$l'(l'+1)$				
4	20	5	30	10	2.06×10^{-21}	3.11×10^{12}	3.12×10^{12}
5	30	6	42	12	2.47	3.73	3.72
6	42	7	56	14	2.88	4.35	4.35
7	56	8	72	16	3.29	4.97	4.97
8	72	9	90	18	3.70	5.59	5.57
9	90	10	110	20	4.12	6.22	6.18
10	110	11	132	22	4.53	6.84	6.80

other; they can also vibrate against each other. The condition for vibration of any system is that a restoring force acts which is proportional to the displacement. Inspection of the potential curve (Fig. 4.11.1) between the two atoms as a function of distance shows that this condition is indeed fulfilled for small displacements. In principle we can compute the value of the spring constant for the classical oscillator from the potential curve and, using the reduced mass μ, calculate the characteristic frequency ω_0. Since in the quantum mechanical harmonic oscillator the energy levels have the spacing $h\nu = \hbar\omega_0$ we can calculate the vibrational levels, being careful not to forget to add the zero-point energy $\frac{1}{2}\hbar\omega_0$. Whereas the pure rotational frequencies are in the far infrared, say in the range of 10^{11} Hz, corresponding to wavelengths of 10^3 μm, the vibrational frequencies are in the range of 10^{13} Hz, or 10 μm, which is in the near infrared.

We finally have to take into account also the change of the state of the electrons. The associated transitions are, as is to be expected, in the same frequency range as electron transitions in atoms, that is, in the visible and ultraviolet. In the same way that the rotational frequencies were superimposed on the vibrational frequencies, these two modes are now superimposed on the electron spectrum. We therefore have a fairly complicated spectrum with three different structures. A hypothetical energy level diagram (Fig. 4.11.5) illustrates the situation. The thick lines correspond to the electron levels, the thin long lines represent the vibrational levels superimposed on the electron spectrum, and the thin short lines are the rotational levels built on each of the vibrational levels. Selection rules similar to the ones of atomic spectra determine here which transitions are allowed. Figure 4.11.6 shows the spectrum of a typical band spectrum, that of BO.

The single lines are due to the rotational structure. The shadings that

Fig. 4.11.5 A section of a hypothetical level diagram of a molecule. Thick lines represent electronic levels, thin long lines vibrational levels, thin short lines rotational levels.

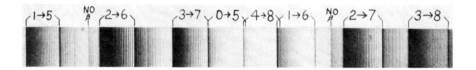

Fig. 4.11.6   Band spectrum of boron monoxide, BO, in the region $\lambda = 2850 - 3120$ Å. Each of the shaded *bands* corresponds to a group of transitions between levels having two specific *vibrational* quantum numbers which are indicated above the photograph. Each *line* in a band corresponds to a transition between levels of different *rotational* quantum numbers. All the bands shown belong to the same electronic transition. The latter is corresponds to a transition between two atomic levels. The bands labeled NO are impurities from nitric oxide.—From R. S. Mulliken (Nobel Prize for Chemistry 1966), *Phys. Rev.* **25**, 259 (1925).

gave rise to the name band spectra when spectrographs of limited resolving power were used are associated with the changes of the vibrational state.

A detailed discussion of molecular spectra is beyond the scope of this book, which will only give an understanding of some of the physical principles. However, we do not want to conclude this section without mentioning one beautiful demonstration of the Pauli principle. We intentionally used as an example a molecule made up of two different atoms. This automatically prevented any complication that could arise from the Pauli principle. Turning now to molecules consisting of identical atoms, we see, for example, that in the molecular spectrum of O_2 every other rotational line is missing. The explanation is the following: Nearly all oxygen molecules are made up of O^{16} atoms. Because these are bosons (they consist of an even number of fermions as explained earlier), the total wave function of the molecules has to be symmetric with regard to the interchange of the two nuclei. The wave function can be represented as a product $\psi_n\psi_{el}\psi_v\psi_{rot}$, where the first factor stands for the nuclear wave function, the second for the electronic wave function, the third for the vibrational one, and the last for the rotational wave function. The first three wave functions are in this case symmetric, but the last alternates between symmetric and antisymmetric because it depends on whether the rotational quantum number is even or odd. Because a symmetric wave function is required, only even rotational levels are possible. The relatively rare molecules of the type $O^{16}O^{15}$ show all rotational lines because the two nuclei are now different. The case of the $O^{16}O^{16}$ molecule is a particularly simple one. However, other molecules with equal atomic nuclei, fermions or bosons, show related effects, which again are drastic manifestations of the general validity of the Pauli exclusion principle.

PROBLEMS

1. An electron is moving in the field of a *nucleus containing Z protons.* (*a*) What is the wave function in the ground state? (*b*) What is the ionization potential of singly ionized helium? Of doubly ionized lithium? (*c*) Find the average value of r for a single electron in the field of an iron nucleus ($Z = 26$); of a silver nucleus ($Z = 47$); of a lead nucleus ($Z = 82$).

2. The nucleus of a *hydrogen atom* is a proton whose radius is approximately 1.2×10^{-15} m (see Fig. 6.2.8). What is the probability to find the electron of a hydrogen atom within the nuclear volume?

3. Compute the radius R, in terms of a_0, at which the probability of finding the electron of a *hydrogen atom* in the first excited spherically symmetric state (the 2s state) is a maximum. The wave function for this state is

$$\psi_{2s}(r) = \frac{A}{4\sqrt{2}}\left(2 - \frac{r}{a_0}\right)e^{-(r/2a_0)}.$$

Compare your result with Fig. 4.1.1(*c*).

4. Calculate the locations of the *maxima and minima* of ψ_{3s} and check your result with Fig. 4.1.1.

5. *Balmer* observed among others the following two lines in the spectrum of hydrogen: $\lambda = 6562$ Å and 4862 Å. (*a*) What is the difference in energy between the states of the hydrogen atom which gives rise to these lines? Express your answer in electron volts. (*b*) What energy levels are involved in the radiation of these two lines?

6. What are the *wavelengths* of the first two lines of the Balmer series? Of the Lyman series?

7. What is the *ionization potential* of the hydrogen atom from the state with $n = 2$?

8. By what fraction does the combined *rest mass* of a proton and an electron change when the two combine to form a hydrogen atom in its ground state?

9. Before an electron and a positron annihilate they form a short-lived system analog to a hydrogen atom. This system is called *positronium*. What are the energies of the states of this system? Express your answers in electron volts.

10. Muons are particles with some of their properties very much like electrons, but they are unstable and have a rest mass 212 times that of an electron. Slow negative muons can be captured by nuclei to form so-called *muonic atoms*, whereby the muon behaves like an electron. (Eventually it will be absorbed by the nucleus or it decays.) (*a*) Calculate energy and radius of the lowest state of a muonic atom (corresponding to a_0 of the

hydrogen atom) and of the second-lowest state with a copper nucleus ($Z = 29$, $A = 63$). Compare this radius with that of the nucleus, using for the latter the formula $R = 1.2 \times 10^{-15} A^{1/3}$ m. (b) If the lead nucleus ($Z = 82$, $A = 207$) were a point nucleus, calculate radius and energy for its lowest state. Compare this radius with the radius of the lead nucleus. The muon can move through nuclear matter fairly unimpeded because of relatively weak interaction forces. Would you expect that the energies of the states of the actual lead-muonic atom lie higher than, lower than, or are equal to those of the hypothetical point nucleus? (Hint: Take Gauss's law into consideration).

11. Under normal laboratory conditions, can one expect to observe the Balmer lines of hydrogen in an *absorption spectrum*? The lines of the Lyman series?

12. With good spectrographs it is possible to record about 30 lines in the *Balmer series* of the hydrogen spectrum. What are the differences in energy and wavelength between the 29th and 30th line? What is the limit for the wavelengths of the Balmer series, the so-called series limit?

13. Because the hydrogen nucleus is not infinitely massive in comparison with the electron, the motions of the electron and the nucleus are actually around the common center of mass. As shown in Section 3.7, such two-body problems can easily be treated with the concept of the reduced mass. For the transition $n = 3$ to $n = 2$ (the red Balmer line) calculate the wavelengths for a hydrogen atom with a nucleus of (a) infinite mass, (b) one proton mass, (c) twice the proton mass, that is the mass of a deuterium atom. The difference in wavelength for different isotopes is called *isotope shift*.

14. According to classical electromagnetic theory the frequency of the radiation emitted by an antenna is equal to the frequency of oscillation of the charges in the antenna. Furthermore, it is known that circular motion can be considered as the resultant of two oscillatory motions at right angles to each other, moving with an appropriate phase shift. Therefore, from classical theory we should expect that the frequency of light emitted by an atom is equal to the frequency of the circulating electron. Show that in the case of very high principal quantum numbers n the frequency of the emitted light for transitions $n \rightarrow n - 1$ is equal to the frequency of the circulating electron in the old theory of Bohr, for circular orbits. (This is one of the manifestations of Bohr's *correspondence principle*, which says that for high quantum numbers quantum mechanics leads to classical physics.)

15. In *positronium* (see problem 9) the spins of the two electrons can be either parallel (orthopositronium) or antiparallel (parapositronium). (a) What are the spectroscopic descriptions of the ground states of these

two kinds of positronium? (b) Considering that a quantum carries a spin of $1\hbar$, show that free orthopositronium cannot decay by the emission of two annihilation quanta and that the annihilation must proceed by emission of three quanta.

16. Compute the ratio of the *velocity of an electron* in the first Bohr orbit of a hydrogen atom to the velocity of light.

17. Several *fundamental lengths of atomic physics* are linked by a dimensionless number, the so-called fine-structure constant $\alpha = (e^2/\hbar c) = 1/137.04$. (a) Calculate the radius a_0 of the first Bohr orbit of an H atom. (b) Calculate the Compton wavelength of the electron divided by 2π, $\lambda_{\text{Compton}}/2\pi$. (In other words use $\hbar$ instead of h in the Compton-effect formula.) (c) Calculate the so-called "classical electron radius" r_e. This is the radius of a sphere with a surface charge equal to an elementary charge e whose electrostatic potential energy is equal to the rest mass of the electron. (It should be noted that this classical electron radius is not the radius of an actual electron.) (d) Show that $a_0 : (\lambda_{\text{Compton}}/2\pi) : r_e = 1 : (137)^{-1} : (137)^{-2}$.

18. Show that the ratio of the *magnetic moment* to the angular momentum of a charged rotating body does not depend on its shape, as long as the charge-to-mass ratio is everywhere the same and the body rotates like a rigid body.

19. Into how many components will a beam of hydrogen atoms split in a *Stern-Gerlach experiment?*

20. In a *Stern-Gerlach experiment* a beam of nickel atoms splits into nine components. What is the angular momentum of the ground state of a nickel atom?

21. A beam of silver atoms splits in a *Stern-Gerlach experiment* into two components (Fig. 4.2.7). This splitting is due solely to the spin. On the other hand, a beam of tin atoms splits into three components, and here the splitting is due solely to the orbital angular momentum. (a) What are the spectroscopic notations of the ground states of silver and tin? (b) Compare the spacing between adjacent components for the two atomic beams.

22. In a *Stern-Gerlach experiment* a beam of Na atoms is sent through two slits 0.1 mm wide and 0.5 m apart. The velocity of the atoms in the beam may be assumed to be 8×10^4 cm/sec. Immediately behind the slits is a magnetic field having a gradient dB/dz at right angles to the beam. The field extends over 10 cm of the beam. At a distance 0.5 m beyond the magnetic field is a photographic plate on which the position of the beam is recorded. The magnetic moment of the sodium atom is 10^{-20} erg/gauss and is always either parallel or antiparallel to the applied field. The force acting on the Na atoms in the field may be computed from Eq. 4.2.3. If μ is in ergs/gauss, B is in gauss, and z is in cm, then F is in dynes. Compute

the least value of the magnetic field gradient, dB/dz, which will resolve the two beams of sodium atoms. The mass of a sodium atom is about 23 times the mass of a proton. In doing this problem be sure to use corresponding units throughout; μ is here given in ergs per gauss because this is the customary way of describing atomic moments.

23. To what values of L can the two *orbital angular momenta* $l_1 = 2$ and $l_2 = 2$ add?

24. In which ways can *two electrons* of orbital angular momentum $l_1 = 2$ and $l_2 = 3$ combine to a resulting angular momentum L? Make a drawing.

25. How many *values of J* result from (a) $L = 3$, $S = 1$? (b) $L = 0$, $S = 1$? (c) $L = 1$, $S = 1$?

26. Which *values of J* can be obtained from an orbital angular momentum $L = 1$ and a spin $S = \frac{3}{2}$?

27. (a) Which value of L and S combine to the *quartet* of ^4D states? (b) Show in drawings the vectors according to the vector model of these four states. (c) What is the spectroscopic notation of these states?

28. The ground state of *oxygen* is $^3P_2$ and is due to the two valence p electrons. (a) Draw the vectors for the orbital angular momentum. (b) Draw the ones for the spin. (c) Draw the ones for L and S which result in the correct total angular momentum.

29. As mentioned in Sect. 4.2, it turns out that the actual value of the orbital angular momentum is not $L = \hbar l$, but $\hbar[l(l+1)]^{1/2}$, and the maximum possible value of its z component is $\hbar m$, where $m = l$, m and l being integers. Show that this implies that the vector L cannot be in the z direction, but precesses around it, and that therefore small x and y components of L must be present which average to zero. Discuss the *sharpness of the z component* in the light of the Heisenberg uncertainty principle. Do the same for the x and y components of L.

30. Show the difference in the energy-level structure for L-S and j-j coupling for two electrons with quantum numbers $l_1 = 1$ and $l_2 = 2$. Draw a diagram analog to Fig. 4.4.7.

31. Two electrons with $j_1 = \frac{3}{2}$ and $j_2 = \frac{5}{2}$ follow the j-j *coupling* scheme. Show in a vector diagram the possible values of J.

32. The ferromagnetism of iron derives from the contributions of approximately two electrons per atom which are unpaired; their spins are parallel, thus also their magnetic moments. The orbital angular momenta do not contribute. In an unmagnetized piece of iron the atoms assume many orientations, but in a strong magnetic field the magnetic moments, and with them the spins, of the unpaired electrons align with that field. The unpaired electrons will therefore have a net angular momentum. Because angular momentum of the system must be conserved, the bulk of the iron will acquire an angular momentum in the opposite direction. Einstein and

de Haas performed this experiment in 1915 by suspending an iron cylinder axially on a thin thread and applying a strong magnetic field in direction of the cylinder axis. (This was Einstein's only experimental paper.) What is the angular velocity of an iron cylinder of 20 cm length and 0.7 mm diameter, originally at rest and unmagnetized, after a field is applied which completely aligns the unpaired spins? Density of iron 7.8 g/cm³, mass number $A = 56$. This effect is called *Einstein-de Haas effect*. (The opposite effect, magnetization by sudden rotation, was discovered by Barnett in 1915.)

33. What would be the *precession frequency* in a field of 10,000 gauss of an atom whose magnetic moment was due to the circulation of a single electron in a circular orbit of radius 0.5×10^{-10} m?

34. Show that a $^3S_1$ state formed by two s electrons with the same principal quantum number would have to be described by a symmetric total wave function and therefore its existence must be ruled out by the *Pauli principle*.

35. Show that assemblies of identical particles for which the Pauli principle does not hold (i.e., *bosons*, as α particles, π mesons, photons) must have symmetric total wave functions.

36. From Fig. 4.6.2 it is obvious that in the actual *sequence of filling shells* it is not such that a new shell is started only after the preceding one is full. (*a*) Using this array of subshells show the actual sequence for the filling of these subshells by drawing a connecting line from subshell to subshell, disregarding small deviations. (*b*) Determine the probable electron configurations of elements 104 and 105. (*c*) Determine the atomic number Z of the next alkali metal.

$$1s$$
$$2s \quad 2p$$
$$3s \quad 3p \quad 3d$$
$$4s \quad 4p \quad 4d \quad 4f$$
$$5s \quad 5p \quad 5d \quad 5f \quad 5g$$
$$6s \quad 6p \quad 6d \quad 6f \quad 6g \quad 6h$$
$$7s \quad 7p \quad 7d \quad 7f \quad 7g \quad 7h \quad 7i$$

37. Fig. 4.7.1 gives the wavelengths for the singlet system in helium which are emitted in transitions from the n^1P_1 states to the ground state $1\,{}^1S_0$. Examine if and how these transition energies can be fitted into a *series formula*.

38. Using the data on the helium atom in Fig. 4.7.1, calculate the value of the *exchange energy* for the $2S$ and $2P$ states.

39. (*a*) For singly ionized *helium* calculate the most probable distance between the nucleus and the remaining electron. (*b*) Assume that in a

neutral helium atom both electrons are at a distance from the nucleus calculated in (a). Assume further that the average distance between the two electrons is roughly of the same magnitude. Calculate the energy due to the Coulomb repulsion between the two electrons this distance apart and compare your result with the value deduced from the energy level diagram of Fig. 4.7.2. From what sources does the discrepancy arise and how should a more precise calculation be done?

40. Show that a *closed shell* or subshell must have an orbital and total angular momentum of zero.

41. Show that one missing electron in an otherwise complete shell, also called a *hole*, will result in the same angular momentum as a single electron in this shell.

42. Comment on the fact that the energy of the $n = 2$ level in hydrogen, counted from the ionization limit, is very closely that of the $2p$ states in *lithium*, but not of its $2s$ state. Likewise explain why the $n = 3$ level of hydrogen has nearly the same energy as the $3d$ states in sodium, but not as the $3p$ or $3s$ states.

43. According to R. G. Parsons and V. F. Weisskopf [*Zeitschrift für Physik* **202**, 492 (1967)], the *spectrum of an alkali atom* can be calculated by assuming that the valence electron (in Na this is a $3s$ electron) behaves like a $1s$ electron in a one-electron atom with an impenetrable core of radius r_c which turns out to be approximately the radius of the first Bohr orbit in hydrogen. The core has one elementary charge. Its impenetrability for this $1s$ valence electron is due to the Pauli principle, because the core contains already two $1s$ electrons. The potential in which this $1s$ valence electron moves is therefore for

$$r < r_c: \quad V = \infty$$

$$r > r_c: \quad V = -\frac{1}{4\pi\epsilon_0}\frac{e}{r}$$

(a) Sketch this potential qualitatively. (b) Sketch the ground state wave function, that is, the $1s$ wave function. (c) Give a reason why its energy is higher than the $1s$ state of hydrogen. (d) How strongly will the states with higher angular momenta be affected by such a core?

44. Assuming that the magnetic moment of the atom shown in Fig. 4.8.5, left, in the excited state is 10^{-23} amp/m², and that the wavelength radiated in the transition shown, in zero field, is 2536.000 Å, compute the three wavelengths due to the *Zeeman effect* radiated in a field of 2 webers/m².

45. The two lines of the Na D doublet have wavelengths of 5890 and 5896 Å, respectively. (a) Calculate the order of magnitude of the *magnetic*

field in the atom. (*b*) At what order of magnitude of the external magnetic field do you expect the Zeeman effect gradually changing into the Paschen-Back effect?

46. In which category of atoms will the *Zeeman effect* be normal, in which anomalous?

47. Draw a frequency spectrum in arbitrary units for the transitions of Fig. 4.8.5, showing the *Zeeman effect*.

48. It is presently believed that *neutron stars*, or *pulsars*, have enormous magnetic fields at their surface which are of the order of 10^{12} or 10^{13} gauss (1 gauss = 10^{-5} weber/m^2). (*a*) Estimate the order of magnitude of the energy shift of a spectral line emitted in a transition from the $2P$ to the $1S$ state in a hydrogen atom. Neglect the electron spin, since this is only an order-of-magnitude calculation. (*b*) Using Bohr's picture of electrons circling in orbits calculate the radius of the first Bohr orbit of a hydrogen-atom electron in such a magnetic field whose direction coincides with the axis of the orbit. (*c*) What is the shape of a hydrogen atom in such a field?

49. If a spectral line is examined with a spectroscopic instrument having a large resolving power, it is possible to find the *shape of the radiated line*, that is, the intensity as a function of wavelength. This is found to have a central maximum which falls off on either side. The width of the intensity curve at half the maximum intensity is called the width of the line. In most spectral lines this width is determined by the Doppler effect. If the atoms were at rest they would radiate a much sharper line, but because of their thermal velocities, they radiate an apparently higher frequency when they are approaching an observer and a lower frequency when they are receding from an observer. The width of the spectral line observed from a radiating gas is determined by the mean velocities of the gas atoms. The change in frequency due to the motion of a radiating source moving in the direction of radiation is

$$\Delta\nu/\nu = v/c$$

where v is the velocity of the source toward the observer and c is the velocity of light. If the probability that an atom has a velocity component along an arbitrary axis between v and $v + dv$ is

$$dw = \sqrt{\frac{\beta}{\pi}} \exp(-\beta v^2) \, dv$$

$$\beta = \frac{M}{2kT}.$$

(*a*) Show that the spectral distribution is

$$I(\nu) = I_0 \exp[-\beta(c^2/\nu^2)(\nu - \nu_0)^2]$$

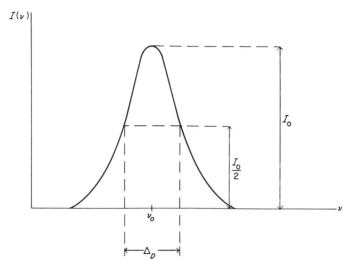

Figure P.4.1 (Problem 49)

and that the width of the line, defined as the width at half maximum, as shown in the figure, is $\Delta_D = 2(\nu_0/c)[(2kT/M) \ln 2]^{1/2}$.

(b) Noting that $\lambda\nu = c$, and therefore that $d\lambda/\lambda = -d\nu/\nu$, show that the Doppler width in wavelength units is

$$\frac{2\lambda_0}{c}\sqrt{\frac{2kT}{M}\ln 2}.$$

50. The width of a spectral line Δ_D broadened by the random motion of the radiating atoms, in frequency units, is

$$\Delta_D = \frac{2\nu_0}{c}\sqrt{\frac{2kT}{M}\ln 2}.$$

Compute the smallest field that can be used to show the *Zeeman effect* of the line discussed in Problem 44, assuming that the radiating atom is mercury $(A = 200)$, that the absolute temperature of the radiating gas is 350° absolute, and that the Zeeman components must be separated by at least the Doppler width to be resolved.

51. How large a magnetic field would be required to show the *Zeeman effect* of the spectral line discussed in Problem 44, if the resolving power of a grating spectrograph is given by nN, where n is the order of the spectrum and N is the total number of lines of the grating, and the spectrum is observed in second order and the grating has 30,000 lines? Neglect Doppler broadening.

52. A low-pressure mercury arc is operated so that the temperature of the electrons is 11,000 K and the ratio of the number of atoms in the first excited state to the number in the ground state corresponds to thermal equilibrium at approximately this temperature. Under these conditions the *spectral intensity* of the emitted radiation in the middle of the spectral line resulting from transitions from the above excited state to the ground state may be estimated by assuming it is equal to that of a black body at the electron temperature. The radiation in the interior of the lamp is absorbed and reemitted as though it were in an insulated container, and comes to thermal equilibrium with the electrons. If the radiation is a single spectral line having the Doppler width appropriate to mercury atoms with a translational energy corresponding to 40°C, approximately 50 Å, and if the wavelength of the line is 2537 Å, what is the total power radiated per meter of length of a tubular lamp 1.5 in. in diameter?

53. Twenty-one electrons are placed in a *cubic box* with impenetrable walls 10^{-10} m long in each dimension. The electrons settle into the lowest possible energy levels. A single electron is now removed from the lowest level by some means. What are the possible wavelengths that this hypothetical system could radiate?

54. The wavelengths of a series of corresponding *x-ray lines* from several elements are given below:

Element	Wavelength in Å	Atomic Number, Z
Fe	17.6	26
Zn	12.22	30
Mo	5.39	42
Ag	4.15	47
Sn	3.59	50
W	1.47	74
Pb	1.17	82
U	0.908	92

Make a plot of $\nu^{1/2}$ as a function of Z using these data, and estimate the effective nuclear charge Z^* for this series of lines. Discuss the significance of this result.

55. The radius of a *mercury nucleus* ($Z = 80$) is approximately 7×10^{-15} m (see Fig. 6.2.8). (*a*) What is the probability for each of the s electrons of the K shell to be inside the nucleus? Assume that the wave functions are not disturbed due to the presence of the other s electron and the other electrons in the atom. (*b*) Sketch the shape of the electrostatic potential inside the nucleus, assuming a uniform charge distribution. (*c*) Do you expect a shift in energy of the s levels because the nucleus is not a point charge? If so, in what direction is this shift? (*d*) How will

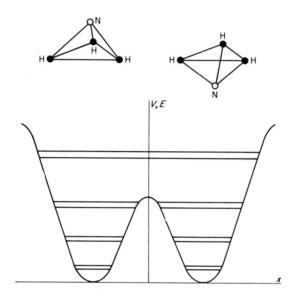

Figure P.4.2 (Problem 63)

the levels of the outer electrons be affected? (*e*) Is a non-relativistic calculation still reasonably justified?

56. In an *atomic photoelectric effect* by a 200-keV quantum on platinum an electron of the *K* shell is ejected from the atom. (*a*) What is the kinetic energy of the ejected electron, the so-called photoelectron? (*b*) What are the energies of the x-ray lines that may be observed?

57. A 100-keV γ quantum interacts with a uranium atom and ejects a photoelectron. Which *x-ray lines* may be emitted due to this process?

58. X-rays of 65 keV energy from platinum, arising from a transition between the *L* and *K* shell, are impinging on a sheet of platinum. Can there be *resonance absorption* of this radiation?

59. An x-ray tube has a molybdenum anode ($Z = 42$). (*a*) Using $Z - Z^* = 3.5$ calculate the *minimum voltage* on the tube with which the K_α line will appear in the x-ray spectrum. (*b*) What is the minimum voltage on the tube which produces the K_β line? (An illustration of the molybdenum x-ray spectrum is in Fig. 2.5.13.)

60. If energetically favorable for the atom, a *K electron* can be *captured* by the nucleus because the wave function of the electrons overlaps the nucleus. The capture of the electron changes a proton inside the nucleus into a neutron. This radioactive transmutation, which is called electron capture (and also can occur with *L* electrons, although with a smaller probability), competes with the positron decay to be discussed in Chapter

6. If the capture of a K electron occurs in an atom with atomic number $Z = 46$, are the resulting x-ray lines those of element 45, 46, or 47?

61. The green line in the mercury spectrum is emitted in a transition from an upper state with angular momentum $J = 1$ to a lower state with $J = 2$. It has been observed that in atoms of the mercury isotope ^{199}Hg the *hyperfine structure* of this line has three components. What is the nuclear angular momentum of ^{199}Hg? Hint: The following selection rule holds: $\Delta F = 0$ or ± 1.

62. The mercury isotope ^{201}Hg has a nuclear angular momentum $I = \frac{3}{2}$. (*a*) Into how many components will the $J = 2$ and $J = 1$ atomic levels split? (*b*) Considering the selection rule $\Delta F = 0$ or ± 1, how many *hyperfine structure* components will the spectral line have which arises from a transition between these two atomic levels of ^{201}Hg?

63. The *ammonia molecule* NH$_3$ (Fig. P.4.2.) looks like a pyramid, the H atoms forming the base and the N atom the top. An energetically equivalent equilibrium configuration is the one of an inverted pyramid. The two configurations are, so to speak, like a glove and an inside-out glove. The position of the N atom in the plane of the H atoms is unstable. (This is because the three p electrons and the core of the N atom tend to arrange themselves in right angles H-N-H, which are however somewhat distorted due to electrostatic forces.) The potential function has accordingly a potential barrier in the center separating the two equilibrium positions through which the N atom can tunnel and therefore oscillate between the two positions. As the figure shows, the levels are split, one component belonging to an even wave function, the other to an odd one. Transitions

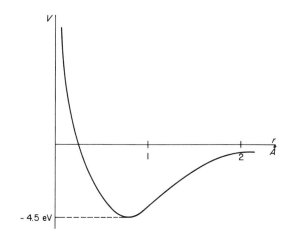

Figure P.4.3 (Problem 64)

between the lowest two states can be induced by microwave radiation of a frequency of 23×10^9 Hz. (a) Sketch for the lowest pair of states the wave function. Is the even or the odd state the lower lying one? (b) Sketch for the second pair the wave functions. (c) What is the energy difference between the lowest pair of states? (d) On what factors does the magnitude of the splitting depend?

64. Estimate the force (or spring) constant for the *vibration* of the H_2 molecule, using the data of the figure.

65. The wavelength of the radiation emitted or absorbed in transitions between vibrational levels in the H_2 molecule is 2.3 μ. Compute the energy differences between the *vibrational levels* and the zero-point energy.

66. What is the *rotational quantum number* of a rotational state in the H_2 molecule which has approximately the same energy as the first excited vibrational level? Use the data of problems 58 and 59.

67. Calculate the *rotational spectrum* of a HF molecule. The distance between the atomic nuclei is 0.917 Å.

68. Calculate the *rotational spectrum* of a $O^{16}O^{16}$ molecule. Internuclear distance 1.207 Å.

Chapter 5

Waves in Solids

5.1 ATOMS AND ELECTRONS IN SOLIDS

In this chapter we confine ourselves to a rather small number of solid-state phenomena which are well understood in terms of the wavelike aspects of the vibrations of atoms and of the motions of electrons in solids.

The first major problem we consider is the disappearance of the heat capacity of a solid toward low temperatures, an effect that contradicts the predictions of classical physics. We are thus led to consider models of a solid in which the concepts of quantized oscillators and density of vibrational modes play a prominent role.

We then start to build a framework that will allow us to understand why some solids are electrical insulators, others metals, and yet others semiconductors. The natural starting point is the free-electron model of a metal in which the interaction between the electrons and the lattice atoms is represented by collisions of the electrons. Although this model predicts Ohm's law and nicely describes the large contribution of free electrons to the thermal conductivity of a metal, it assumes a particular solid type, a metal, and is therefore incapable of leading to predictions as to which assemblies of atoms will be a metal, insulator, or semiconductor. We are thus led to a logical expansion of the ideas considered in the previous chapter concerning the sharing of electrons among the atoms of a molecule.

The wave functions of the outer electrons of isolated atoms are no longer valid when the atoms are brought together, because they overlap. They are replaced by new wave functions according to which the electrons are smeared out or shared by all the atoms. We cannot say electron 1 is in atom A, electron 2 in atom B, and so on. Every electron may be described as having a probability to be in any of the atoms.

If we stick to such a model we must conclude not only that the outer electrons of atoms in solids are shared, but actually all the electrons, those tightly bound near the nuclei as well as the loosely bound outer ones. The difference is only a matter of degree, describable perhaps by a frequency of exchange.

Although at first glance this point of view can hardly help in solving our problem—one might superficially think that all substances should conduct electrical currents—the big step forward is that a new problem is raised. What are the wave functions describing electrons in a metal? And further, what about the periodic potentials of the regularly arranged atoms in a crystal? As we shall see, in answering these questions we shall be making progress. Further, these important periodic fields due to atoms are not fixed, but oscillate as a result of thermal agitation. We shall therefore carry forward two trains of thought: the oscillatory motions of atoms in solids, and the motion of free electrons.

5.2   SPECIFIC HEAT CAPACITIES

The inside of a solid is enormously complex due to atomic and electronic motions. We shall attempt to describe, in part, some of these complexities. We shall begin by studying a model of a solid from which essentially all the complexities have been eliminated and consider in what way, if any, it resembles an actual solid. We then amplify or modify our model by adding manageable complexities. This is more or less the general procedure for studying physical properties, in this case the properties of solid matter, by means of models. The sequence of events is, as a rule: (a) the gathering of limited data; (b) the proposal of a first model to explain at least some of the characteristics of these data, forgetting the exceptions; (c) the acquisition of enough more data to reveal new aspects of the problem; (d) the creation of a new model based not only on further experimental results, but also on new mathematical techniques. Illustrations for such a development can be found in all fields of physics.

An example of this process is the study of specific heat capacity[1] of solids or, in other words, the investigation of where the energy required to raise the temperature of a solid actually goes. The specific heat capacity (the term specific heat is becoming obsolete) can be defined per unit of volume, mass, or per mole. We use it here always per mole, to be exact per gram-mole.

---

[1] According to the first law of thermodynamics, $dQ = dU - pdV$. The specific heat capacity at constant volume is defined as $c_v = (\partial Q/\partial T)_v$. Since we can write dU as $dU = (\partial U/\partial T)_v dT + (\partial U/\partial V)_T dV$, then $dQ = (\partial U/\partial T)_v dT + [(\partial U/\partial V)_T - p]dV$. So for the volume constant $(dV = 0)$, $(\partial Q/\partial T)_v = (\partial U/\partial T)_v = c_v$. In addition, we replace U by the symbol E in the following sections.

For monatomic gases we know that the energy put into the system converts into translational motion of the molecules. Monatomic molecules have three degrees of freedom, namely one translational one in the x, y, and z directions, that is, one for $E_x^{transl} = \frac{1}{2}mv_x^2$, and similarly for E_y^{transl}, and E_z^{transl}. A diatomic gas, in addition to the translational degrees of freedom, can also have rotational and vibrational degrees of freedom. Therefore its specific heat capacity is greater. According to classical statistical mechanics the average energy per degree of freedom of a particle is $\frac{1}{2}kT$ (k being the Boltzmann constant 1.38×10^{-23} joule/K), or for a monatomic gas with N atoms per mole and three degrees of freedom, the molar specific heat capacity would be $\frac{3}{2}Nk = \frac{3}{2}R$, where R is approximately 2 calories per mole.

In a solid the atoms do not have translational or rotational degrees of freedom, but they can vibrate about their equilibrium positions in the lattice. There are three degrees of freedom for the vibrational kinetic energy, corresponding to the three possible directions. In addition, because on the average the vibrating atom has an equal amount of potential energy, there are three more degrees of freedom, or altogether six degrees of freedom

TABLE 5.2.1

Molar Specific Heat Capacities of Solid Elements

Element	Molar Specific Heat Capacity (calories/mole − °C)	Temperature (°C)
Li	5.5	0
Be	3.85	0–100
B	3.35	0–100
N	5.5	−212
Na	6.8	20
Al	5.75	20
Si	4.95	20
Cl	6.7	−113
A	6.2	−223
Fe	5.95	20
Zn	6.0	0–100
Br	5.6	−150
Rb	6.85	0
Mo	6.2	20–100
Sn	6.4	18
W	6.2	20–100
Au	6.15	18
Pb	6.35	20
U	6.7	0–100

per atom. We would therefore expect in a monatomic solid, in which all
the energy supplied to raise its temperature goes into the oscillation of
separate classical particles, the specific heat capacity to be $3R$ or 6 calories/
mole-°C, that is twice that of a monatomic gas, which has only half the
number of degrees of freedom. This is known as the law of Dulong and
Petit[2] who discovered this relationship in 1819 on the basis of the data
available. A review of the data even 150 years later reveals this approximate constancy, as shown in Table 5.2.1. It should perhaps be pointed out
in connection with the above that there seems to be no great difference
between metals and nonmetals. Certainly there is no evidence of any additional 3 calories/mole-°C which one might expect for the "free electrons"
of metals.

Einstein's Theory of the Specific Heat Capacity

A great advance in our understanding of the specific heat capacities of
solids came with a paper published by Einstein in 1907,[3] dealing with the
fact that the specific heat capacities of solids tend toward zero at low temperatures. The experimental facts regarding their temperature dependence
are summarized in Fig. 5.2.1.[4] There are clearly divergences between various substances at high temperatures, but all show this tendency of decreasing to zero at the absolute zero. We need a new model to explore the
effect of the atomic oscillations, and the first aim is to test what a simple
model can achieve.

In Einstein's model the N atoms of a solid body are represented by $3N$
independent oscillators, each having the same characteristic frequency ν.
The factor 3 derives from the fact that each atom is represented by three
one-dimensional oscillators; this is equivalent to one three-dimensional
oscillator, which is somewhat more realistic. The distribution of energy
among many oscillators is given by the Bose-Einstein statistics, according
to which the average energy per one-dimensional oscillator is

$$\overline{E_0} = \frac{h\nu}{e^{h\nu/kT} - 1}. \tag{5.2.1}$$

[2] Pierre Louis Dulong (1785–1838), French chemist and physicist, from 1820 on
professor at the École Polytechnique in Paris whose director he became in 1830. Alexis
Thérèse Petit (1791–1820), French physicist.

[3] *Annalen der Physik* **22,** 180 (1907).

[4] Name and abbreviation of the unit of absolute temperature have recently been
changed by international agreement from degree Kelvin (°K) to Kelvin (K).

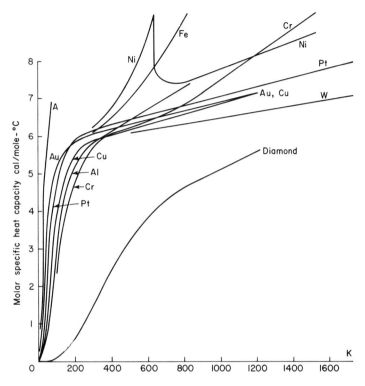

Fig. 5.2.1 Molar specific heat capacity of various substances as a function of temperature. These are measured at constant pressure, whereas calculations below are made for constant volume. The difference is usually negligible at low temperatures because of the small thermal expansion of solids. The peak in the curve for nickel is due to the fact that this metal loses its ferromagnetic character near 620 K. This will be discussed again later.

We have already met this equation in Chapter 2 in the discussion of the distribution of energy among the modes of oscillation of an electromagnetic field. There it led to Planck's law describing black-body radiation. Here it leads to Einstein's expression for the specific heat capacity of monatomic solids. The energy of an assembly of N three-dimensional oscillators, as a function of temperature, becomes

$$E = 3NkT \frac{h\nu/kT}{e^{h\nu/kT} - 1} = 3RT \frac{x}{e^x - 1} \tag{5.2.2}$$

with $x = h\nu/kT$ and $Nk = R$.

At high temperatures x becomes small, hence $e^x \to 1 + x + \ldots$, and the specific heat capacity approaches the Dulong-and-Petit value of $3R$. In

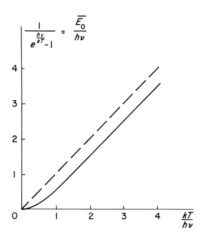

Fig. 5.2.2   A plot of Eq. 5.2.1.

Fig. 5.2.2 we have plotted the expression 5.2.1. The increase in energy with rising temperature at low temperature is small, but this increase becomes bigger and finally (approximately) constant with higher temperature. Qualitatively, this can be understood by the following argument. The oscillators can accept the energy only in finite portions, the quanta $h\nu$. At very low temperatures only a few of the oscillators are in their first excited state, and most are still in their ground state. There is just not enough energy available to distribute it over all oscillators according to the rules of the classical equipartition principle. The oscillators which are, so to speak, passed over in the distribution of the energy do not count for the specific heat capacity. It is as if they did not exist. Therefore the specific heat capacity is smaller than expected from classical theory. These "dormant" oscillators, so to speak, do not have the freedom to take up energy, because there is no energy which can be given to them, and they do not have the freedom to release energy, because they do not have any. Only after most of the oscillators are at least in the first excited state (actually some will be still in their ground state and some already in the second or a higher excited state) can we say that all oscillators have the degrees of freedom they should have according to the classical theory, and consequently also an increased specific heat capacity.

We find for the specific heat capacity at any temperature, by differentiating Eq. 5.2.2 with respect to the temperature,

$$c_v = \left(\frac{dE}{dT}\right)_{v=\text{const}} = 3Nk \left[\frac{h\nu}{kT}\right]^2 \frac{e^{h\nu/kT}}{(e^{h\nu/kT} - 1)^2}. \qquad (5.2.3)$$

Figure 5.2.3 shows a graph of Einstein's expression (5.2.3) for the specific heat capacity of silver and also for comparison of the actual values. The characteristic frequency ν, whose exact value is not provided by Einstein's model, has been chosen such that it gives a good fit to the experimental data at higher temperature. In our example of silver such a fit results when $h\nu/kT = 210$ K$/T$. Each material has its own characteristic frequency ν. One can just as well specify a characteristic temperature, the *Einstein temperature* $\Theta_E = h\nu/k$, which for silver is 210 K. It is clear that the Einstein model retains the correct Dulong-and-Petit result at high temperature, but adds the new feature of a decrease to zero at low temperature.

However, if we examine experimental results more closely and attempt a detailed comparison with Eq. 5.2.3, we find marked discrepancies. Einstein's model at low temperatures obviously overcorrects the experimentally found deviation from Dulong and Petit's value. By choosing a smaller characteristic frequency one could remedy the situation, but at the same time this would cause even more serious discrepancies at higher temperatures. It was soon recognized that a somewhat better fit could be obtained, for example, by introducing a second characteristic frequency of half the value of the first one. This was, however, a purely empirical procedure and was in no way based on theoretical considerations. This unsatisfactory situation called therefore for a further modification of the theory.

Debye's Theory of the Specific Heat Capacity

The next improvement was due to Debye in 1912.[5] Einstein's model was unrealistic insofar as it was based on the assumption that all the atoms of a solid oscillated with the same frequency and independently of each other. Certainly the neighboring atoms will interact with each other and therefore some kind of correlation in their vibratory motion is to be expected. We mentioned in the last chapter that two pendulums of the same frequency, when coupled to each other, display two different modes of oscillation, and three coupled pendulums have three frequency modes and so forth (see Fig. 5.2.4). For just the same reason we can expect, according to Debye, $3N$ different frequency modes in a system of N atoms with a total of $3N$ degrees of freedom. The average energy per mode is, as in Einstein's model, given by the Bose-Einstein statistics.

[5] *Annalen der Physik* **39,** 789 (1912). At about the same time Max Born and Theodore von Kármán, who later became famous as an aerodynamicist, attacked this problem with a somewhat more general method. A vivid account by von Kármán about this competition with Debye is in his very delightful autobiography, *The Wind and Beyond* (Little, Brown, Boston, 1967).

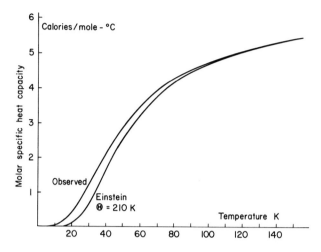

Fig. 5.2.3   Molar specific heat capacity of silver at low temperature.

In order to reduce the mathematical difficulties to manageable proportions, Debye introduced a model in which the solid is considered as a continuum. Such a body can vibrate in many different modes. These modes
of vibration are just the standing acoustic or elastic waves. The atomistic
character of the solid crystal is retained insofar as the total number of
vibrational modes must equal the crystals's $3N$ degrees of freedom contributed by its N atoms.

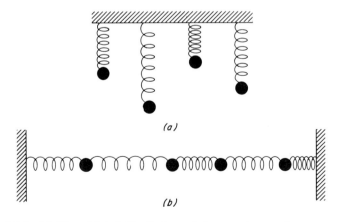

Fig. 5.2.4   (a) Uncorrelated identical pendulums, only one frequency mode: an
analog to the Einstein model. (b) Coupled pendulums, with the number of modes equal
to the number of pendulums: an analog to the Debye model.

In this discussion we shall assume that the velocity of propagation of acoustic waves is independent of frequency, that is, that there is no dispersion, and that it is the same for both longitudinal and transverse waves.[6] The problem is to find out how all these independent modes of oscillation are distributed as a function of frequency. Modes will be quantized just as the energy in an oscillating electromagnetic field is quantized. The acoustic quanta are called *phonons* just as the electromagnetic quanta are called photons. The energy of a quantum is again $h\nu$, or $\hbar\omega$.

A similar computation had been performed earlier by Rayleigh and Jeans for the modes of electromagnetic waves in a cavity which led to the Rayleigh-Jeans law for black-body radiation. Although it is known that this law gives an incorrect result for black-body radiation, its mathematical formalism provided the proper framework for Debye to compute the vibrational modes of a solid.

Let us, however first investigate the much simpler one-dimensional string of length L, which is fixed at both ends. The standing waves on this string are given by

$$Y(x, t) = Y_0 \sin \frac{2\pi x}{\lambda} \sin \omega t.$$

Because the time-dependent factor is of no interest in our present discussion, we may neglect it and simply write

$$Y(x) = Y_0 \sin \frac{2\pi x}{\lambda}. \tag{5.2.4}$$

The boundary conditions of the string require that the amplitude of the standing wave on both ends must be zero. Consequently the wavelengths λ must satisfy the condition

$$n\lambda = 2L \quad n = 1, 2, 3, \ldots.$$

If we substitute for the wavelength with $\lambda = u/\nu$ and assume that the phase velocity u of all waves is the same (that is, there is no dispersion which is, as we shall see later, only partially correct), this condition becomes

$$\nu = n \frac{u}{2L} \quad n = 1, 2, \ldots$$

---

[6] In contrast to the propagation of sound in a gas which proceeds only by way of longitudinal waves, sound waves in solids (and liquids) can also be transverse. These transverse elastic waves are called shear waves, since their propagation involves shear deformations.

or

$$\omega = n\,\frac{\pi u}{L} = n\omega.$$

On an axis representing the frequency the modes are thus equally spaced, as shown in Fig. 5.2.5. Very important for many considerations is the

Fig. 5.2.5   Frequency modes of finite string.

concept of the *density of modes* ρ, which is the number of modes per unit frequency interval. In our case, the density of the modes as a function of frequency is constant, and we may illustrate this in a plot of $\rho(\omega)$ vs. ω, as shown in Fig. 5.2.6. Any density, be it the population density, traffic density, the density of ties on a railroad track, or the density of a solid, is always expressed as a quantity per unit of some other physical quantity, which in the just quoted examples may be square mile, hour, mile, or cubic meter, respectively. For the density of modes of the oscillating string it would be a frequency unit, the hertz.

In contrast to the case of the string we shall now see that in a three-dimensional continuum the density of modes does not stay constant but rises sharply with increasing frequency.

In order to simplify the computation, we will assume that our solid has the shape of a cube. However, it can be shown that the result is independent of the shape of the solid. By analogy to the boundary condition for the string, we will require here that an integral multiple of projections of half-wavelengths fit into each side of length L in order to get standing waves. In addition to the standing waves moving parallel to the axes of the cube, modes are permitted in which waves move in a more or less diagonal direction. The only important point is that the condition be satisfied that an integral number of half-wavelengths fit into each side. The two-dimensional

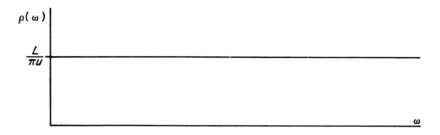

Fig. 5.2.6   Density of modes of a finite string.

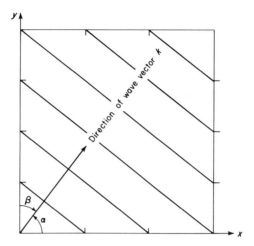

Fig. 5.2.7   An oscillatory mode with the projections of three half-wavelengths in the *x* direction and of four half-wavelengths in the *y* direction.

graph (Fig. 5.2.7) illustrates the situation in which one side includes projections of three half-wavelengths, and the other side four. In three dimensions the direction of the wave is given by the wave vector **k** which can be expressed by the cosines of the angles α, β, and γ.

For one dimension we had written for the wave,

$$Y(x) = Y_0 \sin \frac{2\pi x}{\lambda}.$$

For standing waves in a three-dimensional cube we have

$$Y(x, y, z) = Y_0 \sin\left(\frac{2\pi x \cos \alpha}{\lambda}\right) \sin\left(\frac{2\pi y \cos \beta}{\lambda}\right) \sin\left(\frac{2\pi z \cos \gamma}{\lambda}\right). \quad (5.2.5)$$

Similarly, the condition for one-dimensional standing waves

$$n\lambda = 2L \quad (5.2.5a)$$

becomes

$$n_x\lambda = 2L \cos \alpha$$

$$n_y\lambda = 2L \cos \beta$$

$$n_z\lambda = 2L \cos \gamma$$

where n_x, n_y, and n_z are integers. Squaring and adding these equations, and

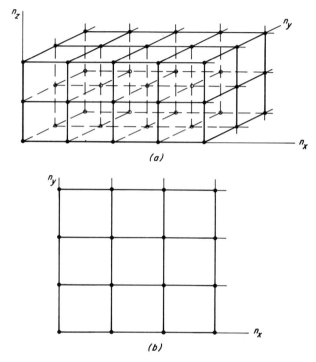

Fig. 5.2.8 Representation of the vibrational states: (a) three-dimensional body; (b) two-dimensional case.

using $\cos^2\alpha + \cos^2\beta + \cos^2\gamma = 1$, we get

$$n_x{}^2 + n_y{}^2 + n_z{}^2 = \frac{4L^2}{\lambda^2}. \tag{5.2.6}$$

Again we are interested in the possible frequencies, not the wavelengths, so that we write this equation as

$$n_x{}^2 + n_y{}^2 + n_z{}^2 = \frac{4L^2\nu^2}{u^2} = \frac{L^2\omega^2}{\pi^2 u^2}. \tag{5.2.7}$$

Each possible combination of n_x, n_y, and n_z represents a possible mode of vibration. Instead of plotting these frequencies as points on a line as we did in the one-dimensional case, we must now use a three-dimensional array, as shown in Fig. 5.2.8 (a). (The two-dimensional case, which is easier to see, is shown in Fig. 5.2.8 (b)).

As n_x, n_y, and n_z are required to be positive, all the states of the vibrating solid fall in the octant for which this condition is met. Furthermore, for each value of ω there is one longitudinal mode and two (because of two states of polarization) transverse modes. For simplicity we assume here that the velocities of the longitudinal and the transverse waves are equal, although this is actually not the case. The total number of modes is therefore three times the number of possible frequencies.

In analogy to the one-dimensional example, the distance of a point from the origin is proportional to the frequency of the mode. For example, the third point on the x axis (not counting the point at zero) represents the frequency $\omega = 3(\pi u/L)$ and has the distance $R = (n_x{}^2 + n_y{}^2 + n_z{}^2)^{1/2}$, which is here $(3^2 + 0 + 0)^{1/2}$, from the origin. Therefore, if we construct a sphere with radius R (only one octant is necessary) with the center at the origin, all the points within the octant represent all the modes with frequencies smaller than the frequency $\omega = R\pi u/L$. Because of their uniform distribution in this mathematical array the number of points of modes within the octant is proportional to the volume, neglecting small fluctuations due to points either barely missed or just included within the spherical surface. Anyway, the more points the octant contains the less important are such fluctuations.

Taking into account that there are three modes per frequency, and because $R = (L\omega/\pi u)$ the number of modes, $3N$, is

$$3N = \frac{3}{8}\frac{4\pi}{3}\left(\frac{L\omega}{\pi u}\right)^3 = \frac{1}{2}\frac{L^3\omega^3}{\pi^3 u^3}. \tag{5.2.8}$$

By differentiation we easily find the number of modes in the frequency

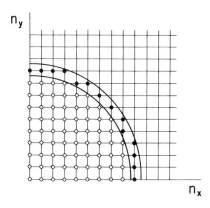

Fig. 5.2.9 The two-dimensional counterpart to the three-dimensional octant of a spherical shell.

interval between ω and $\omega + d\omega$, or the density of modes $\rho(\omega)$,

$$\frac{d(3N)}{d\omega} = \rho(\omega) = \frac{3}{2}\frac{L^3\omega^2}{\pi^2 u^3}. \tag{5.2.9}$$

This is what we had set out to calculate. Instead of differentiating we could have constructed a spherical shell of a thickness corresponding to $d\omega$ and could have counted the modes situated within the wall. Figure 5.2.9 illustrates this approach for the two-dimensional case.

We note that the density of modes for Debye's model increases with the square of the frequency, in contrast to the constant density of modes for the one-dimensional string. Figure 5.2.10 gives a comparison of the frequencies used for the Einstein and the Debye model.

We mentioned earlier that the total number of modes in a crystal with N atoms is $3N$. Hence, there must be a cutoff frequency, the Debye frequency ω_D. Since

$$3N = \int_0^{\omega_D} \rho(\omega)\, d\omega = \int_0^{\omega_D} \frac{3L^3}{2\pi^2 u^3}\omega^2\, d\omega = \frac{L^3\omega_D^3}{2\pi^2 u^3},$$

this Debye frequency is

$$\omega_D = (6\pi^2)^{1/3}\left(\frac{u}{L}\right)N^{1/3} = 3.9\left(\frac{u}{L}\right)N^{1/3}. \tag{5.2.10}$$

We can argue in the following way to see that Eq. 5.2.10 is a reasonable expression for ω_D. It is reasonable to assume that the shortest wavelength that can be propagated in a solid is of the order of magnitude of twice the interatomic spacing a. Waves in a crystal must involve gradually changing

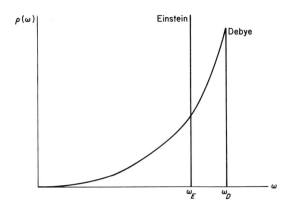

Fig. 5.2.10 Comparison of $\rho(\omega)$ for the Einstein and Debye models.

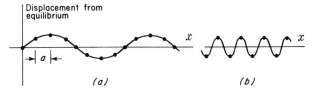

Fig. 5.2.11 Wave in a line of points: (a) general case; (b) shortest possible wavelength, $\lambda = 2a$.

displacements from equilibrium positions in going from one atom to another, as illustrated in Fig. 5.2.11. For example, when $\lambda = a/2$, no point or atom is displaced. The "wave" is no longer a wave in the assembly of points, but in the space between them. We may then, for purposes of making an estimate, put our limits at a longer wavelength $\lambda_D = 2a$, or if we have an assembly of N atoms with a spacing such that $Na^3 = L^3$, $\lambda_D = 2L/N^{1/3}$. The Debye frequency then becomes $\omega_D = 2\pi u/\lambda_D$ or,

$$\omega_D \approx \pi \left(\frac{u}{L}\right) N^{1/3} = 3.14 \left(\frac{u}{L}\right) N^{1/3}. \tag{5.2.11}$$

Equation 5.2.11 is essentially the same as the more rigorous result given in Eq. 5.2.10. The order of magnitude of the Debye frequency in a medium for which $u = 5 \times 10^3$ m/sec, $L/N^{1/3} = 2 \times 10^{-10}$ m is $\omega_D \approx 10^{14}$ sec^{-1}.

This completes the discussion of the physical ideas that go into the Debye specific heat capacity theory. There remain only a few mathematical operations to be performed. The expression for the energy given in Eq. 5.2.2 becomes

$$E = \int_0^{\omega_D} \frac{3L^3\omega^2}{2\pi^2u^3} \frac{\hbar\omega}{e^{\hbar\omega/kT} - 1} \, d\omega. \tag{5.2.12}$$

If we put

$$\frac{\hbar\omega}{kT} = x$$

$$\frac{\hbar\omega_D}{kT} = x_D$$

then Eq. 5.2.12 becomes

$$E = \frac{3L^3k^4T^4}{2\pi^2u^3\hbar^3} \int_0^{x_D} \frac{x^3}{e^x - 1} \, dx.$$

Then, by differentiating Eq. 5.2.12 with respect to the temperature, one finds

$$c_v = \frac{3L^3\hbar^2}{2\pi^2 u^3 kT^2} \int_0^{\omega_D} \frac{\omega^4 e^{\hbar\omega/kT}}{(e^{\hbar\omega/kT} - 1)^2}\, d\omega$$

$$= 9Nkx_D^{-3} \int_0^{x_D} \frac{x^4 e^x\, dx}{(e^x - 1)^2}. \tag{5.2.13}$$

At this point we should notice that since x_D is a dimensionless quantity, it can obviously be viewed as the ratio of two temperatures: $(\hbar\omega_D/k)/T$. We call the numerator the *Debye temperature* Θ_D, hence

$$\Theta_D = \frac{\hbar\omega_D}{k}. \tag{5.2.14}$$

For $\omega_D \sim 10^{14}$ sec^{-1}, $\Theta_D \sim 600$ K. Equation 5.2.13 then can be written as

$$c_v = 9Nk\left(\frac{T}{\Theta_D}\right)^3 \int_0^{\Theta_D/T} \frac{x^4 e^x\, dx}{(e^x - 1)^2}. \tag{5.2.15}$$

This expression is plotted in Fig. 5.2.12. Such a curve can be fitted to experimental data very nicely for many substances over a limited temperature range, usually for T/Θ_D between .02 and .5 as is shown for three substances, Pt, Al, and Cu, in the illustration.

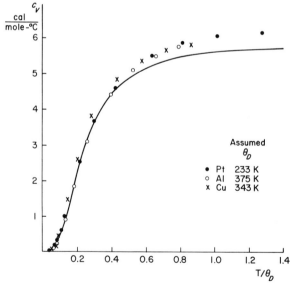

Fig. 5.2.12   A plot of c_v as given by the Debye theory (Eq. 5.2.15), as a function of T/Θ_D, compared to experimental data. The values of Θ_D are those used in Fig. 5.2.13 to give the best fit at low temperatures.

We notice from Eq. 5.2.15 that the temperature dependence of c_v comes on one hand from the factor $(T/\Theta_D)^3$ and on the other hand from the temperature dependence of the integral whose upper limit depends on the temperature T. If we let the upper limit of integration go to infinity, which means that we are looking at c_v for $T \ll \Theta_D$, the integral is no longer dependent on T, and $c_v \sim T^3$. Figure 5.2.12 shows how well some experimental data follow this temperature variation in the region where $T \ll \Theta_D$. This region is referred to as the low temperature region, just as we would define the high temperature region for $T \gg \Theta_D$. In other words, the Debye temperature Θ_D serves to define "low" and "high" temperatures for the lattice of the solid, and herein lies its very important physical significance.

In view of the above considerations, and since

$$\int_0^\infty \frac{x^4 e^x \, dx}{(e^x - 1)^2} = \frac{4\pi^4}{15}$$

the specific heat capacity for low temperatures may be written

$$c_v = \frac{12\pi^4}{5} Nk \left(\frac{T}{\Theta_D}\right)^3 \simeq 468 \left(\frac{T}{\Theta_D}\right)^3 \frac{\text{cal}}{\text{mole } °\text{C}}. \qquad (5.2.16)$$

The experimental values of c_v for various substances as given in the second edition of the *American Institute of Physics Handbook* (Ch. 4), divided by $468 \, (T/\Theta_D)^3$, are plotted in Fig. 5.2.13. From our theory we should expect that the ordinates of all the data points have the value of unity. Even though the data given are not accurate enough for a detailed check, it seems clear that there is rough agreement between theory and experiment for the substances shown. But it is also clear that our model, in order to account for the low-temperature specific heats of solids, still can stand further modifications, and we shall return to this question later.

What about the high temperature value of c_v? By high temperature we, of course, mean $T \gg \Theta_D$. This means that x in Eq. 5.2.15 is very close to zero. Then,

$$\int_0^{\Theta_D/T} \frac{x^4 e^x dx}{(e^x - 1)^2} \rightarrow \int_0^{\Theta_D/T} \frac{x^4 (1) \, dx}{x^2} = \left[\frac{x^3}{3}\right]_0^{\Theta_D/T} = \frac{1}{3}\left(\frac{\Theta_D}{T}\right)^3,$$

in which case

$$c_v = 9Nk \left(\frac{T}{\Theta_D}\right)^3 \frac{1}{3}\left(\frac{\Theta_D}{T}\right)^3 = 3Nk. \qquad (5.2.17)$$

This is just the Dulong-and-Petit value which we expect to find in the

372   FIELDS AND PARTICLES

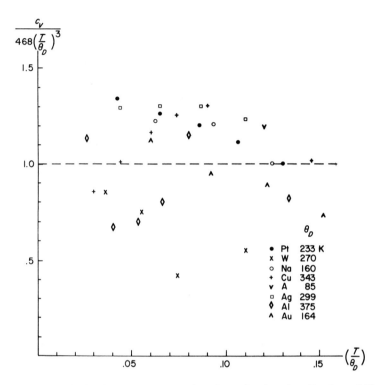

Fig. 5.2.13 A check of Eq. 5.2.16 using data from the *American Institute of Physics Handbook* (Chap. 4). Ferromagnetic substances, such as iron or nickel, have not been plotted because, as already seen in Fig. 5.2.1, additional effects influence their specific heat capacity.

high-temperature classical limit. Again, the Debye model succeeds quite nicely. However, the behavior of each substance must be examined separately.

In nickel, for example, the magnetic moments in a domain are aligned at low temperatures by electromagnetic forces which produce its ferromagnetism. As the temperature is raised, the energy supplied not only produces thermal oscillations but also is used to uncouple the elementary magnets from each other. The temperature at which this latter process is fairly abruptly completed is called the Curie temperature. For Ni it is at 620 K. This process is responsible for the sharp maximum in the specific heat capacity, shown in Fig. 5.2.1, which can be accounted for in detail by magnetic theory. There is a similar behavior in iron, not shown in detail because it is off scale. The Curie temperature of iron is 1030 K, and the specific heat capacity reaches the value of 18 cal/mole − °C.

In our model we have neglected thermal expansion, and the variation of the velocity of sound with temperature. Furthermore, we find that at high temperatures the amplitudes of the oscillations of the atoms become so great that we are no longer dealing with harmonic oscillators. These features, thermal expansion, variation of the sound velocity, and anharmonic behavior, have been shown to be important in determining the high-temperature specific heat capacities of solids. The limited success of our model has perhaps taught us how far we can rely on it in describing the atomic vibrations in solids.

Dispersion of Waves in Solids

The Debye model, in its simplicity, serves to give us physical insight into the problem of vibrations in solids and, in fact, generally gives a good estimate of the lattice specific heat capacity. This model is, of course, limited because it is based on the picture of the solid as a continuous medium. And it is a direct consequence of this assumption of continuity that the density of states turns out to depend on the square of the frequency. The obvious place to look for discrepancies between measured and Debye-model values of the specific heat capacity is the density of states. In principle we would like to calculate the normal frequencies of a three-dimensional system of masses that are connected to each other by something like springs, a formidable problem even when the springs are idealized to follow Hooke's law, that is to say that there is a linear relationship between elongation and force. However, we can gain some insight into the three-dimensional problem by considering the mathematically more simple problem of finding the normal frequencies for a one-dimensional chain of atoms that are held together by springs which obey Hooke's law. The problem has the virtue that it is easily solvable. In addition, we can compare the density of states found using this approach to the constant density of states we found for the one-dimensional continuous medium.

In Fig. 5.2.14 we have a series of atoms of mass M with equilibrium spacing a, which are connected to each other by springs of force constant K. This means that only neighboring atoms exert forces on each other.

Consider the sum of the forces acting on the sth atom which has been displaced to the right into the dotted position by δ_s. The spring to the right is compressed by $\delta_s - \delta_{s+1}$, the δ's measuring the displacements from the equilibrium position. This spring therefore exerts a force to the left. Elongation of the left spring results also in a force to the left, the elongation being $\delta_s - \delta_{s-1}$. Thus, the force acting on the sth atom will be

$$F_s = K(\delta_{s+1} + \delta_{s-1} - 2\delta_s). \tag{5.2.18}$$

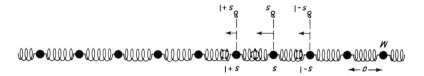

Fig. 5.2.14 A linear chain of atoms.

From the force equation we get

$$M \frac{d^2\delta_s}{dt^2} = K(\delta_{s+1} + \delta_{s-1} - 2\delta_s).$$ (5.2.19)

Because such a displacement will propagate along the chain as a wave, we now assume a wavelike solution of this differential equation of the form

$$\delta_s = Ae^{iska-i\omega t}.$$

$$\delta_{s+1} = Ae^{i(s+1)ka-i\omega t} = \delta_s e^{ika}$$ (5.2.20)

where a is the undistorted lattice spacing, s is a pure number, and k is the wave number. Here we have used Euler's relation (see Appendix III) for the description of a wave. Substituting in Eq. 5.2.19 we get

$$-\omega^2 M \delta_s = K(-2\delta_s + \delta_s e^{ika} + \delta_s e^{-ika})$$

$$-\omega^2 M = K(-2 + e^{ika} + e^{-ika})$$

$$\omega^2 M = K(-2 \cos ka + 2)$$

$$\omega^2 = (2K/M)(1 - \cos ka).$$ (5.2.21)

Recall that in the Debye model we assumed there is no dispersion; that is, $\nu\lambda = w$, with w the phase velocity. This is, because $\omega = 2\pi\nu$ and $k = 2\pi/\lambda$, the same as $\omega = kw$. Equation 5.2.21 shows that we do have dispersion for the linear chain. Hence, we would expect the density of states to differ from the constant value predicted for the Debye model for the case of a linear chain. Before we proceed to calculate the density of states, however, let us turn our attention to a plot of ω vs. k, where we plot ω in units of $(2K/M)^{1/2}$. Here we use the trigonometric relation $2\sin^2(x/2) = 1 - \cos x$. Thus we can write Eq. 5.2.21 also as

$$\omega^2 = \frac{4K}{M} \sin^2 \frac{ka}{2}.$$

This is shown in Fig. 5.2.15. This dispersion relation is shown from $-\pi/a$ to $+\pi/a$, but any interval $2\pi/a$ would have done, as the curve repeats itself. For small values of k, or long wavelengths, it displays the linear characteristics of a continuum with constant velocity, and phase and group velocities are equal. However, for $k = \pm\pi/a$,

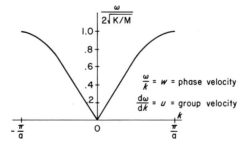

Fig. 5.2.15   Dispersion curve for a linear chain of atoms of mass M elastically bound to their nearest neighbors.

which corresponds to $\lambda = 2a$, it displays zero group velocity, or no transmission of energy just where we had assumed an arbitrary cutoff (see Fig. 5.2.11 (b)) in the Debye theory.[7] In three-dimensional problems, relationships like those shown in Fig. 5.2.15 become complex three-dimensional figures.

It is rather straightforward to calculate the density of states for the chain. First, since $\omega_{max} = (2K/M)^{1/2}$, we can simplify the notation by setting $(2K/M)^{1/2} \equiv \Omega$ in Eq. 5.2.21:

$$\omega^2 = \Omega^2(1 - \cos ka). \tag{5.2.22}$$

If the ends of the chain are held fixed, we can use Eq. 5.2.5a to write

$$2\pi \frac{L}{\lambda} = n\pi = kL, \tag{5.2.23}$$

where $k = 2\pi/\lambda$. Accordingly,

$$\frac{dn}{dk} = \frac{L}{\pi}. \tag{5.2.24}$$

Suppose we now differentiate Eq. 5.2.22 with respect to ω. This gives

$$2\omega = \Omega^2 a \sin ka \cdot \left(\frac{dk}{d\omega}\right),$$

or

$$\frac{dk}{d\omega} = \frac{2\omega}{\Omega^2 a \sin ka}. \tag{5.2.25}$$

As $\rho = \dfrac{dn}{dk} \cdot \dfrac{dk}{d\omega}$,

$$\rho(\omega) = \frac{2L}{\pi a \Omega^2} \frac{\omega}{\sin ka};$$

but from Eq. 5.2.22

$$\sin ka = \sqrt{1 - \cos^2 ka} = \left[1 - \frac{(\Omega^2 - \omega^2)^2}{\Omega^4}\right]^{1/2} = \frac{\omega}{\Omega^2}\sqrt{2\Omega^2 - \omega^2}.$$

Therefore,

$$\rho(\omega) = \frac{2L}{\pi a \Omega^2} \frac{\omega}{(\omega/\Omega^2)\sqrt{2\Omega^2 - \omega^2}}$$

or

$$\rho(\omega) = \frac{2L}{\pi a} \frac{1}{\sqrt{2\Omega^2 - \omega^2}}. \tag{5.2.26}$$

It is apparent from Eq. 5.2.26 that the density of states varies with ω. It is certainly not constant, as was the prediction of the Debye model for a one-dimensional solid.

---

[7] The region of the k axis from $-\pi/a$ to π/a is referred as the first Brillouin zone.

However, we see from Eq. 5.2.26 that for small values of ω (long wavelengths), $\rho(\omega)$ is rather insensitive to variations in ω, because Ω is the dominant quantity, so that we have agreement between the two models in this limit.

Review

We conclude our discussion of specific heat capacities with a short review. The Dulong-Petit law is a quite good approximation at higher temperatures, but it fails badly at low temperatures, and a classical theory cannot remedy this shortcoming. Great progress was due to Einstein who introduced a relatively simple model of atomic oscillators of a single frequency, incorporating the ideas of the then only half-dozen-year-old quantum theory. Again a few years later, Debye (and also Born and von Kármán) refined Einstein's theory by assuming many frequencies and obtained even better agreement between theory and experiment.[8] Also Debye's model contained simplifying assumptions. Because fundamentally it treated the crystal as a homogeneous continuum, the effects of dispersion were ignored. This was fully recognized by Debye who remarked about the resulting consequences in a footnote in his paper. Finally, we discussed the propagation of waves through a one-dimensional crystal (the three-dimensional case being too complicated) instead of a continuum and found that phase and group velocity are different or, in other words, that dispersion occurs. This is because the mass is concentrated in regular intervals in individual atoms and not uniformly smeared out over the whole chain.

5.3 PHONONS: QUANTIZATION OF WAVES IN CRYSTALS

As we have previously remarked, the average energy of a one-dimensional oscillator is given by an expression of the form[9]

$$\bar{E} = \frac{\hbar\omega}{\exp(\hbar\omega/kT) - 1}$$

However, according to Eq. 3.5.9 the nth energy level of a one-dimensional harmonic oscillator is given by

$$E_n = (n + \tfrac{1}{2})\hbar\omega.$$

[8] Debye's theory did not find immediate unanimous approval, as a private letter of the Nobel laureate W. Nernst to Debye indicates: "Dear Mr. Debye: Your last paper shows me that you have understood the quantum theory even less than my worst student. . ." (Private communication by H. B. G. Casimir.)

[9] k here stands for the Boltzmann constant. Since it appears here always in conjunction with a temperature T or Θ, no confusion with the wave number k should arise.

As we recall from Chapter 3, the energy levels are equally spaced. Now let us imagine that the energy of the nth level is due to a number n of vibrational quanta, called *phonons*, each having an amount of energy $\hbar\omega$. The total energy of the n phonons is just $n\hbar\omega$, and to this we add the zero-point energy $\frac{1}{2}\hbar\omega$ to get the level energy E_n.

Now the above expression for E can be viewed as being obtained in the following way. We have a system consisting of many one-dimensional oscillators that do not interact with each other but are all in contact with a thermal reservoir of temperature T. Without disturbing the oscillators too much, we go from one to the other through the entire system of oscillators, making note of the quantum level of each oscillator; we record the level number n for each of the oscillators. If there are N oscillators in the system, and the first oscillator is in the level n_1 (for instance $n_1 = 10$), the second in n_2 (for instance $n_2 = 17$), the third in n_3, and so on, then the average quantum level number for the system, $\langle n \rangle$, is simply given by the arithmetic average of $n_1, n_2, \ldots, n_N$:

$$\langle n \rangle = (n_1 + n_2 + n_3 + n_4 + \ldots + n_N)/N. \tag{5.3.1}$$

So the average energy of an oscillator, ignoring zero-point energy, is given by

$$\bar{E} = \langle n \rangle \hbar\omega. \tag{5.3.2}$$

Therefore, an oscillator at a temperature T has an average number of $\langle n \rangle$ phonons associated with it given by

$$\langle n \rangle \hbar\omega = \frac{\hbar\omega}{\exp(\hbar\omega/kT) - 1}, \tag{5.3.3}$$

or

$$\langle n \rangle = \frac{1}{\exp(\hbar\omega/kT) - 1}. \tag{5.3.4}$$

Equation 5.3.4 gives the average number of these phonons or the average quantum number associated with an oscillator of natural frequency ω in equilibrium with a thermal reservoir of temperature T.

If, on the other hand, we consider a system consisting of oscillators of different natural frequencies, and there are dn oscillators of approximate frequency ω in the frequency interval $d\omega$, then the number of phonons $d\eta$ associated with these oscillators is given by

$$d\eta = \frac{dn}{\exp(\hbar\omega/kT) - 1} = \frac{\rho(\omega)\,d\omega}{\exp(\hbar\omega/kT) - 1}. \tag{5.3.5}$$

The $d\eta$ phonons contribute an amount of energy dE to the system:

$$dE = d\eta\hbar\omega = \frac{\hbar\omega\rho(\omega)\,d\omega}{\exp(\hbar\omega/kT) - 1}. \tag{5.3.6}$$

The total energy of the assembly of oscillators is then given by:

$$E = \int_{\omega=0}^{\omega=\omega_{max}} dE = \int_{\omega=0}^{\omega=\omega_{max}} \frac{\hbar\omega\rho(\omega)\,d\omega}{\exp(\hbar\omega/kT) - 1}, \tag{5.3.7}$$

where ω_{max} could be given by ω_D of the Debye theory. This expression for the system energy, which we have arrived at through a consideration of the vibrational quanta—the phonons, is in exact agreement with Eq. 5.2.12.

Not only can we specify the energy $\hbar\omega$ of each phonon, but we can describe it by its wavelength λ as well. This is entirely reasonable inasmuch as we specify both the frequency ω and wavelength λ of a lattice vibration, and the lattice vibrations are now thought of as being quantized as phonons. Therefore, the phonons comprising a lattice vibration should have the frequency and wavelength of the vibration.

Although we have only considered standing wave solutions to the problem of the vibrations of a continuous medium, there is no reason why we cannot think of a solution to the wave equation that involves traveling waves. For instance, suppose we consider the following expression for the displacement $Y(x, y, z, t)$:

$$Y(x, y, z, t) = Ae^{i(x \cdot k_x + y \cdot k_y + z \cdot k_z - \omega t)} + Be^{-i(x \cdot k_x + y \cdot k_y + z \cdot k_z + \omega t)}, \tag{5.3.8}$$

where

$$\mathbf{k} = \hat{\mathbf{i}}k_x + \hat{\mathbf{j}}k_y + \hat{\mathbf{k}}k_z, \quad k = 2\pi/\lambda.$$

and whereby it is understood that the actual displacement is given by the real part of $Y(x, y, z, t)$; $\hat{\mathbf{i}}$, $\hat{\mathbf{j}}$, and $\hat{\mathbf{k}}$ are unit vectors.

Before we consider the significance of using a solution of this form which involves complex exponentials, it is easy to verify that Eq. 5.3.8 is indeed a solution of the wave equation. Differentiating twice with respect to x, y, and z to form the Laplacian ∇^2, we have

$$\nabla^2 Y = -(k_x{}^2 + k_y{}^2 + k_z{}^2) Y. \tag{5.3.9}$$

Also, by differentiating Y twice with respect to the time t we obtain

$$\frac{\partial^2}{\partial t^2} Y = -\omega^2 Y. \tag{5.3.10}$$

Substituting Eqs. 5.3.9 and 5.3.10 in the wave equation $\nabla^2 Y = w^{-2}(\partial^2 Y/\partial t^2)$, we see that

$$-(k_x{}^2 + k_y{}^2 + k_z{}^2) Y = -k^2 Y = -\left(\frac{\omega^2}{w^2}\right) Y,$$

or

$$k^2 = \frac{\omega^2}{w^2} = \left(\frac{2\pi}{\lambda}\right)^2. \tag{5.3.11}$$

Thus, $Y(x, y, z, t)$ is a solution of the wave equation, and Eq. 5.3.11 tells us that the solution represents a plane wave. In fact, the solution represents two plane waves, one with amplitude A traveling in the $+k$ direction, and one with amplitude B traveling in the $-k$ direction. The standing wave solution that we found before is merely a superposition of traveling plane waves of equal amplitude; that is, $A = \pm B$.

In terms of the idea of traveling waves, we can imagine the phonons propagating through the solid with a phase velocity w, frequency ω, and wave vector $\mathbf{k}$. Since we can see a very great similarity between these phonons and photons, we might be tempted to conclude that just as photons have a momentum given by $\hbar k$, so phonons should carry a momentum $\hbar k$. Although it is sometimes convenient to think of phonons carrying momentum, this momentum is not a real momentum simply because there are no external forces present to give motion to the center of mass of the solid.

We should mention that phonons are playing an important role not only in solid-state physics, but also in nuclear physics, where internal vibrations of nuclei can be described as phonon excitations.

The Mössbauer Effect

An important consequence of the quantization of lattice vibrations is the recoilless emission of γ radiation, or Mössbauer effect. This effect was discovered more or less accidentally in 1958 by Rudolf Mössbauer,[10] a graduate student of the Technical University Munich, who was doing his research at Heidelberg which at that time had more suitable facilities. Mössbauer's thesis project was an investigation of nuclear resonance fluorescence at low temperatures.

When discussing the Heisenberg uncertainty relation $\Delta E \cdot \Delta t \geq h$ in Chapter 3, we pointed out that in nuclei the probability for resonance absorption of γ quanta is generally relatively small due to the recoils of the emitting and absorbing nuclei of the same type and the attendant Doppler shift. If there were a way that this recoil could be eliminated, the probability for resonance absorption should be increased greatly. It is obvious that for nuclei belonging to atoms in the gaseous or liquid state recoil cannot be prevented. However, in solids the situation can be different. Recoil of a nucleus in a crystal involves a sudden displacement of the atom from its normal lattice site, and this motion gives rise to lattice vibrations.

Rudolf L. Mössbauer (born 1929) (Courtesy of American Institute of Physics, Meggers Gallery of Nobel Laureates).

[10] Rudolf Mössbauer (1929–   ). Presently professor at the Technical University Munich. Work in Mössbauer effect and related topics. 1961 Nobel prize in physics for the discovery of recoilless emission of γ-radiation, i.e., the Mössbauer effect.

For simplicity sake we first shall assume that in the crystal only one mode of oscillation is possible, the one given by the Einstein mode of heat capacity, and that the crystal is in its lowest possible state. It is then plausible that, if the energy of the atom which it gains from the recoil is smaller than the energy $h\nu$ associated with an oscillating atom, the atom will not be excited but will stay at rest (neglecting the zero-point energy). There is, hence, no possibility to convert the recoil energy of the atom into vibrational energy of the lattice. The momentum from the recoil must therefore be taken up by the crystal as a whole. Even a very small crystal contains many millions of atoms. Consequently the energy associated with its recoil is negligible. One speaks therefore about recoilless emission of γ radiation although in a very strict sense this is not quite correct. If under such conditions the atom does not move, there will be no Doppler effect and the frequency of the emitted radiation corresponds exactly to the energy difference between the nuclear levels involved in the transition. Similar considerations are valid also for the resonance absorption of such a γ ray by a nucleus which cannot move from its equilibrium position. If the emitting and the absorbing atom cannot move, the energy of such a quantum is therefore just the correct one, and the probability for resonance absorption should be very high.

For an Einstein-model solid we should expect recoilless emission and absorption of photons only for γ energies that could provide an isolated atom at most with a recoil energy which is smaller than the energy of the atomic vibration in the solid. The average energy of an oscillator per degree of freedom is according to Eq. 5.2.1, at not too low temperatures,

$$\bar{E}_0 = \frac{h\nu}{e^{h\nu/kT} - 1} \approx \frac{h\nu}{1 + h\nu/kT - 1},$$

where ν is the frequency of the atomic oscillation which is chosen such that the experimental data for the specific heat fit the theory. Alternatively we can determine a characteristic temperature θ_E, the Einstein temperature, such that $h\nu = k\theta_E$, k being the Boltzmann constant. Therefore the energy of a quantized vibrational mode can be expressed as $k\theta_E$. For example, silver (Fig. 5.2.3) has an Einstein temperature $\theta_E = 210$ K which results for $k\theta_E$ in an energy of 1.38×10^{-23} joule/K $\times$ (1 eV/1.60×10^{-19} joule) = 1.81×10^{-2} eV. The first vibrational mode in a silver atom is expected to be excited only if the recoil energy R is greater than this amount. From our earlier discussion of resonance absorption in connection with the Heisenberg uncertainty principle, it follows that in order to provide the necessary recoil energy R in a silver nucleus of mass number $A = 107$, a γ ray must have an energy of at least

$$E_0 = \sqrt{2RMc^2}$$
$$= \sqrt{2 \times 1.81 \times 10^{-2} \, \text{eV} \times 107 \times 930 \times 10^6 \, \text{eV}}$$
$$= 60 \, \text{keV}, \qquad\qquad (5.3.12)$$

where M is the mass of the atom.

In the radioactive decay of the cadmium isotope with mass number $A = 107$ nuclei of this silver isotope are produced in an excited state of 93 keV energy which subsequently decays to the ground state. Indeed, it has been observed that some of these decays proceed without recoil. The excitation energy of this state is higher than our estimation of 60 keV, but it has to be remembered that the Einstein model does not truly describe the actual situation. Therefore we can be quite satisfied that the estimated energy comes so close. It should also be pointed out that only a fraction of the decays proceeds without recoil; the majority of the decays is usually accompanied by recoil.

Here we must add a note of caution to our considerations which are not correct in all respects. A wave-mechanical treatment will show that even if the available recoil energy of the isolated atom is greater than the energy of the Einstein oscillators it will not cause in each decay a recoil of the atom. Conversely, if the available energy is smaller, there will be still some probability for recoil.

The Einstein model is, as we know, only a rough approximation, and the Debye model approaches reality much closer. According to this latter model, the frequency spectrum of the elastic vibrations does not consist of a monochromatic line, but extends far down, as we saw in Fig. 5.2.10. One could, therefore, expect that no matter how small the recoil momentum is some low frequency could always be excited. However, we should not forget that low frequencies imply long wavelengths. Therefore, several atoms have to move together and because this block of atoms has a greater mass, the available recoil energy becomes smaller as can be verified from Eq. 5.3.12. Hence, the conclusions which we drew for the Einstein model are qualitatively still valid and do not need to be modified much.

The Mössbauer effect is basically detected in an experimental arrangement like the one in Fig. 5.3.1. Gamma radiation from the radioactive source S on the way to the detector D has to pass through a resonance absorber which typically is a few thousandths of an inch thick. If the absorber is at rest, the γ quanta are absorbed in the resonance process and reemitted in all directions; hence, only a few of these "scattered" quanta reach the detector. If, however, the absorber is in forward or backward

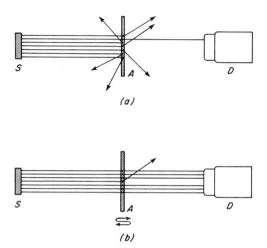

Fig. 5.3.1 A simple arrangement for Mössbauer effect measurements: (a) absorber at rest; (b) absorber in motion. S: source; A: absorber; D: detector.

motion with respect to the source, practically no quanta may be absorbed. The Doppler-shifted frequency ν', which the absorber moving with the velocity v receives, is $\nu' = \nu(1 \pm v/c)$, where ν is the frequency emitted by the stationary source and c is the velocity of light. The relative velocity necessary to destroy the Mössbauer effect is often surprisingly small, only a few mm/sec! This reflects the narrow width of the emitted γ lines. This width is connected to the lifetime of the excited state by the Heisenberg uncertainty relation. The Mössbauer effect can thus serve as a tool to determine short lifetimes of excited states.

Figure 5.3.2 shows data from Mössbauer's first experiment with the 129-keV γ radiation of ^{191}Ir. The effect here was very small; the counting rate changed by only about 1%, and it is very much to the credit of Mössbauer's careful experimentation that he did not overlook the effect for which he had not specifically looked.

Interaction of external magnetic fields with the magnetic moments of the electrons can shift and split the energy levels of an atom. This is known as the Zeeman effect which we have treated in Chapter 4. Similarly, the hyperfine structure splitting of atomic levels, also discussed in that chapter, often has its source in the interaction of magnetic fields of the nucleus with the magnetic moment associated with the electrons. We can also expect a splitting of the nuclear energy levels if the nucleus is brought into a magnetic field. The magnitude of such effects is proportional to the magnetic moments which for nuclei are much smaller than for atoms because nuclei have a 10^4 to 10^5 times greater mass than electrons. The shift in energy is

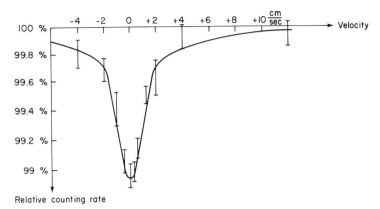

Fig. 5.3.2 Mössbauer's data for the 129-keV radiation of ^{191}Ir. From the width of the resonance curve Mössbauer was able to determine the lifetime of the excited state (see Problem 5.16). [From R. L. Mössbauer, Z. *Naturforsch.* **14a,** 211 (1959).]

therefore very small, but in spite of this it can easily be measured with the Mössbauer effect. For an experiment of this type the absorber is moved with a certain velocity, and the resulting Doppler effect changes frequency and energy of the absorbed γ quanta. Thus the resonance condition can be reestablished for a shifted energy level.

Such experiments have been done on a considerable number of nuclei. Figure 5.3.3 shows the level diagram of the splitting of the ground state and the first excited state of 14.4 keV energy in ^{57}Fe. In Fig. 5.3.4 we see the Mössbauer spectrum of iron. The source was ^{57}Co which decays into the excited state of ^{57}Fe. In order to prevent splitting of the emitted γ rays the iron atoms were embedded in a nonmagnetic material, in this case

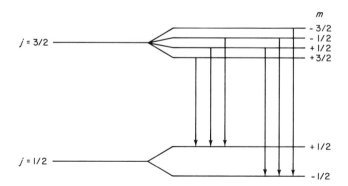

Fig. 5.3.3 Magnetic splitting of the ground state and the 14.4-keV state of ^{57}Fe. The splitting is very much exaggerated.

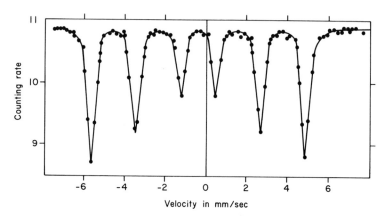

Fig. 5.3.4   The Mössbauer velocity spectrum of ^{57}Fe showing the nuclear Zeeman effect. [From W. Kerler and W. Neuwirth, Z. *Physik* **167**, 176, (1962).]

platinum. On the other hand, the absorber was made from pure iron, and the fields within the magnetic domains cause here the splitting of the levels.

The Mössbauer effect has become nowadays a powerful tool in the fields of solid-state physics, nuclear physics, relativity, and chemistry.

5.4   FREE ELECTRONS IN A BOX

Classical Model

The earliest model of a metal was designed to account for Ohm's law. To this end it was assumed that a metal contained n_e free electrons per unit volume, and that in the presence of an electric field E they acquired a drift velocity v_{dr} such that the energy acquired in falling through a potential energy $eEdx$ was precisely equal to the energy converted into heat by collisions with "scattering centers," which we might think of as atoms for the time being. Let us characterize our model by assuming an average time τ between collisions and call this the mean collision time τ. The average distance, or mean free path λ is then $v\tau$, and the average cross section of the scattering center for collisions is Σ.[11] These quantities are related to the density of the scattering centers n_c by

$$n_c \Sigma \lambda = 1. \qquad (5.4.1)$$

[11] σ is conventionally used to denote cross section, but to avoid confusion later on where σ is used for conductivity, we here use Σ to denote cross section.

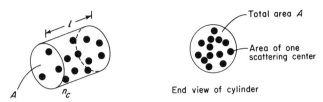

Fig. 5.4.1   Regarding the concept of cross section.

This result is easily demonstrated by the following argument: Imagine the cross section for collision as a purely geometrical quantity. Then the number of scattering centers in a cylinder of cross-sectional area A and length l is simply given by $N = n_c A l$ (Fig. 5.4.1). Hence, if we look down the end of the cylinder the total area for collision presented to an electron by these N scattering centers is simply $N\Sigma = n_c A l \Sigma$. The probability for a collision is, therefore, $N\Sigma/A = n_c A l \Sigma/A = n_c l \Sigma$, as long as the blocked-out area $N\Sigma$ of the scattering centers is much smaller than the cylinder area A so that we can neglect the few instances where the scattering centers are "behind each other." The average distance through which a particle moves until it suffers a collision is called the mean free path λ, and it turns out that for this distance λ the relation $(n_c l \Sigma)_{l=\lambda} = n_c \lambda \Sigma = 1$ holds. This does not mean that the probability for a collision is 1, because some of the scattering centers now overlap but, on the other hand, leave gaps. In fact, a beam of electrons is attenuated through collisions to $1/e$ of its original intensity after having traveled a length λ. The proof is left as an exercise.

The velocity v_{dr} mentioned above is the so-called drift velocity due to the action of the field, and is not be confused with the thermal velocity v of the electrons. The thermal velocity v is given by:

$$\tfrac{1}{2}mv^2 = \tfrac{3}{2}kT.$$

For electrons at 300 K this turns out to be 1.2×10^5 m/sec. This reveals a first point on which the above model is inadequate. It assigns $\tfrac{1}{2}kT$ of energy per electron per degree of freedom, which is in fact not observed, as we shall see later. Moreover, actual electronic velocities tend to be greater by one or two orders of magnitude, another fact which a more adequate model must account for. But at the moment, actual electron velocities do not enter our theory. A cloud of electrons experiences an acceleration eE/m and, if it is initially at rest, in a time τ will attain a drift velocity

$$v_{dr} = \frac{eE}{m}\,\tau.$$

This formula might suggest that the individual electrons after each collision start again with zero velocity. This, however, is not the case, because in being scattered, they will move away from the scattering center with some velocity. The velocity vector can point in any direction, and for many electrons, or for the electron cloud, this averages out to zero.

The mobility μ of the electrons in this cloud is defined as the drift velocity acquired per unit applied field, so that

$$\mu = \frac{v_{\mathrm{dr}}}{E} = \frac{e\tau}{m} \tag{5.4.2}$$

and the conductivity σ, which is the reciprocal of the resistivity ρ, is defined by the current density j[12] due to the drift velocity of this cloud per unit of applied field

$$\sigma = \frac{1}{\rho} = \frac{j}{E} = \frac{n_e e v_{\mathrm{dr}}}{E} = n_e e \mu = \frac{n_e e^2 \tau}{m} \tag{5.4.3}$$

where n_e is the electron density. The model tells us neither the electron density, nor the mean collision time. However, one more measurement in a magnetic field, namely the Hall effect described below, makes it possible to measure n_e. In most normal metals this turns out to give an electron density about equal to the atomic density, or a contribution of about one electron per atom (see Table 5.4.1). Equation 5.4.3 represents Ohm's law $i/V = const. = 1/R$.

With this result, we can use observations of resistivity to estimate τ, using Eq. 5.4.3. A few results are given in Table 5.4.1. Assuming electronic velocities of only 1.2×10^5 m/sec which, as we have said, are much too

TABLE 5.4.1

Metal	Temp. °C	ρ ohm $-$ m	n_e from Hall Effect (per m³)	n atoms (per m³)	τ sec
Cu	20	1.77×10^{-8}	1.1×10^{29}	0.9×10^{29}	1.8×10^{-14}
	-258.6	0.014			2.2×10^{-12}
Au	20	2.44	0.9	0.6	1.6×10^{-14}
	-252.8	0.018			2.1×10^{-12}
Ag	18	1.629	0.7	0.6	3.0×10^{-14}
	-258.6	0.009			5.4×10^{-12}

[12] The current density j is the current per unit area flowing through an infinitesimal area normal to the direction of the current.

low, we get mean free paths at room temperature of the order of 2×10^{-9} m, or about ten interatomic spacings, and from the low temperature conductivities mean free paths of 1,000 to 10,000 interatomic distances. Using more realistic values for the electronic velocities, we get correspondingly greater values. For very low temperatures in very pure substances mean free paths of the order of a centimeter have been calculated; this seems hardly reasonable if we think of electrons as particles making collisions with other particles separated by distances of an order of 10^{-10} m.

The classical model of a metal is capable of accounting for Ohm's law, but it cannot explain why electrons contribute so little to the specific heat capacity, or the difference between insulators and metals, or the very long mean free paths of electrons. There is one further phenomenon that the classical model can account for, namely the large contribution of free electrons to heat conductivity, which we shall now discuss.

If K_e is the thermal conductivity, the heat flow per unit area is

$$Q = K_e \frac{dT}{dx} \tag{5.4.4}$$

and if this flow is due to the drifting of the electron cloud from higher to lower temperatures we have

$$Q = n_e \tfrac{3}{2} k T v_{dr} \tag{5.4.5}$$

where, as in the discussion of electrical conduction

$$v_{dr} = \frac{F}{m} \tau_{th}, \tag{5.4.6}$$

but τ_{th} now being the mean time between collisions for thermal conductivity; F is the force acting on the electron and is discussed below.

Equation 5.4.5 is based on a classical model of the electron gas; that is, an average energy of $(3/2)kT$ is assigned to each electron. Since the flux of electrons is given by the product of the electron density n_e and the drift velocity v_{dr}, the flux of energy Q is then the number flux $n_e v_{dr}$ multiplied by the energy per particle.

Now the ideal gas law applied to this electron gas tells us that the pressure in the gas p, the volume V, and the temperature T are related by the equation

$$p \cdot V = \eta \cdot k \cdot T,$$

where η is the number of electrons in the volume V. Then the pressure exerted by a classical electron cloud is

$$p = \left(\frac{\eta}{V}\right) kT = n_e kT$$

and the difference in pressure on two surfaces differing in temperature by ΔT is

$$\Delta p = n_e k \Delta T.$$

The resulting force on a particle for which the effective collision area is Σ, is therefore

$$F = n_e k \Delta T \Sigma.$$

If we choose the thickness of our layer as one mean free path, then the same pressure will be exerted, on the average, on each particle within the layer. As $\Delta T = (dT/dx)\lambda$, then

$$F = n_e k \frac{dT}{dx} \lambda \Sigma.$$

Using the relation given by Eq. 5.4.1 we then have

$$F = k \frac{dT}{dx}.$$

Substituting this expression for F in Eq. 5.4.6 gives

$$v_{\mathrm{dr}} = \frac{k}{m} \frac{dT}{dx} \tau_{th}.$$

Now we substitute this expression for v_{dr} in Eq. 5.4.5 and obtain

$$Q = n_e \tfrac{3}{2} kT \frac{k}{m} \frac{dT}{dx} \tau_{th}.$$

According to Eq. 5.4.4, the coefficient of the quantity dT/dx in the last equation is the thermal conductivity K_e; that is,

$$K_e = \tfrac{3}{2} n_e k^2 T \tau_{th} m^{-1}. \tag{5.4.7}$$

Combining Eq. 5.4.3 with Eq. 5.4.7 yields the relation

$$\frac{K_e}{\sigma T} = \frac{3}{2} \left(\frac{k}{e}\right)^2 \left(\frac{\tau_{th}}{\tau}\right). \tag{5.4.8}$$

In this very simple model we further assert that the mean times between collisions for both electronic and heat conduction are equal. Then Eq. 5.4.8 becomes

$$\frac{K_e}{\sigma T} = \frac{3}{2} \left(\frac{k}{e}\right)^2 \equiv L. \tag{5.4.9}$$

The quantity L is called the Lorentz number and (based on our calculation) is found to be

$$L = 1.11 \times 10^{-8} \text{ V}^2 \text{ K}^{-2} \qquad (5.4.10)$$

Experimental values are found to be strikingly close to that given by Eq. 5.4.10. The remarkable fact is, however, that there is such a universal constant, and that our classical model can account for it.

We see that by treating the electrons in a solid as a classical gas, we can derive Ohm's law, and a very satisfactory value for the Lorentz number. However, the model fails to explain experimentally observed mean free paths many orders of magnitude greater than the average distance between electrons. The classical model also predicts too low an average velocity for the electrons. These various failures, although occurring along with aforementioned successes, nevertheless push us toward a quantum mechanical treatment of the electrons in a solid. We consider such a treatment after we look at the Hall effect.

The Hall Effect

An electric current in a wire or ribbon consists of moving charges, and under steady conditions the motion of the charges must be along the length of the conductor. The Hall effect,[13] discovered in 1879, deals with the situation brought about by placing such a conductor with its length at right angles to a magnetic field, as shown in Fig. 5.4.2 (a). The current is assumed to be due to the motion of electrons. In the illustration, the current is to the right and the negative conduction electrons therefore move to the left. The magnetic field B, directed into the paper, exerts a magnetic force F_m toward the top of the page on the moving charges. When the

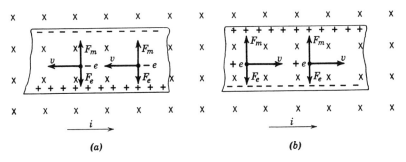

Fig. 5.4.2 The Hall effect.

[13] Edwin H. Hall (1855–1938), American physicist, professor at Harvard University.

current is started, the path of the electrons will be bent upward and nega-tive charge will accumulate on the upper edge of the ribbon until a down-ward electric force F_e, just balancing the magnetic force F_m, prevents a further accumulation of charge on the edge. The current will then have reached a steady condition and will flow along the length of the conductor. There will, however, be a potential difference between points opposite each other on the two edges of the ribbon. The negatively charged upper edge will be at a lower potential than the positively charged lower edge. This potential difference—which is proportional to the field B, vanishes when $B = 0$, and changes its sign when the direction of B is reversed—constitutes the Hall effect. When, under the conditions shown in Fig. 5.4.2 (a), the upper edge is negative, we have what is called a "normal" Hall effect due to the motion of negative charges.

In some metals we find, however, that with the same directions of cur-rent and field, the upper edge is positively charged, as in Fig. 5.4.2 (b). This phenomenon is called the "anomalous" Hall effect and could be ex-plained if we assumed that the current is due to the motion of positive rather than negative charges. If, as in Fig. 5.4.2 (b), the current is to the right, and is due to positive charges also moving to the right, the magnetic force due to a field into the paper will be again upward, but the balancing electric force will now be due to an accumulation of positive charges on the upper edge of the ribbon, and the upper edge will be at a higher potential than the lower edge. The existence of currents apparently due to the motion of positive charges will be discussed in Section 5.5.

So much for the qualitative aspects of the experiment. A quantitative discussion, however, adds greatly to our understanding of the significance of the results obtained. To be more definite, we consider that a strip of metal of width l and thickness t is placed between the poles of a magnet, as shown in Fig. 5.4.3. A current i is passed through the strip, and the difference in potential between two points a and b along a line perpendicu-

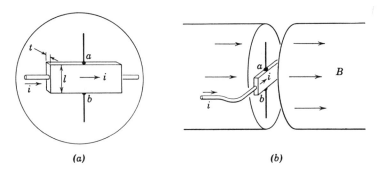

(a) (b)

Fig. 5.4.3 An experimental arrangement for measuring the Hall emf.

lar to the current is observed with a potentiometer. When no magnetic field is applied, $V_{ab} = 0$, as the points are on an equipotential. When a field is present, however, a difference in potential proportional to B appears. This is the Hall emf, $\mathcal{E}_{\text{Hall}}$. It is simply the emf induced when charges are moved at right angles to the field. The induced emf is given by

$$\mathcal{E}_{\text{Hall}} = lv_{dr}B. \tag{5.4.11}$$

But the drift velocity may be calculated in terms of the current and the number of electrons per unit volume n.

$$i = nev_{dr}A = nev_{dr}(l \cdot t). \tag{5.4.12}$$

Solving for the drift velocity, we get

$$v_{\text{dr}} = \frac{i}{nelt}$$

and substituting into Eq. 5.4.11

$$\mathcal{E}_{\text{Hall}} = \frac{iB}{net}.$$

This may be written

$$\mathcal{E}_{\text{Hall}} = C_{\text{H}} \frac{iB}{t} \tag{5.4.13}$$

stating that the Hall emf is proportional to the current and the magnetic field, and inversely proportional to the thickness of the sample. These aspects of the experiment are borne out in fact. The Hall coefficient, C_H, which is measured in an experiment, is, according to our analysis,

$$C_H = \frac{1}{ne}$$

$$n = \frac{1}{C_H e}. \tag{5.4.14}$$

From observations of the Hall effect, we can deduce the number of free electrons per unit volume in the metals investigated. Some experimental results are shown in Table 5.4.2. In the last column the number of atoms per cubic meter, as computed from the density and atomic weight, are given for comparison with the number of electrons per cubic meter, as computed from the Hall effect. We shall discuss the significance of the sign of the Hall coefficient and of these numbers from an atomic point of view in Section 5.5.

TABLE 5.4.2

Hall Constant, Density of Free Electrons and of Atoms in Some Metals

	Substance	C_{Hall} (V/m^3-A-Wb)	$n_e = 1/C_{\text{Hall}}e$ (per m^3)	n_{atoms} (per m^3)
Cu	Copper	-6×10^{-11}	1.1×10^{29}	0.9×10^{29}
Ag	Silver	-9	0.7	0.6
Au	Gold	-7	0.9	0.6
Li	Lithium	-15	0.4	0.5
Na	Sodium	-25	0.2	0.3
Fe	Iron	$+100$	0.06	0.8
Co	Cobalt	$+25$	0.2	0.9
Ni	Nickel	-60	0.1	0.9
Bi	Bismuth	-500	0.01	0.3

Wave-Mechanical Free-Electron Model; Fermi-Gas Model

In this model, often also called the Sommerfeld[14] model, electrons are considered completely free, as in a vacuum. Potential energy appears only at the boundary or surface of a metal to confine the free electrons. The photoelectric effect work function, discussed in Chapter 2, is related to this potential energy. The wave properties of the electrons form the basis of the calculation. In essence, this model is merely an extension of the particle-in-a-box problem. Instead of the box being occupied by only one particle, many particles—the electrons—which are all identical and obey the exclusion principle, are in the well, which represents a piece of metal, for example a wire. These electrons fill, from the bottom level up, as many levels as necessary. Hence, the relationship between one particle in the box, as discussed in Chapter 3, and the Sommerfeld free-electron model is the same as the one between the hydrogen atom with its many energy levels, of which only one is occupied, and a many-electron atom in which the inner shells are completely filled. The potential of the free-electron model and a schematic representation of the occupied energy levels is given in Fig. 5.4.4.

From the photoelectric effect, it is known that some energy, equal to the work function W, has to be expended to remove an electron from the metal. Although this implies that the well is not filled to the brim, it should not

[14] Arnold Sommerfeld (1868–1951). Professor of theoretical physics at the university of Munich. Great contributions to atomic and solid state physics. Among his students were Debye, Heisenberg, and Pauli. The free-electron model was first published in 1927 in *Naturwissenschaften* **15,** 825, and then in *Zeitschrift für Physik* **47,** 1, 43 (1928).

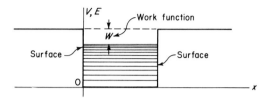

Fig. 5.4.4   The free-electron model.

be interpreted that the well could accommodate more electrons. It means only that work has to be done to extract electrons from a metal.

The applicability of this model is not limited to electrons in a metal. Protons and neutrons, which also are fermions, similarly can fill a well which now represents a nucleus. This more general model, which is not limited to a particular species of fermions, is referred to as the *Fermi-gas model*. Apart from solid-state physics, it is very useful in nuclear physics. An important characteristic of the model is that the particles do not interact with each other.

We shall now calculate the energy levels in the free-electron model. The energy of a free electron is determined by its wavelength

$$\lambda = \frac{h}{p}.$$

In nonrelativistic mechanics $E = p^2/2m$, and in one dimension

$$E_x = \frac{h^2}{2m\lambda_x^2}. \tag{5.4.15}$$

As in counting up the modes of motion of the acoustic waves in a continuous solid, here we want to count up the number of electron waves or modes of motion of electrons in a cube of side L. Here again, if the waves in the x direction are to have nodes at the free surfaces, say $x = 0$ and $x = L$, then L must equal some integral number of half-wavelengths

$$\frac{\lambda_x}{2} = \frac{L}{n_x}$$

where n_x is any positive integer. The same holds true for the y and z axes, and using 5.4.15 we get for the total energy for one particle

$$E = E_x + E_y + E_z = \frac{h^2}{8mL^2} (n_x^2 + n_y^2 + n_z^2). \tag{5.4.16}$$

The possible modes of motion are again uniformly distributed over a lattice with lattice points n_x, n_y, n_z, as previously shown in Fig. 5.2.8, and the energy of any state is given by

$$E = \frac{h^2}{8mL^2} \cdot q^2,$$

(5.4.17)

where

$$q^2 = n_x^2 + n_y^2 + n_z^2.$$

(5.4.17)

It is instructive to compare this equation which we derived for electrons, or in general for particles, with the corresponding Eq. 5.2.7 for elastic waves, or phonons, which we may rewrite as

$$\omega^2 = \frac{\pi^2 u^2}{L^2} (n_x^2 + n_y^2 + n_z^2) = \frac{\pi^2 u^2}{L^2} q^2.$$

Considering that the energy of phonons, just as that of the electromagnetic photons, is given by $E = h\nu = (h/2\pi)\omega$, we have for phonons (or photons)

$$E^2 = \frac{h^2 u^2}{4L^2} q^2.$$

For phonons (and for photons) E is therefore proportional to q, therefore also proportional to the wave vector $\mathbf{k}$, in contrast to the situation for electrons where E is proportional to q^2, or k^2. This is a reflection of the fact that for phonons and photons $E = cp$, where p is the momentum; but for particles at nonrelativistic speeds $E = p^2/2m$.

Equation 5.4.17 is familiar from the problem of the particle in a box which was discussed in Chapter 3. At that time we were only interested in the first few energy levels which a particle could occupy and in the degeneracy of these levels. Now we have to place in the box many electrons which all obey the exclusion principle. In Fig. 5.4.5 we have plotted the

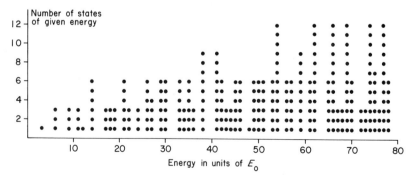

Fig. 5.4.5   The spatial states of a particle in a box up to an energy of 79 E_0.

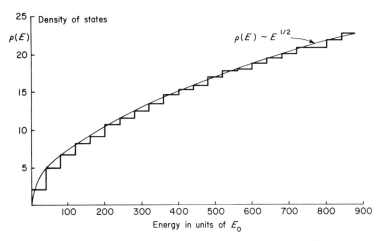

Fig. 5.4.6 The density of spatial states for a particle in a box as a function of energy.

spatial states—which describe the motion of the particles—for energy values $E = E_0 q^2 = (h_2/8mL^2)q^2$ up to 79 E_0. Each spatial state can be occupied by two electrons, one with "spin-up" and one with "spin-down." We observe a general tendency of an increase of states per energy unit. This tendency becomes even more evident when we move toward much higher energies and lump several energy values together (here arbitrarily 40), compute the average of the possible states per energy unit over this interval and thus arrive at the *density of states* $\rho(E)$, which is the number of states per unit energy. This averaging procedure results in a relatively smooth histogram, plotted in Fig. 5.4.6 for energies up to 779 E_0. The trend of the density of states can be represented, particularly for higher energy values, by a smooth curve $\rho(E) \sim E^{1/2}$ which is also drawn in this figure.

In solid-state physics, but also in nuclear physics, it is often very important to know the highest kinetic energy of a particle in a certain enclosure (in nuclear physics, for example, of a proton in a nucleus), assuming that all states, starting with the low-lying ones, are filled up one by one using N particles. The highest energy is called the *Fermi energy* e_F and the corresponding level the *Fermi level*. If the value of q corresponding to the Fermi energy e_F is denoted by q_F, and therefore $e_F = (h^2/8mL^2)q_F^2$, then the total number of states in one octant of a sphere of radius q_F, where q_F is a big number, is given by

$$N = 2 \cdot \frac{1}{8} \cdot \frac{4\pi}{3} q_F^3 = \frac{\pi}{3} q_F^3 = \frac{\pi}{3} \left(e_F \frac{8mL^2}{h^2} \right)^{3/2}.$$

The factor 2 takes care of the two spin orientations and we use the factor

$\frac{1}{8}$ because we take only one octant of the sphere, since n_x, n_y, and n_z all have to be positive. Therefore

$$e_F = \left(\frac{3}{\pi}\frac{N}{L^3}\right)^{2/3}\frac{h^2}{8m}.$$

L^3 is the volume V of the box, and therefore $N/L^3 = N/V$ represents the number of particles per unit volume. Thus we can also write

$$e_F = \left(\frac{3}{\pi}n\right)^{2/3}\frac{h^2}{8m}. \qquad (5.4.18)$$

To get an idea of the size of the Fermi energy e_F in solids we take a typical value for $n(\sim 10^{29}/\text{m}^3)$ and insert it into Eq. 5.4.18 to obtain $e_F \sim 12.7 \times 10^{-19}$ joules $= 8$ eV.

The velocity of an electron at the Fermi energy, the so-called Fermi velocity v_F, may be calculated from its energy, which is purely kinetic (the electrons are free *within* the confines of the box). Thus

$$v_F = \left(\frac{2e_F}{m}\right)^{1/2}. \qquad (5.4.19)$$

Using the value of 8 eV, Eq. 5.4.19 yields a value of 1.7×10^6 m/sec for the Fermi velocity. This turns out to be about 14 times greater than the thermal velocity previously calculated classically. The velocity, and hence the momentum, which the electrons have inside a solid manifests itself in positron-electron annihilation experiments. The two annihilation quanta generally are not being emitted exactly at 180° in the laboratory system if the positron-electron pair has some momentum. The reader is referred to Fig. 2.5.11, which shows measurements of Badoux and Heinrich who employed this effect to deduce the velocity distribution of the electrons in brass.

Now the number of states dn falling into an octant of a spherical shell of radius q and thickness dq is simply given by

$$dn = 2 \cdot \tfrac{1}{8} \cdot 4\pi q^2 dq,$$

or

$$\frac{dn}{dq} = \pi q^2 = \frac{8\pi m L^2 E}{h^2}. \qquad (5.4.20)$$

Now let us differentiate Eq. 5.4.17 with respect to E to obtain

$$1 = \frac{h^2}{4mL^2}q\frac{dq}{dE};$$

or

$$\frac{dq}{dE} = \frac{4mL^2}{h^2} q^{-1} = \frac{4mL^2}{h^2} \left(\frac{h^2}{8mL^2E}\right)^{1/2},$$

or

$$\frac{dq}{dE} = \left(\frac{2mL^2}{h^2}\right)^{1/2} E^{-1/2}. \tag{5.4.21}$$

Then we have for the density of states $\rho(E)$ the following expression:

$$\rho(E) = \frac{dn}{dE} = \frac{dn}{dq} \cdot \frac{dq}{dE} = \frac{8\pi mL^2 E}{h^2} \cdot \left(\frac{2mL^2}{h^2}\right)^{1/2} E^{-1/2},$$

or

$$\rho(E) = 4\pi \left(\frac{2m}{h^2}\right)^{3/2} V E^{1/2}.^{15} \tag{5.4.22}$$

Equation 5.4.21 is plotted against energy in Fig. 5.4.7. The shaded portion of the figure indicates states that are filled at the absolute zero of temperature. The portion of the curve beyond the energy e_F corresponds to unfilled states of the system. So if we are interested in the density of only occupied states, we have the situation shown in Fig. 5.4.8. The density of *occupied* states $\rho_0(E)$ is just equal to the density of *possible* states $\rho(E)$ multiplied by the probability that a state is occupied. The last factor we denote by f_{FD}, and as given in Appendix IV, is found to be:

$$f_{FD} = \left[\exp\left(\frac{E - e_F}{kT}\right) + 1\right]^{-1} \tag{5.4.23}$$

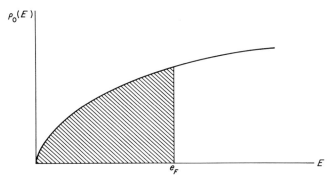

Fig. 5.4.7   A plot of the electronic density of states $\rho(E)$ versus E.

[15] Notice that for electrons $\rho(E) \sim E^{1/2}$, whereas for phonons $\rho(\omega) \sim \omega^2$.

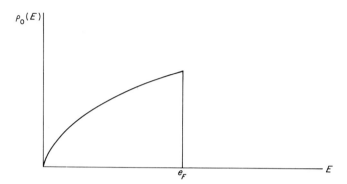

Fig. 5.4.8   Electronic density of occupied states at $T = 0$ K.

where f_{FD} is referred to as the Fermi-Dirac distribution function. We note
that at $T = 0$ K $f_{FD} = 1$ for $0 \leq E \leq e_F$ and $f_{FD} = 0$ for $E \geq e_F$; that is,
the states are completely full up to $E = e_F$, and completely empty above
e_F, for $T = 0$ K. Furthermore, at the energy $E = e_f$ for $T \neq 0$ the distribution function f_{FD} assumes the value $\frac{1}{2}$. Then, since

$$\rho_0(E) = \rho(E)f_{FD}, \qquad (5.4.24)$$

Fig. 5.4.8 obviously results from Fig. 5.4.7. The Fermi-Dirac function for
$T = 0$ K and $T \neq 0$ K is shown in Fig. 5.4.9.

The place in Fig. 5.4.9 where $f_{FD}(0$ K$)$ and $f_{FD}(T \neq 0$ K$)$ start to differ
from each other appreciably is at an energy $\sim kT$ below e_F. Also, it is
found that f_{FD} has a value of nearly zero for an energy $\sim kT$ above e_F.
Thus, we find a zone of partially filled states near the Fermi level e_F, and
$\sim kT$ in width. This is an important region because it is the electrons in
this region that are able to absorb thermal energies and thus get promoted

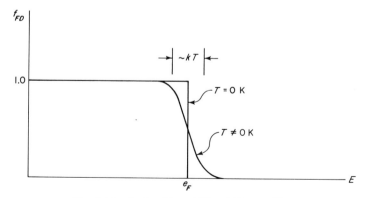

Fig. 5.4.9 f_{FD} for $T = 0$ K and $T \neq 0$ K.

to states of higher energy that were formerly unoccupied. No such situation exists for electrons near the bottom, or even several electron volts from the top, of the Fermi distribution. These latter electrons are "hemmed in," that is, incapable of absorbing thermal amounts of energy. Therefore, only a small fraction of the total number of electrons in a solid can take part in thermal agitation. Let us denote this fraction by ξ; also, we denote the number of electrons in the region of width kT by N_{th}. So we have, approximately:

$$N_{th} = \rho(e_F) \cdot kT \cdot f_{FD}(e_F) = 4\pi \left(\frac{2m}{h^2}\right)^{3/2} Ve_F^{1/2}(kT)(0.5).$$

hence,

$$\xi = \frac{N_{th}}{N} = \frac{4\pi(2m/h^2)^{3/2}Ve_F^{1/2}(kT)(0.5)}{(\pi/3)e_F^{3/2}(8m/h^2)^{3/2}V}$$

$$= 6\left(\frac{kT}{e_F}\right)\left(\frac{2}{8}\right)^{3/2},$$

or

$$\xi \sim \frac{kT}{e_F}. \tag{5.4.25}$$

Therefore, the average increase in energy of a mole of free electrons in a metal would be $E_{el} = 3\,RT\xi$, and the electronic specific heat capacity dE_{el}/dT would be

$$c_{el} \approx \frac{6RTk}{e_f}.$$

This last expression is only approximately correct. An exact calculation of E_{el} involves doing the following integral:

$$E_{el} = \int_0^\infty E\rho(E)f_{FD}\,dE$$

$$= 4\pi\left(\frac{2m}{h^2}\right)^{3/2}V\int_0^\infty \frac{E^{3/2}\,dE}{\exp[(E - e_F)/kT] + 1}.$$

After solving this integral by approximate methods, and differentiating the result with respect to temperature to get the specific heat capacity due to electronic motion, one obtains (to first order in kT/e_F)

$$c_{el} = \frac{\pi^2 RkT}{2e_F} \equiv \gamma T. \tag{5.4.26}$$

The predicted form for the low-temperature specific heat capacities of metals, including both contributions from lattice vibrations (Eq. 5.2.16) and electronic motion, is then, with Θ standing for the Debye temperature,

$$c_{\text{metal}} = c_{\text{lattice}} + c_{el} = 468 \left(\frac{T}{\Theta}\right)^3 + \gamma T. \qquad (5.4.27)$$

This, at last, is a good representation of the observed facts. An example of the good fit of Eq. 5.4.27 to experimental data is shown in Fig. 5.4.10. Comparison with Eq. 5.2.16 which described the specific heat capacity at low temperatures based on Debye's theory shows that the second term of Eq. 5.4.27, containing the contribution of the electrons, is mainly responsible for the correct temperature dependence in this temperature range. Because T enters it only linearly, this term loses its importance in comparison with the first term which varies with the third power of T. Values of γ and Θ are given in Chapter 4 of the *American Institute of Physics Handbook*, of which a few entries are given in Table 5.4.3.

We thus conclude our discussion of specific heat capacities and electrical conduction without going specifically into the crystal structure of metals and the electronic structure of the atoms themselves.

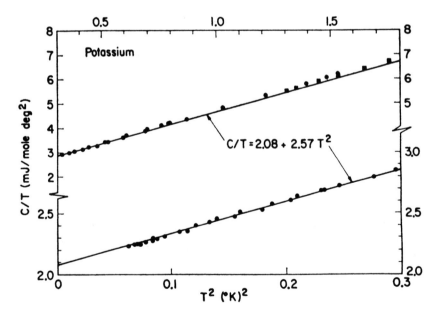

Fig. 5.4.10 c/T versus T^2 for potassium [from W. H. Lien and N. E. Phillips, *Phys. Rev.* **133**, A 1370 (1964)]. Note that the scales for the two parts of the curve are different.

TABLE 5.4.3

Debye Temperatures and Constants γ for Some Metals

Metal	Debye Θ, K	γ, 10^{-4} cal/mole deg^2
Ag	229	1.45–1.60
Al	375	3.27–3.48
Au	164	1.67
Cd	165	1.5–1.7
Cu	345	1.60–1.80
Fe	355	12.0
Mn	410	32.9–43
Mo	360	5.05–5.25
Ni	413	17.4

5.5 ELECTRONS IN CRYSTALS. ENERGY BANDS

In the free-electron models, in the classical model, and in the wave-mechanical model of Sommerfeld, the electrons in metals were treated in two categories. The ones in the first category were either completely free or subject only to retaining forces at the surface. Any disturbance from the atomic cores which would give rise to a periodic variation of the potential was neglected by assuming that it would average out to zero. The electrons which are bound to their atoms constituted the second category and did not play any role in our discussion. These models could account with some success for certain properties of the metals. For example, the classical model explained the connection between the conduction of electricity and heat, and the wave-mechanical model of Sommerfeld the specific heat capacity of metals. On the other hand, these models did not give a useful clue why certain materials are metals, and others insulators or semiconductors. It was therefore suggestive that the Sommerfeld model, although not wrong, was too simple.

We also can take an opposite viewpoint and consider mainly the electrons which are bound to their atoms and which constitute the second category. Obviously, these electrons cannot contribute to electric currents. Their energies are simply given by atomic energy levels. However, when neighboring atoms are introduced, the wave functions overlap, and therefore one cannot localize an electron on a particular atom. Each electron is represented by a wave function spread throughout the lattice. There is still one wave function per electron, but for each electron the wave function differs in the wave vector $\mathbf{k} = mv/\hbar$ describing the motion of the electrons

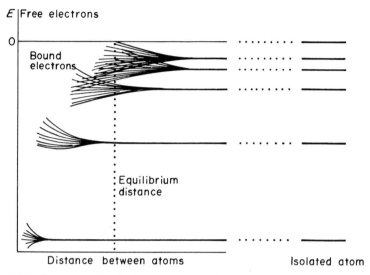

Fig. 5.5.1   The energy levels of bound atomic electrons in solids and isolated atoms.

through the crystal, although near an atom each electron wave function has some similarity with the electron wave function of an isolated atom. The N states describing the N electrons are no longer degenerate but are spread into a band, shown symbolically in Fig. 5.5.1.

The mechanical analogy of coupled equal pendulums which we already used for two-electron atoms might be helpful here too. A single pendulum oscillates in one frequency mode, two coupled pendulums have two frequency modes, three coupled pendulums have three modes, and so on, as shown schematically in Fig. 5.5.2. The difference in the frequency between the various modes depends on the strength of the coupling between the pendulums. Obviously, if the coupling is vanishingly small, the frequencies are all the same.

In a periodic potential with atoms separated by a spacing d, we have a situation much like that shown in Fig. 5.5.3. What had been a level in an isolated atom has now spread into a band. Its width depends on the mutual

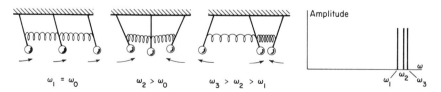

Fig. 5.5.2   The three modes of oscillation of three coupled pendulums.

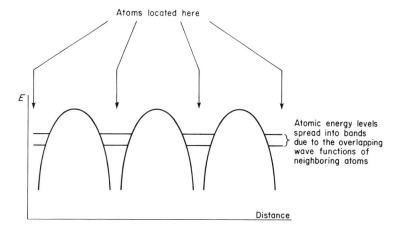

Atoms located here

E

Atomic energy levels spread into bands due to the overlapping wave functions of neighboring atoms

Distance

Fig. 5.5.3 Periodic potential in a one-dimensional, or linear, crystal.

interaction between atoms, and it therefore is also a function of their distance. This model is called the *tight-binding model*. It gives us a good account why the sharp energy levels of the isolated atoms become energy bands in a crystal.

A quite different way to explain the electronic band structure of solids takes its starting point from the Sommerfeld model. We can improve it by taking into consideration the periodicity of the crystal lattice. This improved model is known as the *nearly free electron model*. We might predict that electrons, due to their wave properties, will not propagate through a crystal, but will be impeded in their movement, when the Bragg condition for reflection is satisfied in a one-dimensional, or linear, crystal; therefore for reflection by 180°,

$$n\lambda = 2d$$

or

$$k = \frac{2\pi}{\lambda} = n\frac{\pi}{d}$$

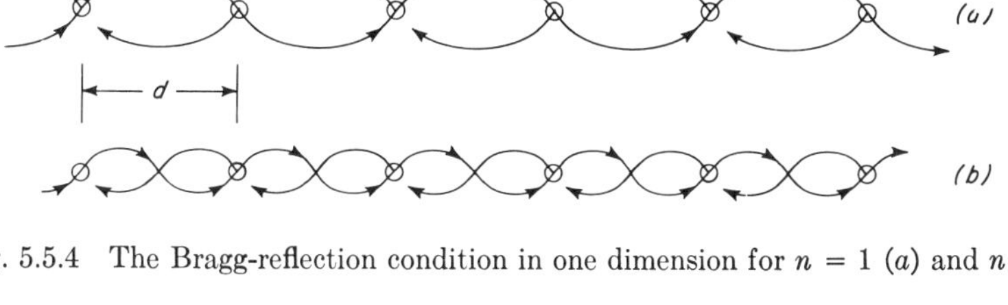

(a)

$\longleftarrow d \longrightarrow$

(b)

Fig. 5.5.4 The Bragg-reflection condition in one dimension for $n = 1$ *(a)* and $n = 2$ *(b)*.

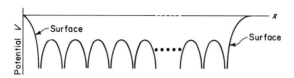

Fig. 5.5.5   The potential of a metallic crystal.

where d is the distance between neighboring atoms, as is shown in Fig. 5.5.4, and k is the wave number. Here, for certain energies, only standing waves can exist and therefore no conduction of electrons can take place for these values of energy. We shall now discuss this problem in more detail.

The square-well potential of the Sommerfeld model has to be replaced by a more realistic one which takes account of the electrostatic potential due to each atom. A potential like that pictured in Fig. 5.5.5 would very well satisfy this requirement.

Most of the electrons of each atom are bound to that atom and, therefore, their states are roughly the ones of the isolated atoms. The outer electrons, however, are not so strongly bound to an individual atom and, even if their energy is somewhat below the humps of the potential between the atoms, the wave functions describing these states penetrate through these humps. This is just what we had pointed out earlier in this chapter, namely that the electrons have a probability to be in any of the atoms.

Because the states of some atoms are relatively easy to calculate, one might think that calculations of the states of a chain of atoms with potentials as pictured in Fig. 5.5.5 might not be a formidable task for a qualified theoretical physicist. Unfortunately this is not the case, but a simplification which still retains the main features gives useful insight about a periodic potential. This results here in a one-dimensional model, known as the Kronig-Penney[16] model, named after the two physicists who introduced it. The potential of Fig. 5.5.5 is replaced by a much simpler one, shown in Fig. 5.5.6.

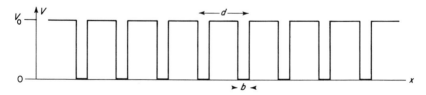

Fig. 5.5.6   The potential of the Kronig-Penney model.

[16] *Proc. Roy. Soc.* (*London*) **A130**, 499 (1931). R. Kronig (1904–   ), Dutch theoretical physicist in Groningen, later at the Technical University Delft, Holland. W. G. Penney (1909–   ), English physicist, later rector of Imperial College, London.

For such a potential we have to set up the Schrödinger equation in two parts, one for the regions within the wells and one for the regions between the wells, which is quite similar to the procedure used in Chapter 3. Choosing for the zero value of the potential energy the bottom of the wells we have for the well regions the wave equation

$$\frac{d^2\psi}{dx^2} + \frac{2m}{\hbar^2} E\psi = 0$$

and for the region between the wells

$$\frac{d^2\psi}{dx^2} = \frac{2m}{\hbar^2} (E - V_0)\psi = 0.$$

For a potential like ours, the time-independent wave function can be shown by group theory to have the general form

$$\psi(x) = u_k(x)e^{ikx} \tag{5.5.1}$$

where

$$e^{ikx} = \cos kx + i \sin kx$$

according to Euler's relation (see Appendix III); $u_k(x)$ is a periodic function with the periodicity of the crystal. Therefore, the wave function $\psi(x)$ can be thought of as being the time-independent part of a plane wave with a variable amplitude $u_k(x)$ which is modulated by the periodicity of the crystal. Figure 5.5.7 shows the real part of the free-electron wave, the electron wave functions for isolated atoms, and the actual wave functions. It

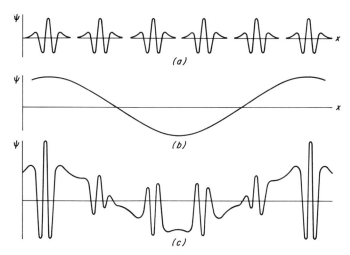

Fig. 5.5.7   (a) Electron wave functions for isolated atoms; (b) free-electron waves; (c) actual electron wave function (Bloch) (real part).

should be pointed out that although this modulation of the wave function seems quite plausible, its justification is not so simple and is due to Bloch.[17] Equation 5.5.1 is therefore known as the Bloch theorem.

The calculations in solving the two parts of the Schrödinger equation are somewhat lengthy, and the interested reader is referred to the textbooks in solid-state physics.[18] Similar to the calculations for the hydrogen atom, the harmonic oscillator, and the rotator, one finds that the usual boundary conditions for ψ and $d\psi/dx$ at the walls of the wells permit only certain values of the energy as solutions of the Schrödinger equations. However, in contrast to the above-mentioned examples the permitted energies lie here in relatively wide energy bands, and are not sharp levels. How this comes about can be seen if we look at one of the last steps of the calculation. In its course one arrives at an equation

$$P \frac{\sin \alpha d}{\alpha d} + \cos \alpha d = \cos kd \qquad (5.5.2)$$

with

$$\alpha = \sqrt{2mE/\hbar^2} \quad \text{and} \quad P = \frac{mV_0 db}{\hbar^2}$$

where d is the distance between the wells and b is the width of a well.

In Fig. 5.5.8 the left-hand side of Eq. 5.5.2 is plotted against αd. Since the value of $\cos kd$ must be between -1 and $+1$, only certain ranges of αd are allowed, which are marked on the abscissa of the graph with a heavy line. The quantity αd, in turn, is a function of the energy E, as seen from the definition of αd. This means that electrons are permitted only in certain energy bands.

The same feature can also be made plausible in a somewhat different way. We again start with the one-dimensional Sommerfeld model. If we plot the electron energy as a function of the wave number k, we obtain a parabola, as shown in Fig. 5.5.9 (a), since

$$E = \tfrac{1}{2}mv^2 = \frac{\hbar^2 k^2}{2m}.$$

[17] Felix Bloch (1905–   ), born in Switzerland; theoretical physicist. Studied with Heisenberg; since 1934 professor at Stanford University. Shared the 1952 Nobel prize in physics with E. Purcell for developing a method for measuring the magnetic moment of nuclei, the so-called nuclear magnetic resonance or nuclear induction.

[18] In these calculations usually one more simplification is made: instead of calculating with wells of finite widths one assumes a very narrow width but compensates for it by making the well much deeper. With this trick, the mathematics of the problem becomes quite manageable.

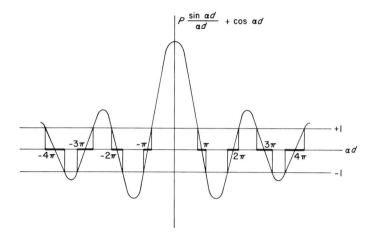

Fig. 5.5.8 The graphical solution of the equation $P(\sin \alpha d)/\alpha d + \cos \alpha d = \cos kd$ (after Kronig and Penney).

For a periodic potential we expect discontinuities for values of k where the Bragg condition is satisfied because traveling waves are suppressed. These discontinuities are shown in Fig. 5.5.9 (b). For example, for $k = \pi/d$ two values for the energy are possible. This can be understood by considering that two different standing-wave patterns with the periodicity of the crystal can be set up, as shown in Fig. 5.5.10. In one of the patterns (a), the anti-nodes of the electron wave functions coincide with the centers of the atoms. Since ψ^2 represents the electron probability density, the electrons in this mode have a high probability to be near these centers. At these locations, due to the electrostatic attraction, the potential energy is much more negative than in the regions between the centers. Because the kinetic

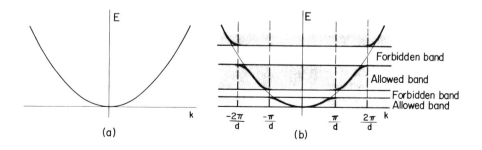

Fig. 5.5.9 The electron energy as a function of k: (a) for the Sommerfeld model; (b) for a potential with periodicity.

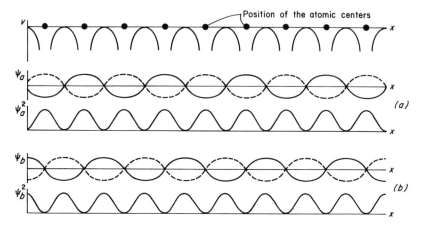

Fig. 5.5.10 The two standing-wave modes for $k = \pi/d$.

energy is not affected, the total energy is in this case usually lower than for the same k value of the Sommerfeld model for which the interaction of individual atoms and traveling electrons were assumed to average out. Conversely, for the second mode (b), the energy of these states is usually higher than in the Sommerfeld model. Between the lower and the higher energy values is a *forbidden energy band*, or a *band gap*. It has its origin in the fact that waves corresponding to this energy cannot propagate, but will be reflected, ending up in generating standing waves. As Bragg reflection occurs not only for $k = \pi/d$, but in general for $k = n\pi/d$, there are several forbidden energy bands, as shown in Fig. 5.5.9.

Before we enter into more detail in our discussion of the *nearly free* electron model, we might ask why Sommerfeld's *free* electron model works so well in explaining the electronic properties of metals and, furthermore, how the energy bands of the tight-binding model fit into the picture.

The free-electron model is in essence only a "stripped down" version of the much more realistic nearly free electron model. As long as we consider only a conduction band that contains about one electron per atom, the E-vs.-k curve is still parabolic in the relevant region in the nearly free electron model, just as for the free-electron model. We have seen this in Fig. 5.5.9. Therefore, the results regarding electric conduction in metals are essentially the same for the two models.

The nearly free electron model and the tight-binding model, on the other hand, complement each other. However, between their respective domains of validity is a broad region where both models yield at best semiquantitative, but often only qualitative results. This intermediate region can be treated only by explicit and highly complicated band-structure calculations. The efforts of a large number of theoretical physicists are today devoted to this area. Figure 5.5.11 shows a possible way to divide the electron states between the tight-binding model and the nearly free electron model. Also indicated in it is the work function W which plays a role in the photoelectric effect discussed in Chapter 2. This representation, given here for a metal, should not be taken too literally, because the situation is different for nearly every metal.

We now shall investigate the behavior of electrons in an energy band somewhat more quantitatively. We recall that in the Sommerfeld free-electron model the kinetic energy of an electron went with the square of its wave vector $k = 2\pi/\lambda$, or with the square of its momentum $p = mv$, which is in accordance with classical physics in this respect. In the nearly free electron model, however, as seen in Fig. 5.5.9 (b), this E–vs.–k parabola is greatly distorted due to the periodicity of the potential and the resulting Bragg reflections which produce standing-wave patterns. We shall begin our discussion with the relationship

$$v = \frac{dE}{dp}$$

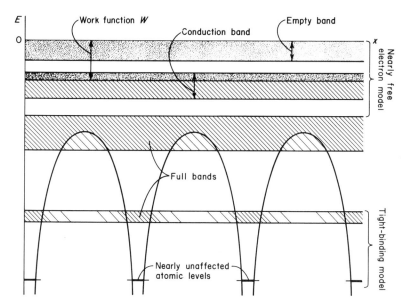

Fig. 5.5.11   Domains of validity of the tight-binding model and the nearly free electron model.

whereby here

$$p = \frac{h}{\lambda} = h \frac{k}{2\pi} = \hbar k.$$

Therefore

$$E = \frac{1}{2m} (\hbar k)^2,$$

and we have in one dimension

$$v = \frac{1}{\hbar} \frac{dE}{dk} . \qquad (5.5.3)$$

Differentiating once more yields

$$\frac{1}{\hbar} \frac{d^2E}{dk^2} = \frac{\hbar}{m}$$

or

$$\frac{1}{m} = \frac{1}{\hbar^2} \frac{d^2E}{dk^2} . \qquad (5.5.4)$$

This equation expresses that the second derivative of E with respect to k is inversely proportional to the mass m. In the E–vs.–k parabola corresponding to the Sommerfeld model the second derivative is obviously constant and, therefore, the mass of the electron is constant, neglecting relativistic effects which are not pertinent in our discussion. In the nearly free electron model, the situation is different. For values of k much smaller than π/d, we still have a parabola, but for higher values the second derivative (which is a measure for the curvature) becomes smaller and finally reverses its sign. This does not mean that the actual mass of the electron changes, but it means that the electron behaves as if it had a mass depending on its momentum. We therefore speak of an *effective mass* of the electron. This effective mass, according to Eq. 5.5.4, is

$$m^* = \frac{\hbar^2}{d^2E/dk^2} \qquad (5.5.5)$$

and is usually designated by m^*. Under the influence of an external force, such as an electric field, the electron will move as if it had a mass m^*.

The effective mass of an electron is given by the curvature of the E–vs.–k curve. If this curve turns upwards (for positive values of E), $m^* > 0$, if downwards, m^* becomes negative. In fact, $|m^*|$ can be greater or smaller than the actual electron mass m. In the upper region of an allowed band the effective mass is therefore negative. At the inflection point, the mass becomes asymptotically $+\infty$ or $-\infty$.

It is also instructive to consider Eq. 5.5.3, which gives the velocity of an electron in different regions of the band. At the bottom and at the top of the band, where the slope is zero, the velocity is zero, and it is greatest at the inflection point.

The concept of effective mass is very fruitful in solid-state physics, and is used also in nuclear physics. It always takes care of interaction forces between the particle and its environment which also contribute to the motion of the particle and must be taken into consideration in some way. With the device of the effective mass this interaction can be disposed of elegantly.

Conductors and Insulators

The behavior of an electron in an empty energy band is quite different from that of a free electron. If, when it is at the bottom of a band, an electric field is applied, it will be accelerated in the usual way, to a degree

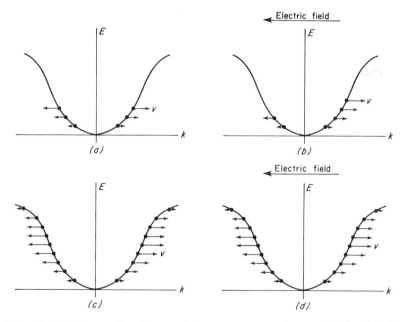

Fig. 5.5.12 Velocity distribution of electrons in a partly occupied band with no external field (a) and external field (b). The same for a full band (c) and (d).

depending on its effective mass. However, when it reaches the upper half of the band, the direction of the acceleration will be reversed, the electron will slow down, come to rest, and reverse its motion. This is really only a manifestation of Bragg reflection which occurs when the critical wavelength is reached (see p. 403). If the electron is undisturbed by collisions, it will oscillate to and fro under the influence of the field. However, if it experiences collisions, the momentum will be frequently redistributed, and the electron cloud will drift under the influence of the field resulting in a current.

Let us now consider a band in a one-dimensional crystal which contains only a few electrons, but is mostly empty, as illustrated in Fig. 5.5.12 (a) and (b). In the absence of a field an equal number of electrons are moving in opposite directions, but when a field is applied, more electrons move in one direction than in the other one, and the net result is a current. This is only possible by occupation of higher-lying previously unoccupied states in the band—if such states are available. It is therefore clear that a full band, as seen from Fig. 5.5.12 (c) and (d), cannot contribute a current.

What factors determine if a band is partly filled, full, or empty? To answer this question we must recall (see Fig. 5.5.1) that an isolated atomic bound state sharply defined at an energy $-E_0$ spreads out into a well defined band of states in a periodic potential. For the band of states there is a well defined density of states, and there are different bands corresponding to different isolated atomic states. The density of states is usually a quite complicated function of the energy, although near the band edges, that is, E_a, E_b, E_c, and E_d, where the energy goes parabolically with k, we expect $\rho(E)_{\text{near } a} \sim (E - E_a)^{1/2}$, and near the upper edge, $\rho(E)_{\text{near } b} \sim (E_b - E)^{1/2}$, and so on, as for a free electron with positive or negative mass. In Fig. 5.5.13 (a) we see a situation where the higher of two consecutive bands is completely void of electrons while the lower has all of its states filled with electrons. In this latter band, band I, there are no empty states or "holes" for electrons in the band to move into and thus change state; therefore, these electrons cannot be accelerated by an external field to produce a current, as we saw in Fig. 5.5.12. This is the case with band I of Fig. 5.5.13. In addition, if the energy difference between the top of band I and the bottom of the next completely empty band, band II, is large compared to kT, then there is no chance for electrons to be thermally excited from band I into band II, and we have an insulator. (For room temperature, i.e., 300 K, kT is 0.025 eV.)

However, in Fig. 5.5.13 (b) we see an entirely different situation, since band II is now only partly filled with electrons. Although bands I and III contribute no current in the presence of an electric field because they are completely full and empty, respectively, band II does contribute current

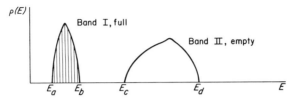

(a)   Energy bands as reflected in density of states for an insulator

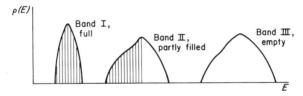

(b)   Energy bands as reflected in density of states for a conductor

Fig. 5.5.13   Density of states and energy bands in an insulator (*a*) and conductor (*b*).

because it contains many unfilled states. Electrons (shaded portion) can now find empty states to be accelerated into by means of the external field. A material with such a band structure is therefore a good conductor.

Although it is extremely difficult to determine the band structure of a solid, nevertheless some general features of the bands can usually be deduced by merely focusing attention on the electronic configuration of the isolated constituent atoms. Consider, for example, the electronic configuration of sodium: $(1s)^2(2s)^2(2p)^6(3s)^1$. If we have N isolated sodium atoms, we have N $3s$ electrons. There are, of course, $2N$ $3s$ *states*, N with spin up and N with spin down. If we assume that, as we bring the atoms together to form a piece of sodium metal, nothing more than spreading into a band of $3s$-like states happens to the atomic $3s$ states, then we have formed a band of $2N$ states (originating from the atomic $3s$ states) in the solid state. This band is only partially filled by the N electrons from the $3s$ levels, so that we expect sodium and, for that matter, all the alkalis to be excellent conductors of electricity.

On the other hand, when considering magnesium with the electronic configuration $(1s)^2(2s)^2(2p)^6(3s)^2$, on the basis of the above arguments one would expect it to be an insulator since the $3s$ band is completely full as well as the $2p$ band and the lower $1s$ and $2s$ bands. In reality, however, magnesium is an excellent conductor of electricity! What we have overlooked is the fact that a real crystal is not a one-dimensional, but a three-dimensional array of atoms. Depending on the direction of the electron motion, Bragg reflection by 180°, which is the cause of the band structure

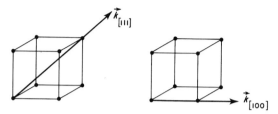

Fig. 5.5.14   The vectors **k** in the [111] and [100] directions in a simple cubic lattice.

in the nearly free electron model, is achieved for different values of λ, hence also for different values of $k = 2\pi/\lambda$. Consequently, different directions have different E–vs.–k curves with the allowed and forbidden energy bands varying according to the direction, for example, the [100] and [111] direction (Fig. 5.5.14). It therefore can happen that allowed bands *overlap* leaving no forbidden energy gap.

This is shown in Fig. 5.5.15 (a), which is drawn for a cubic lattice.[19] Each band is here represented only by the increasing part of the E–vs.–k curve. Because the spacing between crystallographic planes in the [111] direction is smaller than in the [100] direction, the energy for which Bragg reflection impedes the movement of the electrons is higher due to their shorter wavelength. If the lowest band was the only band available to the two $3s$ (valence) electrons of the magnesium atoms, and was filled, no conduction would be possible. This band corresponds according to the tight-binding model to the $3s$ level of the isolated Mg atom. In a crystal this level is spread out into bands of different widths depending on the direction of **k**. The second band in the [100] direction partly overlaps with the

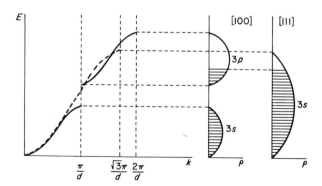

Fig. 5.5.15   Distribution of electrons for overlapping bands.

[19] Magnesium has in reality a hexagonal crystal structure, but the arguments presented here are the same.

lowest band in the [111] direction and is related to the empty $3p$ level in the isolated atom. Because this atomic level has six states, this band has $6N$ states which are now available for occupancy by some of the more energetic electrons from the lower band in the [111] direction. Similar to two connected vessels in which the water fills up to the same level, the electrons will tend to occupy the states of both overlapping bands up to the same energy. Figure 5.5.15 (b) shows this situation.

The upper band of the [100] direction and the band of the [111] direction are only partly filled by all available $3s$ electrons and allow therefore their mobility. Magnesium and the other alkaline earth metals as Be or Ca, which all are divalent, are therefore good conductors.

An interesting situation develops when an allowed band is nearly completely filled. We have seen that an electron near the upper edge of a band has a negative effective mass m^*. We assume now in the following that the uppermost states A and A' in a band are not occupied or, in other words, that there are *holes*, as illustrated in Fig. 5.5.16.

The periodicity of the lattice implies that all atoms in the lattice are equal. We can, therefore, repeat the E–vs.–k curve which in the past we have drawn only for the interval from $k = -\pi/d$ to $k = +\pi/d$. Since the tangent at these two values is horizontal, the curve has neither kinks nor discontinuities. In our figure, we have thus extended the E–vs.–k curve somewhat beyond its earlier limits.

If there is no external electric field, the velocity distribution of the electrons is symmetric with respect to left and right. If an electric field is applied whose direction is to the right, the electron at B, if it were an ordinary electron, would increase its negative velocity and therefore try to move to position C. However, having a negative effective mass, it will do the opposite and move in our diagram to a position with a smaller velocity, which here will be zero. It therefore will occupy the vacant state A. The electron originally at C will move to B and, hence, will also assume a smaller

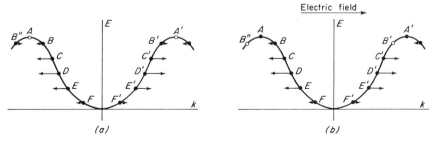

Fig. 5.5.16   A nearly filled conduction band with hole states: (a) no external electric field; (b) electric field present.

negative velocity, and so forth. Also the electron at F, which has a positive effective mass, will move in this diagram to the left, increasing its negative velocity. Similarly, all the electrons on the right side will move one place to the left. The net effect will be that the original vacancy at A has been moved to B'', and the vacancy at A' to B'. Whereas at A and A' the velocity vectors were zero, the states which are newly occupied by the holes have associated with them a velocity vector. If this vector is in the positive or negative direction, we need to investigate closer. We can, however, say that the holes were accelerated because there is an electric field in the positive direction.

The questions arise now: (a) whether the holes have a positive or negative effective electric charge; (b) whether they have a positive or negative effective mass; and (c) whether they are accelerated in the direction of or against the electric field. The first question can be answered by remembering that the electrons carry negative charges. Therefore, a moving hole can be assumed to be a positive charge carrier. From this it follows that if the holes have a positive effective mass, they will be accelerated in the direction of the electric field, and vice versa. Although one can deduce by logical arguments that the holes have a positive effective mass, it is easier to use the results of the anomalous Hall effect to decide this question.

In Section 5.4, when discussing the classical theory of conduction, we mentioned that in some metals the Hall emf ϵ_{Hall} has a sign that is opposite to the one to be expected if negative electrons were the carriers of the electric charge (see Table 5.4.2). We also showed (Fig. 5.4.2) that one could explain the anomalous Hall effect if one assumed positive charge carriers. Tacitly, we made the further assumption that these carriers had a positive mass. It is left as an exercise to the reader to convince himself that neither electrons of negative charge and negative mass, nor holes of negative or positive charge and of negative effective mass can produce an anomalous Hall emf and carry a current in direction of the electric field.

With a positive effective mass and a positive effective charge, the holes behave like positive electrons. However, such holes should not be confused with positrons which almost immediately would annihilate with electrons. The fact that holes have an effective positive mass, not a negative one, as one might first expect, should not come as a complete surprise! The holes are in regions ordinarily occupied by electrons of negative effective mass. Thus, a missing electron might well look like something having a positive mass.

Although we now understand the origin and significance of allowed and forbidden energy bands, and why certain materials are conductors, others insulators, it still remains to explain the electric resistivity of a metal. Experiments show that with increasing purity the conductivity of a material increases. For example, at a temperature of 220 K copper with a 1%-admixture of nickel has twice the resistance of pure copper. The resistance of a conductor also decreases when the temperature is lowered, in contrast to the behavior of semiconductors, which show the opposite temperature dependence and which we shall discuss in the following section. Pure copper at room temperature (300 K) has a resistance which is double that at 170 K. The explanation for this behavior is that any irregularity in the lattice impedes the flow of the conduction electrons. This irregularity might result from lattice defects caused by impurity atoms which take the place of the regular atoms or are squeezed in as so-called interstitial atoms. It also can happen that regular atoms are dislocated or missing in the lattice, for example, due to deformations. Another deviation from the regularity of an ideal lattice stems from the thermal vibrations of the lattice which we have discussed in connection with the specific heat capacities. Here, the phonons, or elastic vibrational quanta, collide with the conduction electrons.

The importance of perfect regularity in a crystal with regard to conduction follows from the fact that in such a case the only scattering that can occur is Bragg scattering, whereas in a crystal with irregularities additional scattering takes place. An electron that undergoes a collision has to change its momentum vector and therefore will occupy another state. Because of the exclusion principle it can only move to an unoccupied state. Since the external electric field has the effect that more electrons move in one direction than in the opposite one, comparatively more vacant states exist for the back direction than the forward direction. Hence, electrons will be scattered slightly more toward the backward direction, or at least their motion is randomized. The net effect is that some velocity equilibrium will be established, as explained in the section on the classical theory of electric conductivity.

Semiconductors

Let us return to the idea of an insulator. We recall that a solid will be an insulator if there is a completely filled band separated from a completely empty band by a gap that is much greater than the available thermal energy kT; that is, gaps in good insulators are typically at least 5 to 10 eV. There are a number of solids, however, in which the band gap is typically 2 or 3 eV or less. This size gap, although some 100 times greater than the available thermal energy at room temperature is, nevertheless, small enough to allow some small amount of conductivity; hence, these solids are known as *semiconductors*.

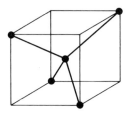

Fig. 5.5.17   The diamond structure of the semiconductors.

The simplest semiconductors, the so-called *intrinsic* semiconductors, are those elements from the fourth column of the periodic table which have the diamond structure: diamond (C), silicon, germanium, and grey tin. These have band gaps of energy E_g = 5.33, 1.14, 0.67, and 0.08 eV, respectively. The electronic configurations of these elements in the atomic state are those of a noble gas-closed shell, surrounded by two s and two p valence electrons. It is energetically favorable for these valence electrons to form covalent bonds between neighboring atoms. (Recall that covalent bonding was previously discussed with regard to the hydrogen molecule.) As a result, each atom is bonded to its nearest neighbors by four strong covalent bonds in a tetrahedral arrangement, as shown in Fig. 5.5.17. The corresponding states for these localized bond electrons completely fill a *valence band* built up from the atomic s and p states, as shown in Fig. 5.5.18. The next higher-lying band, the *conduction band*, is then completely empty at T = 0 K. Thus, at a temperature of absolute zero a semiconductor is a perfect insulator.

The Fermi level lies halfway between the two bands and not, as one might at first expect, at the top of the valence band. The reason can be found in the shape of the Fermi-Dirac function, which was pictured in Fig. 5.4.8. It shows a symmetry about the Fermi level at the energy e_F

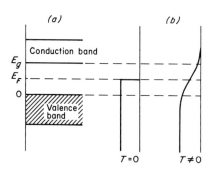

Fig. 5.5.18   (a) Valence and conduction bands of semiconductors. (b) Corresponding Fermi function for T = 0 K and $T \neq 0$ K.

insofar as the number of missing electrons below this level must equal that above it. In this way the Fermi-Dirac function arranges that the number of electrons in the conduction band equals the number of vacant states in the valence band.

As the temperature is raised, a very few electrons are thermally excited into the conduction band and are then free to move under the influence of an applied field. Also, the vacated states or *holes* left behind in the valence band are free to move under the influence of the applied field so that both bands contribute to the conductivity. The conductivity of the specimen thus increases as the temperature increases. This is to be contrasted to the behavior of a metal, in which the atomic vibrations increase with temperature, causing more scattering of electrons and hence the resistivity to increase with increasing temperature.

However, a really dramatic difference between a metal and a semiconductor involves the effect on the resistivity of the addition of very small amounts of an impurity (*impurity doping*). In a metal the change is usually small and proportional to the amount of impurity added. On the other hand, in a semiconductor the conductivity can increase by a factor of 10^3 with the addition of just one impurity atom of every 10^5 atoms of the pure material. However, not any impurity will give this kind of an effect.

For instance, suppose we consider the effect of adding impurity atoms of valence five, such as phosphorus, antimony, or arsenic, to silicon of valence four. If we assume that the phosphorus atoms reside at places previously reserved for silicon atoms, then we have a situation where four of the five valence electrons of phosphorus enter into covalent bonds with the nearest-neighbor silicon atoms. The fifth valence electron is then electrostatically attracted by the single unit of excess positive charge on the phosphorus impurity, so that the excess electron and the core of the impurity atom essentially comprise a hydrogenlike atomic system. This is shown schematically in Fig. 5.5.19.

The electron has a ground state and a series of excited states for which the energies can be approximately determined by a formula analogous to that for a hydrogen atom. The ionization energy, in the present case, is

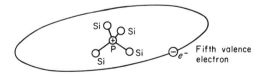

Fig. 5.5.19 Hydrogenlike impurity state in a semiconductor. As in the case of the hydrogen atom, such an orbit should not be taken literally, since *s*-state wave functions are spherically symmetric.

that amount of energy required to excite the electron from the ground state into the continuum of states which now constitute the conduction band. We calculate this energy E' the following way: The energy levels of a hydrogen atom, we recall from Eq. 4.1.15, are determined by the relation

$$E_n = - \frac{1}{n^2} \frac{me^4}{8\epsilon_0^2 \hbar^2} \tag{5.5.6}$$

where n is the principal quantum number. We know that in a dielectric medium of dielectric constant K_e the force between two charges of strength e is just $1/K_e$ of the force between them in vacuum; that is,

$$F_{\text{diel}} = \frac{1}{4\pi\epsilon_0} \left(\frac{1}{K_e}\right) \frac{e^2}{r_{12}^2} = \frac{1}{K_e} F_{\text{vacuum}}. \tag{5.5.7}$$

Therefore, for the electron-impurity system in a semiconductor of dielectric constant K_e, in Eq. 5.5.6 we replace e^2 by e^2/K_e and m by the effective mass m^* to obtain:

$$E'_n = - \frac{1}{n^2} \frac{m^* e^4}{8 K_e^2 \epsilon_0^2 \hbar^2} = - \frac{0.005}{n^2} \text{ eV}. \tag{5.5.8}$$

The last part of Eq. 5.5.8 is a result of using a value of $m^* = .1\,m$ (reasonable for germanium) and $K_e = 16$ (for germanium). The energy is to be calculated from the bottom of the conduction band (and not from the surface of the metal), because if the electron reaches this empty band, it is free to move; in other words, the impurity atom lost its electron and is ionized. So we see that the Bohr model predicts ionization energies of valence five impurities of the order of .005 eV, which is only about a factor of 2 lower than experimentally observed values. In essence, then, the addition of the impurity results in new electronic states in the region of the gap, slightly below the bottom of the conduction band, as shown in Fig. 5.5.20. The impurity is usually called the *donor*.

Thus these states offer in absolute numbers a large reservoir of electrons

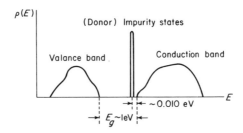

Fig. 5.5.20 Density of states for a pentavalent impurity-doped semiconductor.

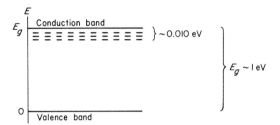

Fig. 5.5.21   Energy level diagram to Fig. 5.5.20.

to the conduction band much closer to the conduction band edge than the electrons at the top of the valence band, although the concentration of these impurities may be only 1 in 10^6. At room temperature, where the available thermal energy is of the order of .03 eV, a reasonably large number of electrons will be ionized from these localized states into the conduction band and thus be available for electronic conduction. These localized states are shown in the energy level diagram of Fig. 5.5.21. These impurity states are then essentially electron donors.

Electron donor states are not the only kind of impurity states that can be present in a semiconductor. Consider, for example, the effect of adding a valence-three impurity, such as boron, to a piece of previously pure silicon. Now we have a situation where all three of the valence electrons of the boron atom enter into covalent bonds with three of the four nearest-neighbor silicon atoms, leaving the fourth bond incomplete; that is, there is a *hole* in the fourth bond. A nearby electron then "hops" into this hole, and after a sequence of such electron hops and hence hole hops in the opposite direction, the hole finds itself at a distance from the negatively charged region corresponding to a stable hydrogenic orbit. In other words, we now have a positively charged hole orbiting the negatively charged impurity region, whereas for the donor impurity we had a negatively charged electron orbiting a positively charged center. At sufficiently low temperatures the hole is in a bound state, but with the addition of thermal energy can be ionized into the top of the valence band. Thus, the ionization energy of the hole is the difference in energies between the ground state of the hole-impurity system and the top of the valence band, as shown in Fig. 5.5.22. We have indicated this difference in energy to be about .010 eV. This is just twice the value that would be obtained from Eq. 5.5.15 for a trivalent impurity in germanium, in which the hole effective mass is comparable to that of an electron in the conduction band. This type of impurity state is called *acceptor*.

Thus, we see that by the addition of controlled amounts of either or

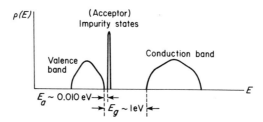

Fig. 5.5.22 Density of states for a trivalent impurity-doped semiconductor.

both valence-three and valence-five impurities, the number and type (electrons and holes) of carriers, and hence, the physical properties can be dramatically influenced. Impurity semiconductors which have (negative) electron donors are called n-type semiconductors; those whose conduction is due to (positive) holes, are p-type semiconductors.

PROBLEMS

1. The lattice energy of an ionic crystal is the energy necessary to separate all its ions to an infinite distance. For an NaCl crystal this energy is 18.3 kcal/mole $= 7.5 \times 10^5$ joule/mole. Compare this value with the one computed for a one-dimensional NaCl crystal, consisting of a string of Na$^+$ and Cl$^-$ atoms which are 2.8 Å apart.

2. An aluminum cube of 1 cm edge length is heated to 400 K and then inserted into a 1-liter vessel filled with argon at room temperature (300 K) and atmospheric pressure. Neglecting heat losses through the walls of the vessel, what will be the equilibrium temperature of the cube and the gas which will be achieved after some time?

3. A piece of copper of 20 g mass with a temperature of 600 K is cooled in a bucket filled with 4 liters of water at 300 K. By how many degrees centigrade will the water temperature be raised?

4. In what way would the curve of the specific heat capacity be modified if Planck's constant h were ten times smaller?

5. What is the characteristic frequency for silver in Einstein's model for the specific heat?

6. Draw a plot of $\bar{E}/kT$ as a function of $h\nu/kT$ and show that for high temperatures $\bar{E}$ is approximately equal to kT, in agreement with Dulong and Petit's value, but that at low temperatures $\bar{E}/kT$ becomes much smaller.

7. Give a semiquantitative estimate of the average amplitude of oscillation of a silver atom based on the Einstein model of specific heat (a) for a temperature of 100 K, (b) for the melting temperature of silver (960°C).

(c) Compare this with the distance between neighboring atoms. Atomic weight of silver: 108; density: 10.5 g/cm³. Crystal structure face-centered cubic.

8. What is the dependence of the density of modes ρ on the frequency ω for a two-dimensional sheet?

9. Show that for a one-dimensional crystal the low-temperature specific heat capacity as calculated with Debye's method is proportional to the temperature T, not T^3 as for a three-dimensional crystal.

10. The velocity of sound in aluminum is approximately 4500 m/sec. Density of aluminum 2.7 g/cm³, atomic weight 27. (a) Calculate the Debye temperature. (b) Calculate the low-temperature specific heat capacity.

11. Draw a graph of the specific heat capacity of copper for the temperature range between 1 and 5 K.

12. In approximately what temperature range would you expect the Debye temperatures to be for Be, Si, Sn, and Pb? See Table 5.2.1.

13. One of the shortcomings of the Debye model for the specific heat capacity is that it neglects dispersion phenomena, as treated for the one-dimensional case. Discuss qualitatively how dispersion will modify the Debye frequency spectrum.

14. Graph the number of phonons as a function of temperature.

15. Disregarding the Mössbauer effect, by what other experimental procedures could the probability for resonance absorption be improved?

16. Design some equipment, a so-called Mössbauer drive, which moves a Mössbauer absorber (a) with controllable constant speed against the source, (b) with sinusoidal varying speed against the source.

17. Calculate the approximate lifetime of the excited state of 129 keV energy in [191]Ir, using Mössbauer's data shown in Fig. 5.3.2.

18. Calculate the energy differences between the individual components of the 14.4-keV level of [57]Fe which is split due to the magnetic interaction, and do the same for the ground state.

19. Assume that in a graph showing absorption versus energy the [191]Ir Mössbauer line is drawn such that its full width at half maximum is 1 cm. (a) How far away is the zero point for the energy scale? (b) What is the ratio $\Delta E/E$?

20. The lifetime of the first-excited state of [119]Sn is 1.9×10^{-9} sec and its energy is 25 keV. The line from the transition to the ground state is partly emitted without recoil and is not split if source and absorber are from metallic tin. What is the minimum relative velocity between source and absorber so that resonance effects will be practically suppressed?

21. Draw a graph for the recoil energy from a 100 keV γ ray versus mass of the nucleus for $A = 20, 100, 240$.

22. Silver of 99.98% purity at $-258.6°C$ has a resistivity of 9×10^{-9}

ohm-cm, the semiconductor germanium at room temperature 50 ohm-cm (depending on its purity this figure can vary by orders of magnitude), and fused quartz, one of the best insulators, 7×10^{19} ohm-cm. Assume a quartz wafer 1/1000 mm thick and of 1 cm² cross section. How long would a germanium bar of 1 cm² cross section have to be to have the same resistance as the insulator? How long would a silver conductor have to be?

23. The current flowing in a copper wire 1 mm in diameter is 5 A. (a) How many electrons flow past a given point in one second? (b) What is their drift velocity assuming the number per cubic meter to be 0.84×10^{29}? (c) Since the drift velocity of the electrons is so small, why does a light bulb turn on almost instantaneously when the switch is snapped?

24. In an experiment on the Hall effect, both a longitudinal and a transverse electric field are present. The equipotentials, which are at right angles to the resultant field, are not parallel to the current. Derive an expression for the angle between the normal to the equipotential surfaces and the current.

25. Prove that the Hall coefficient may be expressed as the product of the resistivity of the material being used and the mobility of the free charges.

26. Discuss the effect of recoil on Bragg diffraction of x-rays.

27. Determine the density of states of a three-dimensional well from Fig. 5.4.5 by using a bin width of 20 E_0.

28. Assume that an insulator may be considered as a rectangular box within which electrons which are added in some way are perfectly free to move about. If free electrons are gradually added in this way and occupy all the lowest energy levels, at what concentration will the maximum energy of an electron (the Fermi energy) be just equal to $\frac{3}{2} kT$, with $T = 300$ K? At this concentration the free electrons would behave more or less like the atoms of an ordinary gas at 300 K. Would they have an appreciable effect on the observed specific heat capacity of the insulator?

29. Comment on the fact that for electrons $\rho(E) \sim E^{1/2}$, whereas for phonons $\rho(\omega) \sim \omega^2$. (See footnote 13.)

30. Draw a plot of the electronic density of occupied states for two temperatures T_1 and $T_2 > T_1$, similar to the one in Fig. 5.4.8 for $T = 0$ K.

31. According to the Fermi-gas model the number of spatial states in the energy interval dE which can be occupied by the electrons of a metal may be written as $CE^{1/2}dE$ where C is a constant. Each spatial state can accommodate two electrons. Assume that a piece of metal contains N free electrons. Find the Fermi energy e_F at 0 K in terms of C and N.

32. At approximately what temperature would the Fermi energy of free electrons in copper be equal to kT?

33. Compute the number of atoms per unit volume of helium at 300 K,

and a pressure of 1 atm. To do so, remember that a perfect gas containing N atoms at a temperature T in a volume V will exert a pressure p on the walls where $pV = NkT$. Suitable units must be used in the above expression. The usual gas constant R is just k times the number of atoms per mole, or $R = 6.02 \times 10^{23}\, k$. What would be the maximum energy of a helium atom in a gas consisting entirely of the isotope ^{3}He which has a spin $S = \frac{1}{2}$ like an electron, and if all the lowest energy levels were occupied? At what temperature could this happen?

34. A piece of copper has a volume V. Assume the validity of the free-electron model and that there are N occupied states. Another piece of copper has the volume $2V$. How many occupied states does this one have?

35. The density of sodium ($A = 23$) is 0.97 g/cm^3. Its valence electrons (one per atom) can be considered as free electrons in the free-electron model. (a) What is the Fermi energy of sodium? (b) What is the Fermi velocity? (c) If a piece of sodium is compressed, will this influence the Fermi energy and the Fermi velocity?

36. A copper single crystal is in the form of a rectangular parallelepiped 0.03 mm by 0.05 mm by 0.06 mm on the edges. The shortest electron wavelength for any of the occupied states is 4.5 Å. (a) What is the Fermi energy for copper? (b) Treating the crystal as a three-dimensional potential well, find the number of free-electron wave functions that are occupied. (Remember the twofold spin degeneracy.) (c) Consider that copper has one conduction-band electron per atom. What fraction is the number of the occupied states with respect to the total number of states in the conduction band?

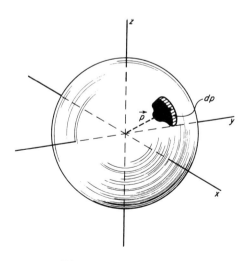

Figure P.5.1 (Problem 38)

37. "Free" electrons in a metal have a quasi-continuous energy distribution. Considering two adjacent electron states with momenta $(h/Na)n_x$ and $(h/Na)(n_x + 1)$, respectively, whereby in both cases $n_y = n_z = 0$, what is the energy difference between the two states? Assume $Na = L = 1$ cm and $n_x = 3 \times 10^7$.

38. Let $N(E)$ be the number of free electrons with energies between E and $E + dE$. These electrons, with respect to their momentum, can be thought of as lying on a spherical shell whose radius is given by the momentum vector $\mathbf{p}$. Thus we can write $N(E)dE \sim 4\pi p^2 dp$. From the known relation between E and p show that $N(E) \sim E^{1/2}$, as has been derived in another way in the text.

39. The Fermi distribution function

$$f_{FD}(E) = \frac{1}{e^{(E-e_F)/kT} + 1}$$

gives the probability that a particular state is occupied. (a) For what values of E is this probability $\frac{1}{4}$? (b) $\frac{1}{2}$? (c) At what temperature would $kT = e_F/4$ if $e_F = 3.1$ eV (a value which is appropriate for sodium)? Compare this with the melting point of sodium which is 97.5°C.

40. The work functions of Ni and Zn are 5.0 V and 4.2 V, respectively. (a) What happens with the electrons when a nickel plate and a zinc plate are brought into close contact? (b) What happens if the two metals are separated again?

41. What fraction do the electrons contribute to the specific heat capacity at room temperature (300 K)?

42. Discuss the relationship between dispersion and Bragg reflection.

43. For a particular metal the electron energy can be expressed as a function of the wave vector $\mathbf{k}$,

$$E(\mathbf{k}) = \frac{\hbar^2}{2m_0}[k^2 - a^2 k^4]$$

where m_0 is the mass of the free electron, a is a constant, and $k^2 = k_x^2 + k_y^2 + k_z^2$. (a) What are the dimensions of a? (b) What is the velocity $\mathbf{v}$ of an electron with $k_x = -1/(4a)$, $k_y = 1/(4a)$, and $k_z = 0$.

44. For a one-dimensional solid the standard tight-binding approximation gives the energy dependence on $\mathbf{k}$ in the form

$$E = -E_0 \cos k_x a.$$

Write an expression for $1/m^*$ and evaluate it for $k_x = \pi/4$, $\pi/3$, $2\pi/3$, and π.

45. The kinetic energy of an electron in a one-dimensional solid is given

by $E = -E_0 \cos ka$. What is the group velocity of the electron when $k = 3\pi/(4a)$?

46. Ten atomic cells, each of length a, are arranged in a straight line to form a one-dimensional solid. (a) Show that the wave function

$$\psi_8 = \frac{1}{\sqrt{L}} e^{16\pi i x/L},$$

where $L = 10\ a$, satisfies the boundary conditions at $x = 0$ and $x = L$. (b) What is the wavelength of this wave function and what is the momentum associated with it? (c) What is the effect of a translation of ψ_8 by a distance a in the x direction, that is, letting $x \to x + a$?

47. Discuss the connection between Bragg reflection and effective mass m^*.

48. Draw graphs for the energy E, the effective mass m^* and the velocity v of an electron in an allowed band in the interval from $k = -\pi/a$ to $+\pi/a$.

49. (a) On which physical quantities do the relative widths of bands and band gaps depend? (b) In which way must these quantities change to yield a narrower gap?

50. Silicon of high purity is doped with a concentration of 10^{20} atoms/m^3 of antimony impurities. (a) Assuming a dielectric constant $K_e = 12$ and $m^*/m = 0.1$, calculate the energy below the conduction band at which one would expect the donor level. (b) What is the radius of the electron orbits around the impurity atoms in the ground state? (c) How many silicon atoms are within a sphere of this radius? Density of silicon 2.4 g/cm^3. (d) What is the ratio of the number of Si atoms to Sb atoms? (e) What would be the sign of the Hall effect? (f) At what temperature would one expect the Sb atoms to start "donating" electrons to the conduction band?

51. In a semiconductor electrons can be lifted by a photoelectric effect from the valence band to the conduction band. What are the maximum wavelengths that will produce this effect in diamond and in germanium? The conduction resulting from this effect is called photoconduction.

52. What sort of impurities are needed to make the Hall effect anomalous ($+$) for germanium? How does the size of this effect depend on the number of doping atoms? How does this number affect the conductivity?

53. By drawing diagrams similar to those of Fig. 5.4.2 show that neither electrons of negative mass and negative charge, nor holes of negative charge and negative mass, nor holes of positive charge and negative effective mass can produce an anomalous Hall emf and can carry a current in direction of the electric field. Show that conduction by holes of positive effective mass and positive charge, however, can explain the experimental situation regarding the anomalous Hall effect.

Chapter 6

Nucleons and Nuclei

6.1 INTRODUCTION

At the beginning of this chapter we shall point out a few basic facts about atomic nuclei. Most of our readers are probably familiar with them from high school or from popular science articles in newspapers or magazines.

We picture the atom as consisting of a nucleus surrounded by the cloud of electrons. Nuclei are very small, in the order of 10^{-12} cm, whereas atoms have radii of approximately 10^{-8} cm. The radius of the atom is essentially the radius of the outermost electron orbit. The building blocks of nuclei are the nucleons. The group of nucleons consists of two species, the protons and the neutrons. Nucleons are much more massive than electrons. The mass of a proton equals 1836.0 electron masses, that of a neutron is slightly greater, namely 1838.6 electron masses. The mass of an atom is therefore almost entirely contained by its nucleus. The proton has a positive charge whose magnitude, 1.6×10^{-19} coulombs, is equal to that of an electron (which is negatively charged). The neutron is uncharged.

As can be seen from the plot in Fig. 6.1.1, the number of protons in nuclei that contain less than approximately 40 nucleons is about equal to the number of neutrons. As we move to more massive nuclei, we find more neutrons than protons, with the ratio in general increasing gradually. In the heaviest elements the ratio of neutrons to protons is about one and one-half. Because a neutral atom must have protons and electrons in equal numbers and, furthermore, because the electronic shell structure determines the chemical properties, such as molecular binding of an atom, it follows that the number of protons in a nucleus is ultimately responsible for the chemical character of an atom. For example, a neutral tin atom has always 50 protons and 50 electrons. One finds, however, stable tin nuclei with the following numbers of neutrons: 62, 64, 65, 66, 67, 68, 69, 70, 72, 74; this is an extreme case. Representative for the other extreme is

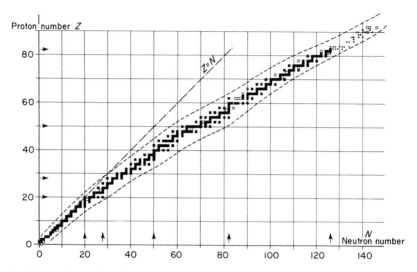

Fig. 6.1.1 Chart of nuclides. Stable nuclides are indicated by black squares, naturally occurring radioactive by open squares. Radioactive nuclides (e.g., radium), which are created in a radioactive decay chain, are shown by dots. The dashed lines delineate the region of the presently known nuclides. Nuclides between the band of stable nuclides and the upper dashed line ordinarily decay by β^+ or α particle emission, nuclides situated on the other side of the stable nuclides decay by β^- decay. Nuclear stability is discussed in Sect. 6.6, nuclear decay in Sect. 6.7. The arrows at 20, 28, 50, 82, and 126 indicate the so-called magic neutron and proton numbers, representing particularly stable configurations, which are discussed in Sect. 6.7.

rhodium: its 45 protons can combine with only one number of neutrons, namely 58, to form a stable nucleus. If the number of neutrons is different, the nucleus will be unstable.[1] A specific nucleus with a definite number of neutrons and protons is called a nuclide. Atoms whose nuclei have the same number of protons are called isotopes (Greek: *isos* = same, *topos* = place; *isotope* = at the same place in the periodic table of elements). Tin, for example, has ten stable isotopes, and rhodium is monoisotopic.

Different isotopes of an element (e.g., tin) behave from the chemical standpoint almost identically with a minor exception regarding the isotopes of hydrogen. The usual hydrogen nucleus consists of a proton; the nucleus of deuterium, the heavy hydrogen, has a proton and a neutron.

---

[1] An even more extreme case is the one of 43 protons. Any combination with any number of neutrons is unstable. This element is therefore unstable and carries the name technetium (Tc) because it was the first element to be produced artifically without naturally existing on the earth. Optical spectral lines of technetium have, however, been observed in the spectrum of certain red giant stars, indicating that it is produced there in nuclear fission reactions.

Finally, there is a third species of hydrogen, the so-called tritium, with one proton and two neutrons. The last kind is not stable. The isotopic abundances of these three hydrogen isotopes in nature are very different: approximately 99.985% is the normal hydrogen, the rest is deuterium. The amount of natural tritium is negligibly small. The unusually large relative mass difference causes slightly different electrochemical potentials and therefore slightly different chemical properties. For this reason the body water in living beings could not be replaced to an appreciable extent by heavy water without seriously or even fatally disturbing the many delicate biochemical equilibria regulating the biological processes. Hydrogen and heavy hydrogen are usually separated by electrolysis of water, making use of the fact that the disintegration potentials of regular and heavy water are slightly different.

In order to discriminate between the isotopes of the same element one uses the following convention: ^A_Z(chemical symbol), where Z is the atomic number, that is, the number of protons (which is equal to the number of electrons in the atom) and A the mass number, that is the number of protons plus neutrons in the nucleus. Two of the isotopes of tin are, therefore, $^{120}_{50}$Sn and $^{122}_{50}$Sn. The former has 70 neutrons, the latter has 72. Since the chemical symbol Sn specifies already the number of protons, the subscript 50 is redundant and is frequently left off. In scientific literature one also finds the mass number A written on the upper right-hand corner, for example, $_{50}$Sn^{120}. In cases where the number of neutrons is of particular importance it is given on the lower right-hand corner, for example, $^{120}_{50}$Sn$_{70}$.

Nuclei can be transformed by bombarding them, e.g., with protons, neutrons, or photons. The bombarded nucleus often absorbs the projectile, but emits another particle. A reaction which is induced by a proton and in which a neutron is emitted can be written in the following way:

$$^{107}_{47}\text{Ag} + p \rightarrow {}^{108}_{48}\text{Cd}^* \rightarrow {}^{107}_{48}\text{Cd} + n + Q.$$

The asterisk in $^{108}_{48}$Cd* signifies that this nuclide is in an excited state. Q is the reaction energy, completely analogous to the Q in a chemical reaction, except that the energies in the nuclear case are usually in the order of MeV, rather than in eV as in chemical reactions. Often a nuclear reaction is written in a shorter way: $^{107}_{47}$Ag(p, n) $^{107}_{48}$Cd whereby Ag is the target and Cd the residual, or product, nucleus. The symbol between parentheses to the left of the comma specifies the bombarding particle, in our case a proton, the symbol after the comma specifies the outgoing particle. Examples of other reactions are $^{107}_{47}$Ag(n, γ) $^{108}_{47}$Ag, with a neutron going into the nucleus and emission of a γ quantum. In an $(n, 2n)$ reaction one neutron enters the nucleus, and two neutrons leave it. The net change is therefore the loss of one neutron.

In the foregoing chapters we have seen that classical physics is a very inadequate tool for the treatment of systems in which interactions at distances of the order of magnitude of the de Broglie wavelength or less play a role. We also saw that quantum mechanics opened the way to an understanding of the behavior and structure of atoms and molecules and of the solid state. The forces playing the dominant role in these areas were those of the electromagnetic theory, although sometimes in the disguise of exchange forces or Van der Waals forces. These electromagnetic forces, even before they were thoroughly understood, gave an excellent account of the physical reality in connection with quantum theory. In nuclear physics the situation is different: the nuclear forces are not nearly so well understood. They are much stronger and decrease much faster with distance than the $1/r^2$ forces of electromagnetic theory. This makes a mathematical treatment very difficult in general, and the same characteristics also often prevent the calculation of reasonable approximations starting with only a few fundamental assumptions. Very frequently the physicist has to assume something, make a model, and use this as a starting point from which he develops his theories, which are necessarily of limited validity. He then compares his predictions with reality, that is, with the experimental data. In many cases the experimenter is ahead of the theorist as, for example, regarding the so-called shell model of the nucleus. (This model is in a crude sense the nuclear counterpart to the atomic shell model which leads to the periodic table of the elements as we have seen earlier.) In this case there was much experimental information available which, however, was unorganized. Analysis of the data led then to the postulation of this model. Often, however, the situation is the reverse; an example is the following: the theorists had postulated the neutrino, a particle with rest mass zero (or at least near zero), charge zero, and spin of $\frac{1}{2}$. This speculation was based on the conservation principle of energy and angular momentum in order to account for experimental observations. Experiments were designed and carried through with the goal of finding this particle. Because of its properties this particle was extremely difficult to detect, and the chance of its being detected accidently in an experiment other than one specifically designed for this purpose would have been about nil.

6.2 NUCLEAR RADII

We shall now make some comparisons between atoms and nuclei. Atoms have most of their mass concentrated in the nucleus which is very small as pointed out above. The atomic radius does not increase with the number of electrons; it depends only on the binding energy of the outer electrons

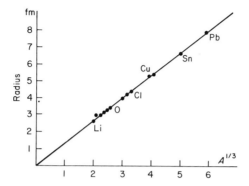

Fig. 6.2.1   Plot of the nuclear radius versus the cube root of the mass number.

or, in other words, the electron configuration. Hence the radius of the sodium atom $(Z = 12)$ is much greater than the radius of the xenon atom $(Z = 54)$. The density of the electrons in an atom is very small and varies greatly within the atom. This fact is reflected in the picture of the Bohr orbits. The nuclear structure is completely different in this regard. Nuclear matter is fairly tightly packed. The nuclear density remains essentially constant when passing from the light to the heavy nuclides. The nuclear volume is therefore closely proportional to the number of nucleons. Since nuclei are spherical to a first approximation, the nuclear radius R varies as

$$R = r_0 A^{1/3}$$

for nuclei with $A = 4$ to $A = 240$, and with $r_0 = 1.2$ fm [1 fm (femtometer) $= 10^{-15}$ m; from the Swedish *femton* $= 15$]. (Often 10^{-15} m is abbreviated as 1 fermi (f), in honor of the famous physicist, Enrico Fermi, to whom physics owes so much and who died in 1953.) It turns out that the unit of 10^{-15} m is a very convenient size in nuclear physics. Figure 6.2.1 shows the nuclear radii as a function of the cube root of the mass number A. In plotting R versus $A^{1/3}$ (rather than just A) we find that the data points fall on a straight line.

Rutherford Scattering

The first indication and proof that nuclei were much smaller than atoms came in 1911 when Rutherford's co-worker Geiger (who later invented with Müller the Geiger-Müller counter) and the student Marsden studied the scattering of α-particles in Manchester, England. In these experiments α-particles that were emitted from naturally radioactive substances and collimated in a narrow beam were let pass through a thin gold foil. Some

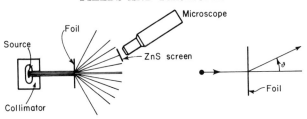

Fig. 6.2.2 A diagram illustrating the main components of Rutherford's scattering experiment.

of the particles underwent some scattering in the foil and of those a few fell on a zinc-sulphide screen which was attached in front of a microscope. The α particles gave rise to a scintillation on the screen of the kind which we can observe with a magnifying glass on a luminous watch dial. The scintillations were observed with a microscope and their number recorded as a function of the deflection angle. Because of the short range of the α particles in air, the source, foil, screen, and parts of the microscope had to be in vacuum (Fig. 6.2.2). About 30 years later Rutherford[2] recalled in a lecture the events of that time:

> "Now I, myself, was very interested in the next stage, . . . and I would like to use this example to show how you often stumble upon facts by accident. In the early days I had observed the scattering of α-particles, and Dr. Geiger in my laboratory had examined it in detail. He found, in these pieces [foils] of heavy metal, that the scattering was usually small, of the order of one degree. One day Geiger came to me and said, 'Don't you think young Marsden, whom I am training in radioactive methods, ought to begin a small research?' Now I had thought that too, so I said, 'Why not let him see if any α-particles can be scattered through a large angle?' I may tell you in confidence that I did not believe they would be, since we knew that the α-particle was a very fast massive particle, with a great deal of energy, and you could show that if the scattering was due to the accumulated effect of a number of small scatterings the chance of α-particles being scattered backwards was very small. Then I remember two or three days later Geiger coming to me in great excitement and saying, 'We have been able to get some of the α-particles coming

---

[2] Lord Ernest Rutherford (1871–1937), born in New Zealand, studied in New Zealand and Cambridge, England. Professor of Physics at McGill University in Montreal where he explained radioactivity as a spontaneous transmutation of elements. Later professor in Manchester and Cambridge where he was director of the Cavendish Laboratory. Produced in 1919 the first artificial nuclear reaction, $^{14}N(\alpha, p)^{17}O$, by using α particles from natural radioactivity. Nobel prize in chemistry 1908.

Ernest Rutherford (1871–1937) in Cambridge 1934 (Photograph by P. Harteck).

backwards. . . .' It was quite the most incredible event that has happened to me in my life. It was almost as incredible as if you fired a 15-inch shell at a piece of tissue paper and it came back and hit you. On consideration I realized that this scattering backwards must be the result of a single collision, and when I made calculations I saw that it was impossible to get anything of that order of magnitude unless you took a system in which the greater part of the mass of the atom was concentrated in a minute nucleus. It was then that I had the idea of an atom with a minute massive center carrying a charge." [3]

Up to that time the physicists were rather inclined to think with J. J. Thomson of the atom as a uniformly positive charged sphere in which the electrons were embedded like plums in a plum pudding. Even a direct hit of an electron by the incoming α particle would have affected the trajectory of the α particle only a little, because the much heavier α particle would have easily pushed the electron to the side. This model allowed therefore only for small angle scattering of α particles even if multiple scattering of a single α particle was taken into account.

[3] *Background to Modern Science*, J. Needham and W. Pagel, eds., (Cambridge University Press, 1938).

Because of the surprising observation of Geiger and Marsden, Rutherford set out to calculate the number of scattered α particles as functions of the angle. It should be kept in mind that the α particles which were used did not have enough energy to come close to the surface of the gold nuclei and hence within the range of the nuclear forces. The forces acting between α particles and nuclei were therefore purely Coulomb forces. Rutherford published his theory in a beautiful and clearly written paper in the *Philosophical Magazine*.[4] Later Rutherford was very proud that quantum mechanics could not improve this result of atomic physics which he had derived on the basis of purely classical physical laws.[5]

Conservation of energy and angular momentum and Coulomb's law are the necessary and sufficient assumptions to calculate the elastic scattering of α particles, which is called Rutherford scattering or Coulomb scattering (although the latter sometimes also includes inelastic scattering).

Because the force acting between α particles and nucleus is the $1/r^2$ Coulomb central force, the laws for planetary motion are valid, although here the interaction force is repulsive. This leads to hyperbolic trajectories instead of elliptical orbits, as shown in Fig. 6.2.3. The interaction force changes the direction of motion of the α particle by the scattering angle φ.

Let us assume that the α particle is approaching the nucleus in such a direction that if it had no charge it would miss the nucleus by a distance p, called the impact parameter. Far away the particle has the velocity v. In approaching the nucleus it loses kinetic energy but gains potential energy because of the Coulomb repulsion. Writing the mass and charge of the α particle m and q_α, respectively, and assuming that the nucleus of charge q_n is much more massive than the α particle and therefore will not gain kinetic energy, we find the following relation at the distance of closest approach

$$\frac{mv'^2}{2} = \frac{mv^2}{2} - \frac{1}{4\pi\epsilon_0}\frac{q_\alpha q_n}{a + c} \qquad (6.2.1)$$

where v' is the velocity at that point and a and c are the quantities given in Fig. 6.2.3 which are related to the geometry of the hyperbola.

Since angular momentum must be conserved, equal areas will be swept out in equal times by the α particle (in the case of planetary orbits this is Kepler's second law), and because of the properties of a hyperbola $b = p$, we have, chosing a distant point on the trajectory and the one of closest approach to the nucleus,

$$vp = vb = v'(a + c)$$

and therefore

$$v' = v\frac{b}{a + c}$$

---

[4] **21,** 669 (1911). Reprinted in *The World of the Atom*, H. A. Boorse and L. Motz, eds. (Basic Books, New York, 1966).

[5] Rutherford was lucky in this respect; only in the case of a $1/r^2$-force law do classical and quantum mechanics yield the same result!

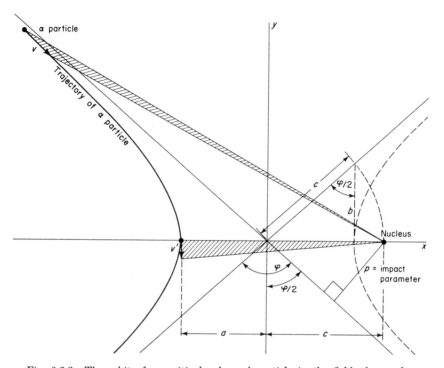

Fig. 6.2.3   The orbit of a positively charged particle in the field of a nucleus.

Inserting this into Eq. 6.2.1 yields

$$\frac{mv^2}{2}\left[1 - \frac{b^2}{(a+c)^2}\right] = \frac{1}{4\pi\epsilon_0}\frac{q_\alpha q_n}{a+c}.$$

Employing the relationship $a^2 + b^2 = c^2$ we get

$$\frac{mv^2}{2}\left[\frac{2a(a+c)}{(a+c)^2}\right] = \frac{1}{4\pi\epsilon_0}\frac{q_\alpha q_n}{a+c}$$

which yields

$$a = \frac{1}{4\pi\epsilon_0}\frac{q_\alpha q_n}{mv^2}.$$

Since $\cot \varphi/2 = b/a$, and $b = p$, we have as final result

$$p = \frac{1}{4\pi\epsilon_0}\frac{q_\alpha q_n}{mv^2}\cot\frac{\varphi}{2}. \tag{6.2.2}$$

This equation relates the scattering angle φ to the impact parameter p. The latter cannot be measured directly. However, if we know that a thin foil contains n nuclei per area A we can calculate what the probability will be for an α particle in traversing the foil to pass by a nucleus with an impact parameter between p and $p + dp$. If there

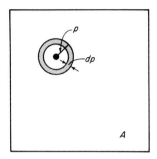

Fig. 6.2.4   The area between impact parameters p and $p + dp$.

were only one nucleus in the area A, the probability P that the impact parameter has the required size would be $P = 2\pi p \, dp/A$ (see Fig. 6.2.4). For n nuclei in the foil this probability becomes $P = n2\pi p \, dp/A$. Obviously we can compute the quantity $p \, dp$ from Eq. 6.2.2. Since

$$dp = \frac{1}{4\pi\epsilon_0} \frac{q_\alpha q_n}{2mv^2} \frac{1}{\sin^2 \varphi/2} \, d\varphi,$$

the probability that an α particle is scattered by an angle which is between φ and $\varphi + d\varphi$ is given by

$$P(\varphi)d\varphi = \frac{n\pi}{A} \left(\frac{1}{4\pi\epsilon_0} \frac{q_\alpha q_n}{mv^2} \right)^2 \frac{1}{\sin^2 \varphi/2} \cot\left(\frac{\varphi}{2} \right) d\varphi.$$

In order to find the probability that an α particle is scattered onto a scintillating screen extending a certain area at a distance r from the scatterer, we have to calculate the solid angle $d\Omega$ which is subtended between the cones φ and $\varphi + d\varphi$. This solid angle (Fig. 6.2.5) is

$$d\Omega = 2\pi \sin \varphi d\varphi.$$

But since $\sin \varphi = 2 \sin(\varphi/2) \cos(\varphi/2)$,

$$d\Omega = 4\pi \sin(\varphi/2) \cos(\varphi/2) d\varphi.$$

The probability $P(\Omega)$ for scattering of an α particle through the angle φ

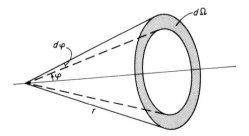

Fig. 6.2.5   The solid-angle element $d\Omega$.

into the solid angle Ω is therefore

$$P(\Omega) = \frac{n}{4A} \left(\frac{1}{4\pi\epsilon_0} \frac{q_\alpha q_n}{mv^2} \right)^2 \frac{d\Omega}{\sin^4 (\varphi/2)}. \qquad (6.2.3)$$

We have here tacitly assumed that the foil is so thin that the probability of an α particle being scattered appreciably a second time is negligible.

The important feature of this result is the very strong angular dependence of the scattering probability which varies inversely as the fourth power of the sine of half the scattering angle. The probability hence decreases very rapidly with increasing angle.

Rutherford found that Geiger and Marsden's measurements were "in substantial agreement with the theory." On the other hand, Geiger and Marsden continued to measure the scattering in variation of different materials, different thicknesses, different angles, and different velocities, in order to verify Rutherford's theory. Since some α particles were even scattered by 180°, an upper limit could be deduced for the radius of nuclei.

It should be pointed out that the model of the nuclear atom (in contrast to the plum pudding model) had been considered even before Rutherford. It has been rejected, however, on the grounds of classical electromagnetic theory according to which electrons circulating in orbits around the nucleus and therefore undergoing continuous acceleration should lose their energy by radiation in a very short time and thus fall into the nucleus.

Modern Methods

The radius of nuclei can be determined in various ways. Here we will describe several very different methods which give an indication of how physicists are able to measure such a quantity. First, we shall discuss the measurements of Hofstadter's[6] group at Stanford, using high-energy electrons which were accelerated in a linear accelerator. These electrons impinge on a foil (e.g., of gold). Most of the electrons pass undeflected through this foil which typically has a thickness of 1/4000 in. but some are scattered by the nuclei. From the angular distribution of the scattered electrons, the shape and size of the nuclei can be calculated. Electrons are ideal projectiles because they are not subject to nuclear forces, but only to the well-known and understood electromagnetic forces. From the standpoint of wave optics and wave mechanics it is also easy to understand that the de Broglie wavelength of the impinging electrons, $\lambda = h/mv$, must be quite a

[6] Robert Hofstadter, born 1915 in New York; professor at Stanford University; Nobel prize in physics 1961 for his work on high-energy electron scattering.

bit smaller than the object under investigation if one wants to "see" some detail. Unless this condition if fulfilled essentially only the recording of the presence of a particle is possible.

The first minimum (in case of a slit, or maximum in the case of an opaque object) in the diffraction pattern of an object of width a_0 for waves of wavelength λ apperars, according to Chapter 2, at an angle α, which is given by the relation $\sin \alpha \approx \lambda/a_0$. If λ is appreciably greater than a_0 the diffraction pattern can no longer yield information about the size of the object, even less about its details. Since the energies of the electrons used for such scattering experiments are highly relativistic, their rest mass energy can be neglected so that $p = E/c$ and $\lambda = h/p = hc/E$. Because the diameters of nuclei are of the order of 10^{-14} m, the condition $\lambda < a_0$ requires energies in the order of 200 MeV. For reasons similar to the ones which were stated in regard to the Heisenberg uncertainty principle (see Chap. 3), footnote 6) the wavelength λ should be replaced by the "reduced wavelength" $\lambda/2\pi$. Therefore, electron scattering performed with 150 MeV energy allows us to explore some details of the nuclear structure.

The main effect in the electron scattering process is naturally some kind of Rutherford scattering, that is, the scattering on electric point charges, which is characterized by a steep fall in intensity with increasing scattering angle. But superimposed upon this decrease in intensity is a diffraction pattern with maxima and minima analogous to the ones we have discussed in wave optics (Fig. 6.2.6). In order to avoid misconceptions we want to emphasize again that this electron diffraction is related to the single slit or single hole optical diffraction, in contrast to the electron diffraction by crystals which has its counterpart to some degree in the optical interference phenomena from multiple slits. From the distance between the relative minima the size of the nuclei can be deduced, from the depth of the diffraction minima conclusions can be drawn about the fuzziness of the nuclear surface. This can be understood from optics: A circular aperture with a distinct, sharp boundary will give a sharper diffraction pattern than an aperture with a gradual transition from transparency to opacity. The conclusion from these experiments is that inside the nucleus the density is fairly constant, but that nuclei have some kind of skin (Fig. 6.2.7). This skin appears to be of about the same thickness, approximately 2 fm, in all nuclei. There the density falls off.[7] Because the electrons interact only with the protons, the tacit assumption has been made in deducing the nuclear radius that protons and neutrons are distributed in the nucleus in like manner, which today seems to be substantiated to a fair degree.

---

[7] The skin thickness is defined by convention as the distance over which the density changes from 90% of its value to 10%.

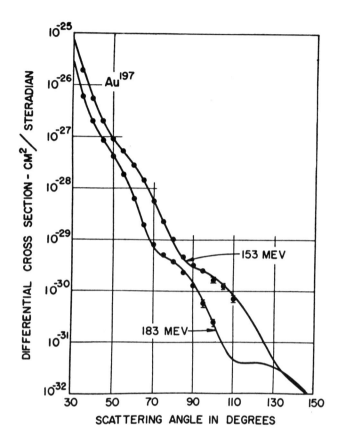

Fig. 6.2.6 Electron scattering in gold at 153 and 183 MeV; measurements and theoretical curves. [From B. Hahn, D. G. Ravenhall and R. Hofstadter, *Phys. Rev.* **101,** 1131 (1956)]. (The differential cross section is a quantity which is proportional to the probability for scattering into a given angle.)

With such a nonuniform charge distribution of the nucleus, if one takes also the region of the skin into consideration, what should be considered as nuclear radius is somewhat arbitrary. Sometimes the half-density radius is given which is the radius at which the charge density has fallen to half its value in comparison with the center.[8]

Another experiment, done by Fitch and Rainwater in the early 1950's at Columbia University, used muons as probing particles. The muon was

---

[8] Frequently, also the root mean square radius is quoted which is calculated from

$$\langle r^2 \rangle_{av} = \int_0^\infty r^2 \rho(r) 4\pi r^2 dr \Big/ \int_0^\infty \rho(r) 4\pi r^2 dr.$$

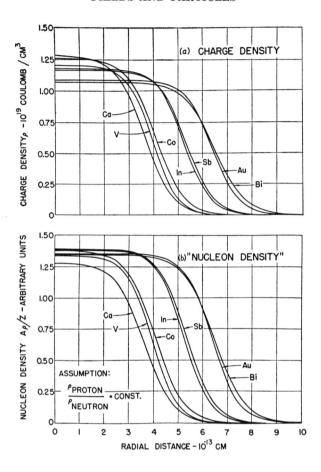

Fig. 6.2.7 Charge density and nucleon density for various nuclei. Note the decrease in average charge density at the center as Z increases. (From Hahn et al.)

discovered in 1937 in cosmic radiation: it was the first particle that did not have the mass of an electron or a nucleon. Its charge is the same as that of the electron. Because its mass is 207 electron masses, and therefore between the mass of electrons and nucleons, it was originally called meson (Greek *mesos* = in between). Later, because other mesons were found, the particle was then given the name μ meson, and finally only muon, the name meson being reserved for particles of different properties. The muon has, in contrast to the proper mesons, properties similar to those of the electron, thus it does not interact strongly with nucleons. Indeed, it is so similar to the electron that it was once jokingly called the overfed twin brother of the electron. A negatively charged muon can, just like an electron, occupy

Bohr orbits around the nucleus. Because its mass is 207 times that of an electron and the radius of a Bohr orbit is $(n\hbar)^2/Ze^2m$ (where m is the mass of the orbiting particle), the radius of the muon's orbit is 207 times smaller than the corresponding one for an electron. Using the "naive," that is the pre-wave mechanical, quantum mechanical picture of Bohr we see that the innermost orbit for lead has a radius of 3.07 fm which is smaller than the radius of the lead nucleus. This means that the muon circles inside the nucleus and according to the laws of electrostatics is therefore attracted only by that fraction of the electric charge of the nucleus which lies inside the radius of the orbit. The next higher orbit ($n = 2$) with a radius of 12.3 fm lies just outside the nuclear surface. If the nucleus were a point charge, the calculation of the energy of transition from the second orbit to the first would give 16.41 MeV. However, the measured value is 6.02 MeV, because the nucleus is of finite size. To do the calculation correctly one should not use the simple Bohr orbit picture, but should do a quantum mechanical calculation. For example, one can calculate the probability of finding the muon at a certain distance from the center. One, then, is able to calculate the radius of the nucleus. The radius found in this way agrees well with the Stanford results.

The experiment was done in the following way: A beam of muons was produced at the 385 MeV cyclotron. (In reality true mesons were produced, which decay after a few meters of flight into muons.) A few of the muons are captured by the nuclei into very high Bohr orbits. They gradually jump to lower and lower orbits, and in each transition the nucleus-muon system loses some energy. In the last steps the energy is given off in the form of quanta. The energy of the quanta emitted in the last transition is measured in counters sensitive to such electromagnetic radiation.

Since about 1965 great progress has been made in the investigation of muonic x-rays. This is due to the invention of new detectors which have a much better energy resolution than the earlier ones. It is now even possible to observe the hyperfine structure of these muonic x-rays and see there the influence of the deformation of those nuclei which are not spherical. An example of a modern muonic x-ray spectrum is given in Fig. 6.2.8.[9]

We finally want to discuss a method for determination of nuclear radii which is not based on electromagnetic interactions, but on nuclear forces. Hence, in contrast to the investigations described above which yield the

[9] Similar x-rays have also been observed with π mesons and K mesons. The latter are one kind of the many more massive mesons. Since these mesons interact strongly with the nucleus through nuclear forces, in contrast to the muons, the quantitative interpretation of such measurements is much more complicated. Examples of such x-ray spectra are also shown in Fig. 6.2.8.

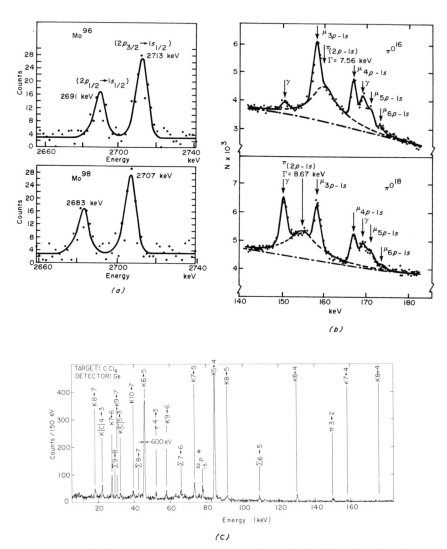

Fig. 6.2.8 (a) K_α muonic x-ray spectra of ^{96}Mo and ^{98}Mo. Note the fine-structure splitting. The effect of the nuclear radius, which varies with $A^{1/3}$, is clearly evident. [Chasman et al., *Phys. Rev. Letters* **14**, 181 (1965).] (b) Pi-mesonic K_α spectra of ^{16}O and ^{18}O. The broad humps are the x-ray lines due to the pions. Superimposed are muonic x-ray spectra and a few γ lines. [Backenstoss et al., *Phys. Letters* **25B**, 365 (1967).] (c) K mesonic x-rays from CCl$_4$. In most events a chlorine nucleus has captured a K$^-$ meson into an orbit. Indicated are the principal quantum numbers involved in subsequent x-ray transitions (e.g. K8 → 7). Also seen are a few x-ray lines due to Σ^- and π^- mesons, some K-mesonic x-ray lines from carbon and one γ line, at 78 keV, from the de-excitation of ^{32}P. [Wiegand, Gallup and Godfrey, *Phys. Rev. Lett.* **28**, 621, (1972).]

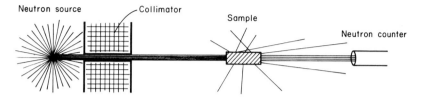

Fig. 6.2.9   A neutron absorption experiment in good geometry.

radius of the charge distribution, the radius of the distribution of the nuclear matter can here be deduced.

Such an estimate of nuclear size, or the range of nuclear forces, is obtained through observing the attentuation of a beam of neutrons passing through a slab of matter containing a known number of nuclei, as illustrated in Fig. 6.2.9. Fast neutrons are eliminated from the incident beam by two processes: absorption by the nuclei with which they collide, and scattering by the nuclei. In such measurements a sample is introduced between the source of the neutrons and the detector. It is important that good geometry be employed. This means that a neutron which has undergone a scattering process should have practically no chance to reach the detector. In the experiment one compares the counting rate when the sample is intercepting the beam with the counting rate when the sample is removed. The ratio of these yields the fraction of neutrons eliminated from the beam.

Let I_0 be the number of neutrons incident on the sample per unit area per second (Fig. 6.2.10). We wish to compute the intensity of the beam which passes without an interaction through an absorber of thickness t. Let us first assume that the neutrons are points, and that the projected

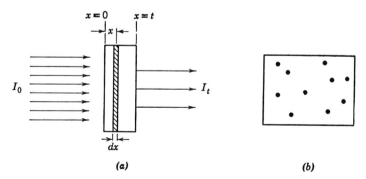

Fig. 6.2.10   (a) Incident and transmitted intensities of a beam of neutrons in passing through an absorber. (b) The black dots represent the area $n\sigma dx$ which is opaque to the beam of neutrons.

area of the nuclei in the absorber is σ. The beam will be attenuated in going through the slab. At a depth x, let the intensity of the beam be $I(x)$. The fraction of the beam removed in going through a further thickness dx is

$$\frac{I(x) - I(x + dx)}{I(x)} = -\frac{dI(x)}{I(x)}. \tag{6.2.4}$$

This fraction may also be expressed in terms of the fraction of the area of the slab within which nuclei interact with the neutron either by absorbing them or by scattering them. If there are n nuclei per unit volume in the slab, then the number in a slab of area A and thickness dx is $nA\,dx$, and the number per unit area of the absorber is $n\,dx$. The fraction of the area A which is within the interaction range is then $\sigma n\,dx$, and we may write

$$\frac{dI(x)}{I(x)} = -\sigma n\,dx. \tag{6.2.5}$$

The solution of this equation is

$$\ln I(x) = -\sigma nx + \text{constant}. \tag{6.2.6}$$

The arbitrary constant must be so chosen that, when $x = 0$, the intensity is the incident intensity I_0. Equation 6.2.6 may be put into the following form, expressing the intensity I_t which can penetrate a slab of thickness t,

$$I_t = I_0 e^{-n\sigma t}. \tag{6.2.7}$$

The cross section σ need not be interpreted in terms of the collisions with rigid spheres. The attenuation of a beam due to any interaction with the particles in its path may be described in terms of an effective cross section, but we must not then expect this cross section to have the properties of a rigid-sphere cross section. For example, a study of the absorption cross section of nuclei for slow neutrons having velocities comparable to those of gas atoms at normal temperatures shows a marked dependence on velocity and even "resonance" maxima. These phenomena can be explained in terms of the detailed energy level structure of the nuclei in question and the wave nature of the impinging neutrons. We shall not study these processes here, but merely point out the generalized meaning of the term cross section.

In nuclear physics, cross sections are generally expressed in barns (b):

$$1\text{ b} = 10^{-24}\text{ cm}^2 = 10^{-28}\text{ m}^2.$$

This term originated during World War II when the very large, slow, neutron cross sections were first observed. They were said to be "as big as a barn," and this term has been officially adopted.

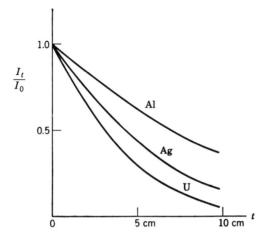

Fig. 6.2.11   The attenuation of a beam of fast neutrons in aluminum, silver, and uranium.

The attenuation of a fast neutron beam in aluminum, silver, and uranium is shown in Fig. 6.2.11. We have here three curves indicating that nuclear size increases as Z and A increase.

In the evaluation of these neutron attenuation experiments we have to take the wave aspects of the neutrons into consideration. For the determination of nuclear radii, neutrons with energies between 10 and 50 MeV have to be used. Neutrons with energies below this range may show resonance phenomena which spoil the picture. This means that the neutron is readily absorbed into an excited level of the nucleus. At energies above 10 MeV the individual levels of a nucleus are so close together and overlap so much that one is no longer justified to speak about resonances. On the other side, for neutrons with energies beyond 50 MeV the nucleus begins to become transparent. The cross section would then appear too small. Neutrons between 10 and 50 MeV have a de Broglie wavelength which is small, but not tremendously small compared with nuclear dimensions. Therefore the nucleus casts a shadow. This shadow does not have a sharp edge due to diffraction effects as was already pointed out in Chapter 2. The incoming wave scatters, so to speak, around the obstacle. According to the laws governing diffraction, the angle with which the dimension of the shadow decreases is of the order $\alpha = \lambda/r$ (Fig. 6.2.12). Therefore the shadow disappears after some distance. This means that some of the neutrons, although they did not hit the obstacle, are deflected from their original direction, and thus they will not reach the detector if the experiment is performed with good geometry. These neutrons have undergone "diffraction scattering."

We will now discuss how big the zone around the nucleus is where the neutrons are diffracted from. We can solve this problem by looking at it in a somewhat different way. We require only that the same shadow should be produced. For this let us replace the spherical nucleus by a round disk of the same radius and let us assume that the disk in Fig. 6.2.12 is not opaque but fully transparent to the neutron waves falling on it from the left.

For simplicity we just assume that the waves of these neutrons are all in phase. In In order to produce a shadow we let the disk emit to the right neutron waves which are by 180° out of phase with the original waves. In order to have complete "darkness" in the region directly behind the disk the number of neutrons emitted from the disk must be the same as the one traversing the disk. A detailed calculation shows that the shadow cone formed by the interference of the two neutron beams has the same shape as the one in the original problem. It follows therefore that the shadow cross section or scattering cross section is also πr^2. Returning to our original problem we hence have to add to the scattering cross section πr^2 the absorption cross section, which in the case of a total absorbing "black" nucleus is also πr^2. The total cross section for fast neutrons in the energy range under consideration is therefore

$$\sigma_{\text{total}} = \sigma_{\text{scattering}} + \sigma_{\text{absorption}} = 2\pi r^2.$$

It should be added that for an accurate determination of the nuclear radius some small corrections and refinements have to be applied which we will not discuss here.

Methods that are based on nuclear force interactions tend to yield slightly greater radii than methods sensitive to the charge distribution in the nuclei. This can be explained by the fact that the nuclear forces reach somewhat beyond the limits of nuclear matter, hence making the nucleus look bigger than it actually is. In addition, if it should be true that the radius of the proton distribution is slightly smaller than the radius of the neutron distribution, this also would help to explain this slight difference in the results.

In Fig. 6.2.13 a graph is reproduced showing the half-density radius of the nuclear charge density as a function of $A^{1/3}$. This radius, with the exception of the very lightest nuclei, can best be represented by the formula

$$r = [1.18\, A^{1/3} - 0.48]\text{fm}.$$

If instead of the half-density radius of the charge distribution another radius is taken, the constant term must be replaced by another one, and also the numerical factor of the A-dependent term changes somewhat.

Disregarding such fine points we can conclude from very different experiments that nuclear radii can approximately be represented by

$$r = 1.20\, A^{1/3}\text{ fm.}$$

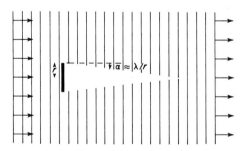

Fig. 6.2.12 Shadow scattering by a disk.

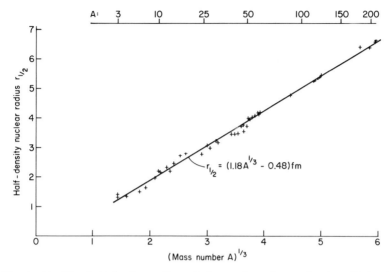

Fig. 6.2.13 The half-density radius of the nuclear charge density. [Data from Hofstadter and Collard, in *Landolt-Börnstein*, New Series I/2, Springer, Berlin (1967).]

We might summarize our findings: nuclear radii are of the order of 10^{-14} m. Nuclear matter has a fairly constant density inside the nuclei which is about the same for all but the lightest nuclei. Toward the nuclear surface the density drops off gradually within a range of approximately 2 fm.

6.3 PROTONS AND NEUTRONS

Before the discovery of the neutron, physicists could not explain satisfactorily how nuclei were made up. They knew for a long time that certain radioactive nuclei emit β particles, which are identical to electrons. An obvious thought was, therefore, that a nucleus of atomic weight A and atomic number Z consists of A protons and $A-Z$ electrons which neutralize some of the charges. Such a hypothesis leads, however, to two serious difficulties.

First, there is an argument about size. We know that nuclei have radii of 10^{-15} to 10^{-14} m. We also know something of the spacing of energy levels in the nucleus. They are of the order of MeV. From our wave mechanical description of the energy levels of particles in a potential energy well, we know certain conditions that must be satisfied. In particular the wavelength associated with the motion of the particle must be equal to or less than twice the dimensions of the confining box. As we have seen, this requirement leads to energy levels whose spacing is of the order

$$E_0 = \frac{h^2}{8mL^2}$$

and, if we take $L = 10^{-14}$ m and $m = 9.1 \times 10^{-31}$ kg for an electron, we get $E_0 \simeq 3000$ MeV, which is far beyond the observed range. However, if instead of the electron mass we take the proton mass we get $E_0 \simeq 1$ MeV. This would seem to be a much more reasonable assumption.

The clinching argument about the composition of nuclei comes from considerations of angular momentum. We shall not discuss how nuclear angular momentum is actually measured; we merely point out that nuclear angular momentum is comparable in magnitude to the electronic angular momentum of atoms, and that these forms of angular momentum are coupled together through atomic and nuclear magnetic fields and can be inferred from the hyperfine structure of atomic spectra (see Sect. 4.10). Protons and electrons each have an intrinsic or spin angular momentum of $\frac{1}{2}(h/2\pi)$ or, in units of $h/2\pi$, a spin of $\frac{1}{2}$. These spins are always coupled parallel or antiparallel to each other, so that the resultant spin of two particles may be 1 or 0, and of three particles may be $\frac{1}{2} + \frac{1}{2} + \frac{1}{2} = \frac{3}{2}$, or $\frac{1}{2} + \frac{1}{2} - \frac{1}{2} = \frac{1}{2}$, and so forth. It will be noticed that the resultant spin angular momentum of an odd number of particles of any kind may be a half-integer, and the resultant spin angular momentum of an even number of particles of any kind must be an integer in units of $(h/2\pi)$, or zero.

To these considerations of spin angular momentum we must add the contributions due to orbital motions of the particles. These, it turns out, are always integral multiples of $(h/2\pi)$. The resultant total angular momentum of an odd number of particles is therefore a half-integral plus an integral, or a total half-integral number of units. Similarly, the resultant total angular momentum of a system containing an even number of particles is necessarily an integral number of units. Measurements of total angular momentum therefore reveal whether we are dealing with an odd or an even number of particles.

The observed results are plotted in Fig. 6.3.1. The interactions of the vertical and diagonal lines in the illustration assign a place to a nucleus with given A and Z. Thus, for example, to find $_2^4\text{He}$, or an α particle with $Z = 2$ and $A = 4$, we find the interaction of the vertical line marked 4 and of the diagonal line marked 2. At the intersection is a cross, indicating that the resultant angular momentum of this nuclide is an integer (actually zero). For $_2^3\text{He}$, the resultant angular momentum on the line $Z = 2$, and in the space reserved for $A = 3$, is indicated by a dot. It is half-integral.

If the hypothesis about nuclear structure that nuclei are made up of protons and electrons were correct, the total number of particles would be

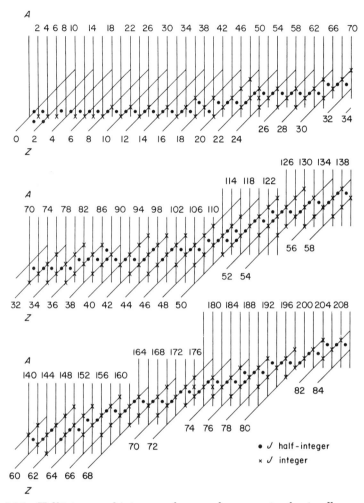

Fig. 6.3.1   Half-integer and integer nuclear angular momenta of naturally occurring nuclides.

the total number of protons, or the number A, plus the number of electrons $(A - Z)$, or $(2A - Z)$ particles all told. But, since $2A$ is always even, we should expect $(2A - Z)$ to be odd or even depending only on whether Z is odd or even. Looking at the figure, we note that the crosses certainly are not restricted to the diagonal lines with even Z. Dots and crosses appear more or less randomly for odd or even values of Z. We conclude that the number of particles in a nucleus is not correctly given by the assumption that the nucleus contains protons and electrons.

When the neutron was detected by Chadwick in 1932, this problem was solved: nuclei consist of protons and neutrons. The neutron has a spin of

$\frac{1}{2}$ like a proton. A nuclide of even mass number always contains an even number of nucleons, and therefore has an integral number of units of angular momentum. An odd nucleus with an odd number of protons and neutrons has a half-integral number of units.

Due to their lack of electric charge neutrons behave very differently from protons. They can easily penetrate through matter because they do not interact with the electrons of the atom and therefore will not be slowed down by energy losses through ionization processes. Hence the most important interactions of neutrons are with the atomic nuclei. By elastic and inelastic collisions with nuclei the neutrons lose energy to their surroundings, until they have only so much kinetic energy left as corresponds to the ambient temperature. At room temperature this energy is approximately 0.025 eV. Besides the collisions, another type of interaction is the capture of neutrons by nuclei with the simultaneous release of the binding energy as electromagnetic radiation. This type of interaction is the (n, γ)-reaction. In most materials the mean free path (that is, between collisions) of neutrons is of the order of a few centimeters and, in general, before a neutron is captured many collisions (in the order of magnitude of 10) take place. From the above remarks it is obvious that one cannot contain neutrons in vessels as one can do with a gas.

In what respects are the two particles, both called nucleons, different, aside from the fact that one is positively charged and the other is neutral? There is a slight mass difference; the neutron is a little bit more massive. It is unstable and can decay into a proton plus an electron plus a neutrino. Although the spin of the neutrino has not been measured, it must be assumed that it is also $\frac{1}{2}$, just like that of the protons, neutrons, and electrons. In the decay of the neutron both the electron and the neutrino each carry away a half-integral number of angular momentum, together either zero or one unit depending upon the relative orientation of the two spins, leaving the proton with a spin $\frac{1}{2}$. The neutrino is therefore necessary to overcome the difficulty which would arise with the spin; it also carries some of the available energy as kinetic energy. The decay of the neutron into a proton is an important example of β decay.

The neutron's half-life, that is the time interval during which half the neutrons, which were present at its beginning, have decayed, is approximately 11 minutes.[10]

---

[10] Such a measurement is very difficult, but an accurate knowledge of the half-life of the neutron is of great importance for the theory of beta decay. Two experiments which claim fairly high precision have been published. Their results, however, are not quite consistent with each other, which illustrates the difficulty of such an experiment. A. N. Sosnovsky, et al. [*Nucl. Phys.* **10**, 395 (1959)] found 11.7 ± 0.3 min, whereas C. J. Christensen, et al. [*Phys. Rev. D***5**, 1628 (1972)] got 10.61 ± 0.16 min.

It is interesting to note that the neutron has a magnetic dipole moment, that is, it acts as if it had a bar magnet inside. How can this be reconciled with its zero charge, since we know that magnetic effects arise from moving charges? An analogy can make clear that there is no contradiction. Assume a rigid sphere with a positively charged spherical core and a shell of equal but opposite charge around it. Both spin with the same angular velocity. We know from the study of electricity and magnetism that the magnetic dipole moment of a current loop is given by $\mu = iA$, A being the area of the current loop. Because of the greater average radius of rotation of the negative charge elements, the magnetism created by the negative charge is greater than the one from the positive charge and is therefore not fully canceled out.

The structure of the nucleons is considerably more complicated than our model of a core and a concentric shell. It was investigated experimentally by Hofstadter's group at Stanford with the same method which had been successfully employed for their work on nuclear radii as soon as high enough electron energies became available. Other research groups also contributed substantially, particularly one at Cornell University.

The Isobaric Quantum Number or Isospin

It has been found (particularly from scattering experiments) that the nuclear forces between two protons are very nearly equal to the forces between two neutrons or between a neutron and a proton.[11] This feature is called *charge independence* of nuclear forces. We can therefore say that the proton and the neutron are very close relatives; in certain respects we can even treat them as the same kind of particle in two different forms. This close relation between protons and neutrons manifests itself also in the structure of nuclei. A good illustration of this point is the striking similarity in the order and spacing of the energy levels of the nuclides $^{11}_{5}B_6$ and $^{11}_{6}C_5$, shown in Fig. 6.3.2. Both nuclides have five protons and five neutrons in common, but the boron isotope has an additional neutron whereas the carbon isotope has an additional proton. Alternatively we may say that the numbers of protons and neutrons are interchanged in these two nuclides. Nuclei that form such a pair are called mirror nuclei.

---

[11] Obviously electrostatic forces exist only in a p-p system. Furthermore, two protons—or two neutrons—with orbital angular momentum zero must have anti-parallel spins because of the Pauli exclusion principle, whereas in a proton-neutron system the two nucleons can have parallel or anti-parallel spins. Because of the spin dependence of nuclear forces, discussed in Section 6.4, one should therefore only compare n-n, n-p, and p-p forces for systems in the same spin state.

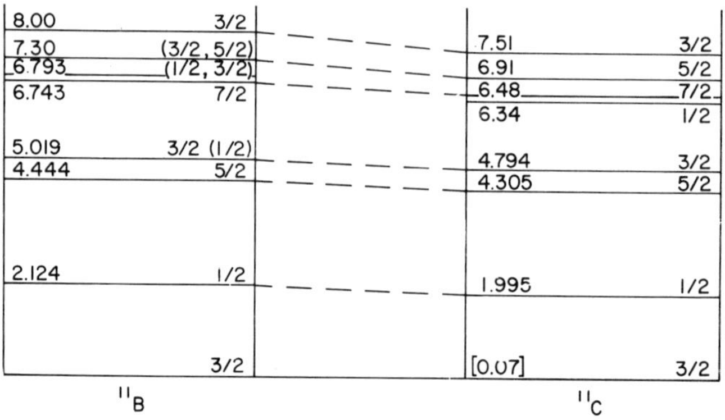

Fig. 6.3.2 The lowest energy levels of the isobars $^{11}_5B_6$ and $^{11}_5C_6$. On the left of each ladder are the energies in MeV; the fractional numbers of the right designate the total angular momentum J of the level. (Uncertain assignments in parentheses.)

This similarity has led Heisenberg[12] to introduce a new quantum number, the so-called isobaric quantum number T. Protons and neutrons have the isobaric quantum number $\frac{1}{2}$. Just as we describe the electron with a spin $s = \frac{1}{2}$ as having two positions with regard to a given direction, usually called the z direction (spin up, $s_z = +\frac{1}{2}$, and spin down, $s_z = -\frac{1}{2}$), we can treat the quantity T in a completely analogous but *formal* way. $T_z = +\frac{1}{2}$ describes a proton and $T_z = -\frac{1}{2}$ describes a neutron. Whereas in the case of the spin its direction in real space is the cause for two different states, it is here the charge or, more generally expressed, the electromagnetic interaction, which makes it possible to distinguish between the two nucleon states, the proton and the neutron. Just as, for example, in a magnetic field the energies of the spin-up and spin-down orientation of an electron are different (which for electrons in an atom gives rise to the Zeeman effect), the energies of the two isobaric quantum number states are also different. The neutron is in the higher state than the proton and for this reason can decay into a proton. Because of the formal mathematical analogy with the ordinary spin, T is now usually named i spin or isospin. But to call it spin has no more justification than to call the inside of a pencil lead, or an aluminum foil a tinfoil.[13] In other words, by introducing a fictitious, only mathematical space, the so-called isospin space, we can think of the isospin as a vector that can be resolved into components, one

---

[12] *Zeitschrift für Physik* **77**, 1 (1932).

[13] Originally, T was called isotopic spin. However, this is a poor designation because T characterizes a common property of isobars rather than of isotopes. To escape this dilemma the name isospin and i spin are now most frequently used. The somewhat more appropriate name isobaric quantum number did not find general acceptance.

of which is the z component. In contrast to its z component the physical significance of the isospin cannot be explained by a classical analog because it belongs fully to the realm of quantum mechanics, just as do, for example, exchange forces. We can only say that the isospin is the quantum number which expresses the charge independence of nuclear forces.

Isospin plays a role also in the description of nuclei. Here, also, the z component describes the charge. The z component of the isospin is given by[14]

$$T_z = \frac{Z}{2} - \frac{N}{2}$$

where Z is the number of protons and N that of neutrons. The T_z component of $^{12}_6C$ is therefore 0, of $^{13}_6C$ it is $-\frac{1}{2}$, and of $^{13}_7N$ it is $+\frac{1}{2}$. Accordingly, the proton has $T_z = +\frac{1}{2}$ and the neutron $T_z = -\frac{1}{2}$, which is in agreement with our earlier statement.

Like atoms, nuclei have ground states and excited states to which one can assign quantum numbers. For a specific nuclide, the z component of the isospin which is a measure of its charge, obviously will be the same for all states. However, T itself can vary, but it never can be smaller than its z component. The nuclide $^{14}_7N_7$ has $T_z = 0$ and may therefore have levels with i spin 0, 1, 2, ... The nuclide $^{14}_8O_6$ with $T_z = +1$ and the nuclide

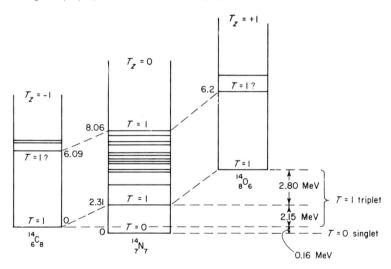

Fig. 6.3.3 Isospin singlet and triplet for mass number $A = 14$.

[14] Many nuclear physicists use the opposite definition for the z component, namely $T_z = N/2 - Z/2$. In high-energy physics, however, the notation is standardized, T_z for the proton being $+\frac{1}{2}$, in accordance with our definition used throughout the text.

$^{14}_{6}C_8$ with $T_z = -1$ on the other hand, cannot have $T = 0$ states, but only $T = 1$ or higher states. An inspection of the lowest levels of the three iso-baric nuclides $^{14}_{6}C_8$, $^{14}_{7}N_7$, and $^{14}_{8}O_6$ (Fig. 6.3.3) reveals that their lowest $T = 1$ levels have a certain relationship. The ground states of each of the three nuclides are drawn here at different heights to take account of the mass differences between them, according to the relation $\Delta E = \Delta mc^2$. (This representation is hence different from that of Fig. 6.3.2 which em-phasized the similarities between nuclides.) With the greatest number of protons and therefore the biggest electric charge, ^{14}O also has the greatest electrostatic or Coulomb energy and hence the greatest mass of the three isobars under consideration. The isospin of the ground state has the small-est possible value which is, as mentioned above, $T = 1$. In ^{14}N the cor-responding level is 2.80 MeV below this state. It is not its ground state but the first excited state. The ground state of ^{14}N is a $T = 0$ state, 2.31 MeV further below. It has, as said above, no counterpart in the other two nu-clides. The ground state of the $^{14}_{6}C_8$ nuclide is 2.15 MeV below the first excited level of $^{14}_{7}N$, because of the further reduced Coulomb energy, but it is slightly higher than the ground state of $^{14}_{7}N$. In analogy to atomic spectroscopy we may say that the three $T = 1$ states form an isospin triplet with $T_z = -1$, 0, $+1$, and the $T = 0$ state of ^{14}N represents a singlet.

If the electric charge had no Coulomb force associated with it, we could expect that the levels of an isospin multiplet are degenerate. We recall that a magnetic field splits the magnetic sublevels of atoms in the Zeeman effect; in the same way the isospin degeneracy is lifted by the Coulomb force.

The concept of isospin and the formation of singlets and multiplets can be made somewhat clearer in the example of the two-nucleon systems. Such a system consists either of two protons (^{2}He), a proton plus a neutron (^{2}H, the deuteron), or two neutrons. We have seen in Section 4.5 that for a system of two electrons the spatial wave function can be symmetric or antisymmetric, or the spin wave function can be symmetric or antisymmetric, as long as only the total wave function, which is the product of the two is antisymmetric. We can now write in a similar manner symmetric and antisymmetric isospin wave functions for our two-nucleon systems. Two protons, 1 and 2, because both their isospins are up are described by a symmetric wave function; thus

$$p\text{-}p: \quad \psi_{\text{isospin}} = \psi_p(1)\psi_p(2)$$

where the subscript p stands for isospin up or proton. Conversely, the two-neutron system has the isospin wave function

$$n\text{-}n: \quad \psi_{\text{isospin}} = \psi_n(1)\psi_n(2)$$

where n stands for isospin down or neutron.

In analogy to the electronic wave function for a system of two electrons with a differ-ent set of quantum numbers we write for the proton-neutron system with a symmetric isospin wave function

$$p\text{-}n: \quad \psi^+{}_{\text{isospin}} = \frac{1}{\sqrt{2}} \left[\psi_p(1)\psi_n(2) + \psi_p(2)\psi_n(1) \right]$$

or an antisymmetric wave function

$$\psi^-{}_{\text{isospin}} = \frac{1}{\sqrt{2}} \left[\psi_p(1)\psi_n(2) - \psi_p(2)\psi_n(1) \right].$$

Altogether we have therefore three symmetric wave functions, composing a triplet, with $T_z = +1$, -1, and 0, belonging to $T = 1$, and one antisymmetric wave function, a singlet, with $T_z = 0$, belonging to $T = 0$.

The proton and the neutron have been treated in our discussion as the same particle, and we can take this into account by generalizing the Pauli exclusion principle. It still says that the total wave function of a system of identical fermions must be antisymmetric. However, the total wave function is now a product of the spatial, spin, and isospin wave functions, or

$$\psi_{\text{total}} = \psi_{\text{spatial}}\psi_{\text{spin}}\psi_{\text{isospin}}.$$

For a system composed only of protons or only of neutrons obviously nothing has changed compared with our earlier, more restricted, version because in these cases ψ_{isospin} is symmetric. However, for a mixture of protons and neutrons a new situation arises. But, as we have seen for the p-n system, the isospin wave function can either be symmetric, and thus have $T = 1$, or antisymmetric, with $T = 0$. The total wave function can therefore result in an antisymmetric one which conforms to the Pauli exclusion principle.

We return now to Fig. 6.3.3 and see that the lowest $T = 0$ state in ^{14}N lies considerably lower than the lowest $T = 1$ state. This becomes plausible if one assumes that in the ground state an equal number of protons and neutrons will result in a symmetric spatial wave function. Concerning the spin part, it has been found that parallel spins have a lower energy than antiparallel ones. This is also the case in atoms, as an inspection of corresponding triplet states (parallel spins) and singlet states (antiparallel spins) shows, for example in the helium atom (Fig. 4.7.1). With spatial and spin wave functions both symmetric, the isospin part must be antisymmetric which means that $T = 0$.

The concept of isospin is in no way limited to the nucleons and nuclei. The π mesons which have a mass of approximately 270 electron masses present another illustrative example for the isospin. These mesons have been found to have either positive, zero, or negative unit charge. The isospin T for all these π mesons is 1, with the T_z components $+1$, 0, -1. Therefore, π mesons form an isospin or charge triplet. Nucleons, on the other hand, as we have seen above, form a doublet.

We end here the discussion of isospin, but we shall see in the next chapter what important role it plays in particle physics.

6.4 THE TWO-BODY PROBLEM; NUCLEAR FORCES

The simplest system on which we can study some aspects of nuclear forces is the one consisting of two nucleons. We have the choice between two protons, a proton and a neutron, or two neutrons. The two-proton system has the disadvantage that in addition to the nuclear forces, Coulomb forces are also acting. Furthermore, the Pauli exclusion principle gives rise to some minor complications. A direct study of the interaction between two neutrons has not yet been made because neutrons cannot be produced in great enough densities to act as targets for experiments. The neutron-proton system is however easily available for investigation.

We can study the interaction between a neutron and a proton by considering the state in which the two nucleons are bound together, constituting the deuteron. This nuclide, $^2_1$H, is the nucleus of the heavy hydrogen, or deuterium, atom. We also can study the force, and hence the potential, between the proton and the neutron by scattering experiments and theoretical analysis of the scattering process. By scattering neutrons on protons with energies ranging from a few eV to several hundred MeV, we can draw far-reaching conclusions about the range of nuclear forces and their potential.

We shall take up the first-mentioned system, the deuteron, in some detail because the mathematical treatment is relatively simple and because it is a good example of the methods of theoretical physics. We first mention some experimental details. The binding energy of the deuteron is 2.22 MeV. This means that this amount of energy is needed in order to dissociate, that is split, the deuteron into a free proton and a free neutron. Experiments to measure this dissociation energy have been performed with x-rays of well-known energy. If the x-ray energy was smaller than the binding energy, no disintegration products could be observed (Fig. 6.4.1). There is also another way to determine this energy. When a very slow neutron, which has negligible kinetic energy, fuses with a proton to make a deuteron or, in other words, when a neutron is captured by a proton, this binding energy must be released. This release can happen only in the form of electromagnetic energy, namely by emission of a quantum. The energy of this γ ray is 2.22 MeV which is, hence, also the value of the binding energy of the deuteron.[15]

We will now take up the discussion of the theory of the deuteron. We know that the force and hence the potential between nucleons must be basically attractive because proton and neutron hold together. We also know from other features that the potential has a short range, much shorter

---

[15] A high-precision measurement of the capture γ ray yielded 2223.35 ± 0.05 keV. To obtain the binding energy one has to correct for the recoil energy of the deuteron due to the emission of the quantum. This results in a binding energy of the deuteron of 2224.67 ± 0.05 keV [H. W. Taylor, N. Neff, and J. D. King, *Physics Letters* **24B**, 659 (1967)].

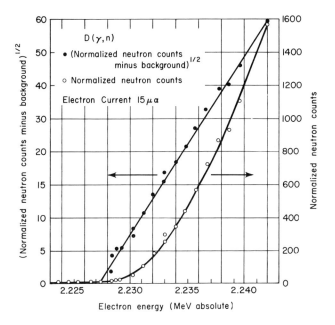

Fig. 6.4.1   Neutron yield from bremsstrahlung irradiation of deuterium. [Mobley and Laubenstein, *Phys. Rev.* **80**, 309 (1950).] (Electron energy = max. x-ray energy.)

than the Coulomb potential which decreases with the reciprocal of the distance. Evidence for the short range of the forces between nucleons is seen, for example, in the fact that scattering of protons due to the nucleon potential is effective only at much shorter distances than the scattering due to the Coulomb potential, the so-called Rutherford scattering. Finally, we know from high-energy experiments, that at very short distances, appreciably shorter than the range of nuclear forces, the potential is repulsive. This means that there is a repulsive or hard core in the nucleon potential.

An example of a potential which satisfies the condition of attraction over a short range but produces repulsion at a very short distance is shown in Fig. 6.4.2 with a solid line. The potential consists of three distinct concentric regions. The innermost one (region I) includes the repulsive core, the next region (II) represents the potential well, and further out (III) the potential is zero. Let us think of the proton as being located at the origin of the coordinate system. As usual, a system of two particles, which are at rest and so far apart that the force between the two is essentially zero, is defined as having zero potential energy and likewise zero kinetic energy. The total energy E is therefore also zero. In our diagram this case

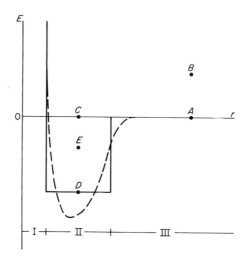

Fig. 6.4.2   The neutron-proton potential: $(-)$ square well with repulsive core; $(- -)$ a more realistic potential.

is represented by a point A. A different situation is illustrated by point B. The neutron here also has no potential energy, however, it has kinetic energy which corresponds to the distance AB on the energy scale. In point C the potential energy is negative and is given by the depth of the potential at this distance from the origin O. The point's vertical distance from the potential curve, in our case CD, represents the kinetic energy of the particle which is naturally always positive. A neutron at A and one at C both have a total energy of zero. A particle at E has the same potential energy as that one at C or D, but less kinetic energy than the one at C and more than the one at D. In order to move it from E to A an amount of energy corresponding to the distance EC must be fed into the system.

It must be said that this square-well potential is not quite realistic and a potential with rounded edges and not quite vertical walls represents reality somewhat better. Such a potential is shown in Fig. 6.4.2 by the dashed line. However, the mathematical difficulties when using the more correct potential are appreciably greater. It was also found that as long as the range of the potential is small compared with the de Broglie wavelength—a condition satisfied at low energies—the assumed shape of the potential (within reasonable limits) does not greatly influence the results. We shall elaborate on this point later. Due to the simplicity of the calculations the square-well potential is still in some favor and gives quite satisfactory results in many cases.

We also should recall here that the potential for the simplest atomic system, the one composed of a proton and an electron, looks very different (Fig. 6.4.3). More important than the fact that the distance and energy scales are of different orders of magnitude, is the gradual flattening out of the slope of the electric potential with increasing distance which, in principle, reaches zero only at infinity.

We shall now apply the Schrödinger equation to our square well and shall try to find a relation between its depth and its width. Furthermore, we may expect to learn something about the form of the ψ function as a function of the distance from the origin.

In calculations of two-body problems it is convenient to introduce the reduced mass (see also Sect. 3.7). Proton and neutron have essentially equal mass M, therefore the reduced mass m is simply:

$$\frac{1}{m} = \frac{1}{M_p} + \frac{1}{M_n} = \frac{2}{M}$$

$$m = \frac{M}{2}.$$

Experimental evidence exists that the deuteron has a nearly spherical shape. We disregard the slight deviation from sphericity and will use for our calculation a spherical coordinate system. Because we assume for this simplified calculation the potential V to depend only on the distance r between proton and neutron and not on the azimuth θ or polar angle φ, the wave function ψ can be written as a product

$$\psi(r, \theta, \varphi) = R(r)\,\Theta(\theta)\,\Phi(\varphi).$$

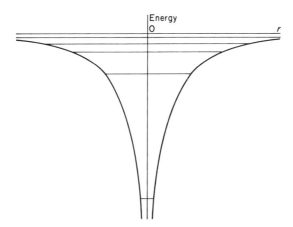

Fig. 6.4.3   The potential for the atomic system proton-electron and its energy levels.

We are interested here only in the simplest solution, which is a spherically symmetric one, as it was also for the hydrogen atom. Therefore Θ and Φ become constants, and we are left with a radial wave equation

$$\frac{1}{r^2}\frac{d}{dr}\left[r^2\frac{dR(r)}{dr}\right] + \frac{2m}{\hbar^2}[E - V(r)]R(r) = 0.$$

If we substitute $R(r)$ by a new function $u(r)$, where $[u(r)/r] = R(r)$ we can write the Schrödinger equation more simply

$$\frac{d^2u}{dr^2} + \frac{M}{\hbar^2}[E - V(r)]u = 0.$$

Note that we have replaced $2m$ by M; $E - V$, as always, is the kinetic energy of the particle, as seen in Fig. 6.4.4. The bottom of the potential well lies below zero, which means that the value of the potential is negative in region II. We write therefore

$$V(r) = -V_0,$$

V_0 being the depth of the potential. Also the binding energy is intrinsically a negative quantity. (This is analogous to the statement that somebody is $5000 in debt. A debt is an intrinsic negative quantity, but is expressed by a positive number, say $+$5000$; however, this man's assets are negative, $-$5000$.) If we designate the binding energy with ϵ and are careful to keep our plus and minus signs straight, we can rewrite our radial Schrö-

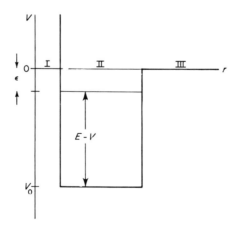

Fig. 6.4.4 Square-well potential with repulsive core describing the deuteron.

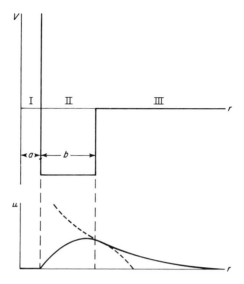

Fig. 6.4.5   The joining of wave functions at boundaries.

dinger equation for the deuteron:

$$\frac{d^2u}{dr^2} + \frac{M}{\hbar^2}\,[V_0 - \epsilon]u = 0, \tag{6.4.1}$$

with V_0 and ϵ both positive. We now have to consider the three regions. Region I extends from the origin through the hard core. Since the probability of a particle being in this region is zero, ψ^2 is zero, and therefore also ψ and u. We have solved the Schrödinger equation in this region before even having written it down!

Region II is not so trivial. The fact that the depth of the potential V_0 is greater than the binding energy ϵ signifies that the particle is not standing still but has kinetic energy. Although we are dealing with the ground state of the deuteron we see that it has a certain amount of kinetic energy. There is nothing strange in this; the electron in the ground state of the hydrogen atom is also not at rest but possesses kinetic energy.

We learned in Chapter 3 that boundary conditions play an eminent role in quantum-mechanical problems, because they lead to the stationary states. We must therefore look for the boundary conditions here. At the boundary (see Fig. 6.4.5) between I and II, ψ, and hence also u, have to be continuous. Because ψ is zero inside I, it must hence fall to zero as one approaches this boundary coming from II. At the boundary between regions II and III ψ must be continuous, but in addition the wave functions must join smoothly. There must be no sudden change in the tangent when crossing the boundary. The reason for this becomes clear when inspecting the Schrödinger equation. A kink in ψ or u would mean that the second derivative would have an infinite value, but this would necessarily mean that $E - V$ would have to be infinite, which would be nonsense. It is left to the reader to convince himself that at the boundary between I and II, ψ is allowed to have a kink.

A solution of the Schrödinger equation for region II of width b which we may try is

$$u = A \sin k(r - a) \qquad (6.4.2$$

where $k = [(M/\hbar^2)(V_0 - \epsilon)]^{1/2}$, because we want to have a standing wave inside. A is a constant which could be determined later, a is the width of region I.

In region III the Schrödinger equation reduces to

$$\frac{d^2u}{dr^2} - \frac{M}{\hbar^2}\epsilon u = 0 \qquad (6.4.3)$$

and has the solution

$$u = Ce^{-r/\rho}, \qquad (6.4.4)$$

where $\rho = [\hbar/(M\epsilon)^{1/2}]$ and C is a constant, which also could be determined. This solution insures that ψ and u will approach zero at big distances.

Since at the boundary between II and III (at $r = a + b$), u must be the same when calculated with the aid of Eq. 6.4.2 or of Eq. 6.4.4, we can write

$$u_{a+b} = A \sin(kb) = Ce^{-b/\rho}, \qquad (6.4.5)$$

where u_{a+b} stands for the value of u at the boundary between II and III.

Since du/dx must also be continuous, which means that the slope should have no kink, we differentiate the wave function on both sides of the boundary, using Eq. 6.4.2 and 6.4.4, and set the two derivatives equal at b. Hence

$$kA \cos(kb) = -\frac{C}{\rho}e^{-b/\rho}. \qquad (6.4.6)$$

We can eliminate A and C by simply dividing Eq. 6.4.6 by Eq. 6.4.5 and obtain

$$k \cot(kb) = -\frac{1}{\rho}. \qquad (6.4.7)$$

Remembering what k and ρ stand for, we can write

$$\cot\sqrt{\frac{M(V_0 - \epsilon)b^2}{\hbar^2}} = -\sqrt{\frac{\epsilon}{V_0 - \epsilon}}. \qquad (6.4.8)$$

There is evidence that V_0 is big compared to ϵ, and thus we can bring our result into more appealing form. Justification for this assumption lies in the fact that the range of nuclear forces is known to be about 2×10^{-15} m. With this value for b we must choose $V_0 = 36$ MeV in order to satisfy Eq. 6.4.8 which is many times greater than ϵ. Hence, $V_0 - \epsilon \approx V_0$, and we can replace the right-hand side of Eq. 6.4.8 by $-(\epsilon/V_0)^{1/2}$ in reasonably good approximation. Because this is a small number, the argument of the cotangent must be approximately $\pi/2$. Equation 6.4.8 becomes thus

$$\left(\frac{\pi}{2}\right)^2 = \frac{MV_0b^2}{\hbar^2}$$

or, putting the two unknown quantities V_0 and b on the left side:

$$V_0b^2 = \left(\frac{\pi}{2}\right)^2 \frac{\hbar^2}{M} = 1.0 \times 10^{-28} \text{ MeV m}^2.$$

In other words, a deep and narrow well satisfies the Schrödinger equation for the deuteron, but also a shallow but wider well will do it. However, using information about b from other experiments, we can determine the depth, which comes out to be approximately 30 MeV.

The wave function u of the deuteron has the shape of the solid line shown in Fig. 6.4.6. The dashed line delineates the shape of the potential. (The ordinate for this, obviously, would have to be labeled energy!) In the

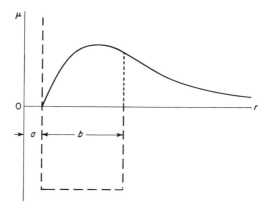

Fig. 6.4.6 The wave function of the deuteron.

region of the well the wave function is sinuosidal, and outside it decreases exponentially. It is interesting to note that it is still quite large beyond the range of the nuclear force, which extends to $a + b$. In other words, for an appreciable fraction of time the separation between the two nucleons is greater than the range of the nuclear forces which hold them together!

Such a situation would be impossible in classical physics, but it is allowed in quantum mechanics. On the other hand, this feature explains why the binding energy of the deuteron of ~ 2.2 MeV is relatively small in comparison to the average binding energy of nucleons in nuclei, which is around 8 MeV.

The extension of the ψ function beyond the walls of the square-well potential is already familiar to us from Chapter 3. There we saw that for wells of finite depth the ψ function reaches into the classically excluded region in which the potential energy is greater than the total energy.

We repeat here the remark made at the beginning: the square-well potential is a very convenient basis for calculations, but it is not very realistic. However, if the potential drawn in Fig. 6.4.2 as a dashed line had been used for such a calculation, it would have given a well-depth and well-width relationship of approximately the same size.

In contrast to a diatomic molecule, which has many excited states below its dissociation energy, the deuteron has no bound excited states. The first excited level is unbound. It is therefore a virtual level (see Sect. 3.5) and lies approximately 50 keV above the dissociation energy of the deuteron. This lack of bound excited levels can be considered as evidence for the relatively weak bond that holds the deuteron together.

We pointed out earlier that the two-body problem could also be studied by scattering measurements and their theoretical analysis. Because the calculations are much more lengthy, although not difficult, we will not go into detail. The important feature is that in scattering experiments we may vary the kinetic energy of the scattering particle from a few eV to many hundreds or even thousands of MeV, whereas in the study of the deuteron we have only the 2.23 MeV binding energy to deal with.

In addition to these neutron-proton scattering experiments, proton-proton scattering experiments have also been performed. Coulomb forces come into play here in addition to the nuclear forces. A most important conclusion from all these scattering experiments is that the nuclear force between neutrons and protons is the same as between two protons and presumably also between two neutrons. The nuclear forces are independent of the charge. The nuclear physicist talks therefore about *charge independence*. Scattering experiments show in addition that the attractive force between two colliding nucleons which have their spins s parallel is greater than if they have their spins anti-parallel. In the first case the spins add up to a total spin of 1: the projections in the z direction can therefore have the values of $+1, 0, -1$. Thus we speak of a triplet state. With the spin anti-parallel, only one state is possible, a singlet state with $S = 0$. We can say that the potential well for triplet forces is deeper than that for singlet forces. In the deuteron the spins of the two nucleons are parallel and add to a total spin 1. The deuteron is a triplet system. Theoretical calculations show that the singlet system of the deuteron is not stable because the attractive forces are too weak to hold the proton and the neutron together in the singlet state.

Our calculation assumed that the force between the two nucleons depends only on their distance, and that the deuteron was spherically symmetric. From our discussion of the hydrogen atom (Sec. 4.2) we know that spherical symmetry implies an orbital angular momentum $L = 0$, that is an S state. Because the spin of the deuteron has the value $S = 1$, the total angular momentum, $J = L + S$, of the deuteron is $J = 1$. We mentioned earlier that there is experimental evidence for a slight deviation from sphericity. One is therefore forced to assume that for some small fraction of the time the deuteron is in a state of angular momentum $L = 2$ (a D state). Since the total angular momentum must stay constant at all times, namely $J = 1$, the vector of the spin angular momentum $S = 1$ must thus be directed opposite to the orbital angular momentum for the D state, or $J = L - S = 2 - 1 = 1$. This fraction of D state admixture to the ground state of the deuteron is presently estimated to be between 2 and 8%, depending on the theory used. The two component states are illustrated in terms of the vector model in Fig. 6.4.7.

Mixing of configurations (as here of the ^3S and ^3D state) occurs also in other nuclei and in atoms. In other words, many states are not pure states but must be described by a combination of component states.

We now discuss the nature of the nuclear forces, or in other words, we ask the crucial question "What holds a proton and a neutron together?" The Japanese physicist Yukawa gave a rough answer to this question in 1935. He postulated, long before the discovery of the meson, that particles of several hundred electron masses were exchanged back and forth between the nucleons. In this process the proton emits a π^+ meson and becomes a neutron; the original neutron receives the π^+ meson and becomes a proton, and so on back and forth. The objection, that it "costs" 145 MeV to create

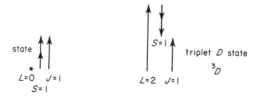

Fig. 6.4.7   The two components of the ground state of the deuteron.

Hideki Yukawa (born 1907) (Courtesy of Niels Bohr Library, American Institute of Physics).

a meson of 270 times the mass of an electron (because mass is energy), can be overcome by invoking the Heisenberg uncertainty principle. Since the mean life τ of the intermediate state in which the meson is traveling is short, the uncertainty in the energy can be enough to remove the problem of energy conservation because $\tau \sim (\hbar/\Delta E)$. This equation enables us also to estimate the range of the nuclear forces. The mesons cannot travel faster than the velocity of light. With $\Delta E = 145$ MeV the distance $c\tau$ comes out to be 2 fm, the range of the nuclear forces!

Such a meson, which is created and very soon absorbed and which violates the law of conservation of energy, is called a *virtual* meson. This is not the only case where the principle of conservation of energy is violated in nuclear physics, but unpunished because of the Heisenberg uncertainty principle. On the other hand, no such principle can be invoked for a violation of the conservation of momentum because the Heisenberg relation connects the momentum and the space coordinate through the expression $\Delta p_x \Delta x \geq \hbar$. Time does not enter. Therefore, momentum is conserved at all times.

It might be added that Yukawa realized that particles of a finite rest mass give rise to short-range forces, whereas photons with rest mass zero are connected with a long-range force, the Coulomb force. This difference comes about because the range of the forces is proportional to the time, which is inversely proportional to the mass. Modern quantum electrodynamics explains the Coulomb forces in a similar way: a charge emits a photon that is absorbed by another charge. Nuclear forces are much more complex than Coulomb forces. Beyond a certain range they are zero, not so far out they are strongly attractive, and at very short distances they are repulsive. In addition, the forces depend also on the spin orientation. The exchange of only one kind of virtual mesons cannot explain all these characteristics. It is therefore assumed that in addition to the virtual π mesons several other species of virtual mesons play a role for the nuclear forces.

6.5 BINDING ENERGY

Now that we have gained some insight into the neutron-proton system which forms one of the lightest nuclei, the deuteron, we shall discuss the structure of nuclei in general. The forces that hold the bigger nuclei together are naturally still the same ones. We shall see, however, that the deuteron was a relatively loosely bound system compared to other nuclides. This is shown implicitly in the fact that the proton and neutron on the average are relatively far apart. In the more massive nuclei a single nucleon has the possibility of exerting attractive forces on several of its neighbors. However, it turns out that a nucleon interacts only with a limited number of other nucleons within the nucleus. We speak therefore about a *saturation* of nuclear forces. With the exception of the lightest nuclides, the average binding energy per nucleon in a nucleus is thus more or less a constant for all nuclides and stays fairly close to 8 MeV.

The total binding energy of a nucleus is the energy one would have to expend in order to separate the nucleus into its individual nucleons. On the other hand, this is also equal to the energy that would be freed if the individual nucleons were to fuse into a nucleus. The binding energy of a nucleus is therefore the energy which is missing in comparison with a system of the same separated nucleons. The binding energy (because $E = mc^2$) manifests itself in the fact that the mass of the nucleus is smaller than the combined mass of the individual protons and neutrons. In an actual experiment, however, one measures atomic masses, not nuclear masses, because it is in general impossible to strip an atom of all its electrons. The atomic mass is therefore the mass of the nucleus plus the mass of the electrons needed to make the atom electrically neutral. The binding energy can, hence, be written as

Binding energy $= [($mass of Z H atoms $+ (A - Z)$ neutrons$) -$

$\qquad$ (mass of atom of mass number A, containing Z protons$)]c^2$,

or

$$\text{Binding energy} = [ZM_H + (A - Z)M_n - {}_Z^A M]c^2.$$

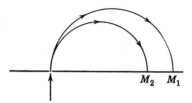

Fig. 6.5.1 Illustration of the principle of a mass spectrograph.

Atomic, and therefore nuclear, masses may be determined very precisely by means of an instrument called the mass spectrograph. Its principle is the following: a beam of ions of known velocity v and equal charge q is directed perpendicularly into a magnetic field B, and the radius R of the circular path of the beam depends on the mass M of the ion according to the equation

$$R = \frac{MV}{qB}.\qquad(6.5.1)$$

Thus in an instrument such as that illustrated in Fig. 6.5.1, ions of mass M_1 and M_2 will travel along circular paths of radius R_1 and R_2, and the point of termination of the path may be detected, for example, by means of a photographic plate whose emulsion is blackened by the ions in question. This sort of instrument determines the ratio of masses particularly reliably, since neither the absolute value of the field nor that of the velocity need then be known. If the velocities are the same for both particles, we

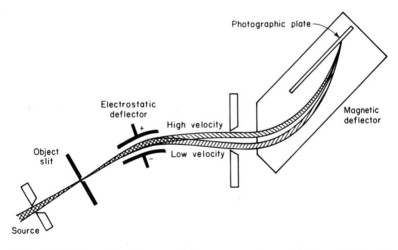

Fig. 6.5.2 Schematic diagram of a mass spectrograph (from Mattauch).

have

$$\frac{M_1}{M_2} = \frac{R_1}{R_2} \qquad (6.5.2)$$

for equally charged ions. Modern mass spectrographs, as for example the one illustrated in Fig. 6.5.2, make use of electric and magnetic focusing and can accept ions of various velocities.

It is now customary to base all measurements on a scale in which the mass of the isotope of carbon having $A = 12$ is taken as exactly 12 mass units abbreviated u. Thus the mass of $^{12}_6C$ is 12 u but the mass of the hydrogen atom with $A = 1$, or ^1_1H, is not 1, but 1.007825 u, and the mass of the helium atom with $A = 4$, or ^4_2He, is not 4, but 4.002603 u. These masses are the masses of the neutral atoms. The binding energy of the electrons can be neglected because its contribution to the mass would be several digits behind the last significant figure of the value of the mass.[16] One mass unit is equal to 1.6605×10^{-27} kg. Because $E = mc^2$, 1 u corresponds to an energy of 149×10^{-12} joule or 931.481 MeV.

The mass loss due to the nuclear binding energy is of the order of about

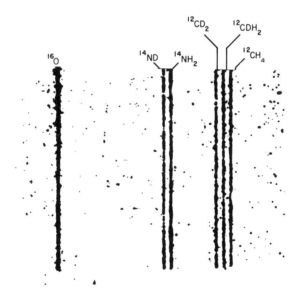

Fig. 6.5.3 Mass multiplet at $A = 16$ showing $^{16}O^+$ and several molecule ions. [R. Bieri, F. Everling, and J. Mattauch, *Zeitschrift für Naturforschung* **10a**, 659 (1955).]

[16] The total binding energy of the electrons is for Sn $(Z = 50)$ 145 keV and for Th $(Z = 90)$ 570 keV.

1% of the mass of a nucleus. It is thus much easier to measure mass differences than to measure absolute masses and then to compute mass differences. Figure 6.5.3 is a photographic record of a mass difference determination. The ions $^{16}O^+$, $^{14}ND^+$ (nitrogen hydride in which the hydrogen is replaced by deuterium, the heavy hydrogen isotope), $^{14}NH_2^+$, $^{12}CD_2^+$, $^{12}CDH_2^+$, and $^{12}CH_4^+$ all have approximately the same mass because they all have 16 nucleons. Such a group of ions is called a mass multiplet. By measuring mass differences within a number of different mass multiplets which are constituted by the same atoms (another such mass multiplet is $^{12}C_2H_4^+$, $^{14}N_2^+$, $^{12}C^{16}O^+$), one will be able to set up enough equations to determine the unknown quantities of interest.

The binding energy per particle, which is a measure of the average loss in mass of a nucleon when it is held in a nucleus, is shown in Fig. 6.5.4. Among the light atoms there are great irregularities. The two protons and two neutrons in an α particle are more strongly bound than are the nucleons in other light atoms. In the vicinity of $Z = 30$ the nucleons are more firmly bound than in light or heavy atoms. In this region of the periodic table (iron, nickel, copper, zinc) the average mass per nucleon has its lowest value. For heavier nuclei the trend is reversed, and the binding energy per particle decreases again. We shall return to these considerations in connection with radioactivity, or the spontaneous disintegration of nuclei, and nuclear reactions induced by bombardment. It is already clear,

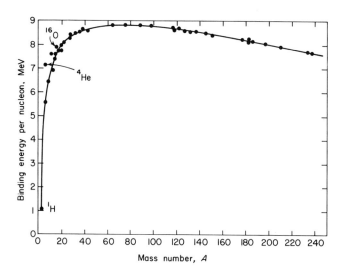

Fig. 6.5.4 The binding energy per nucleon versus mass number A in those nuclei which are, for a given A, the most stable ones.

however, that nuclear energy can be released in two ways, by the fission, or splitting up, of the heaviest stable atoms, or by the fusion, or combining, of the lightest atoms.

6.6 NUCLEAR MODELS

Physicists often resort to models when they understand only certain aspects of a problem. Such models give the researcher guidelines for further research. The results of this research will then decide which aspects of the model can be kept and which ones will have to be modified. A look back into some earlier models of atomic research might clarify the situation. Rutherford proposed the model of a nuclear atom as an alternative to the Thomson model, which pictured the electrons distributed in a homogeneous mass of oppositely charged matter like plums in a plum pudding. The Rutherford model could explain certain facts, such as the scattering of α particles, exceedingly well. However, it was immediately recognized (long before the advent of quantum theory) that the electrons circling around the nucleus should radiate and therefore lose energy and spiral into the nucleus very fast. Such an atom was not at all stable. Should the Rutherford model be considered a poor model, therefore? No! It had its shortcomings, it could not explain everything, but it helped Niels Bohr to make his postulates which were discussed in Chapter 4. On the other hand, the Bohr model, in spite of great progress over the Rutherford model, had its own shortcomings, which only modern wave mechanics has solved. Today we can say that we understand the atom and that we do not need a model for its understanding. For practical reasons we may still make use of a model that intentionally might neglect certain aspects, if it makes certain computational problems easier. In nuclear physics we still need models to help and guide our understanding. We will now discuss such models and delineate their limitations.

The Liquid-Drop Model

One of the earliest models of the nucleus is the liquid-drop model. Its original conception is due to Niels Bohr who realized that certain features could be explained by considering the nucleus as a liquid drop. On this basis H. A. Bethe and C. F. von Weizsäcker[17] developed a formula with which the masses of nuclides can be calculated.

[17] H. A. Bethe (1906–   ), theoretical physicist, born in Germany, came to the United States in 1935. Professor at Cornell University. 1967 Nobel prize in physics for his theory on the energy production in stars which he developed with C. F. von Weizsäcker (1912–   ), German theoretical physicist, now professor of philosophy at the University of Hamburg.

The nucleus is considered to be the analog of a drop of an incompressible liquid. The volume of the nucleus is therefore proportional to its number of nucleons, in agreement with the experimental evidence given earlier. This incompressibility is quite in contrast to the structure of atoms. Omitting from this consideration the lightest atoms and those which in the periodic table of elements are in the neighborhood of the alkalides and noble gases, the atomic radii are fairly constant. For example, vanadium ($Z = 23$) and osmium ($Z = 76$) both have a radius of 1.3×10^{-10} m, although the latter contains more than three times as many electrons as the former. This means that the electrons in the atoms are getting packed tighter and tighter with increasing atomic number. The reason for this trend is that the Coulomb forces that are responsible for the binding become stronger with increasing charge of the atomic nuclei.

In nuclei a number of factors play together which results in the approximate proportionality between nuclear mass and volume. One of these factors is the short range of nuclear forces. Each nucleon can interact only with nucleons in its neighborhood considering that the average distance between nucleons in a nucleus is 1.8 fm. The second factor is that at very close distances, say 0.5 fm, very strong repulsive forces between nucleons are effective. However, this alone would not prevent the nuclei from assuming much smaller radii than they actually have. Another factor is therefore necessary which has its counterpart in the binding energy of molecules. In Chapter 4 we learned that exchange forces play a role. Two hydrogen atoms can form a molecule by sharing both electrons. However, a hydrogen molecule made up of three hydrogen nuclei and three electrons is less stable, in fact unstable, because the Pauli principle requires that one of the three electrons cannot occupy an s state but must be in another state causing much weaker binding. Similarly, two protons (one with spin up, and one with spin down) and two neutrons (likewise) can form a stable configuration, the ^{4}He nucleus, or α particle (Fig. 6.6.1), but five nucleons cannot make up a stable nucleus because the Pauli principle forces one

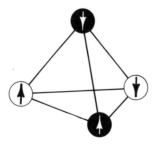

Fig. 6.6.1 Nucleons and bonds in a ^{4}He nucleus.

neutron into a p state. With four nucleons we have hence reached a certain saturation. Although a combination of five nucleons is not stable, six and more nucleons can again combine to a stable nucleus. In these cases each nucleon finds itself in a potential that is due to all the other nucleons. In the evaluation of this common potential the saturation of nuclear forces plays an important role.

Repulsive core, short range of nuclear forces, and exchange forces are thus together responsible for the saturation property of nuclear forces and for the fact that the nucleons inside the nuclei are not as densely packed as would be the case if only strongly attractive nuclear forces were present.

Thus for our model we can first assume that the total number of bonds is proportional to the number of nucleons. Each bond represents a certain amount of binding energy. The sum of all these bonds corresponds to the total binding energy used to hold the nucleus together. The total energy of these bonds is therefore proportional to the number of nucleons and therefore to the volume of the nucleus, or

$$E_b = -C_v A,$$

whereby C_v is a constant, the subscript v standing for volume. A closer inspection, however, reveals that the nucleons at the surface have fewer neighbors and hence must have unsaturated bonds. We have thus overestimated the total binding energy and now have to correct for this. The number of these peripheral nucleons is obviously proportional to the surface of the nucleus. For a closer estimate of the total binding energy the needed correction is proportional to the surface area of the nucleus. The surface of a sphere is proportional to the $\frac{2}{3}$ power of its volume. Because the volume of a nucleus is proportional to its mass number A, the surface correction E_s term for the binding energy becomes

$$E_s = C_s A^{2/3}$$

and has the opposite sign of the first term. A further correction is due to the electrostatic energy of the nucleus. This correction is thus a function of the number of protons in the nucleus. The electrostatic energy is making the nucleus more massive,[18] and therefore also has the opposite sign of the volume energy. If we consider the electrostatic charge uniformly distributed throughout the volume of the nucleus, the correction term for that electrostatic energy is given by

$$E_c = \frac{C_c Z^2}{A^{1/3}}.$$

[18] A notable, and still not really understood, exception is that the neutron has the greater mass than the proton.

The dependence upon A reflects dependence on the radius of the nucleus.

The above terms are essentially of a classical nature. The next two terms, however, are of a specifically nuclear nature. The first one takes into account that a nucleus with equal numbers of protons and neutrons, if one disregards the electrostatic energy, should be the most stable one and therefore should have the smallest mass. This can be understood by the following argument: Assume that a given nucleus contains more protons than neutrons and that the Coulomb energy can be neglected or, in other words, the Coulomb interaction can be "switched off." (Remember that we have already explicitly applied a correction for the Coulomb energy.) For the potential well of a nucleus we have the situation sketched in Fig. 6.6.2(a). Due to the exclusion principle each level in the potential well of the nucleus can be occupied by two protons and two neutrons. The energetically more stable configuration is the one in which the numbers of protons and neutrons are equal, as shown in Fig. 6.6.2(b). However, one reservation has to be made with respect to this last statement and will give rise to the correction term δ discussed later. The correction term which takes care of the fact that the most stable nucleus is symmetric in the number of protons and neutrons is called asymmetry term and has the form

$$E_a = C_a \frac{(N - Z)^2}{A}.$$

The square of $(N - Z)$ insures that a proton excess has the same effect as a neutron excess. The A-dependence shows that the more nucleons there are in a nucleus the smaller is the effect and hence the correction.

The last correction, δ, reflects the fact that even numbers of protons and

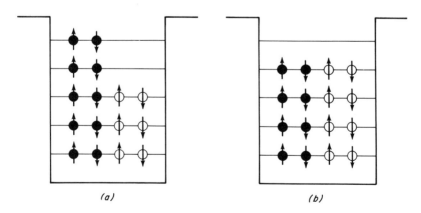

(a) (b)

Fig. 6.6.2 The nucleus with a configuration similar to (b) is more stable than the one with configuration (a). Coulomb effects are neglected.

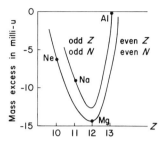

Fig. 6.6.3   The masses of the isobars of mass number 24.

even numbers of neutrons lead to the most stable nuclei. Protons like to go in pairs, so to speak, and neutrons have the same preference. This correction term is therefore called the pairing energy term.

The effect of the symmetry in the number of protons and neutrons and of the pairing energy is nicely seen in Fig. 6.6.3, in which are plotted the

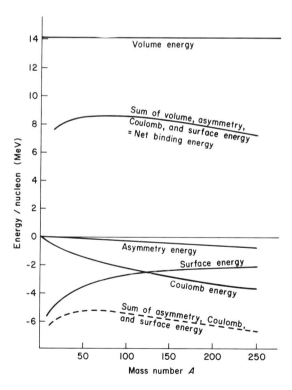

Fig. 6.6.4   Volume, surface, Coulomb, and asymmetry energy per nucleon.

masses of the isobars of mass number 24. In this region of the chart of nuclides the effects of the Coulomb energy are still small.

Figure 6.6.4 gives in a graph, per nucleon, the terms for the volume energy, the surface energy, the Coulomb energy, and the asymmetry energy as a function of the mass number. The sum of these four terms obviously results in the curve of Fig. 6.6.4 which represents the binding energy per nucleon versus the mass number.

Having discussed all the major corrections we can now write the formula for the mass M of an atom (nucleus + electron shell):

$$M = ZM_H + NM_n - C_vA + C_sA^{2/3} + C_cZ^2/A^{1/3} + C_a \frac{(N - Z)^2}{A} \pm \delta.$$

This is the *Bethe-Weizsäcker semi-empirical mass formula*. The constants C_v, C_s, C_c, C_a, and δ must be determined from the measured masses of nuclides. Although there is in general quite good agreement between the experimentally determined masses and the mass formula, certain systematic deviations are manifest which can be explained by the shell model discussed below. In recent years the semi-empirical formula has been improved to take such deviations into account. This formula is often used to estimate the masses of unknown nuclides. Particularly if one deals with nuclear reactions, one would like to have an idea about the energy released or necessary for certain reactions to take place.

The Shell Model

In the liquid-drop model all protons are considered equal, and so also are all neutrons. No nucleon has any individuality left. Certain nucleons stay for a time on the surface and then are treated differently from the interior nucleons, but this is beside the point. When these surface nucleons return to the interior, other nucleons take their places and appear at the surface. The surface nucleons are therefore not particularly distinguished. Furthermore, an important feature of the liquid-drop model is the existence of strong correlations between neighboring nucleons which manifest themselves through the strong binding forces. Although the liquid-drop model gives a good account of the masses and binding energies of the nuclides, the physicists were not successful in extracting information from it about the excited states of nuclei or about the quantum numbers of the states. To ask for such information is quite reasonable because in the case of the atomic model we can get such information. We recall that atoms are in excited states when an electron (much more rarely several electrons) is in an excited state, that is, when it is not in the lowest possible state compatible with the Pauli principle. The energy of these states can be calculated on the basis of wave mechanics. Should such a procedure not be possible also for the nucleus? This question was asked quite early.[19] In order to arrive at an answer several differences between the atom and nucleus must be taken into consideration. The forces in atoms are the well-known electromagnetic forces. Furthermore, the atom has a very conspicuous center, the nucleus, whereas the nucleus does not have such a singularity. Finally, whereas the interactions between electrons due to the mutual Coulomb repulsion often must be taken into account as only a "perturbation," the interactions between the individual nuclei could be of greatest importance, because of the short range of nuclear forces.

In spite of these handicaps the nuclear counterpart to the atomic model, the so-called "shell model," works after a fashion. That is, the quantitative results do not have the precision of the atomic counterpart: in many cases the shell model does not describe the situation correctly even in a qualitative way. Thus we have to keep in mind that the usefulness of a certain model is determined much more by its successes than by its failures. The success of the shell model lies in the correct prediction of characteristics of nuclides like those, for example, which are the counterparts of the alkali metals and the halogens in atomic physics. The number of electrons in these atoms is either one more or one less than in the atoms of the noble gases. The noble gases, however, are the atoms with the most stable electron configuration. The next additional electron is relatively loosely bound and occupies the next principal shell, and the separation of an electron from a noble-gas atom requires a relatively big amount of ionization energy.

The success of the nuclear shell model came when in 1949 Maria Goeppert Mayer[20] in the United States and a German team of two physicists, Jensen[21] and Haxel, and one geophysicist, Suess, independently discovered the clue that yielded the correct closed shells. Up to that time the nuclear shell model had been in some slight discredit, because "reasonable" assumptions led to closed-shell configurations that were not at all in agreement with the experimental facts. There was, for example, evidence in nature that nuclides with 50 and 82 protons or neutrons were particularly stable. The nuclides with 50 protons, as we noted in the beginning of this

[19] The first one to propose a nuclear shell model was W. Elsasser (also the first to point out experimental evidence for matter waves) in 1933 [*Journal de Physique et le Radium* **4,** 549 (1933); **5,** 389 (1934)].

[20] Maria Goeppert Mayer (1906–1972), theoretical nuclear physicist, born in Germany, came to the United States in 1930; in 1949, Mayer was a professor at the University of Chicago. 1963 Nobel prize in physics for the discovery of the nuclear shell model shared with J. H. D. Jensen.

[21] J. H. D. Jensen (1907–1973), German theoretical physicist in Heidelberg.

Maria Goeppert Mayer (1906–1972) (Courtesy of Niels Bohr Library, American Institute of Physics).

J. Hans D. Jensen (1907-1973) (Courtesy of American Institute of Physics, Meggers Gallery of Nobel Laureates).

chapter, are the isotopes of tin, which is among the elements with the greatest number of stable isotopes. This implies that nuclides with 50 protons are particularly stable, although the proton-to-neutron ratio of some of these isotopes might deviate quite considerably from the average for this region of the table of nuclides. There is also a very large number of elements which have stable isotopes containing 50 neutrons. Furthermore, lead, with 82 protons, is the heaviest stable element in nature. These are only some of the features which distinguish the numbers 50 and 82. The situation is similar with the numbers 20 and 126, and to a degree with 28. These proton and neutron numbers are called "magic numbers." We will now discuss how one arrives at these numbers indicating particular stability.

Let us first recall how we arrived at the energy levels in the cases of the hydrogen atom, of a particle in a square well (which is derived from the box), and in the harmonic oscillator. Of these three systems the atom is the most complicated. Its potential is the Coulomb potential (Fig. 6.6.5). The spacings between the levels and the number of electrons occupying each level reflect this form of potential. For the quantum number $n = 1$, 2 places are available, for $n = 2$, 8 places are available, therefore creating another closed shell at $2 + 8 = 10$ electrons. Neon, with this number of electrons, is an atom of great stability. However, the occurrence of the next noble–gas atom, which again is distinguished by a very stable con-

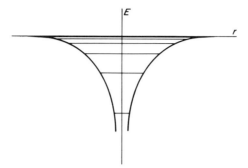

Fig. 6.6.5   An atomic Coulomb-like potential.

figuration, does not coincide with the completion of the $n = 3$ shell; only the p subshell is filled. This subshell contains 8 electrons, so that we now have altogether 18 electrons. This is the number of electrons of an argon atom. It is clear that the Coulomb potential reaches far out because the Coulomb forces are long-range forces. For the description of the nucleus we need a potential without pronounced singularities at the origin, for example, the square well which has a flat bottom. Such a potential is a little bit too radical with its rectangular walls, and a slight rounding seems more realistic. This can be accomplished by chosing some intermediate between a square-well and a harmonic-oscillator potential as shown in Fig. 6.6.6. Figure 6.6.7 gives a schematic energy level diagram for the square well, the harmonic oscillator, and an intermediate potential shape.[22] The labeling of the levels (excepting the principal quantum number) is like that

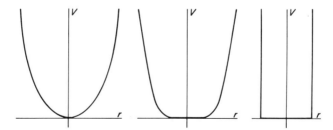

Fig. 6.6.6   The shape of a nuclear potential may be represented by some intermediate between a harmonic oscillator and square-well potential.

[22] A mechanical system having a similar potential function is for example a mass and spring which compresses very easily for small deflections and then becomes very stiff. This can be realized with a spiral coil of changing pitch so that in big compressions some of the windings come in contact with each other and therefore cannot be compressed further. Such an oscillator is an anharmonic oscillator.

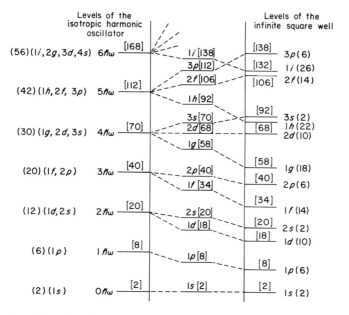

Fig. 6.6.7 The levels of a three-dimensional harmonic oscillator, a square well, and an intermediate potential shape.

for atoms. The numbers between parentheses, for example (20), indicate the maximum possible occupation of each level. The protons have their levels and the neutrons have corresponding ones. The numbers between brackets, for example [40], give the total number of protons or neutrons up to and including that level.

In previous discussions of the potentials of a square box (which is closely related to the square well) and the harmonic oscillator, we used Cartesian coordinates. This had the effect that the angular momentum of the states did not enter into our considerations. A treatment in spherical coordinates, however, yields angular momentum quantum numbers for the states, which are given in the figure. It should be noted that the levels of the harmonic oscillator belonging to the same energy and therefore the same shell can have different quantum numbers and are therefore degenerate. In the square well these levels are split into groups, but are still neighbors, in general. For example, considering for the moment only protons, the third excited harmonic oscillator level can be occupied by 20 protons of angular momentum $l = 3$ and 1, hence being in f states and p states, respectively. In the square well the corresponding f states have a slightly lower energy than the p states. The degeneracy is therefore reduced. In the actual potential, which is an average of the two, the splitting is also manifest. There we expect to see shell closures after a total of 2, 8, 20, 40, 70, 92, and 112 neutrons or protons.

If the characteristics of high stability had indeed been observed to occur at these numbers, the shell model would have been discovered long before 1949. However, there is no indication found in nature that nuclides with a proton or neutron number equal to 40, 70 and so on, are particularly distinguished. To the contrary, the experimental facts pointed to shell closures for 2, 8, 20, 28, 50, 82, and 126 protons or neutrons. Maria Mayer, and independently the German group, found the clue to this riddle by assuming that the levels were split further in a very drastic way by a so-called spin-orbit interaction of unknown origin. Mrs. Mayer got this idea when she discussed these discrepancies with her colleague Fermi. He asked her "Is there any indication of spin-orbit coupling?" [23] She immediately recognized that this was the solution to the difficulties. The existence of a spin-orbit interaction implies that if the orbital angular momentum l of a proton or neutron could combine with the spin angular momentum $s = \frac{1}{2}$ to a state of total angular momentum $j = l + \frac{1}{2}$, this state will be drastically different in energy from the state with $j = l - \frac{1}{2}$. The difference in energy between the two states should increase with the value of l. The energy of the level with $l + \frac{1}{2}$ will be reduced by the spin-orbit interaction, that of the $l - \frac{1}{2}$ level will be raised. This effect is such that the gap between these levels becomes very great. Hence the "magic numbers" occur at 28, 50, 82, and 126. A level of total angular momentum j contains $2j + 1$ substates with different magnetic quantum numbers m_j, namely $j, j - 1, \ldots, -j$. Each of these substates can be occupied by a proton or neutron, respectively. This is quite similar to the filling of levels with electrons in building up the periodic table. The magnitude of the splitting of the levels increases with increasing orbital angular momentum. Because the nucleons in the lowest shells do not have much angular momentum, the shell closures at 2, 8, and 20 protons or neutrons are not changed by the spin-orbit interaction.

Today one believes that the forces which cause the spin-orbit splitting are due to virtual mesons of spin 1 which are different from the virtual π mesons which have zero spin. Electromagnetic forces, which are the source of such a splitting in atoms, are much too weak to account for this considerable splitting here.

The level sequence for protons and neutrons, taking the spin-orbit splitting into account, is given in Fig. 6.6.8. The sequence is slightly different for the two kinds of nucleons because Coulomb repulsion affects the position of the energy levels of the protons somewhat.

[23] *Phys. Rev.* **75**, 1969 (1949).

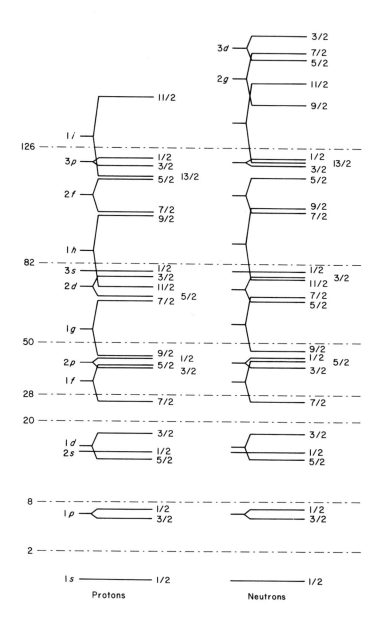

Fig. 6.6.8   Proton and neutron level schemes. [After P. F. A. Klinkenberg, *Rev. Mod. Phys.* **24**, 63 (1952).] Closed shells are indicated by the dash-dotted lines. The orbital angular momentum l is indicated on the left side of each ladder. On the right side, j is given. The occupation number follows from the $2j + 1$ different m_j values.

A further assumption is that all the protons pair off as far as possible, as do all the neutrons. This means that a proton or neutron with a certain angular momentum will form a pair with another proton or neutron, respectively, of the same quantity of angular momentum, but with its angular momentum vector pointed in the opposite direction. Thus as a pair they have zero total angular momentum. If there is an odd number of protons or neutrons in the nucleus, one such nucleon is without a partner, as shown in Fig. 6.6.9. Returning to Fig. 6.6.8 we see that the second shell can accommodate one neutron with total angular momentum $j = \frac{1}{2}$ pointing up, and one neutron with $j = \frac{1}{2}$ pointing down. In addition, there is room for two neutrons with $j = \frac{3}{2}$ down, but also for two with $j = \frac{3}{2}$ up, which again can cancel. The same also holds for protons. Nuclides with an even number of protons and of neutrons should, according to this rule, have a total angular momentum of zero. This is in full agreement with the facts. If there is an even number of protons but an odd number of neutrons, the angular momenta of all the protons cancel, likewise the angular momenta of all but the last neutron. The last unpaired neutron has the angular momentum according to the shell model. Since the other nucleons contribute nothing to the angular momentum of the nucleus, the angular momentum of the nucleus is equal to the angular momentum of the unpaired nucleon. The value of the angular momentum of the last nucleon can now be predicted on the basis of the shell model. Predicted and actual values of the angular momentum agree very well in general as long as the number of nucleons is not too far from a closed shell. $^{95}_{42}Mo_{53}$ and $^{97}_{42}Mo_{55}$ with 53 and 55 neutrons, respectively, have both an angular momentum of $\frac{5}{2}$ in the ground state as predicted by the theory. Also angular momenta of excited states could be predicted from the shell model, corresponding to the next higher energy levels.

The experimental determination of the position of the occupied energy levels is quite difficult and has been done for only a few nuclides. A very

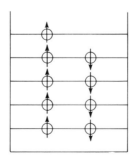

Fig. 6.6.9   The pairing of nucleons.

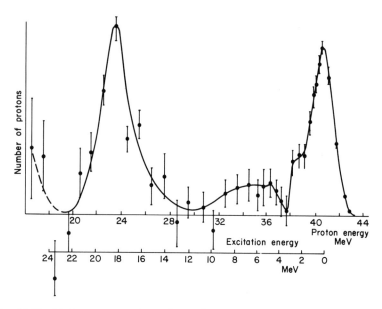

Fig. 6.6.10 Proton spectrum from the nuclear photoeffect on ^{12}C. Preliminary data by S. N. Gardiner, J. L. Matthews, and R. O. Owens (Glasgow University, 1971). Energy of the incoming photons: 60 ± 1 MeV. Energy necessary to separate the least bound proton: 16 MeV. The scale parallel to the abscissa refers to the excitation energy of the ^{11}B nucleus after the emission of a proton. (Recoil of the nucleus has been taken into account.)

direct method employs the nuclear photoeffect, which is the nuclear counterpart to the photoelectric effect in metals and atoms. A photon of sufficiently high energy interacts with the nucleus, and a proton (or neutron) is emitted. From the kinetic energy of this nucleon one can conclude from which shell it came. Preliminary data of such an investigation with 60-MeV photons are given in Fig. 6.6.10 for the ^{12}C nucleus. The peak on the right represents the protons that are removed from the topmost shell, $p_{3/2}$, whose "work function" is therefore smallest and leave the product nucleus ^{11}B in its ground state. The peak to the left, at 24 MeV proton energy, is due to protons that came from the s shell. This shell lies approximately 18 MeV below the $p_{3/2}$ shell. The emitted proton accordingly has less energy. [The small broad hump at 35 MeV and also the shoulder at 39 MeV indicate that sometimes the ^{11}B was at first not in its ground state, but in one of its excited states (see Fig. 6.3.2)].

After the first triumphs of the shell model had been celebrated, quite a number of exceptions from the rules were discovered, and during the next years nuclear physicists tried to explain the discrepancies. Many questions could be answered without tampering with the basic ideas of the shell model. However, certain experimental facts had to await the creation of a new model.

The Collective Model

In the late 1940's it was already recognized that the energy differences between levels in certain nuclides showed remarkable regularities, which up to that time could not be satisfactorily explained. Aage Bohr, the son of Niels Bohr, and B. R. Mottelson were then able to explain some of the features by collective effects. This means that not only one nucleon is responsible for the character of the nucleus as we had seen from the shell model, but many particles. Bohr and Mottelson assumed that the nucleus can vibrate in different modes. If the nucleus is not spherical, it can also rotate in a particular fashion, best comparable to a tidal wave running around a nucleus. Just as the tidal wave in the oceans follows the moon without an actual net flow of water on the Earth, one should not think that a group of nucleons circles the core of the nucleus. Figure 6.6.11(a) represents the rotation of a hypothetical rigid ellipsoidal nucleus. Each nucleon rotates in a circular orbit as indicated by the arrows. Figure 6.6.11(b) illustrates a tidal wave motion. The nucleons move along the lines drawn in the direction of the arrows. This will have the effect that the major axis will turn counterclockwise. Although the particles do not rotate, there is still a rotation of the shape of the nucleus. These two illustrated cases are extreme, and the truth lies somewhere in between.

We will now discuss vibrations of a nucleus. The vibration of water drops, among many other things, was studied by Lord Rayleigh in the last century. Although his were of course not quantum mechanical calculations, much of the formalism could be taken over for the nuclear case. In addi-

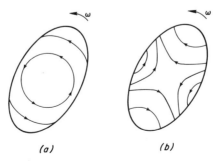

(a) *(b)*

Fig. 6.6.11   Rigid rotation (a) and irrotational motion (b).

tion, the quantum mechanical treatment of vibrational spectra in molecules was similar. It therefore turned out that the mathematical apparatus
to handle the problem of nuclear vibrations was to a great extent available.
We have already discussed the quantum mechanical harmonic oscillator
and will note that its energy levels are spaced in equal intervals (we also
used this characterization in the discussion of the energy levels of the shell
model). Such vibrational levels are, for example, to be found in several
cadmium isotopes (Fig. 6.6.12). The greater the mass of the nucleus, the
lower the excitation energy, as can be seen by comparing the energies of
the vibrational states for the isotopes 110, 112, and 114. This trend is to
be expected, since frequencies of oscillators decrease when the oscillating
mass increases, if everything else can be considered to remain constant.

We shall now discuss the rotational level structure of nuclei. Only deformed nuclei show rotational levels. The reason is that a spherical nucleus
always looks the same from all sides. Quantum mechanically, therefore,
rotation cannot be observed. From our treatment of molecular spectra we
already know that the energies of the levels of a quantum mechanical
rotator are given by

$$E_{\text{rot}} = \frac{\hbar^2}{2\mathscr{g}} J(J + 1)$$

where $\mathscr{g}$ is the moment of inertia. Nuclei with an even number of protons
and neutrons (so-called even-even nuclei) display a particularly simple
level structure. In such nuclei only the even values of J are permitted.
This is for the same reason that every second level in diatomic molecules
of identical atoms is suppressed (see Chap. 4). In an even-even nucleus
the same even number of nucleons is "north" of the equator as is "south."
The two halves of the nucleus can therefore be considered as identical

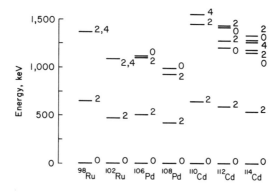

Fig. 6.6.12   Nuclei of even A with vibrational levels.

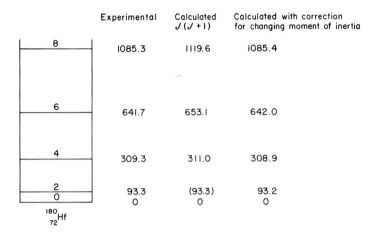

	Experimental	Calculated $J(J+1)$	Calculated with correction for changing moment of inertia
8	1085.3	1119.6	1085.4
6	641.7	653.1	642.0
4	309.3	311.0	308.9
2	93.3	(93.3)	93.2
0	0	0	0

$^{180}_{72}$Hf

Fig. 6.6.13   The rotational levels of $^{180}_{72}$Hf.

bosons. For $J = 2, 4, 6, 8$, therefore we calculate energies of the excited states proportional to $2 \times 3 = 6, 4 \times 5 = 20$, and so on, or taking the first energy interval as unity, energies corresponding to $1, 3\frac{1}{3}, 7, 12$ units of energy. We find, indeed, an appreciable number of nuclides that display this characteristic rotational level structure in nature, for example, $^{180}_{72}$Hf (Fig. 6.6.13). Slight deviations can be disposed of by assuming a slowly changing moment of inertia. Calculated values taking this correction into account are given on the right-hand side of Fig. 6.6.13. An obvious step is now to ask about the moment of inertia of a nucleus. A rigid sphere has a moment of inertia $\mathscr{I} = \frac{2}{5}AMR^2$, where A is the mass number, M the mass of a single nucleon, and R the nuclear radius; AM is therefore the mass of the nucleus. Although we mentioned above that nuclides showing rotational structure are not spherical, the deviation is not very great. It turns out, however, that the moment of inertia calculated from the spectra is only one-quarter to one-half of what one would expect from a rigid rotator. This is an indication that not the whole nucleus is participating in the collective motion. The motion of nuclear matter inside the nucleus seems to be quite complicated.

We have idealized above the situation somewhat by discussing pure rotations and pure vibrations. In reality the boundary between these two modes of excitation is not sharp. In Fig. 6.6.14 we see that nuclei which are spherical, like ^{146}Sm, have a vibrational level structure. As we progress toward more deformed nuclei, like ^{154}Sm, the equidistance of the levels gives way to a spacing typical for rotational levels.

Rotations and vibrations of nuclei can assume various forms; the rota-

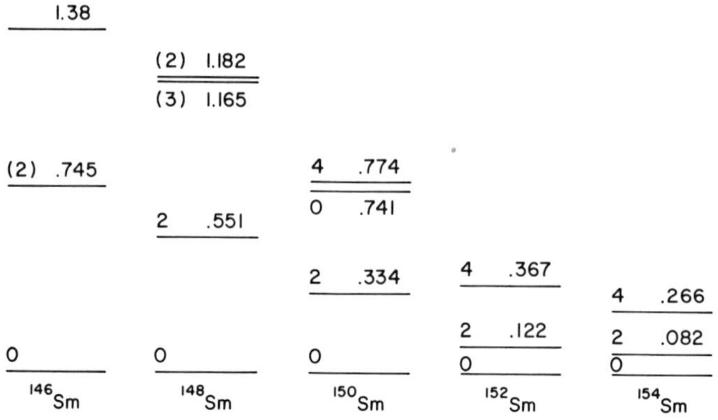

Fig. 6.6.14 The first few energy levels of various even-A samarium isotopes, demonstrating the transition from a vibrational to a rotational spectrum. [From P. Stoler et al., *Phys. Rev.* **155**, 1334 (1967).]

tion of a nucleus may be around various axes, and vibration can occur in simpler or more complicated modes. Also the distortions of nuclei can be such that they can become pear-shaped.

In order to round out the picture, we mention briefly that in addition to the collective effects (as the vibrations and rotations, where many nucleons participate) there are also transitions of single particles, giving rise to so-called single-particle levels. If we deal with a nonspherical nucleus, it is not surprising that we find some splitting of levels that were degenerate in a spherical nucleus. This is analogous to the situation of particles in a cubical box. If one dimension of such a box is changed, so that it is no longer cubical, levels which were degenerate split up. Returning to nuclei, calculations regarding the effect of deformation on nuclear levels were first performed by Nilsson. From the positions of the energy levels relative to each other as found by the experiment, one can deduce the magnitude of the deformation of the nucleus (Fig. 6.6.15).

Much research is going on presently in this field; from year to year more and more levels of nuclei are receiving their interpretation. The close agreement between theoretical predictions and experimental findings is often surprisingly good. Frequently specific experiments are undertaken to fulfill the wishes of the theorists for needed new data.

In conclusion we can say that the present explanations of the level structure of nuclei up to an energy of a few MeV with the aid of models are reasonably satisfactory. This is justification enough for the models, although the models when they were postulated first were based on not very firm theoretical grounds.

In retrospect it is interesting to compare some of the premises for the different nuclear models. In the liquid-drop model we assume strongly interacting nucleons. The nucleons are bound to their neighbors and therefore will move to some degree collectively. This is completely different from the assumptions made for the shell model according to which the

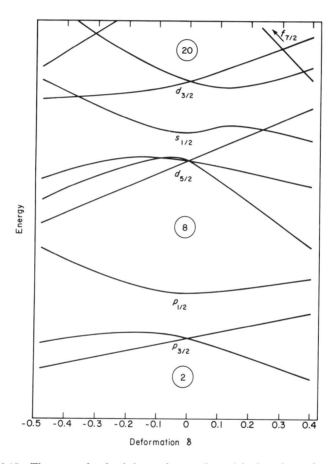

Fig. 6.6.15 The energy levels of the single-particle model when the nuclear potential is not spherically symmetric but ellipsoidal. The abscissa represents the deformation of the sphere $\delta = \Delta R/R$. For $\delta = 0$ the potential is spherically symmetric and results in the usual shell model. The lowest level, the $s_{1/2}$ level, is not shown. It is followed by the $p_{3/2}$, $p_{1/2}$, $d_{5/2}$, $s_{1/2}$, $d_{3/2}$, etc. levels. The deformation removes the degeneracy of the levels in a way similar to the levels in a cubical box which is deformed into a rectangular box. This diagram is known as a Nilsson diagram. The numbers in circles indicate shell closures after 2, 8, and 20 protons or neutrons. [From S. G. Nilsson, *Kgl. Danske Videnskab. Selskab, Mat.-Fys. Medd.* **29**, No. 16 (1955).]

nucleons are considered to move essentially undisturbed by the other particles in their orbits. The orbits are determined by the average potential created by all the other nucleons. The Pauli exclusion principle can give a clue for this undisturbed motion. If two nucleons from inner shells collided, there would be a change in the state of motion of the nucleons and they should go into other orbits. However, all other orbits are fully occupied, with the exception of the ones of very high energy. Therefore, the probability for a collision is much reduced.

The collective model is related to the liquid-drop model insofar as both assume strong correlations between the nucleons. The liquid-drop model is fundamentally classical. The Schrödinger equation plays no part in it. Pairing and asymmetry energies, which have quantum-mechanical origins, are introduced only in an *ad hoc* manner. In contrast, the shell model and the collective model are fully based on quantum mechanics.

6.7 NUCLEAR DECAY

The Formal Description of Radioactive Processes

There are stable and unstable nuclei. Unstable nuclei can transform themselves spontaneously into a new form by emitting a particle. This spontaneous transformation is called radioactivity, and it is a completely statistical process. Regardless of how long a nucleus has survived, the expectancy for its remaining life remains constant until it decays. This is in obvious contrast to the human lifetime. A 20-year-old can expect to live another 50 years, but a 50-year-old man cannot.

Different species of nuclei have different "life expectancies." There is one single law that describes the rate at which all radioactive transformations take place. The number of transformations per second is proportional to the number of decaying unstable atoms present. If N is the number of atoms of the decaying species present, then

$$\frac{dN}{dt} = -\lambda N. \tag{6.7.1}$$

The proportionality constant λ is called the *decay constant*. Its reciprocal, τ, is called the *mean life* of the decaying substance. Thus, the solution of Eq. 6.7.1 is

$$N = N_0 e^{-\lambda t} = N_0 e^{-t/\tau} \tag{6.7.2}$$

where N_0 is the number of decaying atoms present at the time $t = 0$. A quantity related to the mean life τ is the *half-life* $\tau_{1/2}$ or the time required for half of the original number of atoms to decay. This follows from

$$N = \frac{N_0}{2} = N_0 \exp(-\tau_{1/2}/\tau),$$

or

$$\tau_{1/2} = \tau \ln 2 = 0.693\,\tau. \qquad (6.7.3)$$

The activity of radioactive substances is measured in terms of the number of disintegrations per second. It is therefore equal to λN. The activity of one gram of radium is approximately 3.7×10^{10} disintegrations per second. The unit used to express the number of disintegrations per second of any radioactive substance is the curie, abbreviated Ci, and by definition is equal to exactly 3.7×10^{10} disintegrations per second. It is named after the married couple Curie.[24]

Marie (1867–1934) and Pierre (1859–1906) Curie in their laboratory in 1896 (Courtesy of Niels Bohr Library, American Institute of Physics).

[24] Marie Curie Sklodowska (1867–1934), born in Warsaw. Discovered, together with her husband, the French physicist Pierre Curie (1859–1906), in 1898 the elements radium and polonium. For this discovery both shared with H. Becquerel, the discoverer of radioactivity, the 1903 Nobel prize in physics. In 1911 Mme. Curie received the Nobel prize in chemistry for the preparation of pure radium in greater quantities.

Radioactive substances emit three kinds of rays: alpha, beta, and gamma. Alpha particles are helium nuclei and have a mass number of 4. A substance decaying by alpha emission changes its mass number by four units, or $\Delta A = 4$. Beta particles are electrons. Positive as well as negative electrons are found in radioactive radiations. Gamma rays are electromagnetic quanta. Substances undergoing radioactive transformations by beta or gamma decay do so with $\Delta A = 0$. It follows that all radioactive transformations will take place with either $\Delta A = 4$ or $\Delta A = 0$. Although the naturally occurring radioactive elements are concentrated at the heavy end of the table of nuclides, some are in isolated places, such as the β-emitter $^{40}_{19}$K (half-life 1.27×10^9 years) or the α-unstable samarium isotope $^{147}_{62}$Sm (half-life 1.2×10^{11} years).

Examples of radioactive decays are shown in Fig. 6.7.1. A well-known artificial radioisotope is $^{60}_{27}$Co, decaying by emission of electrons and γ radiation into $^{60}_{28}$Ni with a half-life of 5.27 years. The nuclide $^{64}_{29}$Cu can either decay by electron emission into $^{64}_{30}$Zn or can transform by positron emission into $^{64}_{28}$Ni. This is called a dual decay. An example of γ decay is the excited state of $^{107}_{47}$Ag, which decays with 44 sec half-life to the ground state of $^{107}_{47}$Ag.

We have seen in the section on the systematics of nuclei, that certain nuclei are stable and others are unstable. Keeping the number of nucleons constant, the stable system is always the lightest one. Although the emission of α particles is a common mode of decay, particularly among the heaviest nuclides, disintegration of a nucleus in the ground state by emission of a proton or a neutron happens only in a few and very extraordinary cases. Why is this so? The answer is simple. The separation energy of a nucleon, that is the energy necessary to remove a nucleon from the nucleus (or the binding energy of the last nucleon), is in the vicinity of 7 MeV. A condition for emission of nucleons is that the emitting nucleus must be particularly massive (i.e., have a high energy content) in order to be able to afford this expense. These conditions are obviously more favorable if the emitted particle is relatively light. The four nucleons of an α particle are kept together by binding forces that are particularly strong. This is reflected in the quite high total binding energy of 28 MeV. The α particle thus has a relatively low mass; we might say it is "underweight." Therefore, the energy necessary to remove an α particle from a nucleus is comparatively small. We can look at this in a somewhat different way: Let us assume that we have a hypothetical nuclide and remove from it two protons and two neutrons one by one. Each time we have spent 7 MeV in separation energy. Outside our nucleus we will now bring the four nucleons together and form an α particle. In this process we will gain 28 MeV in binding energy. Altogether it did not cost us anything to remove the α

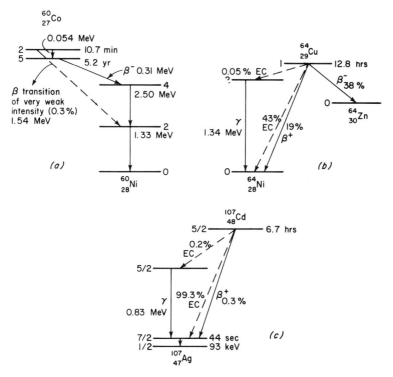

Fig. 6.7.1   Examples of radioactive decays. (a) The radioactive decay of ⁶⁰Co. (b) Dual decay of ⁶⁴Cu. Always competing with positron decay and leading to the same daughter nuclide is the so-called electron capture process (EC). An electron, usually from the K shell, is captured by the nucleus, thus transforming a proton into a neutron; in addition, a neutrino is emitted which carries off most of the decay energy. (c) Decay of ¹⁰⁷Cd to the excited (isomeric) state of ¹⁰⁷Ag which then decays to the ground state with a half-life of 44 sec. Alternatively to the de-excitation by γ-emission, an electron (usually from the K or L shell) can be emitted from the atom and thus carry away the excitation energy of the nucleus. This process is known as internal conversion.

particle. In inspecting the chart of nuclides we can find several cases in which a nuclide with Z protons and N neutrons, abbreviated (Z, N) is heavier than the sum of $(Z-2, N-2)$ plus an α particle. However, the nuclide is considered stable. The solution to this is that the α particle has to overcome a potential barrier. We shall go into the theory of alpha decay a little later.

In beta decay the number of nucleons in a nucleus does not change. What happens instead is that a proton changes into a neutron or vice versa, by emission of an electron, positively or negatively charged, and a neutrino. This transformation is not so strange if one considers that a proton and a neutron are only two different states of the same particle. Here also we shall go into some more detail later. A third possibility for nuclear disintegration is fission, which we mentioned earlier.

Alpha Decay

One of the early triumphs of wave mechanics was the explanation of alpha decay. Without at first going into detail, we can, on the basis of our knowledge of wave mechanics, understand the characteristics of this form of radioactivity. Table 6.7.1 lists some pertinent data. There are two outstanding features of this table which should be noticed. The first is that, although the half-life varies by a wide range of orders of magnitude, actually in the vicinity of 10^{20}, the energies of the α particles vary by a factor of only about 2. The second is that high energies are associated with short lives, whereas low energies are associated with long lives.

The reason can be found in the shape of the nuclear potential for α particles (and protons) which is illustrated in Fig. 6.7.2. This potential acts as a barrier for the charged particles inside (and also outside which is of importance if a nucleus is bombarded). We shall see that this potential barrier is "leaky."

TABLE 6.7.1

Representative Data Concerning Alpha Decay

Nucleus	Half-Life	Energy of Emitted Alpha Rays in MeV
$^{232}_{90}$Th	1.39×10^{10} years	3.98
$^{238}_{92}$U	4.51×10^{9} years	4.18
$^{235}_{92}$U	8.91×10^{8} years	4.56 and 4.40
$^{234}_{92}$U	2.35×10^{5} years	4.76
$^{230}_{90}$Th	8.0×10^{4} years	5.01 and 4.74
$^{226}_{88}$Ra	1622 years	4.79
$^{227}_{89}$Ac	21.7 years	4.95
$^{228}_{90}$Th	1.9 years	5.42 and 5.34
$^{222}_{86}$Rn	3.825 days	5.486
$^{231}_{93}$Np	53 min	6.2
$^{228}_{92}$U	9.3 min	6.72
$^{217}_{86}$Rn	10^{-3} sec	7.74
$^{216}_{85}$At	3×10^{-4} sec	7.79

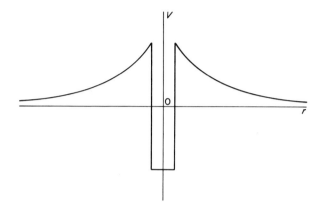

Fig. 6.7.2   The nuclear potential for an α particle.

For an explanation of these facts we return to our wave mechanical discussion of a particle in a box in Chapter 3. When the box was bounded by an infinite potential energy barrier, the wave function had nodes at the surface of the box. For a box with a finite potential energy barrier, however, it was found that the wave penetrated to some extent into the energetically forbidden region outside of the box, as shown in Fig. 3.4.6.

If we now modify the problem still further by limiting the thickness of the potential energy barrier which retains the particle, as shown in Fig. 6.7.3, the barrier penetration leads to a new result. The box is "leaky." We must match wave functions in the box, in the barrier, and outside the barrier. But outside the barrier the particle is unconfined and can move off arbitrarily, and a new formulation of the problem is required. When this is done, we find that solutions of the problem again correspond to certain

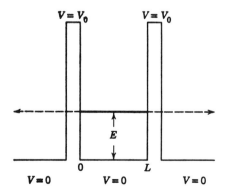

Fig. 6.7.3   A leaky potential barrier.

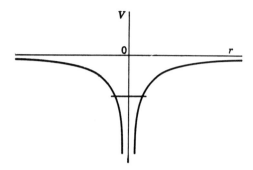

Fig. 6.7.4 The potential energy of an electron in the field of a nucleus.

characteristic energy levels but there is a finite probability that in any given interval of time the particle will appear outside the box. It has been able to penetrate the potential energy barrier. The nearer the energy level is to the top of the barrier, and the thinner the barrier, the greater the probability of having the particle appear beyond the barrier in any given time interval.

For electrons in atoms the attractive Coulomb force provides a potential energy barrier of the form shown in Fig. 6.7.4. The electron can have certain characteristic energies. There will be energy levels within the well, and the wave functions will be limited in space, as for the well shown in Fig. 3.4.6. Electrons cannot leak out of atoms. For nuclei, however, the Coulomb forces on a positively charged particle are repulsive. Inside the nucleus there are strong short-range attractive forces which may be represented by a steep-sided potential energy well as shown in Fig. 6.7.5. These forces do not extend outside the nucleus. Here the Coulomb repulsive

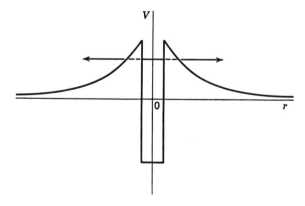

Fig. 6.7.5 The potential energy of a positively charged particle in the vicinity of a nucleus.

forces take over, and we have left a potential energy barrier of finite height and thickness. Positively charged particles having energy levels near the top of such a barrier can leak out.

Before we apply these qualitative considerations to the problems of radioactive nuclei emitting α particles, we shall calculate the somewhat simpler problem of the penetration of a rectangular potential barrier by a beam of particles. Also Gamow's[25] theoretical paper[26] (written when he was working in Born's group) in which alpha decay was explained, starts out with the calculation of the transmission through a rectangular barrier.

The whole calculation is in essence an extension of the reflection and transmission problems which were discussed in Section 3.5. The barrier is shown in Fig. 6.7.6. We have three regions, 1, 2, and 3. In regions 1 and 3 we chose the potential energy to be zero. The kinetic energy of the particles is therefore equal to the total energy E. In region 2 the barrier has a thickness l and its height V exceeds the total energy of the particles. Therefore, what otherwise would correspond to a kinetic energy, namely $E - V$, becomes in this region a negative quantity. With the de Broglie relation

$$\lambda = \frac{2\pi}{k} = \frac{h}{mv} = \frac{h}{\sqrt{2m(E - V)}}$$

we can determine the wave numbers k for the three regions:

$$k_1 = k_3 = \frac{\sqrt{2mE}}{\hbar},$$

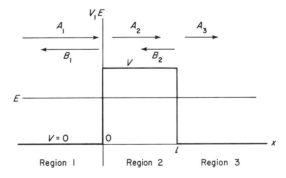

Fig. 6.7.6 Transmission through a rectangular potential barrier.

[25] G. Gamow (1904–1967); born in Russia; professor of physics in Leningrad until 1933, later on at George Washington University in Washington, D.C., and at the University of Colorado. Significant work in astrophysical cosmology and molecular biology.

[26] *Zeitschrift für Physik* **51,** 204 (1928) (in German). Translated in *The World of the Atom,* H. A. Boorse and L. Motz, eds. (Basic Books, New York, 1966).

but for region 2 the corresponding quantity $k_2 = [2m(E - V)]^{1/2}/\hbar$ becomes imaginary because $V > E$. It is therefore convenient to replace it by a real quantity β multiplied by i.

$$k_2 = \frac{\sqrt{2m(E - V)}}{\hbar} = i\frac{\sqrt{2m(V - E)}}{\hbar} = i\beta.$$

In regions 1 and 2 we have particle beams traveling in both directions due to partial reflections at the barrier walls. The amplitudes of particle beams traveling to the right will be designated A with a subscript corresponding to the appropriate region; amplitudes of beams traveling to the left with B.[27] In region 3 we have only the transmitted wave traveling to the right.

The time-independent Schrödinger equation is appropriate in our situation because the stream of particles in any region is constant in time. Therefore the Schrödinger equation for each of the regions is

$$\frac{d^2\psi}{dx^2} + \frac{2m}{\hbar^2}(E - V)\psi = 0$$

where for regions 1 and 3, $V = 0$ and for region 2 $(E - V)$ is negative as stated above. In region 1 the incident and reflected waves together must satisfy the Schrödinger equation. The incident wave (including its time-dependent part) is

$$\Psi_{A_1} = A_1 e^{ik_1 x} e^{-i\omega t},$$

and the reflected wave is

$$\Psi_{B_1} = B_1 e^{-ik_1 x} e^{-i\omega t}.$$

Because in all the expressions for all three regions the time-dependent factor is the same, we can omit it and write for the time-independent wavefunctions simply

$$\psi_{A_1} = A_1 e^{ik_1 x}$$

$$\psi_{B_1} = B_1 e^{-ik_1 x}.$$

The sum is therefore

$$\psi_1 = A_1 e^{ik_1 x} + B_1 e^{-ik_1 x}. \tag{6.7.4}$$

In region 2 we have

$$\psi_{A_2} = A_2 e^{ik_2 x} = A_2 e^{ii\beta_2 x} = A_2 e^{-\beta_2 x}$$

$$\psi_{B_2} = B_2 e^{-ik_2 x} = B_2 e^{-ii\beta_2 x} = B_2 e^{\beta_2 x}.$$

The sum is here

$$\psi_2 = A_2 e^{-\beta_2 x} + B_2 e^{\beta_2 x}. \tag{6.7.5}$$

Because the exponents are real numbers in this region there is no wave but an ex-

---

[27] The reflection at $x = 0$ of the reflected beam B_2 and also its transmission from region 2 to region 1 can be neglected for intensity reasons.

ponential damping. The second term, at first glance, seems to indicate an exponential increase; however, since the corresponding particle beam flows in the negative direction also this exponent represents an attenuation. In region 3, we again have a wave, obviously reduced in amplitude in comparison with the wave in region 1. The situation in the three regions is shown in Fig. 6.7.7.

In region 3 we have only one wave

$$\psi_3 = A_3 e^{ik_1 x}. \tag{6.7.6}$$

We know already from Chapter 3 the importance of the boundary conditions. At $x = 0$ we must have

$$\psi_1 = \psi_2 \tag{6.7.7}$$

and

$$\frac{d\psi_1}{dx} = \frac{d\psi_2}{dx}. \tag{6.7.8}$$

At $x = l$ the boundary conditions are similar:

$$\psi_2 = \psi_3 \tag{6.7.9}$$

$$\frac{d\psi_2}{dx} = \frac{d\psi_3}{dx}. \tag{6.7.10}$$

These boundary conditions, hence, provide us with four equations for the four unknowns B_1, A_2, B_2, A_3. (A_1 is assumed to be known!)

With some algebra, and considering that

$$\frac{e^{ikl} + e^{-ikl}}{2} = \cos(kl),$$

we can obtain the ratio of the squares of the amplitudes of the transmitted to the incident wave:

$$\frac{A_3^2}{A_1^2} = \frac{4k_1^2 k_2^2}{(k_1^2 + k_2^2) - (k_1^2 - k_2^2)^2 \cos^2(k_2 l)}$$

k_2, as pointed out earlier, is imaginary. Using the relation between trigonometric and hyperbolic functions

$$\cos ix = \cosh x$$

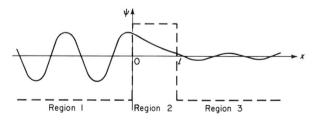

Fig. 6.7.7   The wave functions in the three regions for a beam of particles incident on a rectangular potential barrier.

and replacing k_2 by $i\beta$ we have

$$\frac{A_3{}^2}{A_1{}^2} = \frac{-4k_1{}^2\beta^2}{(k_1{}^2 - \beta^2) - (k_1{}^2 + \beta^2)^2 \cosh^2(\beta l)} \;.$$

(6.7.11)

Because

$$\cosh x = \frac{e^x - e^{-x}}{2}$$

we can write for not too small x

$$\cosh x \approx \frac{e^x}{2} \;.$$

Therefore

$$\frac{A_3{}^2}{A_1{}^2} \approx \frac{4k_1{}^2\beta^2}{(k_1{}^2 + \beta^2)^2} \, e^{-2\beta l}$$

or

$$\frac{A_3{}^2}{A_1{}^2} \approx 16 \, \frac{E(V - E)}{V^2} \, e^{-2\beta l}.$$

In our case, where the potential energy on both sides of the barrier is the same, consequently also the kinetic energies and velocities of the particles, this ratio is equal to the transmission coefficient T. For a thick barrier we have therefore

$$T \approx 16 \, \frac{E(V - E)}{V^2} \, e^{-2\beta l}.$$

(6.7.12)

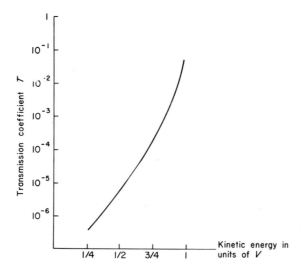

Fig. 6.7.8   The transmission coefficient T for a rectangular barrier as a function of the energy of the incident particle.

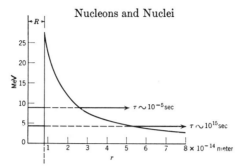

Fig. 6.7.9   The mechanism of alpha decay.

The greater the difference between the total energy of the particle and the height of the potential barrier, and the thicker the barrier, the smaller is the transmission through the barrier. Because β, which is related to this energy difference, and l are in the exponent, small changes in these quantities have a big effect on the transmission coefficient. Figure 6.7.8 shows the transmission coefficient for a barrier for different particle energies. The kinetic energy is given in units of the barrier height. The thickness of the barrier is here 1.5 times the de Broglie wavelength of a particle with a kinetic energy just equal to the barrier height. Even if the kinetic energy is equal to or exceeds slightly the barrier height, the transmission coefficient is far from unity. We expect this behavior on the basis of our discussion on reflection and transmission in Chapter 3.

We now return to our discussion of alpha decay. Instead of a one-dimensional geometry we have now a three-dimensional, spherical one. Furthermore, the barrier changes its height with the radius. This obviously has an effect on the transmission coefficient, but the general features, such as dependence on barrier height and width, are still the same.

We may think of the α particles as retaining their identity to some extent within a nucleus. They may be thought of as existing in energy levels of which two are shown in Fig. 6.7.9. Remembering that particles near the top of a thin barrier may be expected to escape rapidly, whereas particles having energies far below the top of a thick barrier will be much more effectively retained, we proceed to consider the range of energies to be expected of escaping α particles. Particles having energies over 10 MeV are not found because they are effectively not bound at all. They escape "at once." Particles having energies less than 3 or 4 MeV are not found because they cannot escape at all. The barrier is too high and thick. Between these limits lie the observed α-radioactive nuclides, with the understandable trend of higher energies associated with shorter lives. For an explanation of the irregularities in Table 6.7.1 one would have to consider variations in radius and nuclear charge among the nuclei listed.

β-Decay and the Weak Interaction

In contrast to α spectra, in which the α particles show discrete energies as one would expect, because their emission corresponds to a transition between states of well-determined energy, β spectra do not have this discrete character. A β spectrum resulting from plotting the number of particles of a certain momentum interval as a function of the momentum has a maximum somewhere in the middle of its momentum range (Fig. 6.7.10). For a long time it was a great puzzle how a transition between discrete energy states of nuclei could proceed by emission of a particle with kinetic energy, which ranges between zero and some upper limit. In the 1920's Niels Bohr contemplated throwing out the principle of conservation of energy for microscopic processes and considering it as a principle of only statistical validity. It was later found that such a revolutionary approach was not necessary. First it was possible to show, in cases where the decay energy could be determined from the masses of the parent and daughter nuclei, that this energy corresponded to the maximum, and not the average, energy of the β particles emitted from a particular nuclide. Somewhat later Wolfgang Pauli postulated that another particle must be emitted together with the β particle which, because of its characteristics, escaped observation. The energy carried away by this particle and the β particle

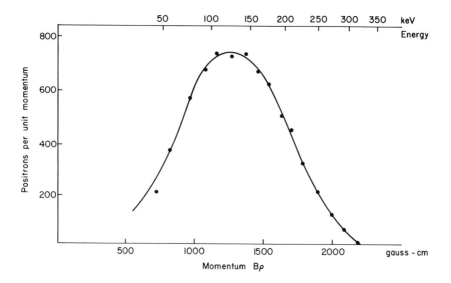

Fig. 6.7.10 Momentum spectrum of the $β^+$ particles from ^{107}Cd. [Bradt, Gugelot, Huber, Medicus, Preiswerk, and Scherrer, *Helv. Phys. Acta* **18**, 351 (1945).] See also Fig. 6.7.1(c).

would then be constant. Also in another respect this second particle saved the situation: in a β transition the number of nucleons in a nucleus does not change. Since each nucleon has spin $\frac{1}{2}$, and orbital angular momentum is always an integer, a nucleus containing an odd number of nucleons (odd A) must have half-integer total angular momentum (e.g., $\frac{1}{2}$, $\frac{3}{2}$, $\frac{5}{2}$), and it must obey Fermi statistics. An even-A nucleus must have integer total angular momentum (e.g., 0, 1, 2) and obey Bose statistics. In a β transition the number of nucleons does not change. On the other hand, the emitted electron removes from the nucleus its half-integer spin, in addition to an integer amount of angular momentum. It is therefore clear that the angular momentum could not be conserved without another particle besides the electron emitted. The comparison of the maximum energy of the β-particles with the available decay energy made it clear that the mass of this particle had to be small. The characteristics of the elusive particle were, therefore: charge zero, mass small, spin $\frac{1}{2}$, does not interact by nuclear forces, indeed has a very weak interaction, because after its emission it does not leave any noticeable trace.

Excerpts of a delightful letter (original in German) addressed to the participants of a physics meeting in Tübingen, Germany, and written with a fine touch of humor, which Pauli sent to Geiger and Meitner,[28] tell the story of the conception of the idea of a neutrino in his own words:

Department of Physics
Swiss Federal Institute of Technology
Zurich

Zurich, December 4, 1930

Dear radioactive ladies and gentlemen:

I ask you most graciously to listen to the carrier of this letter. He will explain to you in some detail that in view of the "wrong" statistics of the N and ^{6}Li nuclei and of the continuous beta spectrum, I have taken a desperate step in order to save the conservation laws of statistics and energy. This is the possibility that electrically neutral particles might exist in the nuclei, which I shall call neutrons[29] and which have spin $\frac{1}{2}$ and obey the exclu-

---

[28] Geiger is known as the co-inventor of the Geiger-Müller counter, and Liese Meitner's work led to the discovery of fission.

[29] When the neutron was discovered in 1932 by Chadwick in England, Fermi (at that time still in Rome) was asked if this was the particle proposed by Pauli. He answered that this was not the same particle, but that Pauli's particle was a little neutron, or neutrino in Italian. This name was henceforth adopted.

sion principle. They are different from light quanta also as they do not travel with the velocity of light. The mass of the neutrons should be of the same order as those of the electrons, in any case not more than 0.01 proton masses. The continuous spectrum would then be understandable if one assumes that in the beta decay an electron is emitted together with a neutron, such that the sum of the energies of neutron and electron is constant. . . .

At present I do not dare to publish something about this idea and I will first entrust myself to you, radioactive people, with the question what you think about the experimental detection of such a neutron, if it actually had a penetrating power about the same or a ten times bigger than gamma rays. [30]

I admit that my remedy immediately may look unlikely because one probably would have seen these neutrons long ago if they were to exist. But only he who dares wins, and the seriousness of the situation with regard to the continuous beta spectrum is clearly shown in the remark of my predecessor, Mr. Debye, who recently said to me in Brussels: 'O, it is best not to think about it at all, just as with the new taxes.' Hence one should seriously discuss every path that may lead to a rescue.—Therefore, dear radioactive people, examine and judge.—Unfortunately I cannot come in person to Tübingen, because I am indispensable here in Zurich due to a ball which takes place on the night of December sixth.

Your most obedient servant,
W. Pauli

First indications of the existence of the neutrino were gained by observing the linear momenta of the emitted electron and of the recoiling nucleus in a β decay. Since the momentum of an atom at rest before disintegration is zero, the sum of the momenta of all the components after the disintegration must also be zero. The beta particle and the recoiling nucleus alone are not enough to fulfill this requirement. In general they do not move in strictly opposite directions, and they do not carry equal magnitudes of momentum. Another particle must therefore participate in this process. Finally, in 1956 Reines and Cowan succeeded in detecting the neutrino in a more direct way.

We now will give an outline of the theory of β decay, which is due to Fermi.[31] This theory was to a considerable extent patterned after the theory for the emission of photons. According to this latter theory the emission of

---

[30] Some of these predicted characteristics were, as one found later, much too modest.
[31] E. Fermi, *Zeitschrift für Physik* **88,** 161 (1934) (in German).

Enrico Fermi (1901–1954) Professor in Rome until 1938, then at Columbia U., from 1945 U. of Chicago. Nobel prize 1938. (Courtesy Niels Bohr Library, Am. Inst. of Physics).

photons arises from the interaction between atoms and the electromagnetic field. When an atom emits a photon, we cannot say that this photon had existed before inside the atom; we rather think of it as being created during the process in which it is emitted. Initially we have an atom in the initial state, afterwards we have an atom in its final state plus a photon. The initial and final states of the atom differ essentially only in the state of one single electron in the atomic shell. Regarding the β decay we can say similarly that we first have a nucleus in an initial state (say with Z protons and N neutrons), and afterwards we have the nucleus in its final state (in case of β^- decay with $Z + 1$ protons, $N - 1$ neutrons) plus a free electron and a neutrino. In this process one nucleon (in our example a neutron) changed its state and was converted into the other kind of nucleon (here a proton). It is easy to understand that because two particles (the electrons and the neutrino) are emitted, the available energy can be shared between the two in any energetically allowed way. In the emission of light only one "particle," the photon, was emitted which therefore took away the full energy difference between the two atomic states and therefore had a discrete energy.

However, it is not so trivial to show that those decays have the highest probability in which the electron and the neutrino have similar energies. We shall do this now, but first refer to Sect. 5.4 where we derived the number of states per energy interval or, in short, the density of states, $\rho(E)$, as a function of the excitation energy. Our starting point was the calculation of the possible energy states in a cube. We found (Eq. 5.4.22)

$$\rho(E) = \frac{dn}{dE} = 4\pi \left(\frac{2m}{h^2}\right)^{3/2} VE^{1/2}. \tag{5.4.22}$$

For our present considerations it is more convenient to express the density of states as the number of states per momentum interval instead of per energy interval. The relationship between the two is

$$\rho(p) = \frac{dn}{dp} = \frac{dn}{dE}\frac{dE}{dp}. \tag{6.7.13}$$

Considering that $E = p^2/2m$ and therefore $dE/dp = 2p/2m$ we find

$$\frac{dn}{dp} = 4\pi \left(\frac{2m}{h^2}\right)^{3/2} V \frac{p}{(2m)^{1/2}} \frac{2p}{2m}$$

$$\rho(p) = \frac{dn}{dp} = 8\pi V \frac{p^2}{h^3} = \text{const } p^2 \tag{6.7.14}$$

$$dn = \left(\frac{2V}{h^3}\right) 4\pi p^2 \, dp. \tag{6.7.15}$$

Therefore, dn is proportional to the volume of a spherical shell of radius p and thickness dp. It is therefore suggestive to speak about momentum space.

The probability for the emission of a particle of momentum between p and $p + dp$ is proportional to the number of states in this momentum interval. Equation 6.7.15 gives us this number of states. The important point to note is that the density of states goes with the square of the momentum. Although the particle, the electron or the neutrino, is emitted into the continuum, the considerations regarding the density of states still hold. The world outside the nucleus can be imagined as an infinitely big box. The infinitely big volume changes the value of the constant and makes the states infinitely closely spaced but it does not change the dependence of $\rho(p)$ on p.

The probability of finding particle 1 in the momentum interval between p_1 and $p_1 + dp$ and the particle 2 between p_2 and $p_2 + dp$ is just the product of the individual probabilities. In beta decay, however, the momenta of the two particles are not independent, because the energies must add up to a constant value. For simplicity's sake we will make the assumption that electron and neutrino both have negligible rest mass. This assumption is correct for the neutrino which has rest mass zero, but is only a very rough approximation for the usual β energies which are of the order of a fraction to a few MeV, whereas the rest mass of the electron is 0.5 MeV. Let the total available energy be E_0. If the electron energy is E_β, its momentum is E_β/c (under our assumption). The density of states with this momentum is proportional to E_β^2. The neutrino, then, must have the energy $E_\nu = E_0 - E_\beta$ and therefore the momentum $(E_0 - E_\beta/c)$. The density of its states is proportional to $(E_0 - E_\beta)^2$. Because the total probability is the product of the two probabilities which in turn are proportional to the densities, this yields a quantity proportional to $E_\beta^2(E_0 - E_\beta)^2$. The maximum of the probability can be found by differentiation in respect to E_β and gives as a result $E_\beta = \frac{1}{2}E$. We arrive at this simple result only, because we neglected the rest mass of the electron. Another correction to our result arises from the electrostatic interaction between the electron and the nucleus.

In some ways more important than the shape of the β spectrum is the speed with which the transformation proceeds. This speed depends on two factors: the availability of momentum space discussed above and a universal constant, the Fermi interaction constant g. The first factor is called the statistical factor. It is clear that the greater the energy or momentum which is available for the transformation, the more momentum space is available and the faster the decay proceeds. The second factor describes the interaction. It is similar to the constant G in the gravitational law $F = G(m_1 m_2/r^2)$. If G were twice as big as it is, processes depending on the gravitational force would proceed faster; stones would fall to earth faster; satellites would orbit faster. In other words, the interaction would be stronger. It now turns out that the interaction responsible for β decay is a weak interaction in comparison to nuclear interaction forces and also electromagnetic forces. It is therefore called *weak interaction*. If the same forces that hold a nucleus together were also responsible for the β decay, this decay would be many orders of magnitude faster. The fastest known β decay is that of ^{12}N (0.0125 sec), while nuclear reactions occur in times varying between 10^{-13} and 10^{-23} sec. The forces in β decay are therefore a completely different kind of forces. In physics we have to deal therefore with gravitational forces, weak forces, electromagnetic forces, and nuclear forces, in ascending order of strength.

We have pointed out above that the decay probability is the product of a factor involving the momentum space, or statistical factor, and a factor containing the universal constant. The half-life, and therefore the decay probability, of a β emitter can be measured experimentally. On the other hand, the hand, the statistical factor can be calculated from the available energy. It is therefore possible to determine the universal constant for the weak interaction with reasonable precision. A word of caution should be added here; in our description we neglected several other effects which also influence the half-life. Coulomb forces and the circumstance that electron and neutrino can carry angular momentum are the most important ones. For these other details we must refer to more advanced textbooks.

The so-called weak interaction is not limited to β-decay. The decay of the muon into an electron and two neutrinos is also governed by this interaction. One of these neutrinos is the same kind of neutrino as in β-decay, the other neutrino, however, is a different neutrino! In which physical properties these neutrinos differ from each other is presently still not known. One only knows that they react differently. Another reaction which is due to this weak-interaction force is the capture of a muon by a nucleon: for example,

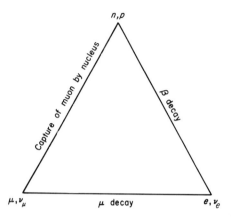

Fig. 6.7.11 The Puppi triangle.

a negatively charged muon is captured by a proton which hereby is converted into a neutron. In this process a neutrino of the second kind is emitted, which carries away most of the energy which was present before as energy in the form of rest mass of the muon. Puppi has described these three processes in a very appealing graph, the so-called Puppi's triangle, Fig. 6.7.11. One side indicates beta decay, in which the four particles $n \rightarrow p + \beta^- + \bar{\nu}_e$ participate.[32] The other sides represent the two other reactions.

We might add that one of the most spectacular features of the weak interactions is their violation of the principle of left-and-right symmetry in elementary processes. We shall discuss this problem in the following chapter in more detail and in the broader context of conservation laws and symmetries.

γ Decay

γ Decay has its counterpart in the de-excitation of an atom by emission of a light quantum. Whereas photons in the visible range of the electromagnetic spectrum have energies in the order of electron volts, most of the electromagnetic transitions of nuclei involve energy differences between a few tens of keV and a few MeV. The quanta which are emitted are called γ quanta. They originate in the nucleus, whereas x-ray quanta that can have energies in the same range originate in the atomic shell or are bremsstrahlung.

---

[32] More correctly, the particle emitted together with the β^- is an anti-neutrino $\bar{\nu}_e$. It is the anti-particle to the neutrino ν_e, just as a β^+ is the anti-particle to the β^-. For more details see Chapter 7.

An atomic or nuclear system is not the source of a steady flow of electromagnetic energy, but it releases its energy in one shot, by emitting a quantum and thereby undergoing a transition between two energy states. The ideas of classical electromagnetic theory therefore need some reinterpretation. The energy of the quantum is $h\nu = \hbar\omega$, and in the average, a quantum is emitted within a time span during which that much energy would have been emitted according to classical theory. The process of the emission of the quantum itself takes much less time in general.

By considering an atom or nucleus as an oscillating dipole, we can roughly estimate the lifetime of an excited state. In the discussion of the radiation of a dipole antenna (Sect. 1.3) we mentioned that the amount of energy emitted per second is

$$W_r = \frac{\omega^4 (Qx_0)^2}{12\pi\epsilon_0 c^3} \tag{1.3.1}$$

where Q and x_0 are charge and dimension of the dipole and ω is its angular frequency $2\pi\nu$, and consequently also of the emitted wave.

In many nuclear systems only one nucleon changes its orbit. Thus we can set for Q the proton charge, and x_0 can be equated in our rough calculation with the nuclear radius. For a nucleus in the region of $A = 200$ this dimension is about 10^{-14} m. For a quantum energy $h\nu = 1$ MeV and the corresponding frequency ν we obtain from Eq. 1.3.1 the energy radiation rate $W_r = 4.3$ joule/sec. Since a quantum of 1 MeV equals 1.6×10^{-13} joule, the lifetime of the excited state is $1.6 \times 10^{-13}/4.3$ sec or roughly 4×10^{-14} sec. This order of magnitude is indeed corroborated by experiments for transitions which have dipole character. A more rigorous quantum-mechanical calculation would proceed along the arguments sketched in Sect. 3.8 by evaluating, among other things, the integral of Eq. 3.8.13, where Ψ_m and Ψ_n are the wave functions of the initial and final state and ex is the dipole moment.

Besides the quantitative difference in energy between quanta emitted from the atomic shell and those from nuclei, another one must be mentioned: In atomic physics nearly all observed transitions arise from atoms which radiate like electric dipoles. This dipole character leads to the selection rule $\Delta L = \pm 1$, known from Sect. 4.8. Quantum mechanics shows that if $\Delta L \neq \pm 1$, the radiation is no more that of a dipole, and furthermore, it proceeds at a considerably slower rate. If dipole radiation is impossible because the selection rule $\Delta L = \pm 1$ cannot be satisfied, this means in general in the case of excited atoms that they will be de-excited rather by collisions either with other atoms or with the walls of the container.

In nuclei the possibilities for de-excitation by other means than emission of quanta are not so overwhelmingly frequent. Therefore transitions with $\Delta L = 2, 3$, or even 4 are fairly common. How much the difference in angular momentum influences the half-life of a transition might be seen from the theoretical data for a transition energy of 200 keV of a medium-heavy nucleus: $\Delta l = 1: 10^{-13}$ sec; $\Delta l = 2: 10^{-7}$ sec; $\Delta l = 3: 1$ sec; $\Delta l = 4: 10^6$ sec. An excited state with an observable half-life is called an isomeric state, in analogy to an isomer in organic chemistry which describes a molecule with a different arrangement of the atoms. Here we have, so to speak, the same nucleus with a different arrangement of nucleons. Nuclear isomers have been found with half-lives ranging up to years. Regarding short-lived isomers there is only a very fluid borderline, because the continued advances in electronics push the time intervals which can be measured further and further down. Today even states with life-times as short as 10^{-9} sec are considered isomeric states.

We will conclude the discussion about nuclear decay by discussion of the decay scheme of the nuclide ^{60}Co, which is used frequently in industry and medicine because of its long half-life of slightly over 5 years, and its relatively energetic γ radiation of more than 1 MeV (Fig. 6.7.1). ^{60}Co usually is produced by exposing the stable ^{59}Co to neutrons from a reactor. These neutrons are captured by the ^{59}Co, transforming it to ^{60}Co. The neutron capture leaves ^{60}Co either in its isomeric state of 10.7 min half-life or in its ground state. The isomeric state is 0.059 MeV above the ground state. The isomeric state has two possibilities for its decay: either it can decay to its ground state, whereby 3 units of angular momentum have to be given off, or by a β transition of 1.54 MeV. Because of the weakness of the β interaction, the first-mentioned mode of decay is much more frequent. The ground state of ^{60}Co decays by β decay to an excited state of ^{60}Ni of 2.50 MeV excitation energy. Two γ rays are emitted in cascade and the ground state is reached. One may ask why the transition from the 2.50 MeV state to the ground state is not made by emission of one γ ray. The answer is that this γ ray would have to carry away 4 units of angular momentum. This makes such a transition quite improbable.

Table 6.7.2 summarizes some of the properties of the diverse particles which play a role in nuclear physics. Added are also the pion, the muon, and its neutrino. Furthermore, to convey an idea about the order of magnitude of the penetrating power, the last column lists the range or mean free path in aluminum for a particle of 2 MeV kinetic energy.

Fission

The more massive a nuclide is, the greater is its electrostatic energy per nucleon because of the rising number of protons. In addition there is also

TABLE 6.7.2

Properties of Particles

Particle	Rest Mass, MeV	Spin	Isospin	Charge Q = 1.6×10^{-19} coul	Stability[a]	Interaction[b]	Range or Mean Free Path for a 2 MeV particle in Al (cm)
Photon, γ quantum	0	1		0	S	EM	9
Electron-neutrino	0	$\frac{1}{2}$		0	S	W	Light years
Electron, β particle	0.511	$\frac{1}{2}$		$-Q$	S	EM, W	0.4
Proton, H ion	938.3	$\frac{1}{2}$	$\frac{1}{2}$	$+Q$	S	S	0.004
Neutron	939.6	$\frac{1}{2}$	$\frac{1}{2}$	0	U	S	5
α particle, ⁴He nucleus	3727.3	0	0	$+2Q$	S	S	0.0006
Muon-neutrino	0	$\frac{1}{2}$		0	S	W	Light years
Muon	106	$\frac{1}{2}$		$-Q$	U	W	0.01
Pion, π meson, π^0	135.0	0	1	0	U	EM	
" " , π^+	139.6	0	1	$+Q$	U	S	0.01

[a] S: stable; U: unstable.
[b] W: weak; EM: electromagnetic; S: strong.

an increase in the asymmetry energy which results from the increasing neutron excess over the protons. For this reason there is a limit to the size of nuclei, because it finally becomes energetically more favorable if a very big nucleus splits into two smaller ones or, in more technical terms, undergoes fission.

Before the fission a nucleus must first deform in a manner illustrated in Fig. 6.7.12. However, small deformations increase the potential energy. (This is similar to a water drop which has the smallest energy when it is spherical, but there is a difference insofar as in many nuclei the equilibrium shape is not spherical.) For modest deformations from the equilibrium shape, for which we assume a deformation a (Fig. 6.7.13), the potential energy increases, until from the deformation b on (which corresponds approximately to shape 3 of Fig. 6.7.12), the scission of the nucleus has gone so far that the system becomes unstable, deforms even more, and fission occurs.

What will cause a nucleus to assume a shape different from the one in which its energy is lowest? The fission of the nuclide ^{235}U (which in natural uranium has an abundance of only 0.7%, the bulk being ^{238}U) may serve as an example: Slow neutrons which have a negligible amount of kinetic energy (<100 keV) can be captured by ^{235}U nuclei. In this process the binding energy of this neutron of approximately 6 MeV becomes available as excitation energy which will set the nucleus into vibrations and will carry it over the potential hump.

In the fission process much electrostatic energy is set free, and the two fission fragments fly apart with kinetic energies between 50 and 100 MeV. In comparison with nuclei of the same mass these fragments are very rich in neutrons. Therefore a few neutrons (on the average 2–3) will be given off per fission process, and by beta decays several more will be changed into protons. The total released energy per fission is about 200 MeV and, by converting into heat the kinetic energy of the fragments, neutrons and beta particles can be used in a reactor as nuclear power.

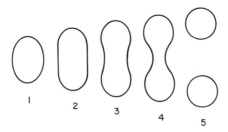

Fig. 6.7.12   The fission of a heavy nucleus.

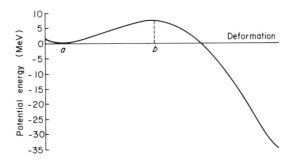

Fig. 6.7.13   The potential energy of a nucleus as a function of its deformation.

One should expect that the nucleus splits most likely into two approximately equal fragments. This is, however, not at all the case. Nearly always the heavier fragment has a mass number A of about 140 ± 10 and the lighter one $A \sim 95 \pm 10$. Today, one-third of a century after the discovery of fission, the reason for this asymmetry is still not understood!

An important feature of fission is the possibility of a chain reaction. The two or three neutrons, which on the average are emitted in fission, can be captured by two or three other ^{235}U nuclei after being slowed down in collisions with other nuclei, and so forth. By absorbing some of the neutrons with boron, which has a very big cross section for capturing neutrons, the multiplication of the fission processes in a reactor can be controlled, thus preventing an explosion as in an atomic bomb.

Fission was discovered in 1938 by the German radiochemist O. Hahn[33] and his co-worker Strassmann. Before that time several famous physicists had seen fission products without recognizing their nature. In 1934 Fermi and his co-workers in Rome had begun to irradiate diverse substances with slow neutrons and produced artificial radioisotopes. (For this work Fermi received the 1938 Nobel prize in physics.) The husband and wife team Joliot-Curie in Paris and also Hahn, Meitner, and Strassmann in Berlin adopted this method, and they all irradiated uranium among other substances. Hahn and Strassmann very carefully separated chemically the resulting activity, expecting radium. Their crucial paper[34] contains the sentences: "We are led to the conclusion: Our 'radium isotopes' have the properties of barium; as chemists we should properly say that the newly formed bodies are not radium, but barium; other elements than radium and barium are out of question." (Barium, however, has a mass number around 138.) Toward the end of this article they wrote: "As 'nuclear chem-

[33] Otto Hahn (1879–1968), director of the Kaiser-Wilhelm Institute for Chemistry; 1944 Nobel prize in chemistry for the discovery of fission.
[34] *Naturwissenschaften* **27,** 11 (1939).

ists' who in some ways are close to physics we are at present still hesitant to undertake the big step which contradicts all previous experience of nuclear physics."

6.8   NUCLEAR REACTIONS

The study of nuclear reactions was started by Rutherford in 1919. He used α particles which were emitted in the α decay of heavy nuclides and let them pass through nitrogen gas. Rutherford found that some nitrogen nuclei were transformed into oxygen nuclei with emission of protons. This reaction can be written either this way

$$^{14}_{7}N + {}^{4}_{2}He \rightarrow {}^{17}_{8}O + {}^{1}_{1}H$$

or in abbreviated and more customary form

$$^{14}_{7}N \; (\alpha, p) \; {}^{17}_{8}O.$$

Other nuclei could also be transformed; however, bombardment of heavier nuclei with natural α particles, the most energetic ones having energies less than about 9 MeV, did not induce a reaction because with increasing charge of the nucleus the electrostatic barrier becomes too high and prevents the bombarding α particles from interacting with the target nucleus. Returning to our original reaction, the α particles amalgamates with the ^{14}N nucleus and forms a highly excited aggregate, the so-called compound system, which in our example breaks up into ^{17}O, i.e., the residual nucleus, and a proton. The compound system in our case is composed of 9 protons and 9 neutrons, and is therefore a fluorine nuclide. It is also possible that the compound system decays by emission of a neutron into $^{17}_{9}F$. This reaction was not seen by Rutherford, because the neutron is not so easy to detect as the proton. In fact only in 1932 was the neutron discovered.

With the coming of accelerators the possibility for study of nuclear reactions was greatly improved. Although today's accelerators work on various principles, they all accelerate particles by means of electric fields. The reader might be familiar with the principle of the Van de Graaff accelerator and the cyclotron. The Van de Graaff accelerator produces an electrostatic field through the transport of charges by a moving belt. Potential differences of up to 10^7 V can be created. An ion, for example a hydrogen nucleus, or a singly ionized carbon ion accelerated by this potential will gain an energy of 10 MeV. If the sign of the charge of the ion can now be reversed by attaching or removing one or two electrons, the ion by transversing this potential again in opposite direction will gain an additional 10 MeV, so that it finally has 20 MeV. This is the principle of the so-called tandem accelerators. In a cyclotron particles are accelerated by an alternating electric field; a constant magnetic field serves to keep particles on nearly circular orbits which, due to electric acceleration, become spirals. Because of the relativistic mass change with velocity of the accelerated particles, which becomes important for proton energies beyond 10 MeV, either the frequency of the alternating electric field must be changed during the acceleration or the magnetic field must vary in space. The first alternative is realized in the frequency-modulated or synchrocyclotron, the second alternative in the isochronous cyclotron. Certain accelerators use an induced electromotive force for the acceleration, as for example the betatron. In linear accelerators the particles are accelerated in a straight line. Usually there are several accelerating sections. The acceleration is effected by high-frequency electric fields in the form of traveling waves. Most of the modern, very large accelerators use these principles either alone, or in combination.[35]

After this short excursion into the different types of accelerators we will now take up some questions about the mechanism of nuclear reactions. There are different types of reactions. Either the whole nucleus is involved in the process, or only one or a few nucleons of the nucleus participate in the reaction. In the first case we can describe a nuclear reaction in the following way: the bombarding particle enters the nucleus. It soon loses its kinetic energy to the other nucleons in the nucleus. The nucleus has now reached the stage called the *compound nucleus*. We can think of this process as if the temperature of the nucleus was raised because of the increase of internal kinetic energy. Similar to a heated water drop in which molecules leave the surface of the drop, nucleons (or α particles) may be evaporated from the nuclear surface. The entering particle shares its kinetic energy with many other nucleons, and usually none of these has enough energy to leave the nucleus, because in order to leave it at least the separation energy has to be overcome. However, there are statistical fluctuations in the distribution of the energy between the nucleons. For this reason there is a small but finite chance that a particle could accumulate a high fraction of the internal energy, that it is at this moment near the nuclear surface, and that it is moving outwards and could leave the nucleus. One might think that protons have a better chance to leave the nucleus because they might be, so to speak, pushed out by electrostatic repulsion by the nucleus. This reasoning, however, is wrong. On the contrary, protons have more difficulty escaping the nucleus because they have to overcome the Coulomb barrier. Only after they are "over the hump" are they repelled! Evaporation of protons is therefore much less probable than evaporation of neutrons

---

[35] More on accelerators may be found in Sect. 7.2.

and, in general, a neutron rather than a proton will be emitted from the compound nucleus. Since a boiled-off particle will usually not carry away all the excitation energy, the nucleus is left in an excited state. If the remaining excitation energy is still high enough for another particle to be emitted, this will usually happen. Alternatively, the nucleus will lose its excess energy by emission of electromagnetic quanta, that is, γ radiation. Examples of reactions proceeding with the emission of several nucleons are $(p, 2n)$ and (α, pn) reactions.

It has been possible to estimate lifetimes of compound nuclei by using the uncertainty relation between time and energy, and it was found that this lifetime is of the order of 10^{-16} or 10^{-17} sec. One of the experimental procedures is the following: A target is irradiated with slow neutrons, and the absorption of the neutrons as a function of their energy is measured. The cross section for neutron absorption shows typical resonances as shown in Fig. 6.8.1. This may be interpreted that only in those cases where the neutron brings along the correct energy can an excited state of the compound nucleus be formed easily. The line width of the resonance is a measure of the lifetime of the excited state on the basis of the Heisenberg relation $\Gamma\tau \sim \hbar$, where Γ is the width of the resonance expressed in units of energy and τ is the lifetime. De-excitation of a compound nucleus which is formed in this way is usually achieved by emission of a few γ rays.

Lifetimes of the compound nucleus also can be measured somewhat more directly by an elegant technique which was developed in the last few years. We will discuss it using the $Ge(\alpha, p)Ga$ reaction as an example. The incoming α particle imparts some momentum to the compound nucleus, which moves some distance d before decaying by emitting a proton. If the lifetime of the compound nucleus is τ_c, this displacement is $d = \tau_c c_c$. The velocity v_c of the còmpound nucleus can easily be calculated from momen-

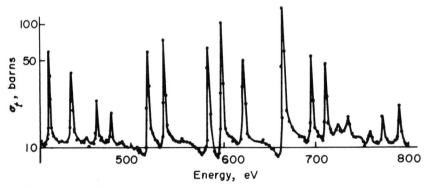

Fig. 6.8.1 Total cross section for neutrons of ^{238}U plotted against neutron energy in the range 400 eV to 800 eV (after Firk, Lynn and Moxon, Proc. Int. Conf. on Nucl. Structure, Kingston, Canada, Univ. of Toronto Press, 1960, p. 757).

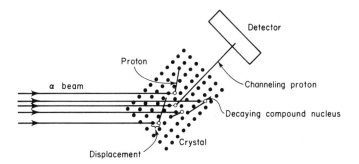

Fig. 6.8.2 Schematic arrangement to measure lifetimes of compound nuclei.

tum considerations, and it turns out to be of the order of 10^6–10^7 m/sec. Since compound-nucleus lifetimes are of the order of 10^{-16} to 10^{-18} sec, the displacement is about 10^{-11} to 10^{-10} m, or 0.1 to 1 Å. It is therefore in general somewhat smaller than the spacing of lattice planes in a crystal.

In the 1960's it was discovered experimentally that protons have a much longer range in single crystals when traveling parallel to lattice planes than when traveling in some random direction. This to some degree plausible effect is called *channeling*, because the proton is thought to move relatively unimpeded between lattice planes. If now an α-particle beam is directed against a thin single crystal of germanium, compound nuclei are formed and are pushed away from the crystallographic plane to which the atomic nucleus originally belonged. The compound nucleus decays when still in motion between two such planes. There is a small but still finite chance that the proton is emitted from the compound nucleus in a direction parallel to these planes. It can therefore channel through the crystal and reach a detector, as shown in Fig. 6.8.2. Obviously only a small fraction of all the protons emitted in a great many (α, p) reactions will happen to move in a direction which favors channeling and thus be able to escape the crystal and to reach the detector. If the displacement of the compound nuclei brings them halfway between two planes of atoms, the probability for channeling is greatest. From the ratio of the channeling protons to all protons released in (α, p) reactions, one can therefore deduce the average displacement and hence can compute the lifetime of the compound nucleus. The lifetimes determined with this method agree with those calculated from the uncertainty relation.

Considering that the kinetic energy of the nucleons inside the nucleus is such that they travel with roughly one-tenth of the velocity of light, and that a representative nuclear diameter is 10^{-12} cm, a nucleon travels a distance of the order of one million nuclear diameters during the life of the compound nucleus! Its chance of escape is indeed small! This long life is one of the main characteristics of the compound nucleus. The compound nucleus has "forgotten" how it has been formed. The mode of decay does not depend therefore on the mode of the formation. It does depend, however, on the excitation energy. Bombardment of ^{63}Cu with protons and of ^{60}Ni with α particles results in the same compound nucleus. If the energies of the protons and α particles are chosen such that the excitation energy of the compound nucleus is the same, the decay in both cases is very similar. For example, the ratios of emission of (a) one neutron to (b) two neutrons to (c) a proton plus a neutron are the same in both cases. An illustration is given in Fig. 6.8.3.

We will now mention reactions in which no compound nucleus is formed. The incoming particle might in its first collision transfer its full energy to one other nucleon which might be successfully knocked out of the nucleus. The time interval between entrance of the bombarding particle and exit of the leaving particle is naturally much shorter than in the compound nucleus case and is in the order of 10^{-20} sec. Finally there is the category of pick-up and stripping reactions (Fig. 6.8.4). In the former, for example, a proton approaches the nucleus, collides with a neutron, picks up this neutron, and the two leave as a deuteron. In the latter case a deuteron

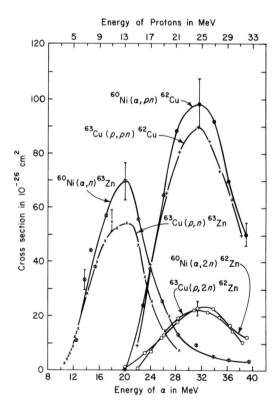

Fig. 6.8.3 The experimental evidence for the compound nucleus hypothesis. [Goshal, *Phys. Rev.* **80**, 939 (1950).]

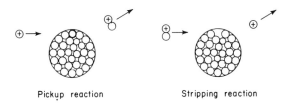

Pickup reaction   Stripping reaction

Fig. 6.8.4   Direct reactions.

might lose its proton or neutron to the nucleus. Such reactions show very pronounced preferred directions for the outgoing particles.

Energy, momentum, and angular momentum are conserved in every nuclear reaction. We discuss here the conservation of energy. When energy is given off in a reaction, this reaction is called *exoergic*, and if a reaction needs energy from the outside in order to be possible, it is an *endoergic* reaction. This is obviously in analogy to chemical reactions.

Let us consider the general case of the reaction $T(b, e)R$, where T stands for the target nucleus, R for the residual nucleus, b for the bombarding particle, and e for the emitted particle or particles. The reaction can also be written

$$b + T \rightarrow R + e + Q$$

where Q (just as in chemistry) is the reaction energy. $Q > 0$ means that energy is given off, and $Q < 0$ means that energy is taken in.

Using, with the appropriate subscripts, K to designate the kinetic energy, M the mass of the nuclei, and m the mass of the bombarding or emitted particles, the energy equation can be written

$$K_b + m_b c^2 + K_T + M_T c^2 = K_R + M_R c^2 + K_e + m_e c^2.$$

If we take the laboratory as reference frame, the target nucleus is usually at rest, therefore, $K_T = 0$. Therefore

$$K_b + [(M_T + m_b) - (M_R + m_e)]c^2 = K_R + K_b.$$

The expression within the brackets is the Q value of the reaction, divided by c^2. We also can write this quantity Q

$$Q = [(M_T + m_b) - (M_R + m_e)]c^2.$$

Experimentally measured Q values give us therefore the possibility to calculate mass differences between the target and the residual nucleus, in addition to the mass spectrographic determinations and those deduced from α and β decay energies.

We shall discuss a few examples. First, deuterium nuclei are bombarded with deuterons, and ^{3}H, tritium, is formed. This reaction can be written as ^{2}H$(d, p)^3$H. Although we are studying nuclear physics and are interested in nuclear masses, it is convenient and general practice to use in the computations the masses of the neutral atoms, that is, to include the mass of the electrons. The tabulated masses are nearly always those of the neutral atoms. Since the sum of the electrons before and after the reaction is constant, their mass drops out of the calculations. To convince the reader we shall do one calculation with nuclear and with atomic masses. Nuclear masses shall be designated by N and n instead of M and m. It is hereby important, not to confuse p, the proton, and its mass with H, the hydrogen atom, and its mass. Similarly one has to discriminate between the deuteron d and the deuterium atom D.

$$Q = [(N_{^2H} + n_d) - (N_{^3H} + n_p)]c^2.$$

We now add one electron mass m_e to each charged particle

$$Q = [(\{N_{^2H} + m_e\} + \{n_d + m_e\}) - (\{N_{^3H} + m_e\} + \{n_p + m_e\})]c^2,$$

or directly in atomic masses

$$Q = [(M_{^2H} + m_D) - (M_{^3H} + m_H)]c^2.$$

Mass tables frequently give the masses of the atoms in mass units u (1 u = 1/12 of the mass of a ^{12}C atom = 931.481 MeV/c^2) ^{1}H: 1.00783 u, ^{2}H: 2.01410 u, ^{3}H: 3.01605 u. Therefore

$$Q = [(2.01410 + 2.01410) - (3.01605 + 1.00783)]u \cdot c^2$$

$$= [4.02820 - 4.02388]u \cdot c^2 = 0.00432\, u \cdot c^2 = 4.02\ \text{MeV}.$$

Since the combined mass of the end product is smaller than the mass of the bombarding particle and target, the reaction is exoergic.

For our second example we modify this reaction slightly, assuming now that a neutron instead of a proton leaves the nucleus. The residual nucleus is therefore ^{3}He, and the equation for Q becomes

$$Q = [(M_{^2H} + m_D) - (M_{^3He} + m_n)]c^2.$$

The mass tables list

$$n\colon 1.00867\ u \qquad ^3\text{He}\colon 3.01603\ u.$$

Hence

$$Q = [4.02820 - 4.02470]u \cdot c^2 = 0.00350\, u \cdot c^2 = 3.26\ \text{MeV}.$$

This reaction is also exoergic.

With fast neutrons as bombarding particles one often observes the reaction $(n, 2n)$, for example ^{12}C$(n, 2n)^{11}$C. With the mass of ^{12}C by definition 12 u exactly, and ^{11}C 11.01143 u we have

$$Q = [(12.00000 + 1.00867) - (11.01143 + 2 \times 1.00867)]$$

$$= -0.02010\, u \cdot c^2 = -18.7\ \text{MeV}.$$

This reaction is endoergic, because 18.7 MeV have to be supplied to make up for the mass difference.

However, in a reaction not only the energy is conserved, but also the momentum. Because the incoming particle carries along momentum, and the center-of-mass of the whole system must move with the same velocity before and after the reaction, some of the energy of the incoming particle may not be available as reaction energy.

Furthermore, in compound-nucleus reactions induced by positively charged particles, that is protons, deuterons, and so on, the bombarding particle must overcome the Coulomb repulsion to reach the nuclear surface or at least successfully tunnel through the Coulomb barrier.

Therefore, in order to determine a Q value of an endoergic reaction, it is usually not sufficient to measure only the inset of the reaction, but one must also measure or at least take into account the kinetic energies of the end products, and possibly their internal excitation energy.

PROBLEMS

1. (a) Calculate the radius of a ^{208}Pb *nucleus*. (b) What is the density (in g/cm³) of nuclear matter? (c) Calculate the average distance between the centers of neighboring nucleons inside a nucleus. (d) What is the energy of a γ quantum which has a wavelength equal to the diameter of a lead nucleus?

2. *Pulsars*, which are fast-pulsating radio sources, are presently believed to be neutron stars which represent a late stage in the life of a star. All the protons and electrons have been transformed into neutrons, and the density of such a star is equal to that of nuclei, or even higher. Assume that our sun becomes a neutron star and has the density of a nucleus. What will then be its radius and its period of rotation? Data of the present sun: radius 7.0×10^8 m; mass: 2.0×10^{30} kg; period of rotation: approx. 25 days.

3. (a) How much *energy* does a proton need in order to strike a silver nucleus whose radius is 7.1×10^{-15} m? Neglect the radius of the proton. The atomic number of silver is 47. (b) How fast would the incident proton be moving?

4. (a) How much *energy* does an α particle need to strike a silver nucleus? (See Problem 3.) The α particle is a helium nucleus. Its atomic number is 2 and its atomic weight is 4. Neglect the radius of the α particle. (b) How fast would the incident α particle be moving?

5. A thorium nucleus having a radius 9.16×10^{-15} m and an atomic number $A = 90$ ejects an α particle (charge $+2e$). Neglect the radius of the α particle. (a) How much *energy*, expressed in electron volts, must the α particle have if it is ejected at rest at the surface of the Th nucleus? (b) Could this α particle reach either gold or silver nuclei?

6. A beam of 50-MeV protons is incident on a thin sheet of gold. The gold nucleus may be assumed to have a radius of 8.7×10^{-15} m. Neglect the radius of the proton. The atomic number of gold is 79, and its atomic weight is 197. At these energies, the Coulomb repulsive force has little effect, and only the protons that make direct hits on gold nuclei are stopped. What thickness must the gold foil have in order to *stop* 1% of the incident *protons* by direct nuclear collisions? The density of gold is 19.3 g/cm³. Hint: How many nuclei per unit area spread on a plane surface would cover 1%

of the area? In what thickness of foil would you find this number per unit area of surface?

7. The average number of ions produced by an α particle in air may be assumed about 10^5 per centimeter. (a) What will then be the *range* of a 5-MeV α *particle* in air if in the average 15 eV are required to produce an ion? (b) What would you expect the range of such α particles to be in your body? What would you expect to be the consequence of exposure to α rays? The number of molecules per mole is 6.02×10^{23}. One mole at normal temperature and pressure occupies 22.4 l. Human tissue may be treated here as though it were water, with a molecular weight of 18 and a density of 1 g/cm^3.

8. Assuming that, from a nuclear point of view, air may be treated as though it were made of nitrogen molecules whose nuclear radii are 5×10^{-15} m and whose atomic number is 7, what fraction of the particles in a beam of α particles such as is treated in Problem 7 should make a *nuclear collision* in 3 cm of path? See hint in Problem 6 and data in Problem 7.

9. In an experiment on the *scattering of α particles*, the number ΔN scattered into a direction making an angle between θ and $\theta + \Delta\theta$ with the direction of incidence are listed below.

θ degrees	$\Delta N/\Delta\theta$	θ degrees	$\Delta N/\Delta\theta$
156	2.05	87.5	20
123.5	6.3	83	22
110	9.0	78.5	25
100.5	12.5	75	33
93	15	72.25	40

Is this scattering due to Coulomb forces?

10. In J. J. *Thomson's atomic model* the positive charge is spread uniformly over the whole atomic volume. Why is such a charge distribution incompatible with the large-angle scattering of α particles?

11. Approximately how many nucleons are located at the *surface of a nucleus* of atomic weight (a) $A = 20$ (e.g., $^{20}_{10}$Ne)? (b) $A = 100$ (e.g., $^{100}_{42}$Mo)? (c) $A = 238$ (e.g., $^{238}_{92}$U)? Disregard the decrease of density in the "skin" region. Before doing the calculation take first a guess!

12. What is the *de Broglie wavelength* of 200-MeV electrons?

13. Determine from the positions of the minima in the *electron-scattering* data in Fig. 6.2.6 the radius of Au nuclei.

14. Figure 6.2.6 shows the *diffraction pattern* from the scattering of 153- and 183-MeV electrons on ^{197}Au nuclei. Qualitatively sketch how the diffraction pattern might look for electron scattering on ^{31}P nuclei at these energies.

15. Show that the *radius R* of the equivalent uniform charge distribution of a nucleus and the mean-square radius of the true charge distribution $\langle r^2 \rangle_{av}$ are connected by the relation

$$\langle r^2 \rangle_{av} = \tfrac{3}{5} R^2.$$

16. Calculate the radius of the first and second *Bohr orbit* for a negative *muon* bound by a molybdenum nucleus $(Z = 42)$, and compare it with the nuclear radius $(A \sim 96)$.

17. Calculate the radius of the first and second *Bohr orbit* for a negative *pion* bound by an oxygen nucleus $(Z = 8)$, and compare it with the nuclear radius.

18. Using the hydrogen wave functions ψ, ψ^2 and $4\pi r^2 \psi^2$ of Chapter 4 sketch the $1s_{1/2}$ *muonic wave function* for $_{42}$Mo and also indicate in this drawing the radii of the ^{96}Mo and ^{98}Mo nuclei. See also Fig. 6.2.8.

19. From the widths Γ of the pionic K_α lines emitted in the transitions $2p$-$1s$ in ^{16}O $(\Gamma = 7.56$ keV$)$ and in ^{18}O $(\Gamma = 8.67$ keV$)$ estimate the *lifetime* from the uncertainty relation $\Delta E \Delta \tau \geq \hbar$. What might be the reason for the difference in Γ between ^{16}O and ^{18}O? What lifetime is being measured?

20. The *radii* of some nuclei can approximately be determined from the mass difference between a nucleus with n protons and $(n + 1)$ neutrons and a nucleus with $(n + 1)$ protons and n neutrons. (Nuclei forming such a pair are called *mirror nuclei*.) This mass difference is partly due to the mass difference between a neutron and a proton which is 1.29 MeV, the neutron being the more massive particle. Another part of the mass difference is due to the difference in the electrostatic energy of the two nuclei. The electrostatic energy of a uniformly charged sphere is, according to electrostatics, $\tfrac{3}{5} Q^2 / 4\pi\epsilon_0 R$ where Q is the charge of the sphere. (a) Calculate from the measured mass difference of the nuclei $^{15}_{8}$O (the more massive one) and $^{15}_{7}$N of 2.413×10^{-3} u the radius of ^{15}O and ^{15}N. (b) Determine the constant r_0. 1 u $= 1/12$ of the mass of a ^{12}C atom $= 931.5$ MeV.

21. A *total neutron-absorption* measurement was performed in good geometry for ^{238}U using a sample of 2.5 cm length. The total neutron cross section for ^{238}U between 18 and 28 MeV is constant and is 6.3 b. (a) By what fraction was the neutron beam attenuated? (b) What is the radius of the ^{238}U nuclei? Density of uranium 18.7 g/cm^3.

22. A hypothetical metal having a specific gravity of 8 and mass number 120 is placed in a *beam of neutrons*. The total neutron cross section is 0.8 b. (a) What thickness is needed to reduce the intensity of the beam to 10% of its incident value? (b) Another sample of the above metal contains an unknown percentage of an impurity having a total cross section of 12,000 b. A slab having the same thickness as that used in part (a) is

found to reduce the beam intensity to 5% of its initial value. What is the concentration of the impurity?

23. A sphere of radius R is made up of two concentric parts, a core of radius $R/2$ having a uniformly distributed charge $+Q$, which is surrounded by a layer of inner radius $R/2$ and outer radius R. This outer part has a uniformly distributed charge $-Q$. The whole sphere is uniformly rotating with an angular velocity ω around an axis passing through its center. The mass of the sphere is M and is distributed uniformly. Compute the *gyro-magnetic ratio* γ (see p. 279) of this sphere.

24. The *magnetic moment* of a proton μ_p is $+2.79$ nuclear magnetons, abbreviated μ_N, and that of a neutron μ_n is -1.91 μ_N. 1 $\mu_N = (e\hbar/2M_p)$, where M_p is the mass of a proton. Therefore, 1 μ_N is 1837 times smaller than the Bohr magneton μ_B of atomic physics. That the magnetic moment of the proton $\mu_p \neq \mu_N$, and that of a neutron, μ_n, is not equal to zero, may be explained by assuming that for a fraction t of the time the proton is dissociated into a neutron and a π^+ meson, and likewise the neutron may dissociate into a proton and a π^- meson, or

$$p \leftrightarrow n + \pi^+ \qquad n \leftrightarrow p + \pi^-$$

The pions have a magnetic moment which is greater than μ_N because of the smaller meson mass. Show that such a model can explain the fact that $\mu_p + \mu_n \approx 1 \ \mu_N$. (Meson mass $\approx \frac{1}{7}$ nucleon mass.)

25. (a) What is the z component, T_z, of the *isospin* of $^9_5$B? (b) What is the isospin T of its ground state?

26. The nuclide ^{51}V has 23 protons. (a) What is the value of the z component of the *isospin* of the ground state? (b) of the excited states? (c) Which values can the isospin T assume?

27. Redraw Fig. 6.3.3 showing an *isospin triplet* to conform to the representation of Fig. 6.3.2.

28. Given are some energy levels of ^{6}He, ^{6}Li, and ^{6}Be which either have isospin $T = 0$ or $T = 1$. Give assignments for the most probable isospin T for each level and for the z component T_z.

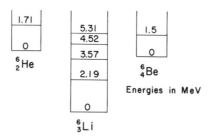

Figure P.6.1 (Problem 28)

29. Show that the total wave function of the deuteron is antisymmetric, as it should be according to the *generalized exclusion principle* which also takes the isospin into account.

30. Calculate the Bragg angle obtained with a NaCl crystal for the 2.23 MeV γ radiation which results from the *capture of a neutron* by a proton. Lattice constant 2.8 Å.

31. A *deuteron* can be *disintegrated* by the action of an energetic γ quantum. This process is called photodisintegration of the deuteron and was investigated first in 1935 by Chadwick (the discoverer of the neutron) and Goldhaber [*Proc. Roy. Soc. (London)* **A 151**, 479 (1935)]. γ Rays from the natural radioactive thorium C″ which have an energy of 2.62 MeV passed through deuterium gas, and pulses from the freed protons were electronically detected. The energy of these protons was determined to be 0.24 ± 0.08 MeV. (*a*) Compute from the given data the binding energy of the deuteron. Assume that the masses of the proton and the neutron are equal. (*b*) Was the limit of error for the proton energy realistic, considering the actual value of the binding energy?

32. A ball of mass m moves frictionless with modest velocity v across a trench of depth V_0, never losing contact with the ground, as shown in the figure. (*a*) Draw a *diagram* showing the total *energy*, the potential energy, and the kinetic energy of the ball as a function of the distance x from the origin O. (*b*) Assume now that the initial velocity is high enough that the ball temporarily loses contact with the ground, reaching it at the center of the well, and from there on rolls further along. Assume that no energy is lost by heat. Draw the appropriate diagram for this situation.

33. Given a *one-dimensional two-particle system*, similar to a deuteron, with a potential and a ψ function as given in the figure. (Assume that one of the particles, located at $x = 0$, has a much greater mass than the other particle, which was mass m, so that the reduced mass can be approximated by the mass m of the lighter particle.) (*a*) From the inspection of the graphs in the figure state if the two particles are bound. Justify your answer in one or two sentences. (*b*) From the figure estimate the fraction of time for which the two particles are farther apart than the range of the potential. (*c*) What is the kinetic energy of the lighter particle with this wave function when inside the well? Express your answer in terms of m, a, and h.

Figure P.6.2 (Problem 32)

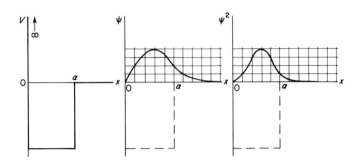

Figure P.6.3 (Problem 33)

34. Without too great error the *wave function of the deuteron* $u(r) = \psi(r)r$ as derived from a square-well potential with repulsive core (Fig. 6.4.6) can be approximated over the whole range of r by a simpler one, namely $u(r) = ce^{-r/\rho}$, where c is a constant slightly different from C, but ρ has the same value as in the calculation using the square well with repulsive core. (*a*) Normalize the wave function by choosing the appropriate value for c. (With regard to the normalization of a wave function see pp. 211–212 and 263–264.) (*b*) Calculate the probability that the distance between the two nucleons is greater than the range of the nuclear force which, based on the chosen potential (square well with repulsive core), is $a + b = 2.4$ fm.

35. *Compare* the potential of the H_2 *molecule* with the potential of the *deuteron*. Consider the size, the existence of excited states, the ratio of zero-point energy to binding energy.

36. Draw a diagram similar to Fig. 6.6.2 for a massive nucleus where $N > Z$, taking *electrostatic effects* into account.

37. A very simple nuclear model is the *Fermi-gas model*. (See Sect. 5.4.) Consider the nuclide ${}^{78}_{34}$Se. (*a*) What is its nuclear volume? (*b*) Assume a cubical box of the same volume and determine the kinetic energy of the protons and of the neutrons which are at the Fermi level. (*c*) The energy necessary to separate the least bound proton is for this nuclide 10.4 MeV, and for a neutron 10.5 MeV. What is the depth of the proton potential well? Of the neutron potential well? (*d*) By how many MeV is a proton bound which is at the lowest proton level? What is the corresponding energy for a neutron?

38. On the basis of the *Fermi-gas model* (see Sect. 5.4) calculate the density of states just above the Fermi level. Assume a cubical box of edge length a filled with N identical particles of spin $\frac{1}{2}$.

39. (*a*) Plot the *mass parabola* for the isobars of mass number $A = 133$.

Nuclide	Atomic Mass (u)	Nuclide	Atomic Mass (u)
$_{51}$Sb	132.921000	$_{55}$Cs	132.911913
$_{52}$Te	132.917100	$_{56}$Ba	132.912428
$_{53}$I	132.914140	$_{57}$La	132.914330
$_{54}$Xe	132.912340	$_{58}$Ce	132.917630

(b) Discuss the stability of these nuclides.

40. Some of the nuclides of mass number $A = 100$ have the following *masses*:

$$^{100}_{41}\text{Nb}: \quad 99.914020 \text{ u}$$

$$^{100}_{42}\text{Mo}: \quad 99.907475 \text{ u}$$

$$^{100}_{43}\text{Tc}: \quad 99.907840 \text{ u}$$

$$^{100}_{44}\text{Ru}: \quad 99.904218 \text{ u}$$

$$^{100}_{45}\text{Rh}: \quad 99.908126 \text{ u}$$

$$^{100}_{46}\text{Pd}: \quad 99.908770 \text{ u}$$

(a) Plot the masses as a function of Z and sketch the appropriate parabolas. (b) Indicate which nuclides are stable, which decay by β^- decay and which by β^+ decay. (c) Estimate the magnitude (in MeV) of the pairing energy δ.

41. (a) Set up a table with the heading given below and give the *quantum numbers* for each of the nine nucleons of $^9_5$B in its ground state. Note that to some extent the quantum numbers m_j are not determined.

protons			neutrons		
l	j	m_j	l	j	m_j

(b) What is the expected angular momentum of the ground state of $^9_5$B?

42. Check if the *angular momenta of the ground states* of the following nuclides are in agreement with the diagram of Fig. 6.6.8: $^{79}_{35}$Br $(p_{3/2})$, $^{83}_{36}$K $(g_{9/2})$, $^{86}_{36}$K (0), $^{95}_{40}$Zr $(d_{5/2})$, $^{95}_{42}$Mo $(d_{5/2})$, $^{127}_{53}$I $(d_{5/2})$, $^{129}_{53}$I $(g_{7/2})$, $^{131}_{56}$Ba $(s_{1/2})$.

43. The ground state of $^{59}_{29}$Cu is a $p_{3/2}$ state; the first excited state is a $p_{1/2}$ state and has an energy of 0.669 MeV. The next higher state is $f_{5/2}$ at 0.962 MeV. (a) Check if the actual level sequence agrees with the *shell-*

model scheme of Fig. 6.6.8. (*b*) What is the magnitude of the spin-orbit splitting of the *p* levels? (*c*) If we assume that the spin-orbit splitting in a nucleus is roughly proportional to the angular momentum, what is the expected magnitude of the energy difference between the $f_{7/2}$ and $f_{5/2}$ levels? (*d*) Where is the $f_{7/2}$ level and how could one determine its energy?

44. The ground state of $^{209}_{82}$Pb is a $g_{9/2}$ state. The next levels are $i_{11/2}$, then $j_{15/2}$ and $d_{5/2}$ close together, $4s_{1/2}$, and $g_{7/2}$ and $d_{3/2}$ close together. Discuss this sequence in terms of the *shell model*.

45. The square-well potential, and therefore also the nuclear potential appropriate for the shell model, has a great similarity with the potential of a *cubical box*. However, certain differences exist. In particular, no angular momentum is associated with the states in a cubical box. Hence, it is not surprising that for the filling of shells in a square-well potential *without spin-orbit splitting* and in a cubical box different numbers of protons (or neutrons) would be required. What would be the first seven "magic numbers" if the nucleus could be accurately described by a cubical box?

46. The nuclide ^{172}Hf has the following series of *rotational levels* (energies in keV, angular momentum in parentheses): 0 (0), 94 (2), 308 (4), 627 (6), 1036 (8), 1519 (10), 2063 (12), 2651 (14), 3273 (16), 3915 (18). Taking the energy difference between the states of angular momentum 0 and 2 as basis for the computation, construct a table of the differences between the calculated and the actual energy differences between adjacent levels as a function of their average angular momentum. (*a*) From this set up an empirical correction formula. (*b*) Calculate the moment of inertia from the energy difference of the two lowest states and compare it with the one which one should expect from a rigid rotating sphere of mass and average nuclear radius $R = r_0 A^{1/3}$ (with $r_0 = 1.2$ fm) of this nuclide.

47. A particle of the mass of a nucleon is confined in a cubical box of side length 10^{-14} m. (*a*) What is the energy in MeV of the first excited state? What is the degeneracy? (*b*) The box is now deformed by lengthening one of its dimensions by 20% and by reducing the other two by 8.5% each, thus keeping the volume of the box constant. What energy values corresponding to the first excited state of part *a* result from this rectangular box? (*c*) Instead of lengthening it, one side of the box is shortened by 20%, and the other dimensions are adjusted accordingly to keep the volume constant. What are the energies now? (*d*) Plot in a diagram the energies and the deformations for cases *a*, *b*, and *c*, similarly to a *Nilsson diagram*.

48. Most of the nuclei in the region of uranium in the table of nuclides are not spherical but football-shaped (in technical terms: they have a positive *quadrupole moment*). Would one expect that the α particles emitted by some of these nuclides are emitted preferentially in the direction of the major axis or perpendicularly to it? Give reasons.

49. The samarium isotope $^{147}_{62}$Sm decays by alpha decay with a half-life of 1.2×10^{11} years. How many *disintegrations* of this isotope occur per minute in one mole of natural samarium which contains 15% ^{147}Sm?

50. ^{40}K is a β emitter with a half-life of 1.27×10^9 years. What percentage of this isotope has *decayed* into ^{40}A since the earth was formed, 4.6×10^9 years ago?

51. The nuclide $^{238}_{92}$U is unstable and *decays* via a number of intermediate nuclides into a stable lead isotope $(Z = 82)$. Lead has the following stable isotopes of mass number $A = 204, 206, 207,$ and 208. (*a*) In which isotope does the radioactive decay chain end? (*b*) How many α particles are emitted? (*c*) How many β^- particles?

52. If the *age of the earth* is taken as 4.6×10^9 years, how much of the original U^{238} has decayed since the earth was formed?

53. From experiment it is known that 1 gram of pure radium forms 0.042 cm^3 of helium per year. It is also known from counting the number of α particles emitted that 3.7×10^{10} α particles are emitted per second. From this information and the fact that 1 gram-molecule of helium has a volume of 22.4 l under standard conditions, compute *Avogadro's number*.

54. (*a*) Calculate the probability for *penetration* of a rectangular *barrier* of 17 MeV height and 10 fm width by an α particle whose kinetic energy outside the nucleus is 8 MeV. (*b*) Assuming that the α particle is bouncing back and forth with one-tenth the speed of light between two rectangular barriers as shown in Fig. 6.7.3 which are 16 fm apart (see Fig. 6.7.9), after how long has the α particle probably succeeded in escaping from the well?

55. The mass difference between a neutron and a proton is 1.29 MeV. (*a*) What is the maximum kinetic energy of the electrons which are emitted in the *beta decay* of the neutron? Neglect the recoil energy of the neutron. (*b*) What is the mass difference between a hydrogen *atom* and a neutron?

56. Which ones of W. Pauli's preliminary assumptions regarding the *neutrino* were correct and which ones turned out to be wrong?

57. If the *neutrino* has a rest mass equal to that of an electron, how could one find out?

58. The gound state of $^{60}_{27}$Co has an angular momentum $J = 5$ and decays by β^- emission into an excited state of $^{60}_{28}$Ni with $J = 4$. What must be the *relative spin directions* of the Co nucleus, the β particle, the antineutrino, and the Ni nucleus?

59. $^{25}_{13}$Al decays by positron emission into the ground state of $^{25}_{12}$Mg. The Al nucleus has a spin of $J = 5/2$ and the magnesium nucleus also has $J = 5/2$. How must the *spins* of the positron and the neutrino be *oriented* to each other?

60. What is the order of magnitude of the *lifetime* of a state with 2 MeV excitation energy which can decay by emission of electric dipole radiation?

61. The maximum energy of the β^- spectrum from the decay of tritium (^{3}H) has been found to be $E_{\beta\,max} = 18.72 \pm 0.10$ keV. This result can be used, in connection with the Q value of the reaction ^{3}H (p, n) ^{3}He of 763.77 $\pm$ 0.08 keV, for a determination of the *mass difference* between a neutron and a hydrogen atom. (*a*) What is this mass difference in keV? (*b*) What error must be attached to this result? (*c*) What is the mass difference between a neutron and a proton?

62. By which *reactions* could $^1_1$H, $^2_1$H, $^3_1$H, $^3_2$He, or $^4_2$He be produced from stable elements? The stable elements at the beginning of the periodic table are $^1_1$H, $^2_1$H, $^3_2$He, $^4_2$He, $^6_3$Li, $^7_3$Li, $^9_4$Be, $^{10}_5$B, $^{11}_5$B, $^{12}_6$C, $^{13}_6$C. Write your answer in the form

$$^1_1\text{H } (n, \gamma) \, ^2_1\text{H}.$$

63. How much *energy* in MeV is *released* in the following reactions?

$$^3_1\text{H } (p, \gamma) \, ^4_2\text{He} \qquad \text{Masses: } ^4_2\text{He:} \quad 4.00260 \text{ u}$$

$$^2_1\text{H } (n, \gamma) \, ^3_1\text{H} \qquad\qquad\quad\; ^6_3\text{Li:} \quad 6.01513$$

$$^6_3\text{Li } (d, n) \, ^7_4\text{Be} \qquad\qquad\quad ^7_3\text{Li:} \quad 7.01600$$

$$^7_3\text{Li } (\gamma, n) \, ^6_3\text{Li} \qquad\qquad\quad ^7_4\text{Be:} \quad 7.01693$$

$$^9_4\text{Be:} \quad 9.01219$$

$$^{10}_4\text{Be:} \quad 10.01353$$

$$^{10}_5\text{B:} \quad 10.01294$$

64. Could an accelerator producing 4 MeV protons initiate the *reaction*

$$^{127}_{53}\text{I } (p, \gamma) \, ^{128}_{54}\text{Xe}?$$

65. Through *bombarding* ^{9}Be by various particles the following products may be obtained:

$$^6\text{He}, \; ^{10}\text{Be}, \; ^{10}\text{B}.$$

What projectile may be used in each case and what would be its minimum energy and the energies of the products? See masses in Problem 63.

66. In the *proton-proton cycle*, which provides the energy of the sun and other similar stars, protons merge to form $^4_2$He nuclei. This process proceeds in several steps. What is the number of protons necessary to form one $^4_2$He nucleus and how many positrons and neutrinos are emitted in this process?

67. The energy production in the sun is based on the *proton-proton cycle*. Due to the high temperature in the sun's interior, the protons have enough kinetic energy to form deuterons by collision. These, in turn, collide again with protons and produce ^{3}He. Two such ^{3}He nuclei can transmute into ^{4}He and two protons. Now the cycle can start over again. This thermo-

nuclear reaction cycle is thus

$$^1\text{H} + {}^1\text{H} \rightarrow {}^2\text{H} + \beta^+ + \nu + 0.4 \text{ MeV}$$
$$\rightarrow \gamma + \gamma \;(1.02 \text{ MeV})$$

$$^2\text{H} + {}^1\text{H} \rightarrow {}^3\text{He} + 5.5 \text{ MeV}$$

$$^3\text{He} + {}^3\text{He} \rightarrow {}^4\text{He} + {}^1\text{H} + {}^1\text{H} + 12.9 \text{ MeV}$$

(a) How many protons are consumed to produce one He nucleus? (b) How much energy is set free to form a He nucleus? (c) How much energy escapes from the sun as kinetic energy of neutrinos? Mass of ^{4}He: 4.0026 u.

68. (a) Calculate the *potential energy* in MeV of a system consisting of a spherical $^{92}_{36}$Kr nucleus touching a spherical $^{144}_{56}$Ba nucleus. (b) Compare this energy with the energy released in the reaction

$$^{235}_{92}\text{U} + {}^1_0 n \rightarrow {}^{236}_{92}\text{U} \rightarrow {}^{91}_{36}\text{Kr} + {}^{142}_{56}\text{Ba} + 3({}^1_0 n)$$

$$^{235}_{92}\text{U} = 235.044 \text{ u} \qquad {}^{142}_{56}\text{Ba} = 141.916 \text{ u}$$

$$^{91}_{36}\text{Kr} = 90.881 \text{ u} \qquad {}^1_0 n = 1.009 \text{ u}$$

69. In a *reactor* the neutrons released in the fission process are "moderated" in graphite. On colliding with a C atom, a neutron is sometimes captured but usually bounces off with reduced energy in accordance with the laws of conservation of energy and momentum. (a) If, on the average, a neutron gives up 15% of its energy at each collision, retaining 85%, how many collisions are required to reduce a 1-MeV neutron to an energy of 1 eV? (b) Assume that, of a large number of neutrons making one collision· each with a C atom, about 99.90% would bounce off, the rest being captured. For 10^{10} neutrons starting off at 1 MeV, how many will be reduced to 1 eV in energy without being captured? (c) If no other neutron losses were involved, what minimum number of neutrons would have to be released, on the average, per fission to sustain the chain reaction in the reactor, assuming that every neutron that reaches an energy of 1 eV will produce fission? (d) What other losses would be present in an actual reactor?

70. How much *energy* in MeV is *released* in the reactions $^2_1\text{H} + {}^2_1\text{H} \rightarrow {}^3_1\text{H} + {}^1_1\text{H}$ and $^3_1\text{H} + {}^2_1\text{H} \rightarrow {}^4_2\text{He} + {}^1_0 n$?

71. The first *atomic bombs* made were said to be the equivalent in destructive power to 20,000 tons of T.N.T. Assuming that destructive power is a measure of the energy released, and that 1 lb of T.N.T. releases about 1.7×10^6 joules, estimate the number of pounds of ^{235}U consumed in the explosion. The density of uranium metal is about 18.5 g/cm³. Estimate the total decrease of nuclear mass resulting from the explosion.

72. A nuclear reactor is operating at a level of 1000 kW. Assuming that 200 MeV are released per ^{235}U *fission*, how many fissions are occurring per second? How long will it take to use up 10 g of fissionable material?

73. Compute the *"heat of fission"* of ^{235}U in calories per gram. (See Problem 72.)

74. Assume that when the *sun* is directly overhead, the power radiated to the earth by the sun is 1.42 kW/m². (*a*) If the radius of the earth is 6000 km, what is the equivalent mass of the energy falling on the earth per second? (*b*) Compute the mass of the earth from the known acceleration due to gravity at the earth's surface. Compute, then, the mass of the sun from the fact that it is moving in an almost circular orbit having a radius of 150 million km, and that the time taken for one revolution is 365 days. Compute, finally, the total radiation from the sun. What fraction of its mass does the sun radiate per year? (*c*) If the temperature of the sun were not maintained by a nuclear reaction, but if the sun could be regarded as a reservoir of energy containing $\frac{3}{2}kT$ for every nucleon in it, and if the average temperature of the sun were x million degrees centigrade, how long would it take the sun to lose all of its energy at the present rate of loss? Express your answer in terms of the unknown x above.

Chapter 7

Particles and Symmetries

7.1 THE ROOTS OF HIGH-ENERGY PHYSICS

After World War II nuclear physics became an extremely active field. To a great extent this was due to the wartime effort in nuclear-weapons research and development and to the postwar interest in nuclear energy. Through the theoretical and experimental endeavors in nuclear physics it became increasingly clear that the clue to the deeper secrets contained in the nuclei would have to be found in the nucleons. Nuclear physics is concerned with the structure and forces of nuclei which can best be studied by observing what happens when energy is fed into a nuclear system, for example, by bombardment with protons. The study of the subnuclear structures needed higher energies than the study of nuclei because, as was obvious, the de Broglie wavelength of the bombarding particles would have to be smaller than nucleon diameters.

Nuclear physics can be considered as one parent of high-energy physics; its other parent is cosmic radiation physics which is, in fact, a branch of science nearly as old as nuclear physics. It had its origin early in this century in observations that led to the discovery of an ionizing agent in the atmosphere which made charged electroscopes and electrometers discharge. In order to escape the natural radioactivity of the ground due to the ever-present traces of uranium, potassium, and so on in soil and rocks, such experiments were performed at the beginning of the century on the Eiffel Tower and in manned balloons. It soon was discovered that the intensity of the ionizing radiation strongly increased with altitude. This was correctly interpreted as being due to a filtering effect by the atmosphere on radiation of extraterrestrial origin. Today it is believed that this radiation has its origin mostly in our galaxy, but partly, according to current hypotheses, also in extragalactic regions. It is assumed that protons in space are accelerated to energies up to $> 2 \times 10^{21}$ eV[1] by changing electric and

[1] See for example *Sov. J. Nucl. Phys.* **13**, 453 (1971); K. Suga *et al.*, Phys. Rev. Lett. **27**, 1604 (1971).

magnetic fields in the galaxy or in intergalactic space, probably by mechanisms similar to those which accelerate charged particles in betatrons and synchrotrons and which will be discussed later. In short, by some combination of changing electric and magnetic fields, the particles are accelerated and kept in orbit. Such accelerated protons vehemently collide in the upper atmosphere of the earth with atoms, causing explosions of their nuclei which result in the emission of many high-energy protons and neutrons and subsequently, by way of Compton effects, bremsstrahlung, and pair production, electron showers and high-energy photons. In addition, during these collisions and explosions, particles are created which do not occur in ordinary low-energy nuclear reactions and decays. The first such particle which was discovered in 1937 was the muon, for several years mistaken for the particle which had previously been predicted by Yukawa to be responsible for nuclear forces. The true Yukawa particle finally was discovered in cosmic radiation in 1947. The significant contributions of cosmic radiation research go far beyond the discoveries of the muons and π-mesons to include other unexpected new particles, mesons as well as hyperons, that is, particles more massive than nucleons. Their characteristics made it necessary to introduce a new quantum number into physics, which we will discuss later.

However, cosmic radiation is in some sense a very diluted radiation, and therefore experiments in this field are very tedious and time-consuming, and in certain circumstances just impossible. Cosmic radiation is a mixture of all kinds of particles of all kinds of energies; hence, selecting the right particle with the right energy is no easy matter. It was therefore obvious that high-energy accelerators would have great advantages, although the very highest energies will still be reserved for the cosmic-ray scientists because the biggest accelerators under construction have energies of 500 GeV.[2]

Another incentive for the construction of big accelerators was the expectation of producing anti-protons and anti-neutrons according to the predictions of the theory of Dirac. The relationship of a proton to an anti-proton is the same as that of an electron to a positron. Proton and anti-proton hence have exactly the same mass but opposite charge and also the opposite magnetic moment. Neutron and anti-neutron obviously both have zero charge, but the magnetic moments of both are different in their signs. The rest mass of a nucleon and thus also that of an anti-nucleon is close to 1 GeV. In order to produce a nucleon–anti-nucleon pair, corresponding

---

[2] 1 GeV $= 10^9$ eV, where G stands for giga, Greek for giant. In the American literature one occasionally still finds the expression BeV, B standing for billion. Since in Europe a billion means 10^{12}, the abbreviation GeV came more and more into use when the monopoly on high-energy machines which the United States held for many years came to an end and when American and European physicists started to work closely together.

to an electron–positron pair, at least 2 GeV are necessary under the most favorable conditions. However, these conditions at the present time are not usually fulfilled. This point will be taken up in the next section.

The roots of high-energy physics, which today is synonymous with particle physics, are therefore "classical" nuclear physics, cosmic-ray physics, and the study of anti-particles. Today the situation is such that the cosmic-ray physicists, because of the competition from the high-energy physicists working on accelerators, either joined the accelerator people or had to transfer their interest to problems that could not be studied with accelerators. The Van Allen belts, which are regions of high electron or proton density around the Earth, are a good example of the new problems in cosmic-ray physics. Another such example is that of the study of electron showers created by primary particles of energies of up to $\sim 10^{21}$ eV.

7.2 ACCELERATORS OF HIGH-ENERGY PHYSICS*

In general we have refrained from describing apparatus used in physics. If we make an exception in this chapter, it is because the costs for the equipment in this branch of physics are now on such a scale that a certain understanding of the purpose for which the taxpayers' money is being spent seems well justified.

The big accelerators, those which have at least the capability of producing mesons, are either of a circular or a linear type, and are built for the acceleration of either protons or electrons. The maximum energy obtainable is not the only important factor, but also the number of particles accelerated in a burst (most of these machines accelerate particles only in bursts of very short duration of the approximate order of magnitude of milliseconds) and the frequency of these bursts, which for most of these big accelerators is of the order of magnitude of one burst per second.

Certain accelerators are being built to do certain jobs particularly well. For example, the so-called "meson factories" provide a copious beam of π-mesons which are then used for scattering experiments and reactions with nucleons and nuclei. The term "factory" should be taken with a grain of salt as they are no more than a 500–800 MeV proton accelerator of high beam intensity for a specialized purpose. Projects exist furthermore for accelerators of high intensity to produce anti-proton and anti-neutron beams and beams of K mesons, which are mesons of approximately three times greater mass than the π mesons.

It is quite interesting to consider some of the salient principles of ac-

* This section may be omitted without loss in continuity.

celerator design. We must first, however, discuss the fundamentals and limitations of the ordinary cyclotron which may be regarded as one of the ancestors of all modern circular accelerators.

The Cyclotron

Principal components of a cyclotron (Fig. 7.2.1) are a powerful electromagnet (field usually 1–2 Wb/m²), and the chamber in which the particles (usually protons, deuterons, or α-particles) are accelerated. This chamber is evacuated in order to obtain a sufficiently long mean free path of the particles. The particles are accelerated by an electric potential difference between two electrodes which have the shape of a pillbox cut in half along a diameter. Because of their shape the electrodes are called dees. An ion source at the center provides the particles, which are mostly ionized hydrogen, deuterium, or helium gas. As will be explained below, these ions will spiral outwards during their acceleration. If they have reached the desired energy they may be deflected by an extra electrode. The particle beam after leaving the accelerator chamber may then be used for experiments.

The particles are accelerated in the gap between the two dees to which a voltage is applied from a high-frequency oscillator. There is no electric field inside the dees, just as there is no field inside a charged hollow body. During the time in which the particles describe, under the influence of the magnetic field, a semicircle within the dee, the potential difference between the dees changes sign and therefore the particle will again be accelerated in the gap. The magnetic field, exerting a force perpendicular to the motion of the particles, evidently does no work and therefore does not contribute to the acceleration. Its only function is to keep the particle in an orbit.

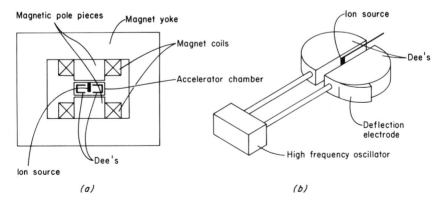

Fig. 7.2.1   Schematic cut through a cyclotron (*a*) and Dee system (*b*).

Ernest O. Lawrence (1901–1958) (right), and M. Stanley Livingston (born 1905) at the University of California in Berkeley next to the 27½-inch cyclotron completed in 1934 which produced 5-MeV deuterons. The 74-ton electromagnet formerly had been used in an Poulsen-arc radio transmitter. Lawrence conceived the idea of the cyclotron in 1929, and in 1931 he and his, to that time, graduate student Livingston built the first operating one which accelerated H_2^+ ions to 80 keV. Lawrence received the Nobel prize in physics in 1939 for the invention of the cyclotron. (Courtesy of University of California, Lawrence Berkeley Laboratory).

If a particle of mass m and charge q moves with velocity $\boldsymbol{v}$ perpendicular to the lines of force of a homogeneous magnetic field $\boldsymbol{B}$, a force $\boldsymbol{F} = q[\boldsymbol{v} \times \boldsymbol{B}]$ will act on the particle. This force is at right angles to $\boldsymbol{v}$ and $\boldsymbol{B}$. The particle will therefore move on a circular trajectory because

$$\boldsymbol{F} = qvB = m\frac{v^2}{r}$$

$$rB = \frac{mv}{q}.$$

The angular velocity $\omega = v/r$ is therefore

$$\omega = 2\pi\nu = \frac{qB}{m}. \tag{7.2.1}$$

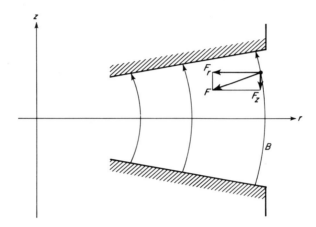

Fig. 7.2.2   Focusing force F_z on a particle moving above the median plane.

It is an important point that the frequency of rotation ν is independent of v and r. This means that particles of equal mass and charge need the same time to complete a semicircle regardless of their velocity, the slower particles describing smaller orbits than the faster ones. Equation 7.2.1 is therefore an expression of the condition that the particles are isochronous. In a cyclotron the particles that are orbiting isochronously are all passing through the same accelerating electric field. This field alternates with the frequency ν so that after a half-period the particles are accelerated again. In a cyclotron a particle usually makes several hundred turns. The total path is therefore quite long. One might think that if a particle does not start out precisely perpendicularly to the magnetic field it should hit one of the pole faces. Fortunately two focusing effects are freely furnished by nature, which was recognized only after the successful operation of the first cyclotrons. One is the electrostatic focusing which plays a role only at low energies and which we will not discuss further here, the other one is the magnetic focusing. The magnetic field between two circular pole faces is not completely homogeneous (Fig. 7.2.2). The lines of force are slightly bulging outwards. If a particle is moving away from the median plane a restoring magnetic force will bring it back to it. The particles are automatically focused on the median plane, performing small oscillations around it, resulting in orbits of axial stability.

Frequency-Modulated Cyclotrons and Synchrotrons

The limitation of the conventional cyclotron is that the relativistic mass increase at high particle velocities causes the condition of isochrony (Eq.

7.2.1) no longer to be satisfied. As the particle gains speed and travels in orbits of increasing radius, its mass also increases according to the laws of the special theory of relativity. There are two obvious fundamental possibilities to keep the particles in step with the oscillating electric field which provides the acceleration. One of them is, while keeping the angular frequency ω constant, to increase the magnetic field B radially outward, the other alternative is to decrease the applied acceleration frequency ω as the particles are becoming more and more massive. Both means have been employed in the construction of accelerators. The second way leads to the family of frequency-modulated cyclotrons, also called synchrocyclotrons. The frequency of the high-frequency oscillator may be changed by having parts of the capacitance of the oscillating circuit residing in an enormous tuning fork-like vibrating capacitor which, because of the changing distance between its ends, varies its capacitance and causes the desired frequency changes. Theoretical calculations, which in this instance were carried out before accelerators employing this principle had been built, showed that how the angular frequency varies as a function of time is not particularly critical. The particles tend to stay in phase with the applied field. They remain, so to speak, in "holding orbits" (to use an analogy from air traffic over congested airports) until the frequency is again the right one for further acceleration. It is this "phase stability," discovered in 1944 by V. I. Veksler in Russia and independently in 1945 by E. M. MacMillan in Berkeley, that led the two physicists to the invention of the synchrotron and the synchrocyclotron. These names derive from the fact that electric synchronous motors also use such a phase stability. If the rotor in such a motor, for instance, is lagging an increased torque brings it back in step. This principle is also applied in the linear accelerators.

The biggest synchrocyclotron is at the University of California in Berkeley. This accelerator was started before World War II and before the principle of frequency modulation was known. E. O. Lawrence, who had invented the cyclotron in 1931, hoped to reach with it by brute-force techniques an energy of around 100 MeV. During the war the development was suspended, and the magnet was used to separate uranium isotopes. Afterwards, when E. M. MacMillan, also at Berkeley, discovered the principle of phase stability, the original plans were changed to make it a synchrocyclotron. It came into operation in 1946 and first accelerated deuterons and helium ions. It also produced protons of a maximum energy of 350 MeV. In 1956 it was rebuilt to reach proton energies of 730 MeV.

In synchrotrons, in contrast to the cyclotrons described above, the frequency stays constant but the magnetic field varies with time. Such synchrotrons have been built for the acceleration of electrons and protons. In contrast to a cyclotron where the orbit radius varies greatly with energy, the orbit radius in synchrotrons remains constant.

Cyclotrons are only suitable for the acceleration of massive particles, because electrons gain velocity too fast and even at 1 MeV almost reach the velocity of light so that isochronism for different orbits cannot be achieved in practice. On the other hand, the first synchrotrons were designed for electrons, and only later the principle was also used for protons. There is however a certain practical energy limit for electrons. Orbiting electrons, because they undergo a centripetal acceleration, radiate energy, as does any accelerated charge. In the big electron synchrotrons, such as, the MIT-Harvard 6 GeV Cambridge Electron Accelerator (abbreviated CEA), 40% of the energy fed into the electrons is lost again by radiation. This is the synchrotron radiation already mentioned in Chapter 2. In the CEA the losses at 6 GeV are 4.5 MeV per turn. This energy is emitted in discrete quanta as a bremsstrahlumg spectrum with a maximum energy of 18 keV. Hence electron synchrotrons are a powerful source of ultraviolet radiation and x-rays.

Alternate Gradient or Strong Focusing

Another important principle incorporated into the machines of the last decade must be mentioned, the so-called strong focusing. Its application keeps the particles, which tend to oscillate around an equilibrium orbit, under the influence of the magnetic restoring forces on a very narrow path and therefore allows relatively small magnet gaps and consequently a great saving in magnet iron because the magnet dimensions can be made much smaller. For example, a 10-GeV proton synchrotron in Dubna (near Moscow), U.S.S.R., which does not employ this principle has a magnet of a weight of 35,000 tons, whereas the magnet of the 33-GeV AGS (= Alternate Gradient Synchrotron) in Brookhaven, Long Island, in which this principle is incorporated weighs only 4000 tons. In the Russian accelerator the magnet poles are 40 cm apart; in the Brookhaven machine, however, the vertical dimension of the vacuum chamber in which the protons are accelerated is only about 8 cm.

The strong-focusing principle was first discovered by a then unknown electrical engineer, N. Christofilos, whose hobby was accelerator design and who earned his living in Athens as an elevator specialist. In the United States he applied for a patent and also sent a report about the new focusing principle to experts in this country. Possibly because the description was couched in somewhat unusual and inelegant mathematics due to his being essentially an autodidact, the experts did not spend enough time to fully understand his paper and considered it at best irrelevant and, thus, missed its importance. A short time later, a group of American physicists from the

"Establishment" made fundamentally the same discovery and applied for a patent. The same experts who before had not taken Christofilos' theory seriously now had to give an opinion about the new version. In reading the later proposal, which was written in the proper jargon, they recalled the earlier one and found it essentially identical. Therefore, no patent was granted to the physicists, and Christofilos' contribution was rewarded by the offer of a job with the accelerator construction group at Brookhaven National Laboratory.

In an ordinary cyclotron or a synchrocyclotron the magnetic field decreases with increasing radius. The resulting negative field gradient has a focusing effect on particles above or below the equilibrium plane. In the case of alternate gradient focusing the particle passes alternately through regions of positive and negative field gradients. As illustrated in Fig. 7.2.3 (a) a particle in position A will be focused under the influence of this negative field gradient. In contrast, a particle in the analog position A', but this time in a positive field gradient (Fig. 7.2.3 (b)), will be defocused. Let us now consider a particle in the equilibrium plane but moving on a radius that is greater than the equilibrium orbit. This case is illustrated in the figure by the positions B and B'. In Fig. 7.2.3(a) the particle is in a field that is too weak; hence it is bound to go even more and more astray. On the other hand, in Fig. 7.2.3(b) the particle at B' finds itself in too strong a field and consequently will be bent back into the equilibrium orbit. Thus we find that in both cases—the negative and positive gradients—the field has a focusing effect in one direction but a defocusing effect in the other one perpendicular to it. A beam of particles passing through fields with alternating gradient will therefore alternately be focused and defocused horizontally and vertically, but at different times. It is a consequence of Maxwell's equations that it is not possible to have focusing action in both planes at the same time, as an optical lens does with light rays for example. Only a mathematical analysis can show that the effect of a com-

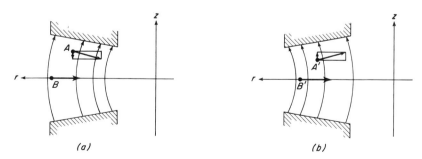

Fig. 7.2.3 Focusing in negative (a) and defocusing in positive (b) magnetic field gradients.

bination of focusing and defocusing elements as a whole is one of focusing, but it can at least be made plausible by an optical analogy: A system of convex and concave lenses of focal lengths f and $-f$, respectively, have on the whole a focusing effect if the lenses are spaced apart. We see in Fig. 7.2.4(a) a system consisting of a convex lens, followed by a concave lens, and in Fig. 7.2.4(b) the same lenses in reversed order. In both cases the net result is focusing, although with different effective focal lengths.

It is left as an exercise to trace the rays through a system of several alternating convex and concave lenses. Whereas in the optical case focusing and defocusing in the vertical and horizontal planes were in phase, this is not so in the case of magnetic lenses. The same magnetic lens acts as a focusing element in one plane and as a defocusing element in the other plane. To speak in optical terms these magnetic lenses are highly astigmatic. The beam is therefore broadest in the x plane when it is narrowest in the y plane and vice versa.

Phase stability and alternate gradient focusing made the enormous accelerators possible. At present the biggest one in operation is the proton synchrotron of the National Accelerator Laboratory at Batavia, Ill. Later, it will accelerate protons to a maximum energy of 500 GeV; in the summer of 1972 it operated routinely at 200 GeV. At 200 GeV it will accelerate eventually 1.5×10^{13} protons/second, at 500 GeV 10 to 100 times less. The gigantic dimensions of this accelerator are seen in Fig. 7.2.5.

The accelerators which have contributed most to our recently acquired knowledge on particles are the AGS at Brookhaven, which came into operation in 1961 with an energy of 33 GeV, and the PS (= Proton synchrotron) at CERN, the European Organization for Nuclear Research in Geneva, Switzerland with 28 GeV, in service since 1960.

Fixed Field Alternate Gradient (FFAG) Cyclotrons

Accelerators incorporating time-varying magnetic fields or variable frequency have the drawback that the beam currents are intermittent and

(a)   (b)

Fig. 7.2.4   The focusing action of a system of a convex and a concave lens with focal lengths $+f$ and $-f$, respectively.

Fig. 7.2.5   Aerial view of the National Accelerator Laboratory at Batavia, Ill., near
Chicago. The main ring has a diameter of 1.24 miles. The protons are first accelerated
to an energy of 0.75 MeV in a Cockcroft-Walton accelerator, then to 200 MeV in a
linear accelerator located between the 16-story Central Laboratory Building and the
small circle to the right. This circle is the booster accelerator which brings the protons
to an energy of 8 GeV. The protons are then injected into the main ring for acceleration
to an energy of up to, presently, 300 GeV. The maximum energy will be raised in the
future to 400 or 500 GeV. After the protons have attained the desired energy, they are
extracted and guided towards experimental areas which are about one mile to the left,
outside the picture. (Courtesy of National Accelerator Laboratory).

in the time-average relatively weak. For many experiments it would be
much more advantageous to have available a steady current of protons or
electrons. Equation 7.2.1 showed that the frequency in a cyclotron could be
held constant if the magnetic field increased with increasing radius but, as
Fig. 7.2.3(b) illustrates, this results in defocusing, in contrast to the decreasing magnetic field of Fig. 7.2.3(a). In 1938 Thomas showed that this
defocusing effect of a field which increases radially can be overcome by
varying the field also periodically in a horizontal direction. This variation
is in space only, not in time. The frequency of the electric field cannot be

kept constant. This idea remained dormant for about 20 years, mostly because of the popularity of frequency-modulated cyclotrons. However,
there is presently strong interest in accelerators capable of producing great
beam intensities at a constant rate. Several accelerators have been built
using this principle whose important points we shall now explain.

The magnetic field is divided into sectors that alternately contain strong
and weak fields (Fig. 7.2.6(a)). The field of each of the sectors increases
toward the outside in order to take care of the relativistic mass increase.
In the sectors with strong field the curvature of the orbit is greater than in
the other sectors. Thus, the particles traverse the boundaries between the
sectors not at right angles but obliquely. At each boundary they pass a
region which has a field gradient that decreases against the outside. This
just provides for the necessary focusing according to Fig. 7.2.2. This idea
was later improved. Replacing the sectors by spirals (Fig. 7.2.6(b)), the
particles were made to traverse the boundaries between weak and strong
fields under even more oblique angles, and focusing became better. The
result was the spiral-ridge cyclotron, also called isochronous cyclotron or
Fixed-Field Alternate-Gradient cyclotron, abbreviated FFAG.

Figure 7.2.7 shows the schematic drawing of a 585-MeV sector-focusing
cyclotron being built in Switzerland as a "meson factory." For technical
reasons it was found advantageous to divide the accelerator into two accelerators in series. An injector cyclotron, also of the spiral-ridge type,
accelerates the protons to an energy of 72 MeV. The resulting accelerated
protons are then injected into the main accelerator which is doughnut
shaped. Because this accelerator does not have to deal with the low-energy
protons, the magnetic field requirements are of much more manageable
proportions. In addition, the injector cyclotron can also be used for research in low-energy nuclear physics.

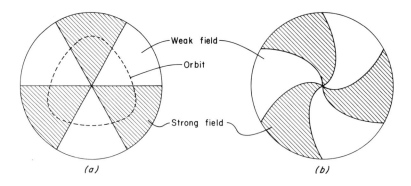

Fig. 7.2.6 Schematic diagram of the magnetic field of sector-focusing cyclotrons:
(a) radial sectors: (b) spiral ridges.

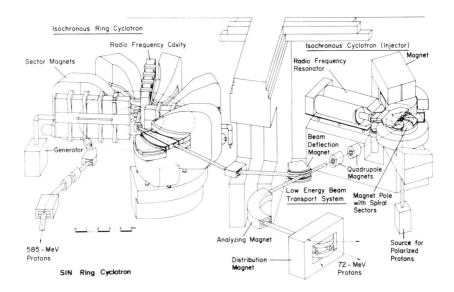

Fig. 7.2.7 The two isochronous cyclotrons in series at the "meson factory" in Switzerland. The first cyclotron serves as injector for the second accelerator. The ring accelerator uses instead of "D's" four RF cavities in which the protons are accelerated by the electric field inside during the traversal. The inner dotted circle corresponds approximately to the proton orbit at the injector energy of 72 MeV, the outer circle to the 585-MeV orbit. The beam emerging from the injector can also be used for nuclear research at lower energies. (SIN Swiss Institute for Nuclear Research.)

Linear Accelerators

Linear accelerators have been built for electrons and heavy particles, usually protons. However, in the high-energy field only the electron linacs, as the linear accelerators are usually called, are represented. Low-energy (approx. 50–100 MeV) proton linacs are nevertheless often used as injectors to circular accelerators. The Brookhaven and the CERN proton synchrotrons have such injectors, as has the Batavia accelerator.

In regard to electron linacs the electrons are injected into the accelerator with velocities close to that of light. They then ride in a wave guide (like a surfboard rider on an ocean wave) near the crest of a traveling electromagnetic wave of the order of 10 cm wavelength, corresponding to a frequency of about 3000 MHz. It should be borne in mind that 5 MeV electrons already have a velocity of 0.995 c. Consequently the phase velocity of this guided traveling wave has to be slowed down only by very little in comparison to the speed of an electromagnetic wave in free space. This slowdown of the traveling wave is accomplished by giving the wave guide an appropriate shape. (In proton linacs, because of the much lower velocity of the protons, the method of acceleration is somewhat different.) Since for high-energy accelerators it is not practical to let such a wave run through its whole length, linacs are built in sections, each section or a group of sections receiving its microwave power from a klystron, which is a powerful microwave generator also used for radar. The electrons pass from one section to the next one. Hence, the traveling waves of each section must have the correct phase relationship with each other. This is accomplished by sending timing pulses from a master oscillator to all the klystrons along the linac. As remarked earlier the principle of phase stability is of importance also in linacs. Focusing of the beam is not a particular problem because the Lorentz contraction tremendously shortens the length of the linac as seen by the electron. The Mark III accelerator of Stanford University on which the electron scattering experiments for the determination of nuclear and nucleon radii have been performed, as described in the previous chapter, has a length of 66 m and accelerates electrons to 1 GeV. The relativistic length of this machine is only 26 cm!

The most spectacular linac is the Stanford University Linear Accelerator, nicknamed SLAC, which is 2 miles long and has been in operation since 1967.[3] It contains 960 acceleration sections, each 3 m long. Each of the 243 klystrons feeds energy into four sections. Up to 360 bursts of electrons can be accelerated per second. At present the maximum energy is approximately 22 GeV, but there are plans to increase the number of klystrons by a factor of four to double the energy with simultaneous doubling of the beam current. The present electron peak beam current is between 25 and 50 mA. The electron-beam pulse length can be varied between 0.01 and 2.1 μsec.

Whereas the Brookhaven AGS delivers a proton burst of 10^{12} particles every 3 seconds, SLAC accelerates approximately the same number of electrons in a burst, but 360 times per second. However, the cross sections for the production of mesons and baryons, that is, particles with at least nucleon mass, are about 200 times smaller for electrons than for protons, the reason being that electrons can only interact through electromagnetic interactions and not through strong interactions as protons can. Combining all these factors the result is that SLAC produces some five times more strongly interacting particles, that is mesons and baryons, per time unit than the Brookhaven AGS.

***

[3] Two very good survey articles on SLAC appeared in the April 1967 issue of *Physics Today* written by R. B. Neal and J. Ballam. Also the journal, *Scientific Research* in the November 1966 issue carried an informative article by H. L. Davis.

Storage Rings for Colliding Beams

In Section 7.1 in connection with the creation of anti-protons, we mentioned that, in general, far more than 2 GeV are necessary for the production of a nucleon–anti-nucleon pair although its rest mass is somewhat less than 2 GeV. The cause of this apparent discrepancy is the following: a proton–anti-proton pair is usually produced by the reaction $p + p \rightarrow p + p + p + \bar{p}$. Before the collision, one of the protons is at rest and the bombarding one contains kinetic energy and momentum. Because momentum must always be conserved, the system has to have the same momentum before and after the reaction. A portion of the original kinetic energy is hence consumed in the motion of the center of mass of the four resulting constituents. The energy available for producing the proton–anti-proton pair (or in general for any inelastic process) is therefore less than the original kinetic energy of the bombarding particle before the collision. The whole situation can be compared with the case of two railroad freight cars in a switch yard, one standing still with brakes released and the other bumping into it. After the engagement of the automatic coupler both cars move along. The energy which is transformed into heat making this an inelastic collision process is obviously only a fraction of the kinetic energy of the approaching freight car. Returning again to particle collisions the fraction of the energy available for inelastic processes becomes even smaller if the bombarding particle approaches relativistic velocities. In the limiting case when the velocities are so high that the rest mass of the particles is negligible compared with its total energy, the available energy in a collision between a moving particle and a particle at rest, both having a rest energy E_0, is

$$E_{\text{available}} \approx \sqrt{2E_{\text{lab}}E_0}$$

where E_{lab} is the energy of the particle in the laboratory system, and therefore (in our limiting case) also the energy of the accelerator. The 28-GeV proton synchrotron of CERN thus provides only 7.4 GeV available energy in proton-proton collisions.

On the other hand, if two proton beams each of 28 GeV laboratory energy are made to collide with each other, the full 56 GeV becomes available because the center of mass of the proton-proton system has zero velocity. To get 56 GeV available energy in a conventional operation an accelerator with an energy of 1700 GeV would be necessary.

The obvious problem with experiments on colliding beams is that the probability of collisions between particles is very small. As mentioned earlier, a burst of the Brookhaven AGS contains approximately 10^{12} protons. If such a burst is directed against another similar one, the probability for a hit is very small, considering that in conventional experiments with stationary targets 1 cubic centimeter of liquid hydrogen contains 4×10^{22} protons. The only feasible way to achieve success is to boost the intensity of each burst as much as possible and then to store the accelerated protons in two storage rings, one for the protons moving clockwise and the other for the protons moving counterclockwise, bunch them in each ring and then let the bunches intersect at predetermined places.

Storage rings for electron beams were successfully put into use in 1967 for particle physics experiments in the U.S.S.R. and in France. In 1971 a colliding-beam device for protons became operative at CERN which uses the 28-GeV particles of the proton synchrotron (Fig. 7.2.8). The beam from the accelerator can be fed in a clockwise or counterclockwise sense into two storage rings of 150 m radius. The two opposing orbits intersect each other at several locations. In order to increase the collision probability the protons are not uniformly distributed over the ring but travel in 30 "buckets." Each ring, when filled, will contain 4×10^{14} protons. This corresponds to a current of 20 A. The vacuum of the rings is so high that the protons can circulate in it for half a day.

It is interesting to note that the accelerator is located in Switzerland but the storage ring is on French territory. Besides technical, physical, and financial problems (the storage ring project costs about \$70 million) there were also some by no means minor diplomatic hurdles to be overcome.

Particle Beams

If the interaction of protons or electrons with nucleons or nuclei is the aim of the study, the particle beam is brought from the accelerator to the

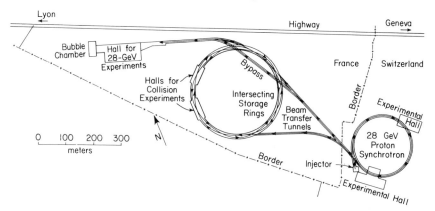

Fig. 7.2.8 The intersecting storage ring of the CERN Laboratory near Geneva, Switzerland.

equipment of the experimenter through holes in the many feet of shielding material around the accelerator. If, on the other hand, interactions of mesons or other artificially produced particles are the object of the investigation these particles must first be produced in collisions of protons or electrons with targets of hydrogen or other elements. In such collisions a great variety of particles may be produced. Through magnetic separation, sometimes also with electrostatic deflection, it is often possible to obtain fairly clean beams of only one kind of particle. Of great importance for example are the beams of K mesons, a species of mesons over three times as massive than the π mesons.

7.3 DETECTION AND EVALUATION METHODS*

Accelerators in conjunction with particle beam-handling systems provide only the rough material, that is the particles, for the experiments. However, one of the principal phases in every investigation is the detection of particles and the examination of their characteristics. Particle detectors and data-processing equipment thus play an eminent role in each experiment.

The basic principle of all particle detectors rests in the interaction of charged particles with matter. If the primary particle impinging on a counter is charged it will produce a certain amount of ionization in the matter or, as in the Cerenkov counter, it will produce some light. If the particle is uncharged its presence can only be detected indirectly, for example, by an interaction with other nucleons which produces moving charged particles. Also the deficits in the energy and momentum balances in a reaction are used for pinning down neutral particles, quite similar to one of the clues that led to the postulation of the neutrino. The existence of an unstable neutral particle may also be deduced from the observation of its charged decay products.

There are two groups of particle detectors. The first group comprises the counters, which simply transform the passage of a particle into a signal whose magnitude is usually (an exception is the Geiger-Müller counter discussed below) a function of the energy loss of the particle in the counter. A most important feature of a good counter is its ability to time an event with high precision, of the order of nanoseconds ($= 10^{-9}$ sec, the prefix nano $= 10^{-9}$). The second group consists of the detectors that record the tracks of the particles.

* This section may be omitted without loss of continuity.

Counters

Of the first group the detector best known to the layman is probably the *Geiger-Müller* counter which, however, has come into nearly complete disuse in nuclear and particle physics because of its poor timing capabilities and because its pulses, regardless of the particle energy, all have the same size. It still plays a role in cosmic-ray experiments and space physics research with satellites. Such a counter consists of a tube with a fine wire inside along its axis. The wire is at a positive potential in the neighborhood of 1000 V above the tube. The counter is filled with a gas or gas mixture (e.g., argon and alcohol vapor) at reduced pressure, approximately one tenth of an atmosphere. If a particle passes through the gas the electrons released by the ionization move toward the wire and induce a gas discharge of short duration which gives rise to an electron pulse.

A type of counter in extended use in low- and high-energy physics is the *scintillation counter*. Its functioning is similar to that of a luminous material in watch dials in which zinc sulphide scintillates because of its excitation by the radioactivity of substances embedded in it. In the scintillation counters for nuclear and particle physics the usual scintillating material consists either of sodium iodide crystals with minute additions of thallium or of certain organic substances, which may be crystals or may be dissolved in organic solvents or in plastic. The light whose output is in general proportional to the energy loss of the particle in the detector is collected into a photomultiplier and converted into an electronic pulse.

Another counter, used only in high-energy physics, is the *Cerenkov counter*. Its principle can best be understood by an acoustical analogy. If an object, such as a plane, moves faster through the air than the velocity of sound, a sonic boom appears because of the creation of a shock wave. Similarly if charged particles move through a transparent medium, such as glass, with a velocity faster than the speed of light in that medium, a shock wave of light is created whose direction of propagation in relation to the direction of the particle is a function of the ratio of the velocities of the particle and the light. This light is picked up by photomultipliers and converted into a signal.

Devices Recording Tracks

Of the second group of detectors, that is, the group registering the traces left by the particles, the nuclear emulsions, but particularly the bubble chamber and the spark chamber, are the most important ones.

Chronologically the *nuclear emulsions* were the first of these detectors, and they were of particular importance after the war and through the 1950's. They are basically photographic emulsions with a very high proportion of silver bromide in the gelatin compared with regular photographic emulsions. The sensitive layer can have a thickness of up to 1 mm. The thickness is limited due to the difficulty in developing thicker emulsions. An ionizing particle traversing the emulsion reacts with the grains of the emulsion in a similar manner to light and thus leaves after development a visible track of silver grains. The density of a track, that is the number of developed silver grains per unit length, is a function mainly of the charge and the speed of the particle because the probability of interaction with an atom along its path depends on the length of time spent in the neighborhood of the atom; consequently a fast-moving particle will not leave as dense a track in an emulsion than a slower-moving particle. Since these interactions are mostly electromagnetic phenomena (ionization, excitation), the interaction probability increases with increasing charge. Electrons which because of their small mass travel with speeds close to the velocity of light, even if they have only a few MeV energy, therefore cause only faint tracks. Protons of the same energy produce much denser tracks, and the effect of mesons is intermediate. α-Particles with twice the charge of a proton ionize more and hence give heavier tracks than protons. In many experiments stacks of several layers of nuclear emulsions are used. A particle might traverse several layers before coming to a stop. After their development the emulsions are scanned under a microscope for tracks. If a track seems to be interesting its total length and also the density of the developed silver grains in the track may be determined. From such data the kind of particle and its energy can be deduced. The direction of the track in respect to the direction of the incident beam from the accelerator is also of interest. At the end of a track of an unstable particle one or more new particles might appear, depending on the mode of decay. Sometimes it can be deduced from the shape and density of a track that the original particle came to rest and did not decay in flight. Conservation of momentum requires then that the sum of the momenta of the newly created particles be zero. If the observed momenta do not cancel, the conclusion must be drawn that one or more neutral particles have escaped without leaving a track; this might be a neutrino, a neutron, a neutral meson, or something else. One of the particles which was discovered with the aid of nuclear emulsions was the π meson. It was found by C. F. Powell and co-workers in Bristol, England, in 1947 (Fig. 7.3.1). Analysis of the tracks showed that the π meson came to rest, but that another particle appeared, which is now called a muon. These muons have all a range of approximately 0.6 mm in a nuclear emulsion, because their original kinetic energy is the same. Together with the muon an invisible neutrino is emitted. Also the muon

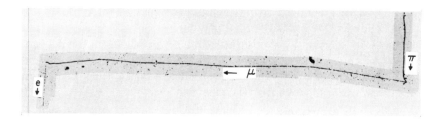

Fig. 7.3.1 A $\pi \to \mu \to e$ decay in a nuclear emulsion. [R. Brown, U. Camerini, P. H. Fowler, H. Muirhead, C. F. Powell (Nobel Prize in Physics 1950) and D. M. Ritson, *Nature* **163**, 47 (1949)].

is an unstable particle—it decays into an electron that leaves a faint track in the emulsion, and two neutrinos.

The bubble chamber has a predecessor, the *cloud chamber*, one of the oldest tools in nuclear and particle physics, invented in 1911. In a cloud chamber ionizing particles passing through a region of slightly supersaturated air, alcohol, or hydrogen vapor produce a trail of condensed droplets. This process is well known from the vapor trails caused by the ionized gases of airplanes if the right atmospheric conditions prevail. The discoveries of the neutron, the positron, and the muon are due to the cloud chamber. Today this tool which for decades was eminently useful is now superseded by the bubble chamber and the spark chamber.

Whereas the cloud chamber uses a saturated vapor as a medium, the *bubble chamber* (Fig. 7.3.2) contains a slightly superheated liquid. If an ionizing particle passes through the liquid, local bubbles which can be photographed appear along the path. Also this operating principle can be explained by an analogy. Soda water in a full closed bottle does not bubble, but as soon as the bottle is opened and the pressure released, bubbles form at the impurities of the inner walls of the bottle, detach themselves and rise. Similarly, the liquid in the bubble chamber is held at a temperature and pressure at which it does not quite boil. At the right moment, often triggered by a pulse from the accelerator or by particles passing through detectors outside the chamber, the pressure is suddenly slightly reduced so that along the path of an ionizing particle the liquid boils and forms small bubbles. The tracks consisting of these bubbles can be stereoscopically photographed. The bubble chambers are usually in a strong magnetic field to allow a determination of the sign of charge and of the momentum of the particle from the curvature of the track. Since many experiments need thousands of photographs, physicists try to mechanize the evaluation of these photographs as much as possible and let computers do much of the evaluation, as for example determination of the energy and momentum balance. The most frequently used liquids are liquid hydrogen at 25 K, propane, and freon. Hydrogen is clearly the ideal liquid for the study of interactions with free protons. In addition, because of the small charge of hydrogen nuclei in comparison with other atoms, the scattering of the particles due to Coulomb forces is relatively small, thus permitting accurate measurements of the momentum. On the other hand, in the denser liquids the ranges of particles are shorter and therefore extend range measurements

Fig. 7.3.2   The 80-inch liquid-hydrogen bubble chamber of Brookhaven National Laboratory. The chamber is 80 inches long, 26 inches high and 27 inches deep and contains 900 liters of liquid hydrogen. It is surrounded by a vacuum chamber, large magnet coils and a massive steel magnet yoke. The field throughout the chamber is 20 Wb/m². One side of the chamber consists of a glass window 6½ inches thick through which the chamber is illuminated and photographed with three cameras. (Courtesy of Brookhaven National Laboratory).

to higher energies. Some of the great bubble chambers are several feet in diameter and hold hundreds of gallons of liquid hydrogen. One advantage of the bubble chamber over the cloud chamber is the much greater density of the medium, which keeps the tracks shorter. The bubble chamber is also superior to the nuclear emulsion in several respects. For example, the nuclide in which the observed interactions arise is better defined, in contrast to the emulsion which contains, besides silver and bromide, the carbon and hydrogen of the gelatin. With nuclear emulsions one is often not sure with what kind of nucleus a particle has reacted. On the other hand, the cumulative property of the nuclear emulsion can be of great advantage in many cases when one is looking for rare events. This means that the emulsion is continuously sensitive for long periods of time which may be in the order of months; afterwards there is some gradual fading of the latent image. The bubble chamber, however, is sensitive only for approximately

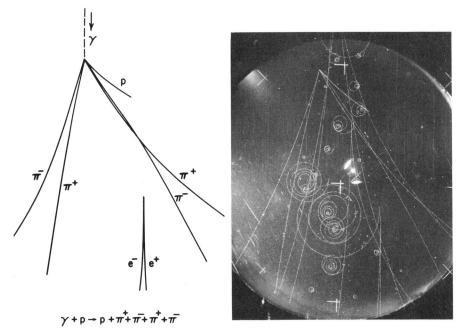

$$\gamma + p \rightarrow p + \pi^+ + \pi^- + \pi^+ + \pi^-$$

Fig. 7.3.3 Production of four mesons by interaction of a high-energy photon with a proton $\gamma + p \rightarrow p\pi^+\pi^-\pi^+\pi^-$. γ energy between 1 and 6 GeV. 15″ hydrogen bubble chamber at Cambridge Electron accelerator. In the lower right quadrant is the very narrow fork of an e^+e^- pair. $B = 1.32$ Wb/m². The interested reader may determine the approximate energy of the incident quantum from the curvatures of the tracks. Assume that all tracks are in a plane parallel to the picture and that no neutral particles were created. The curvature of a track can be derived from the measurement of its chord and sagitta. (Courtesy of MIT Bubble Chamber Group).

Fig. 7.3.4 A large array of spark chambers during assembly for the neutrino experiment at CERN (Courtesy of Photo CERN).

1/100 sec followed by a fairly long recovery time. Figure 7.3.3 shows two events in a bubble chamber.

A development more recent than the bubble chamber is the *spark chamber*. In its simplest form it functions in the following way. Two parallel plates form a capacitor. An electric field is applied between the plates of such high intensity that an ionizing particle passing from one plate to the other gives rise to a spark along its path. Usually there are several plates behind each other. This spark is either photographed or the arrival time of the "thunder" of this "lighting" at two or more microphones is recorded. The spark chamber at CERN, used for the detection of neutrino-induced reactions, is shown in Fig. 7.3.4. Two such events are shown in Fig. 7.3.5. In comparison with bubble chambers, spark chambers have a much better time resolution but their spatial resolution is inferior.

Lifetimes of particles often can be deduced from the distance they travel before they decay. Since the particles have in general a speed close to that of the velocity of light, the lifetime of the particles in the laboratory system can easily be calculated, but with the aid of the appropriate Lorentz transformations the more important lifetime in the system of the particles can also be found. In cases where a decay product is neutral and unstable, the

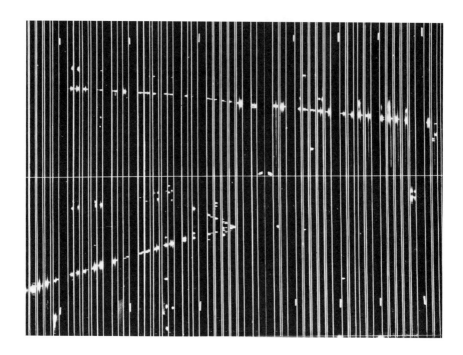

Fig. 7.3.5 Photograph of the spark chamber set-up during the neutrino experiment. The photograph is unusual in the sense that two neutrino events were obtained accidently during the same 2×10^{-6} sec interval of beam. The fact that such coincidences do occur, in spite of the low cross section of neutrino reactions, is an illustration of the high intensity of the neutrino beam. The two events in the picture represent the two most commonly encountered types, which are both examples of the "elastic" neutrino reaction: $\nu + n \rightarrow \mu^- + p$. The neutrino ($\nu$) is not seen, being without charge, but is incident from the right. It hits a neutron (n), bound in the nuclei of the aluminum and brass 5 mm plates which constitute the electrodes of the spark chamber. Most of the energy is given to the muon (μ^-) which is the long track in the two events. In the upper event the "recoiling" proton (p) gets little energy and is hardly seen, and the μ continues almost undeflected in the direction of the neutrino. In the lower event the recoiling proton gives a clear track, and the muon goes off at an angle (Photo CERN).

principles of conservation of energy, momentum, and charge often help to relate separated tracks in the same photograph. Such an example is given in Fig. 7.3.6.

In most experiments combinations of several detectors are used. Particles passing through counters may, for example, trigger bubble or spark chambers. Often a number of counters are positioned one behind the other or side by side, forming a counter telescope or hodoscope (*hodos* = way) in order to ascertain the direction of a particle. Or by way of requiring a certain size of pulse from each counter one can identify the particle. In a certain situation it may be required that only certain counters respond, but others remain silent.

As an example a complicated system is shown in Fig. 7.3.7, called a missing-mass spectrometer. It serves for the determination of masses of unknown particles and resonances resulting from the reaction

$$\pi^- + p \rightarrow p + X^-$$

with X^- the "missing mass" to be determined. This "missing mass" in short represents an excited state of mesons and decays into a number of π mesons. It turns out that a measurement of the deflection angle of the outgoing proton is already sufficient for this mass determination because direction and momentum of the incoming π^- mesons are known. However, as a check, the energy of the proton is also measured and the mesons from the X^- decay are recorded. The important data about the mass spectrum are discussed in Section 7.11.

Finally, Fig. 7.3.8 gives a view into an experimental area at CERN.

Plots

If a reaction or a decay of a particle leads to a final state that consists of three or more particles, one of the questions that arise is whether these particles were all created at the same time or in stages. The reaction

$$A + B \rightarrow C + D + E + F$$

might proceed as a one-stage reaction as just written. One of the several alternate ways of decay, however, is the following two-stage process

$$A + B \rightarrow X \quad\quad\quad + Y$$
$$\searrow C + D \quad\quad \searrow E + F.$$

The answer to such questions often can be found by assuming hypothetically each of the different modes of decay and then plotting the experimental data in a manner appropriate for each of these possibilities. An

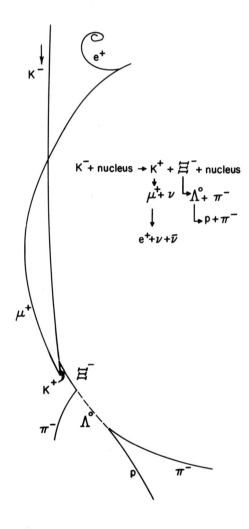

Fig. 7.3.6   Event in C₃F₅Cl (light freon) in heavy-liquid bubble chamber operated at CERN in the 1.6 GeV/cK^- beam. (Courtesy of Rutherford High Energy Laboratory, Chilton, England).

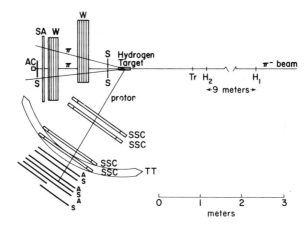

Fig. 7.3.7 The "missing mass" spectrometer at CERN. H: hodoscopes, Tr: trigger detector, S: scintillation counters, W: spark chambers with parallel wire planes, SA: array of scintillation counters. AC: anticoincidence counter (to prevent registration of pions from the original beam), SSC: sonic spark chambers, A: absorbers, TT: turntable.

Fig. 7.3.8 Experimental hall of the CERN proton synchrotron. Beneath the concrete shielding blocks left of the center is a beam line leading to a bubble chamber. In the center is a beam line with three electrostatic particle separators. To the right is another beam line. (Courtesy of Photo CERN).

example is the inelastic scattering of K mesons from protons

$$K^+ + p \rightarrow K^+ + \pi^+ + \pi^- + p.$$

Are all the particles flying apart at the same instant? Or is a $(\pi^+\pi^-)$ pair created that decays later? Or are there other groupings? The answer is easy to see from inspection of the plot in Fig. 7.3.9.

For the construction of this plot the assumption was made that the decay is a two-stage decay (as indeed it often is), the system first splitting into two systems which then decay further in approximately 10^{-23} seconds (a time much too short to move any noticeable distance) into p and π^+, and K^+ and π^-, respectively. Each point in this plot represents the so-called invariant energies of both two-particle systems. By invariant energy (often called invariant mass) of a group of particles is understood their total (that is, relativistic) energy in their center of mass system. The graph shows a high density of points in the region of 0.9 GeV for the $(K^+\pi^-)$ system and another such region, although not as pronounced as the former one, at 1.2 GeV for the $(p\pi^+)$ system. Corresponding plots for the $(p\pi^-)$ and $(K^+\pi^+)$ invariant energies fail to show such regions, as do plots for

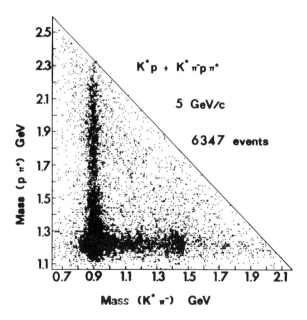

Fig. 7.3.9 Scatter plot of the invariant energies of the two-particle system $(p\pi^+)$ and $(K\pi^-)$ produced in the reaction $K^+ + p \rightarrow K^+ + \pi^+ + \pi^- + p$ at 5.0 GeV/c. The triangle corresponds to the region allowed by the conservation of energy and momentum. [W. De Baere, et al., *Nuovo Cimento* **61 A**, 397 (1969).]

other combinations. It should be pointed out that by no means all decays of this reaction follow this two-stage pattern; if that were so, all the points would lie close to the intersection of the two bands. It can only be concluded that there is a certain preference for this decay mode.

The plot discussed above is called scatter plot. For break-ups into three particles another plot is frequently used, the Dalitz plot (named after its originator) which yields even much more information, but its discussion is beyond the scope of this chapter.

Finally, the role of computers must at least be mentioned because without them progress in high-energy physics would have been much slower. It is obvious that rough data from counters can easily be fed into computers, and also the registrations from sonic spark chambers (as those with acoustic receptors are called) present no problems. However, the evaluation of tracks in emulsions and bubble chamber pictures is more complicated, but is gradually becoming more automated.

In some cases the data from the registering instruments are fed directly into the computer. The computer is then used "on-line." However, for economical reasons usually the data are initially stored on punch tape or magnetic tape. The information is later transferred to a computer, which in such cases is used "off-line." The writing of computer programs has now become an integral part of nearly every experiment in particle physics.

7.4 ATOMS, NUCLEI, AND PARTICLES

Until 1932 only two subatomic particles were known, the proton and the electron. In that year the neutron was discovered, and this relieved the physicists from great headaches. For example, it was no longer necessary to assume the existence of electrons inside nuclei, and the integer and half-integer units of angular momentum of the nuclides could be explained. Also the postulation of a neutrino removed difficulties for the nuclear theory in connection with beta decay. The discovery of the positron in 1932 was to some degree forecast in 1928 by Dirac's theory. There were therefore no difficulties in the interpretation of this particle after its discovery. Yukawa (Sec. 6.4) explained the short range of nuclear forces in 1935 with the hypothesis that particles of some hundred times the rest mass of the electron were the agent for the attraction between nucleons. Thus the existence of the meson was also postulated on theoretical grounds before its discovery. The joy of finding soon afterwards, in 1937, a particle with a mass of the expected order of magnitude, however, slowly gave place to consternation because with the exception of its mass and charge the characteristics of the particle were not at all the expected ones. Yukawa's particles were predicted to interact strongly with nuclei but the new particles, which were found in the cosmic radiation, were very penetrating, going through many meters of material without being absorbed, therefore hardly interacting with nuclei. This puzzle was solved when the true meson, now called the π meson or pion, was found in 1947. The first-discovered particle, now carrying the name muon, is related to the electron which likewise does not interact with the nucleus through the strong nuclear forces. With the exception of the muon all other particles could immediately and easily be fitted into a coherent system of nuclear physics. For the future it was hoped that in due time the anti-proton and the anti-neutron would be discovered, either in man-made processes or in cosmic radiation.

If things had stayed this way this chapter might well be only an adjunct to the chapter on nuclear physics. However, from 1947 on a few strange tracks were observed, most unexpectedly, in cloud chambers that were set up to observe cosmic radiation. Some of the observed tracks started inside the cloud chamber. Often two tracks started from the same point.[4] Therefore, they had to be the decay products of a neutral particle. From their length and density one had to conclude that the mass of the neutral particle had to be between that of a π meson and a nucleon. Other tracks were caused by charged particles of similar mass. Some of the tracks had to come from neutral particles of mass appreciably greater than that of a meson but less than that of a nucleon, and some from particles which had charge. A little later the first accelerators capable of accelerating protons to a few GeV came into operation. Soon a number of different particles were discovered and produced in great quantity. With sophisticated methods the lifetimes could be measured and also the modes of their decay could be determined. The Latin and Greek alphabets (capitals and lower-case letters) were extensively used to name these newly found particles.

No real systematic trends in this deluge of particles could be recognized for a long time. In classifying the particles one spoke during the early stages of the work about a "zoology of elementary particles" and an "elementary particle zoo," but even this was euphemistic because the ordering principle in classical zoology was much further advanced. We know that a dog is closer related to a sparrow than to a carp. Corresponding statements in particle physics could for a long time not be made in good faith. However, the fog has now begun to lift. At last we see some ordering principle, although we still do not know by what agent it is caused. Atomic phenomena are due to electric forces and nuclear phenomena to nuclear forces. In the latter case we have a reasonably workable conception, and

---

[4] The particles were first called V particles because of the geometry of the tracks. Today they are known as K mesons.

in the former one we have a very precise conception of the character of the fields and forces involved. The phenomena of particle physics, however, are not at all understood. It is since only recently that we have something corresponding to the formula describing the Balmer series of the hydrogen atom. The Balmer formula did not explain the hydrogen atom but was an important step toward the hydrogen atom model. In essence, in particle physics we are at about that level of understanding today, which makes this research field so exciting to the human intellect. A number of physicists—among them V. F. Weisskopf—showed the way to a deeper general understanding of high-energy phenomena and their place in the whole of physics. To some degree we shall follow Weisskopf's ideas.

We might first ask ourselves by playing a game with extrapolations, what new knowledge we might expect from the pursuit of high-energy physics. In atomic physics, which deals with energies of electron volts, the interaction is the well-understood electromagnetic interaction, and transitions from one state to the other proceed by emission or absorption of electromagnetic quanta which, as we know, have a rest mass of zero. The important quantum numbers are, besides the principal quantum number, the angular momentum quantum numbers and their component in some preferred direction, the so-called magnetic quantum numbers. In nuclear physics much more energy is available. The appropriate unit of energy, instead of the eV, is here the MeV. In addition to the electromagnetic transitions we also observe transitions by way of emission of a pair of light particles, that is, an electron and neutrino, which bring the nucleus from one quantum state to another. As we recall these particles are due to the weak interaction. In addition to the quantum numbers with which we are familiar from atomic physics there is a new one in nuclear physics: the i spin and its component in the z direction. The i spin reflects the fact that the nucleon has a proton state and a neutron state. It should be remembered that in the range of nuclear physics (in contrast to particle physics) the electron-neutrino pairs of the weak interaction and the γ quanta of the electromagnetic interaction are real entities, whereas the mesons which are the agents for the strong interaction are only virtual mesons. As already discussed in Sect. 6.4, this is so because the real meson has a rest mass of approximately 140 MeV, an amount of energy which is more than the usual energy difference between nuclear states. On similar grounds the weak interaction cannot play a role in atomic physics because it is associated with particles of half an MeV rest mass, much more than the representative energy differences in atoms.

Keeping these considerations in mind we now can guess that we might expect to discover in high-energy physics new quantum numbers involving new selection rules and the emission of particles more massive than the photon or the leptons. Whereas the energy of the quantum states in atoms is of the order of eV, and in nuclei of the order of MeV, it will be here again about a thousand times more of the order of GeV (= 10^9 eV), and we might find energy differences between these states in the order of some hundred MeV.

7.5 THE PARTICLES AND THEIR CONSERVATION LAWS

Over the years a large number of particles has been discovered; presently more than one hundred are known if the anti-particles are counted separately. This makes it obvious that they should not be called elementary particles as they were named optimistically when their number was small. Table 7.5.1 gives an incomplete list of these particles.

The bubble chamber photographs of Figs. 7.5.1–7.5.3 illustrate the production of particles by high-energy collisions and their decay. Figure 7.5.1, taken at the Argonne National Laboratory near Chicago, shows a reaction induced by a π^+ meson. Figure 7.5.2, from the Rutherford High Energy Laboratory in England, contains two K^- meson events, and Fig. 7.5.3, from CERN, Switzerland, shows the reaction of an antiproton with a proton. In this process, among other particles, a K^- meson is produced which happens to produce in a further reaction with a proton a Σ particle. The famous bubble chamber photograph of the Brookhaven National Laboratory on Long Island with the first Ω^- particle, produced in a reaction of a K^- meson with a proton, is shown in Fig. 7.10.6. A photon-induced reaction, from the Cambridge Electron Accelerator, was shown in Fig. 7.3.3, two neutrino-induced events in a spark chamber at CERN in Fig. 7.3.5, and a reaction in which the bombarded target is a nucleus rather than a proton in Fig. 7.3.6.

In general, to each particle belongs an anti-particle. The anti-particle has the opposite charge of the particle, and the magnetic moment has the opposite sign. Therefore the neutron and the anti-neutron are two distinct particles although both have zero charge. If the neutron is imagined as having a positive core and a negative shell which both rotate with the same angular velocity as mentioned in Section 6.3, and therefore having spin angular momentum and magnetic moment vector in opposite directions, the anti-neutron will have a negative core and a positive shell, with the consequence of parallelity of both vectors. In some cases, however, particle and anti-particle are identical. The π^0 meson, for example, is its own anti-particle. The same holds true for the photon. Anti-particles are often so designated by the bar above their symbol, as for example $\bar{p}$, $\bar{n}$. Σ^+ is the anti-particle to Σ^- but it is often also written as $\overline{\Sigma^-}$.

TABLE 7.5.1

Table of Particles and Resonant States[a]

Particle	Charge	Antiparticle	Mass (MeV)	Spin[b] J	i-Spin T	Hypercharge Y	Interaction in Decay	Mean Life (Sec)	or Width (Mev)	Principal Decay Modes ($>10\%$)
PHOTON (Baryon Number = 0, Lepton Number = 0)										
γ	0	same	0	1^-				stable		
LEPTONS (Baryon Number = 0, Lepton Number = 1)										
ν_e	0	$\bar{\nu}_e$	0	$\frac{1}{2}$				stable		
ν_μ	0	$\bar{\nu}_\mu$	0	$\frac{1}{2}$				stable		
e^-	-1	e^+	0.511	$\frac{1}{2}$				stable		
μ^-	-1	μ^+	105.7	$\frac{1}{2}$			W	2.2×10^{-6}		$e\bar{\nu}_e\nu_\mu$
HADRONS										
(a) MESONS (Baryon Number = 0, Lepton Number = 0)										
π^0	0	same	135.0	0^-	1	0	EM	0.84×10^{-16}		$\gamma\gamma$
π^+	$+1$	π^-	139.6	0^-	1	0	W	2.6×10^{-8}		$\mu\nu_\mu$, $\pi\pi^0$
K^+	$+1$	K^-	493.7	0^-	$\frac{1}{2}$	1	W	1.2×10^{-8}		$\mu\nu_\mu$, $\pi^0\pi^0$
K^0	0	$\overline{K^0}$	497.8	0^-	$\frac{1}{2}$	1	W	K_S^0 8.82×10^{-11} K_L^0 5.2×10^{-8}		$\pi^+\pi^-$, $\pi^0\pi^0$ $\pi e\nu_e$, $\pi\mu\nu_\mu$, $\pi^0\pi^0\pi^0$, $\pi^+\pi^-\pi^0$
η	0	same	548.8	0^-	0	0	EM	$\Gamma = 0.0026$		$\gamma\gamma$, $\pi^0\pi^0\pi^0$, $\pi^+\pi^-\pi^0$, $\pi^+\pi^-\pi^0$
ρ^+	$+1$	ρ^-	765	1^-	1	0	S	135		$\pi\pi$
ρ^0	0	same								
ω	0	same	784	1^-	0	0	S	13		$\pi^+\pi^-\pi^0$, $\pi^0\gamma$

Particle	Q	Antiparticle	Mass	J^P	I	Y	Int.	Γ / τ	Decay modes
K^{*+}	+1	$\overline{K^{*+}} \equiv K^{*-}$	892	1^-	$\tfrac12$	1	S	50	$K\pi$
K^{*0}	0	$\overline{K^{*0}}$ same	899	1^-	$\tfrac12$	1	S	50	$K\pi$
φ	0	same	1019	1^-	0	0	S	4.4	$K^+K^-,\ K_S^0 K_L^0,$ $\pi^+\pi^-\pi^0,\ \rho\pi$
A_1^+	+1	A_1^-	~ 1070	1^+	1	0	S	200–400	$\rho\pi$
A_1^0	0	same		1^+	1	0			
B^+	+1	B^-	1233 ± 10	1^+	1	0	S	100	$\omega\pi$
B^0	0	same		1^+	1	0			
f	0	same	1269 ± 10	2^+	0	0	S	156	$\pi\pi$
A_2^+	+1	A_2^-	1310 ± 10	2^+	1	0	S	100	$\rho\pi,\ \eta\pi$
A_2^0	0	same		2^+	1	0			
K_N^+	+1	$\overline{K_N^+} \equiv K_N^-$	1421	2^+	$\tfrac12$	1	S	100	$K^*\pi,\ K\rho$
K_N^0	0	same							
f'	0	same	1514	2^+	0	0	S	~ 70	$K\bar K$
g	$\pm 1, 0$	g	1680 ± 20	3^-	1	0	S	~ 160	$\pi\pi\pi\pi,\ \pi\pi$

(b) BARYONS (Baryon Number = 1, Lepton Number = 0)

Particle	Q	Antiparticle	Mass	J^P	I	Y	Int.	Γ / τ	Decay modes
$N\{\ p$	+1	$\bar p$	938.259	$\tfrac12^+$	$\tfrac12$	+1		stable	
$\quad n$	0	$\bar n$	939.553	$\tfrac12^+$	$\tfrac12$	+1	W	918 sec	$pe\bar\nu$
Λ	0	$\bar\Lambda$	1115.6	$\tfrac12^+$	0	0	W	2.52×10^{-10}	$p\pi^-,\ n\pi^0$
Σ^+	+1	$\bar\Sigma^+$	1189.4	$\tfrac12^+$	1	0	W	0.80×10^{-10}	$p\pi^0,\ n\pi^+$
Σ^0	0	$\bar\Sigma^0$	1192.5	$\tfrac12^+$	1	0	EM	$<1.0 \times 10^{-14}$	$\Lambda\gamma$
Σ^-	-1	$\bar\Sigma^-$	1197.3	$\tfrac12^+$	1	0	W	1.48×10^{-10}	$n\pi^-$
$\Delta(1236)^{++,+,0,-}$	$2,1,0,-1$	$\overline{\Delta(1236)}$	1236	$\tfrac32^+$	$\tfrac32$	+1	S	120	$N\pi$
Ξ^0	0	$\bar\Xi^0$	1315	$\tfrac12^+$	$\tfrac12$	-1	W	3.0×10^{-10}	$\Lambda\pi^0$
Ξ^-	-1	$\bar\Xi^-$	1321	$\tfrac12^+$	$\tfrac12$	-1	W	1.7×10^{-10}	$\Lambda\pi^-$
$\Sigma(1385)^{+,0,-}$	$1,0,-1$	$\overline{\Sigma(1385)}$	$1383(+)$ $1386(-)$	$\tfrac32^+$	1	0	S	36	$\Lambda\pi,\ \Sigma\pi$

TABLE 7.5.1 (Continued)

Particle	Charge	Antiparticle	Mass (MeV)	Spin[b] J	i-Spin T	Hyper-charge Y	Inter-action in Decay	Mean Life or Width	Principal Decay Modes (>10%)
Baryons (cont.)									
$\Lambda(1405)$	0	$\overline{\Lambda(1405)}$	1405	$\frac{1}{2}^-$	0	0	S	40	$\Sigma\pi$
$\Lambda(1520)$	0	$\overline{\Lambda(1520)}$	1518	$\frac{3}{2}^-$	0	0	S	16	$N\bar{K},\ \Sigma\pi,\ \Lambda\pi\pi$
$N(1520)^{+,0}$	1, 0	$\overline{N(1520)}$	~1520	$\frac{3}{2}^-$	$\frac{1}{2}$	+1	S	130	$N\pi,\ N\pi\pi$
$\Xi\begin{cases}\Xi^0(1530)\\ \Xi^-(1530)\end{cases}$	0	$\overline{\Xi^0(1530)}$	1531	$\frac{3}{2}^+$	$\frac{1}{2}$	-1	S	9	$\Xi\pi$
	-1	$\overline{\Xi^-(1530)}$	1536	$\frac{3}{2}^+$	$\frac{1}{2}$	-1	S	16	$\Xi\pi$
$\Delta(1650)$	2, 1, 0, -1	$\overline{\Delta(1650)}$	~1650	$\frac{1}{2}^-$	$\frac{3}{2}$	+1	S	~160	$N\pi\pi,\ N\pi$
$N(1670)$		$\overline{N(1670)}$	~1670	$\frac{5}{2}^-$	$\frac{1}{2}$	+1	S	~140	$N\pi\pi,\ N\pi$
$\Lambda(1670)$			1670	$\frac{1}{2}^-$	0	+1	S	~30	$\Sigma\pi,\ \Lambda\eta,\ N\bar{K}$
Ω^-	-1	$\overline{\Omega}^-$	1672.5	$\frac{3}{2}^+$	0	-2	W	1.3×10^{-10}	$\Xi^0\pi^-,\ \Xi^-\pi^0,$ ΛK^-
$N(1688)$			1688	$\frac{5}{2}^+$	$\frac{1}{2}$	1	S	~140	$N\pi,\ N\pi\pi$
$\Lambda(1690)$			1690	$\frac{3}{2}^-$	0	0	S	~60	$\Sigma\pi,\ N\bar{K},\ \Sigma\pi\pi$
$N(1700)$			~1710	$\frac{1}{2}^-$	$\frac{1}{2}$	1	S	~200	$N\pi$
$\Sigma(1765)$			1765	$\frac{5}{2}^-$	1	0	S	~120	$N\bar{K},\ \Lambda\pi,$ $\Lambda(1520)\,\pi$
$\Lambda(1815)$			~1820	$\frac{5}{2}^+$	0	0	S	~80	$N\bar{K},\ \Sigma\pi$
$\Lambda(1830)$			1835	$\frac{5}{2}^-$	0	0	S	~110	$\Sigma\pi,\ \Lambda\pi\pi,\ N\bar{K}$
$\Delta(1910)$			~1910	$\frac{1}{2}^+$	$\frac{3}{2}$	+1	S	~330	$N\pi$
$\Delta(1950)$			~1950	$\frac{7}{2}^+$	$\frac{3}{2}$	+1	S	~180	$\Delta(1236)\,\pi,\ N\pi$
$\Sigma(2030)$			2030	$\frac{7}{2}^+$	1	0	S	~140	$N\bar{K},\ \Lambda\pi$
$\Lambda(2100)$			2100	$\frac{7}{2}^-$	0	0	S	~100	$N\bar{K},\ \Lambda\omega$
$N(2190)$			~2190	$\frac{1}{2}^-$	$\frac{1}{2}$	+1	S	~300	$N\pi$

a Most of the entries are taken from the extensive tables in *Physics Letters* **39B**, 1 (1972). This table does not contain particles and resonant states about which only little or uncertain data are available. The designation of several particles and resonances is presently still not uniform. In an alternate notation the letter N stands for all baryons with hypercharge $Y = 1$. Those with $T = \frac{1}{2}$ are designated $N_{1/2}$, and those with $T = \frac{3}{2}$ are $N_{3/2}$. $N_{1/2}$ and $N_{3/2}$ correspond therefore to N and Δ in our table, e.g. $N_{3/2}(1236) = \Delta(1236)$. Similarly, the $Y = 0$ baryons are designated as Y in the alternate notation, with subscripts 0 and 1 indicating their i spin. Y is therefore identical with Λ, and Y_1 with Σ. Primes, e.g. Λ'', may be used to differentiate between baryons having the same set of quantum numbers. Also for the mesons very often the mass is attached to the letter, e.g. $f(1260)$. In this case the asterisks are sometimes omitted for the excited states.

In the column "mean life or width" an entry with a power-of-ten factor signifies the mean life in seconds, without such a factor the width of the resonance in MeV. S: Strong, EM: Electromagnetic, W: Weak.

For the heaviest N, Λ, Δ, and Σ hadrons charges and designations of the antiparticles are omitted since they are analog to the lighter N, Λ, … hadrons.

b In addition to the spin J another property of the particle or resonant state is listed, its *intrinsic parity*, which is either even $(+)$ or odd $(-)$. However, we shall not discuss or make use of it.

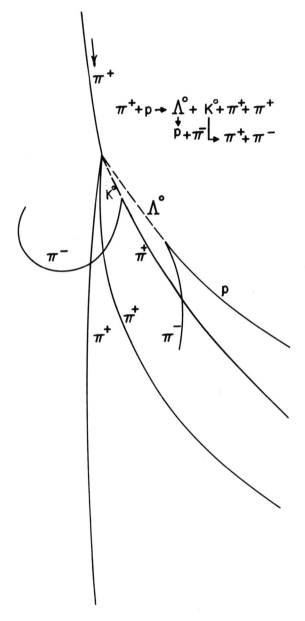

Fig. 7.5.1   A π^+ meson of momentum 3.9 GeV/c from the pion beam of the Argonne National Laboratory accelerator interacting with a proton in a 30-inch hydrogen bubble chamber according to the reaction $\pi^+ + p \to \Lambda^0 + K^0 + \pi^+ + \pi^+$. The Λ^0 decays into p and π^-, and the K^0 into π^+ and π^-. (Courtesy of MIT Bubble Chamber Group).

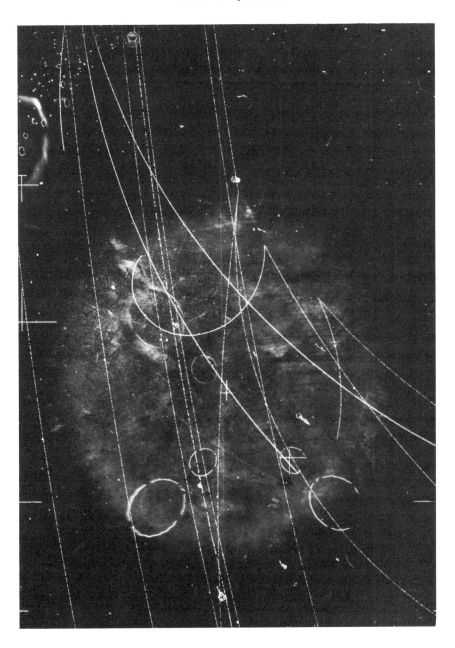

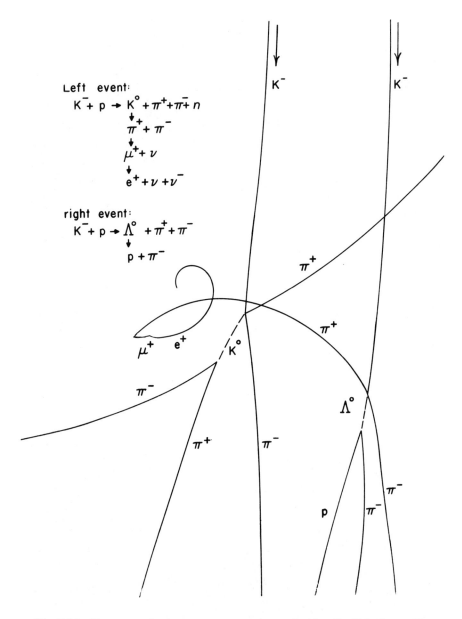

Fig. 7.5.2 Two events in the same exposure observed with a liquid-hydrogen 82-cm bubble chamber in the K^- beam (momentum 1.7 GeV/c) of the Rutherford High Energy Laboratory in Chilton, England. Right event: $K^- + p \to \Lambda^0 \pi^+ \pi^-$. The invisible Λ^0 decays into a proton and π^-. The π^+ undergoes $\pi^+ \to \mu^+ \to e^+$ decay accompanied by the appropriate neutrinos. Left event: $K^- + p \to K^0 \pi^+ \pi^- n$. The invisible K^0 decays into a pair of charged pions. (Courtesy of RHEL.)

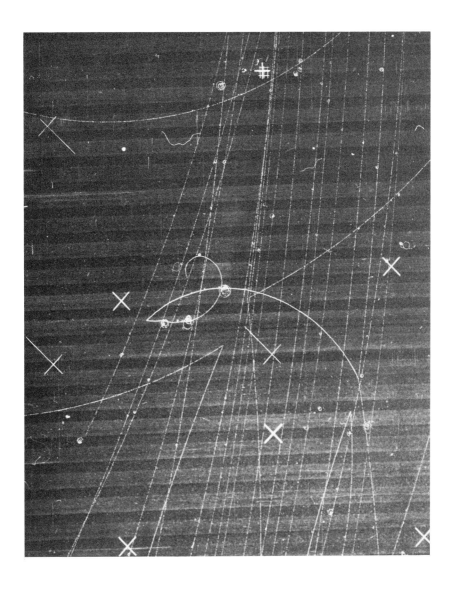

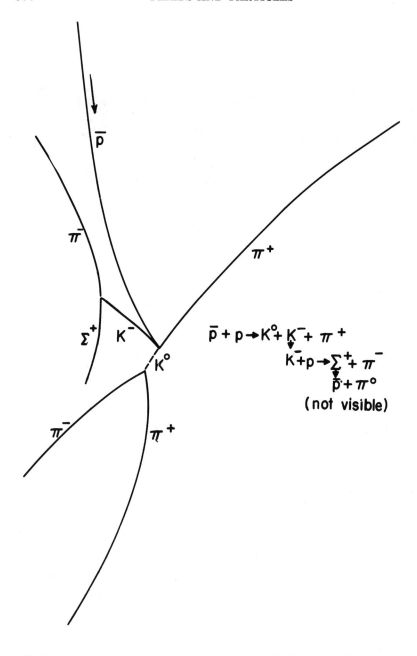

Fig. 7.5.3 A slow antiproton comes to a rest in a hydrogen bubble chamber and annihilates with a proton. In the annihilation a neutral K° meson, a K^- meson and a π^+ meson are created. The K^0 decays into π^+ and π^-. The K^- interacts with a second proton producing a Σ^+ and a π^-. The Σ^+ decays into a proton and a π° (Photo CERN).

Many particles have such a short life that they cannot really be called particles and therefore go under the name "resonances." A famous such resonance discovered in the early 1950's is the so-called $(\frac{3}{2}, \frac{3}{2})$ resonance (because spin and i spin both have the value $\frac{3}{2}$) in the scattering of π^+ mesons of 195 MeV kinetic energy by protons. This resonance corresponds to a combined pion-proton mass of 1236 MeV. The cross section as a function of the pion energy shows a distinct maximum (Fig. 7.5.4). (Another, but smaller, maximum appears at 1920 MeV). The encounter of the two particles lasts only for 10^{-23} sec as can be deduced from the width of the resonance curve by applying the uncertainty relation. It represents an excited state of a nucleon. The difference between a resonance and a particle is only that the particle has a longer life. The resonances decay by strong interactions, whereas the particles do it by weak interactions. As we shall see many of the particles are only excited states of nucleons which by certain selection rules are prevented from decaying in such short time as the $(\frac{3}{2}, \frac{3}{2})$ resonance but have a much longer life of the order of 10^{-10} sec. Resonances have designations like particles. The $(\frac{3}{2}, \frac{3}{2})$ resonance has the name $\Delta(1236)$ or $N_{3/2}(1236)$, as seen in Table 7.5.1. Its decay mode is a nucleon and a pion. The scattering process leading to the formation and decay of this resonance can therefore be written

$$\pi^+ + p \rightarrow \Delta^{++}(1236) \rightarrow \pi^+ + p.$$

All particles can be classed into the groups of either *leptons* (from the

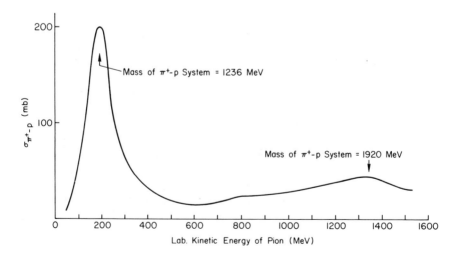

Fig. 7.5.4   The $(\frac{3}{2}, \frac{3}{2})$ resonance in the scattering of positive pions on protons, showing excited states of the nucleon of masses of 1236 and 1920 MeV.

Greek *leptos* = small), *mesons* (*mesos* = middle) or *baryons* (*barys* = heavy). In addition, the *photon* is in a category by itself. The leptons, that is, electrons, muons, and neutrinos, cannot interact by a strong interaction force, but only by the weak one or, if charged, by the electromagnetic interaction. As already known from classical physics, electrons can also interact with the photon electromagnetically. Some leptons have zero mass, namely the electron neutrino, that is the neutrino associated with the electron of the beta decay, and the muon neutrino,[5] which is associated with the muon. The two neutrinos have also their anti-particles, the anti-neutrinos. Electron and muon, as discussed in Chapter 6, seem to be different only with respect to their mass. All leptons have half-integer spin, therefore obeying the Pauli exclusion principle and Fermi statistics. They are hence fermions.

The main difference between baryons and mesons is that all baryons, like all leptons, have half-integer spin and thus observe Fermi statistics, whereas all mesons have integer spin and follow Bose statistics. The mesons are therefore bosons. On the other hand, baryons and mesons also have much in common and, therefore, are grouped together into the class of *hadrons* (*hadros* = large, strong). All hadrons interact strongly with each other and, in addition, are also capable of interacting through forces of weak interaction. Consequently, if selection rules forbid the strong interaction, or in their interaction with leptons, the weak interaction comes into play. Furthermore, hadrons can also interact electromagnetically with other hadrons and leptons. The baryons are, as their name implies, in general more massive than the mesons. However, there are many exceptions to this rule.

Empirically it has been found that for the leptons the law of the conservation of the number of leptons holds. In other words, the number of leptons remains constant. The anti-particles are hereby put into the balance as negative numbers. A simple example: in the beta decay of the neutron, an electron and an anti-neutrino are created, making the total number of leptons equal to zero before and after the beta decay. Another example is the decay of the muon into a positron, a muon antineutrino, and an electron neutrino, as shown in Figs. 7.3.6 and 7.5.2.

A similar law holds for the conservation of baryons. It has been found advantageous to attribute to all particles a baryon number. Baryons have the baryon number 1, anti-baryons −1, whereas the mesons and leptons have the baryon number 0. To date, conservation of lepton number and conservation of baryon number seem absolute, that is, no exceptions have

---

[5] The muon neutrino sometimes is also called neutretto in order to differentiate it from the electron neutrino.

been found yet. In this respect that is similar to the law of conservation of ordinary charge. The lepton number and the baryon number can be thought of as internal quantum numbers, just like the spin. This absolute conservation of baryon and lepton numbers explains the stability of the proton because it is the lightest baryon. If this law did not hold, the decay of a proton into a positron and a neutral pion should be possible. However, efforts to detect such a decay have all been negative, and the conclusion can be drawn that the mean life of a proton is $> 10^{21}$ years. This must be set in relation to the age of the universe which is of the order of 10^{10} years.

Mesons—and also photons which, as we know from atomic physics, can be created and absorbed—do not obey such a law regarding the conservation of their number. Hence, the facts are that for fermions—the leptons and baryons—this conservation law holds, but not for bosons, that is the mesons and photons.

In all reactions between elementary particles and in their decays it has been found empirically that the charge Q is conserved. Examples are the production of an electron–positron pair by a high-energy γ quantum or the annihilation of such a pair. The annihilation of a neutral π^0 meson into two γ quanta is another example. Charge is also conserved when pions are produced in nucleon-nucleon collisions, for example

$$n + p \rightarrow p + p + \pi^-$$
$$\rightarrow n + p + \pi^0$$
$$\rightarrow n + n + \pi^+.$$

Furthermore, a pion-induced reaction like $\pi^- + p \rightarrow \Lambda^0 + K^0$ also conserves the charge.

In the last chapter we introduced the concept of i spin whose root is in the charge independence of nuclear forces. This means that if in a nucleus a proton is substituted by a neutron of the same angular momentum state or vice versa the nucleus remains unaltered in its major characteristics. We have given some examples of i spin multiplets consisting of nuclei having the same i spin but different orientation of this fictitious vector. The simplest such multiplet is the nucleon with i spin $T = \frac{1}{2}$ which can have two different components in the z direction, namely $T_z = +\frac{1}{2}$ representing the proton and $T_z = -\frac{1}{2}$ representing the neutron.[6]

The i spin is of greatest importance in particle physics. However,

[6] Although in high-energy physics the letter I is mostly used for the i spin, we shall adhere to our old designation T for this concept as commonly used in low-energy physics, in order to prevent confusion. We shall, however, switch in this chapter to the name i spin, because it is somewhat more frequently used in particle physics than the name isospin.

whereas the ordinary, mechanical spin is conserved in all types of interaction the i spin is only conserved in strong interactions. Conservation of
i spin is therefore not one of the absolute conservation laws.

We also mentioned earlier that the concept of i spin can be extended to
other particles. For example, π-mesons form an i spin triplet, all having
$T = 1$, with $T_z = +1$ for π^+, $T_z = 0$ for π^0 and $T_z = -1$ for π^-. The conservation of i spin in strong interactions can be illustrated on the $(\frac{3}{2}, \frac{3}{2})$
resonance which we used earlier as an example for a particular resonance.

Figure 7.5.5 shows again the scattering cross section of pions on protons,
this time not only for positive but also for negative pions. The obvious
difference between the two curves is that the π^- scattering cross section at
the $(\frac{3}{2}, \frac{3}{2})$ resonance is only about one-third of that for π^+. In addition,
other resonances are apparent. As pointed out earlier, the $(\frac{3}{2}, \frac{3}{2})$ resonance
can be considered as an excited state of the nucleon, today customarily
designated[7] as $\Delta(1236)$. In the case of π^+ mesons the process leading to our
resonance, its i spin balance and its balance of the z component of the i spin
can be written

$$\pi^+ + p \rightarrow \Delta(1236) \rightarrow \pi^+ + p$$

$$T: \quad 1 \qquad \tfrac{1}{2} \qquad\qquad \tfrac{3}{2} \qquad\qquad 1 \qquad \tfrac{1}{2}$$

$$T_z: +1 \quad +\tfrac{1}{2} \qquad\quad +\tfrac{3}{2} \qquad\quad +1 \quad +\tfrac{1}{2}$$

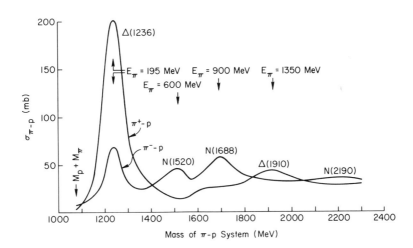

Fig. 7.5.5   The scattering cross sections for π^+ and π^- mesons on protons.

[7] In the alternate notation it is $N^* \frac{3}{2}$ (1236) read "en star three-half 1236." N stands
here for nucleon, the star for an excited state (which, however, may be omitted), 1236
for the mass in MeV of this excited state, and the subscript $\frac{3}{2}$ for the value of the i spin.

A $T = \frac{1}{2}$ state for the resonance (by assuming that the $T = 1$ vector and the $T = \frac{1}{2}$ vector are anti-parallel) is not possible because the T_z component which must be $+\frac{3}{2}$ clearly cannot be greater than the vector itself. This argument is completely analogous to the one with which we had ruled out $T = 0$ states in ^{14}C and ^{14}O.

Let us now look at the process with π^- mesons:

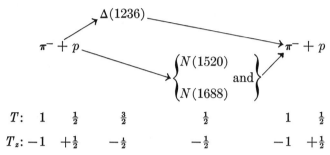

$$T: \quad 1 \quad \frac{1}{2} \quad \frac{3}{2} \quad \frac{1}{2} \quad 1 \quad \frac{1}{2}$$

$$T_z: -1 \quad +\frac{1}{2} \quad -\frac{1}{2} \quad -\frac{1}{2} \quad -1 \quad +\frac{1}{2}$$

Here we see that in addition to the i spin state $T = \frac{3}{2}$, the state $T = \frac{1}{2}$ is also permitted. In fact two such resonances belonging to $T = \frac{1}{2}$ appear in the general region, corresponding to masses of 1520 MeV and 1688 MeV. The conservation of the i spin of a system implies that its value remains the same before, during, and after a reaction. This means that the π^+-p system has $T = \frac{3}{2}$, whereas the π^--p system can be either in a $T = \frac{1}{2}$ or $T = \frac{3}{2}$ state. The z components of the two systems are $T_z = \frac{3}{2}$ and $\frac{1}{2}$, respectively.

In addition to the scattering of the π^- mesons on protons, a charge-exchange reaction is also possible, during which the charges are redistributed such that the outgoing meson and the nucleon both are neutral

$$\pi^- + p \to \Delta(1236) \to \pi^0 + n.$$

It is left as an exercise to set up the T and T_z balance for this reaction. The possibility of competition from $T = \frac{1}{2}$ states and the charge-exchange reaction result in the cross section at the $\Delta(1236)$ resonance peak for π^- mesons being only about one-third of that for π^+-mesons as a detailed analysis shows which requires quantum mechanics above the level of this book.

The i spin is a concept that is appropriate only for strongly interacting particles. One cannot therefore attribute i spin quantum numbers to leptons. Because electromagnetic interactions are not charge independent, but on the contrary by their very nature depend on charge, they do not conserve i spin. Electromagnetic interactions are also responsible for the members of a multiplet having slightly different masses. The π^0 meson is slightly less massive than the π^+ or π^- mesons; proton and neutron too have slightly different masses. There is therefore a small amount of violation of charge independence due to the electromagnetic interaction. Also, in weak interactions i spin is not conserved.

A somewhat more complicated conservation law, the law of conservation of *hypercharge*, has been deduced empirically. It is, however, not a universal law because it holds only for strong and electromagnetic interactions, but not for weak interactions. Hypercharge can also be considered as a quantum number and is denoted by Y. We have already mentioned in Section 6.3 of the last chapter that the proton and the neutron form a charge doublet and the three π mesons a charge triplet. The average charge in the nucleon doublet is $\frac{1}{2}$, in the meson triplet it is zero. The hypercharge Y is defined as twice the average charge of the multiplet. The nucleons thus have $Y = 1$ and the pions $Y = 0$. Anti-proton and anti-neutron clearly have $Y = -1$. The conservation law says that in a strong interaction hypercharge must be conserved. On the basis of experimental evidence the particles have been given the appropriate hypercharge numbers. Examples of reactions conserving hypercharge are the following:

$$n + p \rightarrow p + p + \pi^-$$

$$\pi^- + p \rightarrow \Sigma^- + K^+$$

$$\pi^- + p \rightarrow \Lambda^0 + K^0$$

$$\pi^+ + p \rightarrow \Lambda^0 + K^0 + \pi^+ + \pi^-.$$

The last reaction is seen in the bubble chamber photograph of Fig. 7.5.1. All these reactions are strong interactions as evidenced by their relatively large cross sections. In the two last reactions the pions have $Y = 0$, the proton $Y = +1$, and the Λ^0 has $Y = 0$ (there are no charged Λ's). The K meson doublet consists of the neutral K^0 and the positive K^+, and therefore $Y = 1$ for the K's. An example of the violation of the conservation of hypercharge in weak interactions is the decay of the K^0. Because this meson has a mass of 498 MeV there is enough energy available for its decay into two or three π mesons, since these have a mass of 137 ± 2 MeV. These decays have indeed been observed, but the decay is relatively slow at 10^{-10} sec.[8] This can easily be explained by the fact that hypercharge is not conserved, since π mesons have a hypercharge $Y = 0$. The decay of the K^0 can therefore only proceed through a weak interaction. Also the Λ^0 can decay only by weak interaction into a meson and a nucleon. Such decays are shown in Figs. 7.5.1–7.5.3.

---

[8] The case of the K^0 mesons is particularly complicated, because there are two different types, the K_S^0 and K_L^0. The K_S^0 has the above-quoted lifetime, the K_L^0 decays approximately 60 times slower! Problems relating to these two modes are presently of greatest interest and are discussed later in this chapter.

What led to the introduction of the concept of hypercharge was the fact that in pion-nucleon collisions a Σ or Λ baryon was never produced alone but was always accompanied by an equal number of K mesons. Furthermore, if a Ξ baryon was produced it was always accompanied by two K mesons. For this reason one spoke of "associated production." The particles that had such strange tendencies were therefore called "strange particles." Since such strangeness[9] has now become so frequent the name "strange particle" is used somewhat less in favor of simply "particle."

Finally it should be mentioned that the z component of the i spin is also conserved in strong and electromagnetic interactions, and in all types of interactions with the ordinary spin. Parity, which will be discussed in detail in Section 7.8, is another quantity which is conserved only in some types of interactions. It is not conserved in weak interactions. This refers not only to beta-decay but to all processes involving weak interactions, for example, the decay of baryons and mesons. Parity is however conserved in electromagnetic and strong interactions.

Tables 7.5.2 and 7.5.3 summarize the characteristics of the different groups of particles and their various interactions.

7.6　THE EXCITED STATES OF THE NUCLEON

In the introduction to this chapter we pointed out that with increasing energies we might expect new kinds of "quanta," having rest masses much greater than the lepton pairs, rather in the order of magnitude of the

TABLE 7.5.2

Characteristics of Particles

Particles		Statistics	Interactions			Conservation of Number
			Weak	Electro-magnetic	Strong	
Photon		Bose		✓		No
Leptons		Fermi	✓	✓		Yes
Mesons	⎫Hadrons	Bose	✓	✓	✓	No
Baryons	⎭	Fermi	✓	✓	✓	Yes

[9] Historically the quantum number Y was preceded by the quantum number for the "strangeness," S. The connection between Y and S is given by $Y = S + B$. Since B, the baryon number, is always conserved, S is conserved just as well as Y.

TABLE 7.5.3

Interactions and Conservation Laws

Interaction	Conservation of				
	Baryons	Parity	Hyper-change	i Spin	z Component of i Spin
Gravitation	√				
Weak	√				
Electromagnetic	√	√	√		√
Strong	√	√	√	√	√

mesons, associated with the force field of the strong forces. We also re-marked that new quantum numbers would come into play.

The theoretical physicist Weisskopf emphasized that nature repeats itself, so to speak, by having a "quantum ladder" in atomic, nuclear, and particle physics.[10] He pointed out that the different mesons represented nothing but the "quanta" emitted during the transitions between different quantum states. All these states are states of the nucleon, the ground state being our familiar proton and the other states the excited states. Even the neutron in the strictest sense can be considered as an excited state of the proton into which it decays through emission of a lepton pair. The states can be grouped into multiplets, according to their i spin (in atomic physics it was the regular spin), with singlets when $T = 0$, doublets when $T = \frac{1}{2}$, triplets when $T = 1$, and so on. Figure 7.6.1 shows the spectrum of the baryons according to Weisskopf. The states are either baryons, or their resonances, depending on their lifetime which, in turn, depends only on whether the particle can decay by strong interaction or whether it has to decay by weak interaction.

Whereas electromagnetic transitions take effect with the emission of one kind of quantum, we have here a large number of different mesons which may even decay into other mesons or into leptons. Because the excited states have various states of charge and of strangeness, a certain variety of mesons is plausible. However, some mesons decay into other mesons or into leptons. Weisskopf's explanation for this is that the strong interaction is so strong that it can produce such effects. In other words, the strong interaction can produce "quanta" that have some similarity with the

[10] For example, see the article "Quantum Theory and Elementary Particles" in *Physics in the 20th Century*, selected essays by V. F. Weisskopf (MIT Press, Cambridge, 1972). This book contains several highly recommended articles on modern physics.

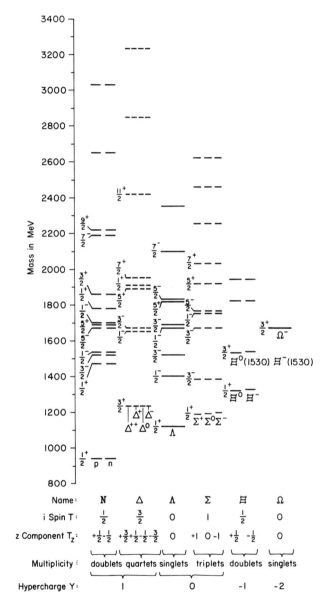

Fig. 7.6.1 Spectrum of the energy states of the baryon. Each ladder represents the states of a particular i spin, z-component of the i spin, hypercharge and charge. Angular momentum J and parity ($+$: even, $-$: odd, discussed in the following section) are given at the left of each level. The individual states, or particles, have names like Δ^+ (1910).

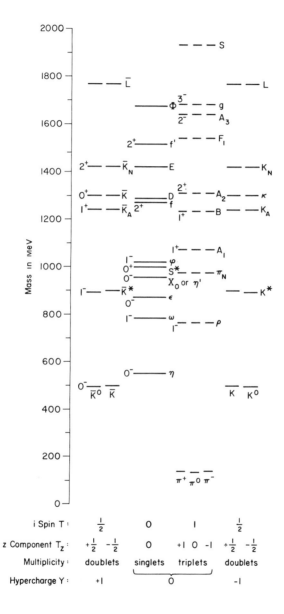

Fig. 7.6.2 Spectrum of the energy states of the meson. See also caption to Fig. 7.6.1. The names of the mesons, Greek and Latin upper-case and lower-case letters, with and without sub- and superscripts, nearly devoid of all systematics, are given at the right of each level.

original baryons from which they were emitted inasmuch as they too can emit new particles. There is one difference: these "quanta" (mesons) have the baryon number 0 in contrast to the baryons which have the baryon number 1. Therefore mesons may disintegrate into mesons and photons without violating the law of conservation of baryon number. On the other hand, similar to baryons the mesons also have excited states and different quantum numbers, so that here we again can construct a level diagram, as seen in Fig. 7.6.2.

7.7 SYMMETRIES AND CONSERVATION LAWS

It was not recognized until this century that the familiar conservation laws of physics are connected with certain inherent symmetries of nature. This connection has also some esthetic attraction since symmetry is fundamentally associated with the concept of order. Some of these symmetries under discussion are of a geometrical character whereas others are abstract.

We speak of a symmetry operation if this operation brings a system into a state identical with the one in which it was before. That is, the system is invariant with regard to the symmetry operation. Invariance is hence the principal feature of symmetry. If the symmetry is not perfect we speak about a broken symmetry. The degree to which symmetry is broken may vary greatly. We shall see later that this symmetry breaking is of considerable importance especially in particle physics.

Crystallography is an ideal discipline to elucidate the concept of symmetry. A crystal of sodium periodate trihydrate (Fig. 7.7.1(a)) appears from the top (i.e., in the direction of the crystallographic c axis) as shown

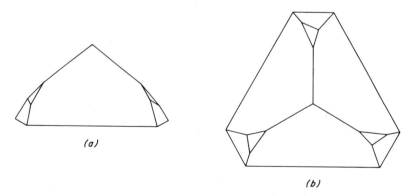

(a)

(b)

Fig. 7.7.1 A crystal of sodium periodate trihydrate with a threefold axis, displaying trigonal symmetry, side view (a) and top view (b).

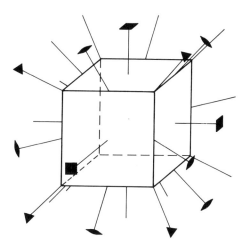

Fig. 7.7.2   The rotational axes of a cube; (♦), twofold axis: (▲), threefold axis; (■), fourfold axis.

in Fig. 7.7.1(b). A rotation of the figure by 120° will transform it into one that looks identical. The symmetry operation which has been applied here is one of rotation. Since three such successive operations are here necessary for a full turn of 360°, the rotation axis is called a threefold axis. Twofold, fourfold, and sixfold axes also occur in the world of crystals. A cube, for example a rock salt crystal, in addition to three fourfold axes connecting the centers of opposite faces has four threefold axes along the body diagonals and six twofold axes passing through the centers of opposite edges as illustrated in Fig. 7.7.2.

Rotational symmetries are only one kind of symmetry found in crystals. There are also mirror symmetries. Ammonium sulphate (Fig. 7.7.3) is an example of a crystal displaying several mirror symmetry planes.

Crystals are classified into crystal classes according to the symmetry elements present. Group theory shows that for crystals 32 different symmetry classes are possible (however, not all of these are realized in nature). Each crystal class has its group-theoretical designation, as C_3 (as for sodium periodate trihydrate), D_{4h} (sodium chloride), or D_{2h} (ammonium sulphate).

After this excursion into crystallography whose only purpose was to stress the diversity of symmetries, we return now to our discussion of symmetry and conservation laws. It has been found that the law of conservation of momentum is connected with the homogeneity of space. This means that no point of space is preferred to any other point. This homogeneity of space is a symmetry property. Translations in space do not change physical laws. A physical experiment will have the same outcome in New

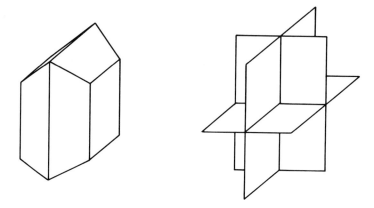

Fig. 7.7.3   An ammonium sulphate crystal and its symmetry planes.

York and in San Francisco. If this were not so momentum would no longer be conserved.

In a similar manner the symmetry property of the isotropy of space, that is, the property that all directions in space are equivalent, is connected with the conservation of angular momentum. The laws of physics are invariant against the orientation of the coordinate system.

The uniformity of time is related to the conservation of energy. The special theory of relativity combines some of these symmetries into a space-time symmetry.

The above conservation laws of classical physics are all associated with continuous symmetries. This will say that a displacement or rotation can assume any value, in contrast to the symmetry properties displayed in crystals where only rotations of 60 or 90°, or a multiple of these, satisfied the requirements of the internal crystal structure. Quantum mechanics, in addition to the above conservation laws, has others which are connected with discontinuous symmetries. We shall discuss these in the following sections. Surprisingly for the physicists, experiments gave evidence that in weak interactions at least two of a group of three conservation laws are violated. These three conservation laws concern parity, charge conjugation, and time reversal.

The parity operation P is the symmetry of spatial reflection which brings r into $-r$. The second symmetry concept is the charge conjugation C, which is a "mirror" operation working on the charge. For example, it converts an electron into a positron, a neutron into an anti-neutron, and so on. The last concept is that of time reversal T. This operation reverses the sense of time in physical processes.

7.8 PARITY AND ITS NONCONSERVATION IN WEAK INTERACTIONS

Weak interactions, like the beta decay, the decay of the charged π mesons into a muon and a neutrino, the decay of a muon into an electron and two neutrinos, or the decay of K mesons into pions, have one important aspect which was discovered only in 1956, although beta decay had been studied in many laboratories for several decades. In 1956 it was found that parity is not conserved in weak interactions. The consequence of this fact is that nature is not quite so symmetric as the physicists had always assumed it was. Parity is a wave mechanical concept, which we shall now discuss.

The wave functions we used to describe a particle in a one-dimensional tube can be classed into two different kinds: in one class are the wave functions which are symmetric about the origin (Fig. 7.8.1(a)); in the other class are wave functions which, when reflected at the origin, have to be multiplied by -1 in order that the mirror image should look the same as the original (Fig. 7.8.1(b)). We can express this in a somewhat more mathematical form. If we replace in our ψ function the $+x$ values by $-x$ values, the ψ function will either stay as it was or it will change sign. We can apply these considerations to three-dimensional space and can then write

$$\psi(x, y, z) = \pm\psi(-x, -y, -z) \qquad (7.8.1)$$

where the plus sign is for functions of the first class which are said to be of even parity, and the minus sign for the functions of our second class, the odd-parity functions. Since, as we pointed out earlier, not ψ but ψ^2 contains the physical reality, the even or odd character of the wave function does not manifest itself in a direct way. We will now show that our expressions for the energy are not affected by an inversion of the coordi-

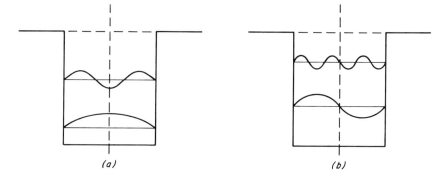

Fig. 7.8.1 Wave functions of even (a) and odd (b) parity.

nates. Kinetic energy is given by the expression $\frac{1}{2}mv^2$. It therefore makes no difference whether the velocity is in the positive or in the negative direction. If we consider the potential energy of a harmonic oscillator which is equal to $\frac{1}{2}kx^2$, we see again that inversion of the coordinates has no influence on the potential energy, as is expected from any scalar quantity.

Until 1956 it was considered a dogma by the physicists that physical events on the atomic scale were not influenced by inversion of the coordinates or, in somewhat more physical jargon, were invariant under the parity operation. Each physical process on the nuclear or atomic scale when looked at in a mirror should look like a physical process which also happens in reality. We have to point out that looking at an object in a mirror has the same effect as the parity operation (if one disregards an additional rotation of the whole coordinate system) (Fig. 7.8.2). The mirror reverses one coordinate, say the x coordinate but does not affect the other coordinates. The result is that a right hand looks like a left hand. The combination of two mirrors (as in some vanity mirrors) at right angles to each other (or mathematically two mirror operations) yields again the original right hand. But a third mirror operation will produce again a left hand. We are therefore justified to illustrate the parity operation by the use of only one mirror. The reader is invited to use his two hands to convince himself that a reflection at one plane (a mirror operation) is equivalent to a reflection at the origin of all three coordinates (the parity operation) plus a rotation of the coordinates (Fig. 7.8.3) by 180° about the x axis.

We will now discuss the parity operation on a physical event using as an example a current-carrying coil which is deflected by a magnetic field from a straight wire beneath with current passing through it (Fig. 7.8.4). The

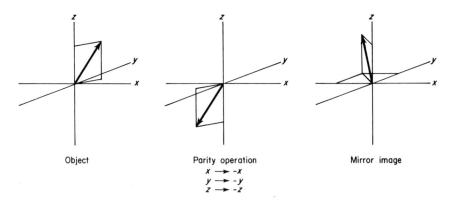

Fig. 7.8.2 The parity operation.

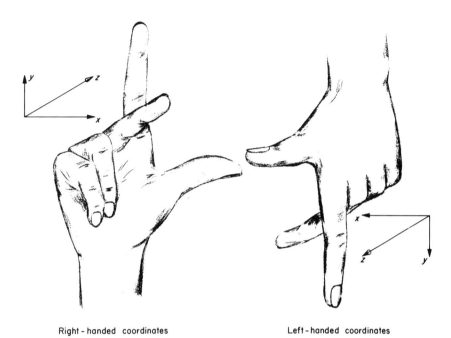

Right - handed coordinates   Left - handed coordinates

Fig. 7.8.3   The parity operation demonstrated with a pair of hands.

real coil turns clockwise because the magnetic field lines of the straight wire and those of the coil tend to line up. In the mirror image the situation is as follows: the current in the straight wire flows to the left and therefore sets up the field as drawn in the picture. The coil with its magnetic field will turn counterclockwise as shown. The currents in the mirror image are the true mirror images of the real currents. Note that magnetic field lines, however, are not mirror images. We should keep in mind that the direction of the magnetic field is pure man-made convention. This is not true in

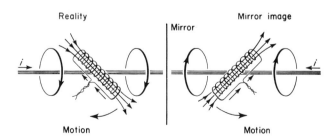

Fig. 7.8.4   The interaction of two magnetic fields in reality and its mirror image.

the same degree with the direction of the current, because in principle we could observe the flow of the electron in the wires with some kind of microscope, and therefore observe physical reality.

We should add a word of caution: macroscopic processes do not follow the rule that each real object has a real counterpart that looks like its mirror image. There are very few humans with the heart on the right-hand side; certain types of sugar turn the plane of polarization of light to the right, but others do it to the left. Some species of plants wind around poles in a preferred direction. Each real object could have a real counterpart that looks like its mirror image. However, by some historical accident this is not always the case.

A further example is a macroscopic counterpart of our magnetic coil. Such a coil has a magnetic moment, and therefore we can replace it with a compass needle, as is done in Fig. 7.8.5.

The real compass needle will be deflected as shown in the figure. What we now see in the mirror, however, is something that does not happen in reality: a current flowing to the left should deflect the black-painted north pole clockwise, not counterclockwise as indicated by the arrow and as seen in the mirror. The original atomic picture based on the electron flow yielded a realistic mirror image. The macroscopic paint on the north pole of the magnet needle on the other hand resulted in an unrealistic image.

Let us now go back to the beginning of this section where we showed that if we can write

$$\psi(x, y, z) = \pm\psi(-x, -y, -z),$$

energy expressions like $\frac{1}{2} mv^2$ or $\frac{1}{2} kx^2$ are invariant against the parity operation. We might therefore assume that if

$$\psi(x, y, z) \neq \pm\psi(-x, -y, -z)$$

this might no longer be the case. We may therefore search for physical qualities that do not remain the same under coordinate inversion.

For a long time it was known to mathematicians and physicists that

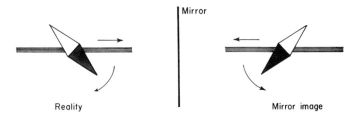

Fig. 7.8.5 A macroscopic magnet needle in a magnetic field and its mirror image.

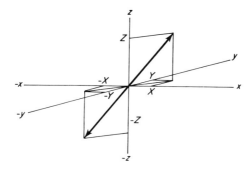

Fig. 7.8.6   Behavior of a polar vector under coordinate inversion.

there are two different kinds of vectors: the polar vectors, as displacement, velocity, acceleration, electric field intensity E, and the axial or pseudo-vectors, as angular momentum, torque, and angular velocity which are all concerned with rotation. In changing the coordinates from $+x, +y, +z$ to $-x, -y, -z$, a polar vector changes its direction (Fig. 7.8.6).

Axial vectors, on the other hand, do not change direction under coordinate inversion, as can be demonstrated using the example of angular momentum. We know that the angular momentum vector is the cross-product of the two vectors mv and r. Both these vectors are polar vectors, and both change sign on being reversed. The resulting product, the angular momentum vector, will therefore not change sign since "minus" times "minus" yields "plus." Another way of looking at this situation is to consider that the cross-product of the vectors A and B is equal to the cross-product of $-A$ and $-B$, say C, in both cases (Fig. 7.8.7). Because the axial vectors do not behave like ordinary vectors with regard to coordinate reflection they are called pseudo-vectors.

We will now go one step further in our discussion of vector analysis before we return to our physical problem. We will ask what happens to the scalar product, or dot product, of a polar vector and an axial vector under coordinate reflection. Evidently, because one of the factors changes sign, and the other does not, the product too will change sign. (The naive reader probably would not have expected that a scalar product would reverse its

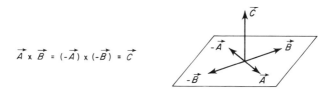

Fig. 7.8.7   Behavior of an axial vector under coordinate inversion.

sign.) The quantity that results here is called a pseudo-scalar because it does not behave quite like an ordinary scalar. The dot product of two polar vectors forms, however, a true scalar which does not change sign under coordinate reflection of the two vectors.

After this mathematical excursion we are ready to go back to physics. We stated earlier that the expressions for the energy are invariant with regard to the parity operation and mentioned as examples the potential and kinetic energy. But how would it be if certain physical quantities should be represented by pseudo-scalars instead of true scalars? That such quantities could play a role in atomic physics was discussed several decades ago, but these ideas were rejected because there was the strong belief that nature could not be asymmetric. In 1956 it became manifest through certain experiments that nature is not symmetric when weak interactions are involved.

The experimental facts which first cast some suspicion that parity might not be conserved in weak interactions were in the field of particle physics. However, one of the two first experiments which gave actual proof that parity was not conserved was a study involving beta decay. (The other

Wolfgang Pauli (1900–1958) and Chien Shiung Wu (born 1913) in 1957. (Courtesy of Niels Bohr Library, Segrè Collection, American Institute of Physics).

Tsung Dao Lee (born 1926) (Courtesy of American Institute of Physics, Meggers Gallery of Nobel Laureates).

experiment concerned the decay of muons). T. D. Lee and C. N. Yang proposed the following experiment. Beta-unstable nuclei should be aligned so that their angular momentum vectors were all parallel. Would the rates of emission of beta particles in the direction of the angular momentum vector be the same as in the opposite direction? Before 1956 the answer of physicists to this question was an unqualified "yes," because parity had to be conserved according to every book on quantum mechanics. After the experiment was carried out the answer was "no." *The New York Times* had the story on its front page, and Lee and Yang received the Nobel Prize. The magnitude of the upheaval in the physicists' minds in those days can well be seen from excerpts of a handwritten letter of Pauli to Prof. Weisskopf at MIT. The facsimile of this letter and its translation from the German are published in Pauli's collected works.[11]

[11] W. Pauli, *Collected Scientific Papers*, R. Kronig and V. F. Weisskopf, eds., Interscience, 1964. These volumes also contain Pauli's excellent articles on the history and philosophy of physics.

Chen Ning Yang (born 1922) (Courtesy of American Institute of Physics, Meggers Gallery of Nobel Laureates).

27 January 1957

Dear Weisskopf,

Now the first shock is over and I begin to collect myself again (as one says in Munich).

Yes, it was very dramatic. On Monday 21st at 8:15 p.m. I was supposed to give a talk about "past and recent history of the neutrino." At 5 p.m. the mail brought me three experimental papers: C. S. Wu, Lederman and Telegdi; the latter was so kind to send them to me. The same morning I received two theoretical papers, one by Yang, Lee and Oehme, the second by Yang and Lee about the two-component spinor theory. The latter was essentially identical with the paper by Salam, which I received as a preprint already six to eight weeks ago and to which I referred in my last short letter to you. (Was this paper known in the U.S.A.?) (At the same time came a special delivery letter from Geneva by Villars with the *New York Times* article.)

Now, where shall I start? It is good that I did not make a bet. It would have resulted in a heavy loss of money (which I cannot afford); I did make a fool of myself, however (which I think I can afford to do)—incidentally, only in letters or orally and not in anything that was printed. But the others now have the right to laugh at me.

What shocks me is not the fact that "God is just left-handed" but the fact that in spite of this He exhibits Himself as left/right symmetric when He expresses Himself strongly. In short, the real problem now is why the strong interactions are left/right symmetric. How can the strength of an interaction produce or create symmetry groups, invariances or conservation laws? This question prompted me to my premature and wrong prognosis. I don't know any good answer to that question but one should consider that already there exists a precedent: the rotational group in isotopic spin-space, which is not valid for the electromagnetic field. One does not understand either why it is valid at all. It seems that there is a certain analogy here!

In my lecture I described how Bohr (Faraday lecture, 1932, Solvay Conference, 1932), as my main opponent in regard to the neutrino, considered plausible the violation of the energy law in the beta-decay (what one calls today "weak interaction"), how his opposition then became weaker and how he said in a more general way (1933) that one must be "prepared for surprises" not anywhere but specifically with the beta-decay. Then I said spontaneously (on the spur of the moment) that at the end of my talk I would come back to the surprises which Professor Bohr had foreseen here.

He was not right with the energy law* but, who knows, will there be any stop after this new principle? According to it, perhaps the beta interactions are still "too strong" to violate also the energy law; but what if there are still weaker interactions for which also the energy law does no longer hold (as Bohr wanted it originally)?

---

*Only in *Nature*, 1936, did he give in!

Not only Pauli, also at least Yang and Wu were very much startled[12] by this complete violation of parity conservation, and the later Nobel laureate R. P. Feynman is said to have indeed lost a bet.

The experiment used the β^--decay of ^{60}Co. The decay scheme of ^{60}Co has been given in Fig. 6.7.12. The ground state of this nuclide has an angular momentum of 5 units of $\hbar$, whereas the excited state of ^{60}Ni which is reached after the emission of the electron and the anti-neutrino has an angular momentum of 4 units. Hence, one unit of angular momentum is removed from the parent nucleus, half a unit as the spin of the beta particle, the other half as the spin of the anti-neutrino. We now can make two assumptions. Referring to Fig. 7.8.8 the electron is emitted either in the upward direction from the ^{60}Co nucleus in our figure, as illustrated at the right, or in the downward direction, as shown at the left. Looking from a position above the nucleus, the emitted electron in either case must spin in a counterclockwise direction in order to remove $\frac{1}{2}$ unit of angular momentum. If we assume that the electron is emitted in the direction of the angular momentum vector of the nucleus, the linear momentum and spin angular momentum of the electron will then behave like a right-hand

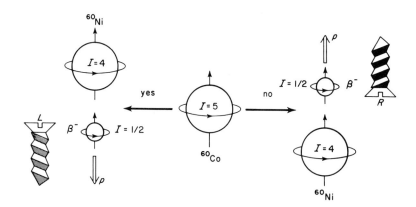

Fig. 7.8.8 Two possible ways to remove half a unit of angular momentum from the nucleus. (The neutrino which carries away an equal amount is left out in this figure)

[12] Private communication to one of the authors.

Chen Ning Yang, born 1922 in China. At the time of his work on parity professor for theoretical physics at the Institute for Advanced Study in Princeton, now professor at the State University of New York at Stony Brook. Shared the 1957 Nobel prize in physics with his collaborator. Tsung Dao Lee, born 1926 in China, professor for theoretical physics at Columbia University.

Chien Shiung Wu, born 1913 in China, professor of physics at Columbia University. Pioneering experimental work in beta decay.

screw as shown at the right. If, however, the electron leaves the Co-nucleus in the opposite direction, its linear and circular motions are those of a left-handed screw. Up to that time it was assumed that both cases are realized. The experiment showed that all the emitted β^--particles behave like left-handed screws, against the expectations of even the experimenters themselves. Nature proved to be asymmetric.

The experiment on ^{60}Co was done in the following way. Cobalt was chosen, among other reasons, because it is ferromagnetic. This implies that the electron spins of the cobalt atoms are aligned in a strong external magnetic field. Because of the hyperfine interaction between the magnetic moments of the electrons and the nucleus the latter tends to align too. Because the interaction energy is small the perturbing heat motion has to be eliminated. The cobalt sample was therefore cooled down to 0.01 K. A β-counter measured the number of β particles emitted parallel and anti-parallel to the externally applied magnetic field. This experiment was a team effort of Chien Shiung Wu of Columbia University, one of the leading experts in β-decay, and E. Ambler and his co-workers at the National Bureau of Standards who had great experience in aligning nuclei at low temperatures.

When similar experiments were performed with positrons, it was found that these particles are right-handed. Their screw sense, or helicity (from *helix* = screw), was right-handed. By considering electrons and positrons together we have therefore regained some of the lost symmetry in nature. An electron looking into a mirror sees a particle that spins like a positron, and vice versa. Whereas the relationship between left and right is expressed by the parity P, the relationship between positive and negative charge is described by an analogous operator, the charge conjugation C. Although P and C are not conserved individually in weak interactions the combination of both, (CP) is conserved to a very high degree, with the today still puzzling exception of the K^0 mesons discussed in the next section. Figure 7.8.9 represents in the example of the muon, decaying into an electron and two neutrinos, the parity operation P and the charge conjugation operation C. Just as in the nuclear β decay, the negative electron which is emitted in the decay of a μ^- has left-hand helicity, and a positron from the μ^+ decay right-hand helicity. A C or P operation alone on the negative or positive muon yields an unnatural particle, but the combination of both operations produces the anti-particle, that is, the μ^+ or the μ^-.

The neutrino has also an inherent helicity, being purely left-handed, and conversely, the anti-neutrino is purely right-handed. This could be deduced from measurements of the recoil of the nuclei which give information about the direction of the neutrino or anti-neutrino, and from the conservation of angular momentum. In fact, it has been found that the neutrinos must

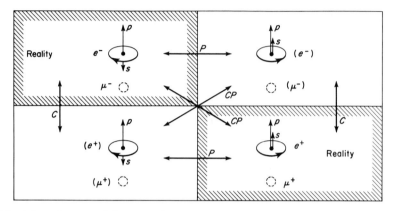

Fig. 7.8.9   Parity and charge-conjugation operation in the beta decay of the muon.

be blamed as the primary source for the violation of parity conservation.

Earlier we pointed out that symmetries are associated with conservation laws. The violation of the symmetry of left and right in this case is equivalent to a violation of the conservation of parity.

We conclude this section with a few historical remarks to give an indication of how entrenched in the minds of physicists the preconceived notions about the conservation of parity have been.

W. Pauli in 1933 in an article, "The General Principles of Wave Mechanics," [13] which has since become one of the standard works of quantum mechanics, briefly treated the formalism for a theory which would not conserve parity, taking up an idea which had already been conceived in 1929.[14] In his discussion he wrote: "However, these wave equations, as is evident from their derivation, are not invariant with regard to mirror operations (interchange of left and right). Therefore they are not applicable to physical reality." In 1958, the article was again reprinted with almost no changes, but the second quoted sentence was dropped and the following footnote added: "Nowadays these equations have been applied to the neutrino in order to represent parity-non-invariant weak interactions."

The theoretical tools were hence there and ready, but nobody picked

[13] In *Handbuch der Physik*, 2nd ed., Springer, 1933, Vol. 24/1, p. 226. The new version is in *Handbuch der Physik* (Encyclopedia of Physics), 3rd ed., Springer, 1958, Vol. V/1, p. 150.

[14] H. Weyl, *Zeitschrift für Physik* **56**, 330 (1929). On p. 332 Weyl writes: "We shall see that two components are enough if the symmetry of left and right is relinquished"; and on p. 334: "Only this in fact in nature existing left-and-right symmetry will force us to the introduction of a second pair of ψ-components."

them up for a long time. In addition, an interesting experiment had been performed on β-particles and published in 1928[15] which gave a strong indication of a left-right asymmetry. In their article the authors remarked: "Since the apparatus is symmetrical in design as between the two settings at 90° and 270°, the source of the asymmetry must be looked for in an accidental asymmetry of construction or in some asymmetry of the electron itself." The authors ruled out the first alternative as very improbable. Unfortunately, due to external circumstances the experiments were discontinued and soon went into oblivion. A great chance to nail down the effect and to do an important experiment was not taken. It took another 28 years to take up the matter again although hundreds of laboratories all over the world were busy measuring beta spectra.

7.9 TIME REVERSAL AND CPT INVARIANCE

In our discussion on the nonconservation of parity we stated that although P and C are not conserved singly in weak interactions, (CP) is conserved, at least to a high degree. We now want to discuss an experiment and its consequences which justifies the caution and qualifying remark with which the last sentence ended. It has been found that (CP) is in some cases not completely conserved. Whereas P and C conservation are as much as possible violated, (CP) conservation possibly is only violated to a small degree.

It came as one of the surprises of physics that the experiment which was designed to prove the invariance of (CP) turned out to disprove it. This experiment concerned the decay of some of the K mesons.

K mesons can be either positively charged, negatively charged or neutral. The antiparticle of the positive K^+ meson is the K^- meson. What, however, is the anti-particle of the K^0 meson? In the case of the π^0 meson it turns out that this particle is its own anti-particle. Similarly, the photon and the ρ^0 meson are their own anti-particles. On the other hand, we know that the anti-particles of the neutrino and the neutron are different from the particles. It turns out that the $\bar{K}^0$ particle is also different from the K^0 particle. [Evidence for this comes for example from the fact that the reaction $n + n \rightarrow \Lambda^0 + \Lambda^0$ does not occur (see problem 41)]. A collision between a K^0 and a $\bar{K}^0$ could therefore lead to the annihilation of both. Transitions between K^0 and $\bar{K}^0$ are possible due to the weak interaction in which, as we know, the hypercharge does not have to be conserved. K^0 and $\bar{K}^0$ can convert into each other, for example, by a virtual state formed by two π mesons.

$$K^0 \leftrightarrows \pi^+ + \pi^- \leftrightarrows \bar{K}^0.$$

[15] R. T. Cox, C. G. McIlwraith, and B. Kurrelmeyer, *Proc. Nat. Acad. Sciences* **14**, 544 (1928).

Because of this interaction between K^0 and $\bar{K}^0$, which is known as particle mixing, we have a situation which mathematically somewhat resembles that of coupled pendulums, of a two-electron system, or that of interference. The wave functions associated with the K^0 and $\bar{K}^0$ can combine to form a new set of wave functions, one symmetric and one antisymmetric. (Because the particles involved are bosons the Pauli principle plays no role here.) The new states have the following wave functions

$$(K_S^0) = \frac{1}{\sqrt{2}} [\psi(K^0) + \psi(\bar{K}^0)] \tag{7.9.1}$$

$$(K_L^0) = \frac{1}{\sqrt{2}} [\psi(K^0) - \psi(\bar{K}^0)]. \tag{7.9.2}$$

The subscripts S and L stand for "short" and "long" [16] and refer to the lifetime.

Performing the (CP) transformation by application of the (CP) operator to these equations means that we interchange the K^0 and $\bar{K}^0$ (which has the effect that the second particle in each equation goes in first place and vice versa) and change also the "charge" (the anti-particle becomes the particle and vice versa). This operation, hence, has the following result:

$$\psi(K_S^0) \rightarrow \psi(K_S^0) \tag{7.9.3}$$

under (CP) transformation

$$\psi(K_L^0) \rightarrow -\psi(K_L^0). \tag{7.9.4}$$

The (CP) operator, therefore, in the first case has the value $+1$ and in the second case -1. Experiments show that some of the neutral K mesons decay into two π mesons, some into three π mesons, besides other decay modes. Let us now consider the decay into a $\pi^+\pi^-$ pair and let us assume for simplicity that the K meson is at rest. The two pions will therefore fly in opposite directions. If we apply the (CP) transformation on this two-pion system the effect will be that nothing has changed. The pion flying to the left with one kind of charge flies now to the right and has the opposite charge. The (CP) operator had the same effect therefore on the decay products (that is, no effect!) as on the K_S^0 meson itself. The consequence is that the K_S^0 meson can decay into two π mesons without violating (CP). In contrast, the K_L^0 meson cannot decay into two pions because before the decay (CP) had the value -1, and after the decay into two pions it must have the value $+1$. If the two-pion decay mode occurs also with K_L^0 mesons, it has to be considered as a sign that the value of (CP) is not conserved. One of the possible allowed ways for decay of the K_L^0 mesons is the one into three pions, π^+, π^0, and π^-. Such a combination gives the correct value for (CP), namely -1, which is stated here without proof.[17]

The decay of the K_S^0 mesons into two π mesons corresponds to a lifetime of $(8.82 \pm 0.08) \times 10^{-11}$ sec, whereas the decay of the K_L^0 into three π mesons is a much slower process because the available energy now has to be shared among three particles. The lifetime of the K_L^0 mesons is about three orders of magnitude longer, namely $(5.18 \pm$

[16] Sometimes one still finds in the literature the designations K_1^0 and K_2^0.

[17] The argument hinges on the fact that all particles have an *intrinsic* parity, a concept not used further in this elementary book. Protons and neutrons have even intrinsic parity $(+)$, mesons an odd one $(-)$. Two mesons, because $(-)(-) = (+)$ will not change the parity of the system, but three mesons will, since $(-)(-)(-) = (-)$.

Fig. 7.9.1 The separation of $K_S°$ and $K_L°$ mesons and their decay.

0.04) $\times 10^{-8}$ sec. If in an experiment a beam of K^0 mesons is created which is a mixture of K_S^0 and K_L^0 particles, the K_S^0 will decay rapidly so that in a distance of a few meters from the area of production a pure beam of K_L^0 is left. The situation is represented schematically in Fig. 7.9.1.

As mentioned this experiment was performed to prove the invariance of (CP). To the surprise and somewhat to the consternation of the physicists, a few two-pion decays were found among the three-pion decays of the K_L^0 a sufficient distance away from the K-producing target. The arrangement for this experiment is shown in Fig. 7.9.2. The $\pi^+\pi^-$ decay mode was recognized by the requirement that the combined momentum of the two pions was in line with the beam direction and that their total energy was equal to that of the K^0. It was found that approximately one out of 500 K_L^0 decays takes place by two-pion decay. This means that (CP) invariance is violated.

The decay of the K_L^0 into two, instead of three, mesons is not the only indication for a (CP) violation. Two other decay modes of the K_L^0 are the decays $e^+\pi^-\nu_e$ and $e^-\pi^+\bar\nu_e$. If (CP) were invariant one should expect that

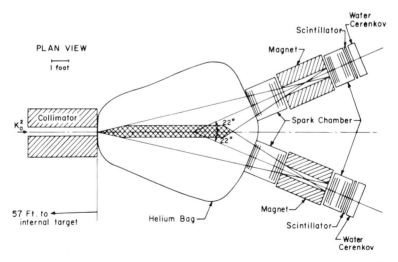

Fig. 7.9.2 The experimental arrangement for the detection of the two-pion decay of the $K_L°$ mesons. [J. H. Christenson, J. W. Cronin, V. L. Fitch, and R. Turlay, *Phys. Rev. Letters* **13,** 138 (1964).]

these two modes are equally probable. However, it has been found that there are about twice as many $e^+\pi^-\nu_e$ decays than $e^-\pi^+\bar{\nu}_e$ decays. Also this result speaks for a (CP) violation.

The consequences of the nonconservation of (CP) in weak interactions are indeed very serious. Certainly in 1956 the downfall of the principle of conservation of parity in weak interactions was already a shock to physicists, but the theoreticians stayed immediately masters of the situation by pulling, so to speak, the appropriate theory from some old drawers. Historically, as soon as it seemed possible that parity might not be conserved the theoreticians had the theory ready and suggested the crucial and by now famous experiments to prove or disprove the nonconservation of parity. To the great satisfaction of physicists it was found that in general the nonconservation of parity P goes hand-in-hand with the nonconservation of charge conjugation C, as we have seen in our discussion of beta decay.

There exists a very general principle, the (CPT) theorem, which was formulated by Pauli and Lüders in 1956, where T stands for the time-reversal operation. Before discussing this theorem in further detail we must explain the significance of time-reversal invariance. In essence it means that physical processes can run forwards and backwards in time. If we take a moving picture of a physical phenomenon, the playback of the movie in reverse also represents a physical situation. Everyday experience can easily furnish examples in support of time reversal invariance, but there are also examples that seem to refute this principle. An elastic ball falls on a horizontal plane and bounces back. The playback in reverse of a movie of this event is certainly again a representation of a possible physical situation. In this case the two situations even look identical but this is not necessary. Another example, again from the field of mechanics, is the disintegration in flight of a moving object into two fragments, as

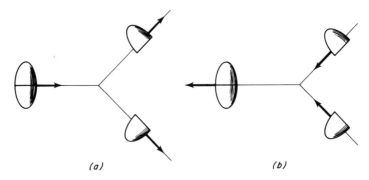

(a)   *(b)*

Fig. 7.9.3 The disintegration of an object when time runs forward (*a*) appears as an inelastic collision when the time runs backward (*b*).

illustrated in Fig. 7.9.3. A motion picture of this process projected in reverse looks simply like an inelastic collision between the two bodies A and B.

If three fragments are involved, the reverse process looks already slightly suspicious regarding its probability. And how about a breaking china cup? Certainly motion pictures of this and similar events running backwards always impress us as miraculous and seem to contradict the idea of time reversal. However, if we specify before the breakage of the cup to the greatest and finest detail in which fragment each single molecule will be, in which direction each fragment shall fly, and so on, we will see that the probability for a particular decay of the cup is also very nearly equal to zero. Only the sum of the probabilities of all the great many possible ways of disintegration of the cup falling on a stone floor is close to unity! There is only one way for fragments to fit together, but many ways for fragments to fly apart. If we picked only one of these ways the probabilities for the event taking its course forwards or backwards in time would be equal. Our example of the breaking china cup is therefore not a flagrant contradiction of the time-reversal invariance principle. However, as we have already found with parity, macroscopic objects are often not good examples. Nuclear reactions offer other fine examples of time reversal invariance. A (p, n) reaction has its counterpart in the (n, p) reaction, and so forth.

We now return to the discussion of the CPT theorem. This theorem states that physical laws and events must be invariant under the combined operation of C, P, and T. If one of them is not invariant, another must therefore not be invariant too in order to make (CPT) invariant. In beta decay P and C are both violated, with the consequence that (CP) is already invariant. Physicists do not like to give up the time-reversal invariance T. For this reason the results of the K^0 decay disturb them very much at present.

Could it be that (CP) is not invariant but that T is? In other words, that the (CPT) theorem does not hold? Pauli and Lüders showed that this theorem is in some sense a corner stone of the special theory of relativity and of the quantum theory as applied to electromagnetic fields, the so-called quantum electrodynamics. A breakdown of the (CPT) theorem would have the gravest consequences for the formulation of the two theories. The violation of (CP) invariance as evidenced in the two-pion decay of the K_L^0 mesons is therefore considered as evidence for the violation of time-reversal invariance.

Obviously the K_L^0 decay experiments are quite an indirect way to see if time-reversal invariance may be violated. Hence, more direct tests are of crucial importance. One such test is based on the comparison of the decay rate ratios $K_L{}^0 \rightarrow \pi^+\pi^-/K_S{}^0 \rightarrow \pi^+\pi^-$ and $K_L{}^0 \rightarrow \pi^0\pi^0/K_S{}^0 \rightarrow \pi^0\pi^0$. However, even hints, how this argument[18] runs are unfortunately far above the level of this book. We thus have to be content to say that the evaluation of these experimental data shows that T is violated, without having to infer this via the CPT theorem.

7.10 PARTICLE SYMMETRIES

Earlier in this chapter we discussed symmetries in connection with conservation laws. Symmetries also play a role as an ordering principle in other respects. In our examples taken from crystallography we saw that different symmetry operations lead to different crystallographic symmetry groups. Lower symmetries have fewer symmetry elements, that is, mirror planes, rotational axes in our examples taken from crystallography, than higher symmetries. Certain symmetry groups can be developed from simpler ones by the addition of new symmetry elements. The mathematical apparatus for the treatment of problems of symmetry is furnished by group theory. Group theory has thus become progressively more important with the increasing popularity of symmetry considerations in physics in the last decades. A group is defined as a set of abstract elements. These elements have to satisfy certain rules. The elements of a group may be operations, for example, rotations or reflections.

It turns out that the particles also can be classified according to group theory. Let us look first at a very simple form of symmetry in the nuclear case, the nuclei $_6C_7{}^{13}$ and $_7N_6{}^{13}$. The former contains six protons and seven neutrons, and in the latter the numbers of both kinds of nucleons are interchanged. The two nuclides are therefore symmetric to each other. One is so to speak the mirror image of the other, and we call such a pair mirror nuclei.[19] Another symmetry of this kind is displayed by the three kinds of π mesons, the π^-, π^0, and π^+. In both cases the symmetry is based on the aspect of charge. However, physicists and mathematicians already see a symmetry in the structure of atomic multiplets. A level of angular momentum l splits in a magnetic field into $2l + 1$ equally spaced substates. For $l = 2$ we get therefore the substates with $m = -2, -1, 0, +1, +2$ (Fig. 7.10.1). The z component of l, m, represents the component of l in the direction of the magnetic field. Schematically we can represent the multiplet belonging to the same l in the following way (Fig. 7.10.2). A similar representation can evidently be made for the i spin T. In this

---

[18] R. C. Casella, Phys. Rev. Lett. *21*, 1128 (1968).

[19] This "mirror" should not be confused with the "mirror" in the parity operation!

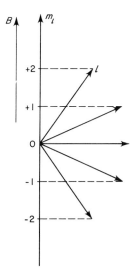

Fig. 7.10.1 The splitting of an $l = 2$ state into $2l + 1$ substates.

case T corresponds to l, and T_z corresponds to $l_z \equiv m$. It should again be emphasized that T does not represent a physical quantity which in classical, macroscopical physics has a meaning, like angular momentum, length, or temperature. On the other hand, what we call its z component has a very direct connection with reality, namely with the charge of the particle. In the case of the π mesons the charges are distributed symmetrically around zero, because of their charges -1, 0, and $+1$. The nucleon pair, that is the proton and the neutron, has an average charge of $\frac{1}{2}$ in units of the elementary charge. Because average charge of a multiplet plays an important role in elementary particle physics, the concept of hypercharge Y, which is twice the average charge of a multiplet has therefore been introduced as mentioned earlier. Members of the same multiplet all have the same hypercharge. Nucleons have therefore $Y = 1$, π mesons $Y = 0$.

One can now ask if there exists a symmetry scheme more comprehensive than that of the i spin which would also include hypercharge. This would make it possible to consider, for example, all the eight baryons of spin $\frac{1}{2}$ as different states of the same particle. These eight baryons are the Λ^0, a singlet having therefore $T = 0$, furthermore a group of particles belonging to $T = 1$ and hence forming a triplet, namely Σ^+, Σ^0, Σ^-, and two doublets,

Fig. 7.10.2 The $l = 2$ multiplet.

Fig. 7.10.3   An i spin multiplet.

both with $T = \frac{1}{2}$, namely, the doublet Ξ^0, Ξ^-, and the doublet constituted by the proton and the neutron, which we might designate here with N^+ and N^0.

There are several symmetry groups which could be used, but only one, the so-called SU_3 symmetry seems to correspond to reality. We recall that in the case of the angular momentum we represented the values of the l_z component as points lying on a straight line. We also mentioned that a similar representation was possible for the z component of the i spin (Fig. 7.10.3). We have here a one-dimensional lattice (because we deal only with T_z) which has twofold symmetry. This latter statement means that we can rotate the arrangement around its center first by 180° and have again the same picture, and a second time by 180° to arrive at the original constellation.

We shall now try to form a related operation with an arrangement of different values of T_z and of Y. Necessarily, we will have a two-dimensional lattice which we will construct in such a way as to be in agreement with nature. This turns out to be an arrangement with a threefold axis (Fig. 7.10.4). The underlying symmetry associated with it is called SU_3, whereas that associated with a twofold axis is SU_2 symmetry. We hasten to point out that the fundamental connection between the twofold rotational symmetry of Fig. 7.10.3 and SU_2 and also of the threefold rotational symmetry of Fig. 7.10.4 and SU_3 is considerably more complex and subtle than we could sketch here. In Fig. 7.10.4 we find our two doublets, the nucleons and

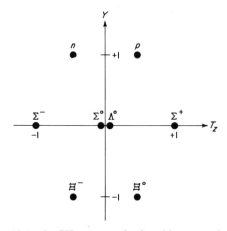

Fig. 7.10.4   An SU_3 super-multiplet of baryons of spin $\frac{1}{2}$.

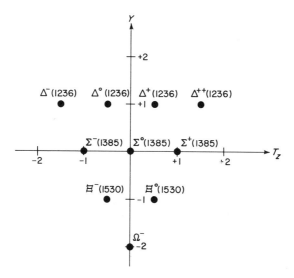

Fig. 7.10.5 An SU₃ super-multiplet of baryons of spin $\frac{3}{2}$.

the Ξ's, the Σ-triplet and the Λ^0 singlet. The arrangement of these eight particles into a super-multiplet was named, very poetically, by Gell-Mann and Ne'eman who discovered this scheme, the "eightfold way."

Other particles similarly can be grouped into super-multiplets. One such array is the one shown in Fig. 7.10.5 of ten baryons. This decuplet, (Greek *deka* = ten) whose members all have an ordinary spin of $\frac{3}{2}$, has an interesting history. When this scheme was postulated, one particle, the Ω^- had not yet been discovered. Experiments were therefore undertaken with the goal of finding the missing particle. Physicists at Brookhaven National Laboratory succeeded in 1964 in finding the Ω^- in a bubble chamber photograph. This was indeed a great triumph for the theory. The first picture, on which this Ω^- particle appears is reproduced in Fig. 7.10.6. The Ω^- appears as one of the products of the reaction induced by the K^- particles which entered the bubble chamber. The dotted lines in the schematic representation indicate invisible tracks of neutral particles. The production and the complicated decay chain are as follows:

$$K^- + p \rightarrow K^0 + K^+ + \Omega^-$$
$$\searrow \Xi^0 + \pi^-$$
$$\searrow \gamma \quad + \quad \Lambda^0 \quad\quad + \gamma$$
$$\searrow e^+ + e^- \quad \searrow \pi^- + p \quad \searrow e^+ + e^-$$

Other decay modes of the Ω^- have since been observed.

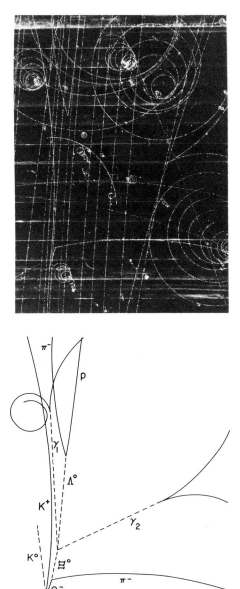

Fig. 7.10.6   The first bubble chamber photograph of the Ω^- particle. (Brookhaven National Laboratory).

We can easily understand that the proton and the neutron are basically the same particle since their masses only differ by approximately 1% or less. The same holds true for the Σ's or the Ξ's. How can be justify the placing of the nucleons with a rest mass of 939 MeV, the Σ's with 1192 MeV, the Λ⁰ with 1115 MeV, and the Ξ with approximately 1320 MeV into one group? The answer is that the situation is only quantitatively different. Perfect symmetry would require perfectly identical masses of the two nucleons, the proton and neutron. This perfect symmetry is however broken; the observed mass difference between the nucleons or between the Σ's is due to the electromagnetic interaction. For the mass difference of the order of hundreds of MeV between the multiplets we may therefore postulate a stronger interaction than the electromagnetic one. It has been possible to find empirical formulas for the mass differences between multiplets. In the case of the decuplet of Fig. 7.10.5 the situation is particularly striking. The differences between adjacent multiplets are equal within the limits of error and amount to 146 MeV. Because the mass difference be-

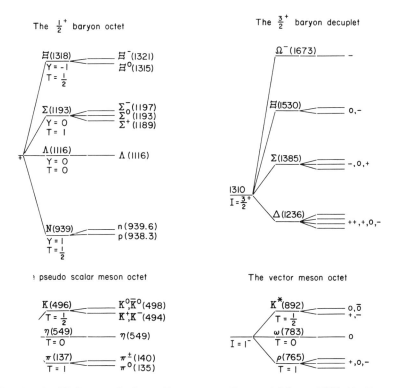

Fig. 7.10.7 Hadron multiplets. [From Yuan, *Nature of Matter*, BNL-888 Report, p. 149.]

tween the Δ's and Σ^*'s, and between the Σ^*'s and the Ξ^*'s were known to be equal, an educated guess for the mass the Ω^- could be made before it had been discovered. This guess proved to be correct. In general, however, the mass formulas are not quite as simple and there are also some deviations which have to be explained away.

In order to drive home the point that a super-multiplet deals with different manifestations of the same entity, we can construct a kind of energy level scheme. The situation is analogous to the Zeeman effect in atomic physics where levels are being split because the degeneracy of the substates of l is removed through the interaction of an external magnetic field with the atom. We give here examples of some of these super-multiplets just as an illustration (Fig. 7.10.7). The names "pseudo-scalar" and "vector" mesons are concerned with the interactions of these mesons which will not be explained here.

After the successful step from the i spin multiplets to the super-multiplets, the high-energy physicists became bold and tried another step. What

Murray Gell-Mann (born 1929) (Courtesy of American Institute of Physics, Meggers Gallery of Nobel Laureates).

TABLE 7.10.1

The Quantum Numbers of Quarks and Anti-Quarks

	Quarks			Anti-Quarks		
	$\mathfrak{P}$	$\mathfrak{N}$	λ	$\bar{\mathfrak{P}}$	$\bar{\mathfrak{N}}$	$\bar{\lambda}$
Charge Q	$+\frac{2}{3}$	$-\frac{1}{3}$	$-\frac{1}{3}$	$-\frac{2}{3}$	$+\frac{1}{3}$	$+\frac{1}{3}$
i Spin T	$\frac{1}{2}$	$\frac{1}{2}$	0	$\frac{1}{2}$	$\frac{1}{2}$	0
Member of	i Spin doublet $\longrightarrow$		singlet $\longrightarrow$	i Spin doublet $\longrightarrow$		singlet $\longrightarrow$
	$\longleftarrow$ SU$_3$ triplet $\longrightarrow$			$\longleftarrow$ SU$_3$ triplet $\longrightarrow$		
z Component T_z	$+\frac{1}{2}$	$-\frac{1}{2}$	0	$-\frac{1}{2}$	$+\frac{1}{2}$	0
Hypercharge Y	$+\frac{1}{3}$	$+\frac{1}{3}$	$-\frac{2}{3}$	$-\frac{1}{3}$	$-\frac{1}{3}$	$+\frac{2}{3}$
Baryon number B	$+\frac{1}{3}$	$+\frac{1}{3}$	$+\frac{1}{3}$	$-\frac{1}{3}$	$-\frac{1}{3}$	$-\frac{1}{3}$
Spin J	$\frac{1}{2}$	$\frac{1}{2}$	$\frac{1}{2}$	$\frac{1}{2}$	$\frac{1}{2}$	$\frac{1}{2}$

if the super-multiplets were members of a super-super-multiplet? Without going further into these questions, let us say that this leads to an even higher symmetry, the SU$_6$ symmetry.

Now comes the big question. Of what are fundamental particles made? One theory is that they are made from "quarks"! Gell-Mann[20] gave these postulated basic particles this name which he took from the beginning of a poem in James Joyce's "Finnegan's Wake." [21] There are three quark states $\mathfrak{P}$, $\mathfrak{N}$, λ (Table 7.10.1) which we can again arrange in a diagram and three anti-quark states $\bar{\mathfrak{P}}$, $\bar{\mathfrak{N}}$, $\bar{\lambda}$ with a similar diagram (Fig. 7.10.8). We can now build up our octet, decuplet, or other structures from these basic particles. Combination of a quark with an anti-quark gives nine different particles, an octet, and a singlet. We will sketch how this is done, without giving here the mathematical justification for this procedure, but it may be mentioned that basically the same procedure can be used (one-dimensionally) to combine ordinary spins or i spins. The procedure is therefore sound and justified. We superimpose the figure representing the anti-quarks (Fig. 7.10.9(b)) on the figure of the quarks (Fig. 7.10.9(a)) letting the origin of the coordinate of the anti-quarks coincide with each of the three quarks. If we represent the displacement of a quark or anti-quark from the origin of its T_z-Y coordinate system by a vector and add

[20] M. Gell-Mann (1929–); professor of theoretical physics at California Institute of Technology; Nobel prize 1969.

[21] (p. 383, Viking Press, New York 1939) "Three quarks for Muster Mark!/Sure he hasn't got much of a bark/ And sure any he has it's all beside the mark. . . " The quarks are the mocking calls of the seagulls for King Mark, who is about to lose Iseult to Tristan.

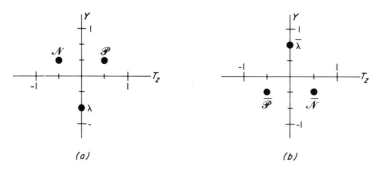

Fig. 7.10.8 The three quark states and the three anti-quark states.

now vectorially a quark and an anti-quark in all possible combinations we will get the constellation pictured in Fig. 7.10.9(c)). This configuration can be split into a singlet and an octet as already mentioned (Fig. 7.10.10). It should be pointed out that this octet is not the octet that contains the proton and the neutron as a number, but an octet of mesons. The quarks are assumed to have ordinary spin $\frac{1}{2}$. Therefore a quark–anti-quark system has a spin of either 0 or 1.

Alternatively, we can add the respective quantum numbers Y and T_z (and also Q and B) of a quark and an anti-quark to obtain the quantum number of a meson. For example, the combination of an $\mathfrak{N}$ quark ($Y = +\frac{1}{3}$, $T_z = +\frac{1}{2}$) and a $\bar{\lambda}$ quark ($Y = +\frac{2}{3}$, $T_z = 0$) yields the quantum numbers $Y = 1$ and $T_z = +\frac{1}{2}$, which are those of a K^+ meson, either the K^+ (494) with spin 0 or the K^+ (892) with spin 1. In both cases the baryon number is naturally zero.

The super-multiplet containing the nucleons is formed from three quarks and therefore contains particles of half-integer spin. The proton, for ex-

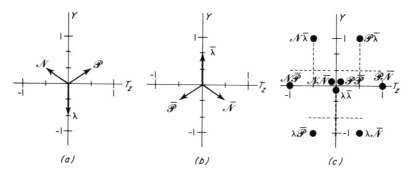

Fig. 7.10.9 Quark and anti-quark states (a and b) and their superposition to represent meson states (c).

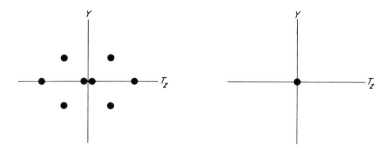

Fig. 7.10.10   Separation of the meson states into an octet and a singlet.

ample, is composed of two $\mathscr{P}$ quarks, each having $Y = +\frac{1}{3}$ and $T_z = +\frac{1}{2}$, and an $\mathscr{N}$ quark, with $Y = +\frac{1}{3}$ and $T_z = -\frac{1}{2}$, which adds up to $Y = +1$ and $T_z = +\frac{1}{2}$.[22] The ordinary spins of the three quarks combine to $\frac{1}{2}$. The peculiar thing is that two of the quarks must have a charge of $+\frac{2}{3}$ elementary (that is, proton) charges, and the third quark $-\frac{1}{3}$. Such particles, however, have not yet been found in spite of intensive searches by many groups of physicists using different methods. Also the originator of the concept of the quarks, Gell-Mann, is inclined to consider the quarks as fictitious particles or, in his own words, mathematical indices. It might very well be that quarks only exist in theory and in the minds of physicists.

In the last century Mendeleyev set up the periodic table of elements. His guideline was also some kind of symmetry, namely the repetition of the chemical properties of the elements. With regard to the physics of particles a similar achievement has now been reached. At Mendeleyev's time quantum mechanics and the Pauli principle were unknown. Thus a deeper understanding of the foundation of the periodic table was not possible then. To some degree we find ourselves today in the same position with our understanding of the world of particles which are sometimes given the adjective "elementary."

PROBLEMS

1. The most energetic *air shower* so far found in *cosmic radiation* seems to have been originated by a particle with an energy of $\sim 4 \times 10^{21}$ eV. (*a*) How much is this energy in foot-pounds? (*b*) Assume that one could harness the energy of one mole (6×10^{23}) particles of this energy. To what

[22] The designations of the quarks are not yet standardized. We have chosen here the one which is easy to remember, since the *p*roton and the *n*eutron consist of two-thirds of $\mathscr{P}$ and $\mathscr{N}$ quarks, respectively, and the Λ_0 baryon contains one λ quark.

velocity could one accelerate a slab of the area of the United States without Alaska and Hawaii (8×10^6 km²) and a thickness of 100 m. Assume a density of 3×10^3 kg/m³.

2. (a) What is the *velocity of a proton* that has a kinetic energy of 6 GeV? (b) What is its mass in terms of its rest mass?

3. A single magnetic *quadrupole lens* focuses a beam of charged particles in one plane and defocuses it in a plane perpendicular to the first one. Sketch an arrangement of several quadrupole lenses which brings a parallel beam with a circular cross section to a point focus.

4. (a) An object of mass m moves with the velocity v in the laboratory system, where $v \ll c$, and *collides* with another object of equal mass. Show that in this nonrelativistic case $E_{\text{available}}$, the *energy available* for inelastic processes, such as deformation or the generation of heat, is $\frac{1}{2}(\frac{1}{2}mv^2)$. (b) If the mass of the moving particle is five times the mass of the particle at rest, what is the available energy?

5. A particle of rest mass m_0 and kinetic energy E_{kin} in the laboratory system, where E_{kin} is of the order of magnitude of m_0c^2, *collides* with another particle of the same rest mass m_0 which is at rest. (a) Show that the maximum *available energy* in the center-of-mass system—that is, the energy that can produce other particles, or bring one of the collisions partners into an excited state—is

$$E_{\text{available}} = \sqrt{2E_{\text{kin}}m_0c^2 + (2m_0c^2)^2} - 2m_0c^2.$$

(b) Show that for energies where $E_{\text{kin}} \gg m_0c^2$ this formula reduces to

$$E_{\text{available}} \approx \sqrt{2E_{\text{kin}}m_0c^2}.$$

6. For the production of a *proton–anti-proton pair* in a collision between two protons at least 2×981 MeV kinetic energy is required in the center-of-mass system. What minimum kinetic energy, as measured in the laboratory system, must a proton have in order to produce such a pair in a collision with a proton at rest?

7. (a) Consider protons of total energy $E = 200$ GeV in the Batavia *accelerator*. Estimate the radius of the orbit and the angular velocity ω from the pertinent equations in Sect. 7.2. Use a magnetic field $B \approx 1$ Wb/m². (The momentum mv is related to E by relativistic mechanics. Can you use the approximation $mv \approx E/c$?) (b) The Batavia accelerator costs approximately $250 million. Estimate the percent of the present GNP (gross national product) needed to construct an accelerator of 200,000 GeV $= 2 \times 10^{15}$ eV. (Does the cost increase linearly with energy? More rapidly, or less rapidly than linearly?)

8. In nuclear decays the *electron-capture* process competes with the β^+ decay; in massive nuclei it even dominates strongly. An electron of the atomic shell, usually the K shell, is absorbed by the nucleus, and a proton

thereby changes into a neutron. Most of the nuclear decay energy is carried off by a simultaneously emitted neutrino or anti-neutrino. Which one of the two must it be?

9. ^{64}Cu (Fig. 6.7.1(b)) can decay either by β^- or by β^+ decay or by electron capture. Indicate for each decay mode if a *neutrino or anti-neutrino* is emitted.

10. Approximately two-thirds of the *decays of the K^+ and K^-* mesons proceed by emission of a muon and a (anti-) neutrino. In which case is it a neutrino and in which case an anti-neutrino?

11. Must the *decay mode of the K^- meson* by emission of an electron and a neutrino or anti-neutrino be ruled out?

12. Discuss the possibility or impossibility of the following *reactions*: (a) $n + p \rightarrow p + p + \bar{p}$. ($b$) $n + n \rightarrow n + \bar{n}$. ($c$) $p + p \rightarrow p + p + p + \bar{p}$.

13. A *pion* at rest decays by the *decay* mode $\pi^+ \rightarrow \mu^+ + \nu_\mu$. ($a$) Using rest masses from Table 7.5.1 find the magnitudes of the momenta of muon and neutrino, using conservation of momentum and of total energy. (b) Suppose the pion has a velocity of 0.99 c, find the maximum energy of the neutrino in the laboratory system. (Neutrinos have the same relativistic kinematics as photons, since both have zero rest mass.) In what direction is the neutrino emitted in the rest system of the pion to achieve this maximum value of energy in the laboratory system?

14. A *pion* having a velocity 0.99 c in the laboratory system *decays* into a muon and a neutrino. Assume that a neutrino is emitted at 90° with respect to the pion direction in the rest system of the pion. (a) What is the neutrino direction in the laboratory system? (Hint: aberration of light) (b) What is the neutrino energy in the laboratory system? (Hint: Doppler shift)

15. Figure 6.2.9(c) shows the K^- *mesonic x-ray spectrum* of chlorine, besides some other lines. (a) From the observed lines construct an "atomic" energy level diagram. (b) What may be the reasons that transitions to orbits with $n < 4$ are not observed? (c) In the spectrum there also appears a γ line from ^{32}P which is emitted in a transition from an excited state to the ground state. By what reaction may this nuclide have been formed, assuming the target nuclide in this case was ^{35}Cl and the bombarding particle was indeed a K^- meson?

16. Which mesons, in their virtual state, may be ruled out as being responsible for the *spin-orbit interaction* of nuclear forces which is clearly in evidence in the nuclear shell model.

17. (a) Write the balancing equations of the i spin and its z component for the *charge-exchange reaction* $p + \pi^- \rightarrow \Delta(1236) \rightarrow n + \pi^0$. ($b$) Can this charge-exchange reaction also proceed through the $N(1520)$ or $N(1688)$ resonance?

18. The $\Delta^+(1236)$ *resonance* has been observed to decay to 99.4% by

emission of a pion. In 0.6% the decay goes by emission of a γ quantum. Explain why this second mode is so much less frequent than the first one.

19. (a) What is the charge of the $\Delta(1236)$ *resonance* in the $\pi^+ + p$ reaction (see Fig. 7.5.5). (b) What is its charge in the $\pi^- + p$ reaction? (c) From the width of the resonance (see Table 7.5.1) determine its lifetime.

20. At approximately which energies should one expect *resonances* in the scattering of π^- mesons on neutrons?

21. Complete the equations of the following *reactions*: (a) $\pi^- + p \rightarrow \Sigma^- + \ldots$, (b) $K^- + p \rightarrow \Xi^- + \ldots$, (c) $K^- + d \rightarrow \Lambda + \pi^0 + \ldots$, (d) $\Xi^- + p \rightarrow \Lambda + \ldots$.

22. Balance the following equations for *particle decays*: (a) $\pi^+ \rightarrow \nu_e + ---$, (b) $K^+ \rightarrow \pi^0 + ---$, (c) $\Sigma^0 \rightarrow \Lambda^0 + ---$, (d) $\bar{\Lambda} \rightarrow \bar{p} + ---$. Should the decay be fast or slow? Explain briefly.

23. Each of the following decays never occurs because it *violates* at least one *strict* conservation law. State the violation. (a) $p \rightarrow n + e^+ + \nu$. (b) $p \rightarrow \pi^+ + \pi^0$. (c) $\pi^0 \rightarrow \gamma$. (d) $\pi^+ \rightarrow \gamma + \gamma$. (e) $\pi^+ \rightarrow \mu^+ + \gamma$.

24. A Ξ^- particle, assumed to be at rest, decays into a Λ particle and a π^- meson. What is the sum of the *kinetic energies* of the decay products?

25. In the preceding problem, how is the *kinetic energy* shared between the two particles?

26. What is the experimental evidence that Ξ^- is the *particle* and Ξ^+ is the *anti-particle*, and not vice versa?

27. Why is the Σ^- particle not the *anti-particle* of the Σ^+?

28. The *scatter plot* of Fig. 7.3.9 reveals the existence of $p\pi^+$ and $K\pi^-$ systems. Which resonances do these systems represent?

29. Check if the i *spin* and its z component are conserved in the reaction $p + p \rightarrow p + n + \pi^+$.

30. Figure 7.10.6 is a bubble chamber picture of the reaction $K^- + p \rightarrow K^0 + K^- + \Omega^-$. (a) Check if B, T, T_z, and Y are *conserved* in this reaction. (b) The Ω^-, Ξ^0, and Λ^0 decay after their formation. Check the conservation of B, T, T_z, and Y and determine if the decays are by strong, electromagnetic, or weak interaction.

31. Figure 7.5.3 shows the *reaction* $\bar{p} + p \rightarrow K^0 + K^- + \pi^+$. (a) Which type of interaction is responsible for this reaction? (b) Check the conservation of B, T, T_z, and Y. (c) What is the sum of the kinetic energies of the three new particles? (d) The K^0 meson decays into a π^+ and π^-. Check if B, T, T_z, and Y are conserved. By what interaction does this decay proceed? (e) In the same photograph is also the reaction $K^- + p \rightarrow \Sigma^+ + \pi^-$. Is this reaction exoergic or endoergic? (f) Check the conservation of T, T_z, and Y in this decay.

32. In the *energy level diagram* of Fig. 7.6.1 show by connecting lines between two levels in analogy to transitions in atoms (see, e.g., Fig. 4.8.2

for sodium) a few possible transitions where (a) π mesons are emitted. (b) K mesons are emitted.

33. (a) Would the $1s$ state of a *hydrogen atom* look the same or different in a mirror? What is its *parity*? (see Eq. 7.8.1.) (b) Is the Coulomb potential energy $V(r) = -(e^2/4\pi\epsilon_0 r)$ a scalar or a pseudoscalar?

34. Which of the following are scalars? Which pseudoscalars? Which polar vectors? Which pseudovectors? (a) displacement $\boldsymbol{r}$. (b) energy density $\frac{1}{2}\epsilon_0 \boldsymbol{E} \cdot \boldsymbol{E}$. (c) kinetic energy $\boldsymbol{p} \cdot \boldsymbol{p}/(2m)$. (d) angular momentum $\boldsymbol{r} \times \boldsymbol{p} = \boldsymbol{I}$. (e) helicity $\boldsymbol{I} \cdot \boldsymbol{p}$.

35. Suppose you had *anti-matter*, with radioactive anti-cobalt-60, $^{60}_{27}$Co. (a) What would it decay into? (b) Redraw Fig. 7.8.8 for its decay.

36. The nuclide ^{12}B, with $J = 1$, decays by β^- *decay* into the ground state of ^{12}C, with $J = 0$. In this case the two emitted leptons carry off the difference in angular momentum not as orbital angular momentum but as spin. (a) Will the electron and the antineutrino preferentially be emitted in the same direction, in the opposite direction, or at a right angle to each other? (b) The nuclide ^{12}N, with $J = 1$, decays by β^+ decay into ^{12}C. Also here the angular momentum is carried off as spin. What is the preferential *angle of emission* between the two leptons?

37. The nuclide ^{35}S, with a ground state $D_{3/2}$, decays by β^- *decay* into ^{35}Cl, also with $D_{3/2}$. What is the most probable *angle of emission* between the two leptons?

38. A π^+ meson at rest decays by emitting a muon in the positive x direction. The *muon* is slowed down appreciably by passing through matter, but retains its original direction, and decays in flight into a positron, an electron neutrino, and a muon anti-neutrino. These three particles share the available energy quite similar to the sharing of energy by the two leptons in ordinary β decay, within the limits of the conservation laws of energy and momentum. (a) In what direction are the most energetic positrons emitted? Draw a graph, indicating the momentum and angular momentum of each lepton. (b) Do the same for the decays where the positron carries away very little kinetic energy.

39. A π^+ *meson* at rest decays by the following decay mode: $\pi^+ \rightarrow \mu^+ + \nu_\mu$ (1). (a) The ν_μ is left-handed (negative helicity). Suppose the μ^+ is emitted along the positive z axis. Find the direction of its spin, find its helicity. (b) Write the decay of the anti-particle, $\pi^- \rightarrow \ldots$. (2) Find the helicity of the emitted muon. (c) Consider the combination CP where C transforms (1) into (2), and P is the parity operation. Compare decay (1) with decay (2) seen in a mirror. Do they agree on mirror helicity?

40. Under the *time-reversal* operation T the momentum $\boldsymbol{p}$ changes to $-\boldsymbol{p}$ and the angular momentum $\boldsymbol{J}$ changes to $-\boldsymbol{J}$. Show that the functions $\boldsymbol{J} \cdot (\boldsymbol{p}_1 \times \boldsymbol{p}_2)$ and $\boldsymbol{p}_1 \cdot (\boldsymbol{p}_2 \times \boldsymbol{p}_3)$ change signs under time reversal.

41. Show that the nonoccurrence of the reaction $n + n \rightarrow \Lambda^0 + \Lambda^0$ implies that the *anti-particle* $\boldsymbol{K^0}$ is different from the particle K^0.

42. Construct a diagram with T_z as abscissa and Y as ordinate for the spin-0^- *octet* and *singlet*, consisting of the three π mesons, the K^0 and K^+ mesons and their anti-particles, and the η meson.

43. (a) Draw graphs, similar to Fig. 7.10.4, for the $\frac{3}{2}^-$ baryons and the $\frac{5}{2}^-$ baryons, which form two *octets*. In addition, one of the known $\frac{3}{2}^-$ baryons forms a singlet. Take the data from Fig. 7.6.1. (b) Which of the two Ξ baryons of presently unknown spin and parity is a good candidate for the $\frac{3}{2}^-$ octet and which one for the $\frac{5}{2}^-$ octet? (c) Which $\frac{3}{2}^-$ baryon is probably the singlet?

44. The *mass* of the proton and the neutron can be expressed by a nucleon mass m_N plus a mass correction δ^+ for the proton and δ^0 for the neutron. Similarly, it has been suggested that the masses of Σ^+ and Σ^- can be written as $m_{\Sigma^+} = m_\Sigma + \delta^+$ and $m_{\Sigma^-} = m_\Sigma + \delta^-$, where δ^+ has about the same value as in the expression for the proton mass, because the mass correction is in either case due to the same electric charge. Since the Ξ^- and Ξ^0 particles belong to the same octet we can assume that their masses can also be expressed in such a way, with the correction terms δ^- and δ^0 being approximately the same as for the above particles of the corresponding charge. (a) Express the mass difference between Ξ^- and Ξ^0 in terms of the masses of the proton, the neutron, the Σ^- and the Σ^+. (b) Check the accuracy of this approximation by comparing the calculated mass difference with the actual one.

45. Represent the baryons of Fig. 7.10.4 by *quarks*.

46. Represent the baryons of Fig. 7.10.5 by *quarks*.

47. Represent the reaction $K^- + p \rightarrow K^+ + \Omega^-$ by *quarks*.

48. (a) In the diagrams for *quarks* and anti-quarks (Fig. 7.10.8) construct an axis representing the charge Q. (b) Check if such an axis can be drawn also in the diagrams of Figs. 7.10.4 and 7.10.5. (c) Express Q in terms of Y and T_z.

49. The ladders for N, Δ, Λ, etc., contain particles and resonances of different spins and parities. (a) In the ladder for N look up the least massive members with $J = \frac{1}{2}^+, \frac{5}{2}^+, \frac{9}{2}^+$. Plot the squares of their masses versus their angular momentum and draw a straight line through the points. (b) Into the same graph plot the Δ baryons with angular momentum $\frac{3}{2}^+, \frac{7}{2}^+$, and $\frac{11}{2}^+$ and draw a straight line. Such lines are called *Regge trajectories*. (c) Look for other Regge trajectories among the baryons.

Appendix I

The Poynting Vector and Electromagnetic Waves

I.1 THE POYNTING VECTOR

Energy can be transmitted through empty space. Broadcasting towers send out radio and television signals which are received at distant points. The sun transmits heat and light through the high vacuum in interplanetary space. An energy flow through space is best described by means of a vector. The direction of this vector will indicate the direction of movement of the energy. The magnitude of the vector may conveniently be so chosen that it specifies the magnitude of the energy flow, or the number of joules per second which cross unit area measured on a plane perpendicular to the vector.

The vector describing energy flow through space is called the Poynting vector, after J. H. Poynting (1852–1914), and is designated by $\mathbf{S}$. Its magnitude gives the watts per square meter moving in the direction of $\mathbf{S}$. Thus, if $\mathbf{S}$ is along the x axis of some rectangular coordinate system, the magnitude of $\mathbf{S}$ would be S_x. The total flow of energy through some area A measured on the y–z plane would be S_xA, where A is in square meters.

The transmission of energy through space is an electromagnetic phenomenon and must be related to the electric and magnetic fields. Wherever there is an electric field E, we have an energy per unit volume equal to $ED/2$. Wherever there is a magnetic field, we may expect to find additional energy per unit volume equal to $HB/2$. In order to describe the flow of this energy from its sources into space, we must consider some volume element of space in which the total energy is increasing. This energy can be increasing only if energy is flowing inward through the surface. The mathematical derivation of the Poynting vector consists of finding an expression for $\mathbf{S}$ such that the integral of the normal component of $\mathbf{S}$ over a closed surface is numerically equal to the time rate of increase of energy in the volume bounded by this closed surface. If A is the surface area of a volume

623

of space containing a total energy U, we must find a vector $\mathbf{S}$ such that

$$\int_A \mathbf{S} \cdot d\mathbf{A} = \frac{dU}{dt} .$$

The derivation of the Poynting vector is given below. The result is

$$\mathbf{S} = \mathbf{E} \times \mathbf{H} \tag{I.1}$$

Since the electric field in mks is in volts/meter, and the magnetic field is in amps/meter, the product is (volt·amp)/meter², or watts/meter². Wherever nonparallel electric and magnetic fields are simultaneously present, there will be a flow of energy at right angles to the plane containing the two. According to the rules of vector multiplication, the magnitude of S is $EH \sin \phi$ where ϕ is the angle between E and H. The direction of S is the direction of advance of a right-handed screw when the sense of rotation is that of a rotation of the electric vector E into the direction of H on the shortest way.

I.2   THE DERIVATION OF THE POYNTING VECTOR

The energy density in the electric field surrounding the charged metallic parts of a capacitor is

$$u_e = \frac{ED}{2}$$

and the energy density in the static magnetic field surrounding a conductor in which there exists a constant current is

$$u_m = \frac{HB}{2} .$$

We shall now consider how to describe the movement of energy in space. It is clear that, since we shall be dealing with changing energy densities, we shall be concerned with changing fields and therefore with simultaneously present electric and magnetic fields. For example, when the energy density in the field of a capacitor is changing, the electric field must be changing, there must be a charging current, and this, in turn, will be associated with a magnetic field. Similarly, when a magnetic field is changing, induced emf's must appear and therefore also electric fields. The flow of energy in space must therefore be associated with the simultaneous appearance of electric and magnetic fields, and the description of this flow of energy must somehow be contained in the fundamental equations relating the two fields, namely, Maxwell's equations. For a vacuum, which we shall first consider, the circuital relations may be written

$$\oint \mathbf{H} \cdot d\mathbf{s} = \int_S \dot{\mathbf{D}} \cdot d\mathbf{A}$$

and   (I.2)

$$\oint \mathbf{E} \cdot d\mathbf{s} = -\int_S \dot{\mathbf{B}} \cdot d\mathbf{A}.$$

We shall apply these equations to an infinitesimal volume element dv in an attempt to relate the fields at the surface of the volume element to the change in total energy content. The rate of increase of energy within the volume element may be written

$$\frac{\partial U}{\partial t} = \frac{\partial u}{\partial t} \, dv = \frac{\partial}{\partial t} \left(\frac{HB}{2} + \frac{ED}{2} \right) dv. \qquad (I.3)$$

The next step is to select a particular volume element to study. This will be a cube oriented in a particular way with respect to the fields we are considering. To begin with, we choose the y axis in the direction of the electric field. The magnetic field will in general have a component at right angles to the electric field. We shall see that this normal component only is involved in the description of energy flow in space, and that the special case of E parallel to H is of no interest. We now choose the z axis in the direction of the component of H perpendicular to E, and choose the x axis

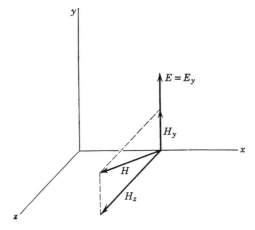

Fig. I.1   The specification of the coordinate system to be used in describing the Poynting vector.

in the usual way so that x, y, z form a right-handed coordinate system, shown in Fig. I.1. The volume element which we shall use will be a cube whose volume is $dx\,dy\,dz$, shown in Fig. I.2. The electric field and the z component of the magnetic field are shown. The magnetic field may also have a y component. Expressing our starting point, which is Eq. I.3, in this coordinate system, we get, since

$$E_x = E_z = 0$$

$$H_z = 0$$

and since

$$HB = \mu_0 H^2 = \mu_0(H_x^2 + H_y^2 + H_z^2) = \mu_0 H_y^2 + \mu_0 H_z^2$$

$$ED = \epsilon_0 E^2 = \epsilon_0(E_x^2 + E_y^2 + E_z^2) = \epsilon_0 E_y^2$$

that

$$\frac{\partial U}{\partial t} = \left(\mu_0 H_y \frac{\partial H_y}{\partial t} + \mu_0 H_z \frac{\partial H_z}{\partial t} + \epsilon_0 E_y \frac{\partial E_y}{\partial t}\right) dx\,dy\,dz$$

$$= (H_y \dot{B}_y + H_z \dot{B}_z + E_y \dot{D}_y)\,dx\,dy\,dz. \tag{I.4}$$

Let us now apply the second of Eqs. I.2, to the various faces of the cube shown in Fig. I.2. In order to express B_y in terms of an electric field, we must choose a face of the cube at right angles to B_y, which could be only the upper or lower faces. One of these is redrawn in Fig. I.3. It is clear that the line integral of E around either of these squares must vanish, since E_t, which in this case is either E_x or E_z, vanishes. We conclude that, if E is in the direction of the y axis, then B_y must necessarily be zero, and the first term of Eq. I.4, is also zero.

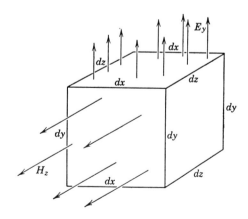

Fig. I.2   The volume element being considered.

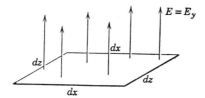

Fig. I.3   The evaluation of $\int E_t ds = -\int_s \dot{B}_y \, dA$.

Before evaluating the second term, notice that since the volume element we are dealing with is assumed to contain no free charges, the total electric flux going in is equal to that going out. Further, since electric flux enters and leaves only on the lower and upper faces, which have the same area, the flux density must be the same on both faces. We therefore conclude that in our volume element E_y is independent of y, as shown in Fig. I.4.

We now take up the second term in Eq. I.4, and identify B_z with the $\dot{B}$ of Eq. I.2. The surface area to be considered is one having sides dx and dy, as shown in Fig. I.5. Along the sides dx, the contour integral has no contribution to make, since the tangential component of E, namely E_x, is zero. We are left, then, with the contribution of the vertical sides. All along

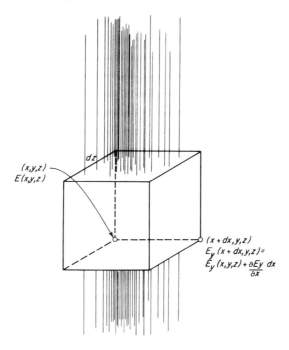

Fig. I.4 E_y is independent of y but varies with x and z.

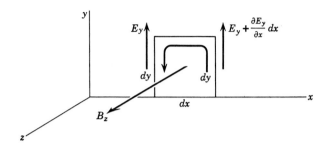

Fig. I.5. The evaluation of $\int \mathbf{E} \cdot d\mathbf{s} = -\int_s \dot{\mathbf{B}} \cdot d\mathbf{A}$.

the left-hand side, the electrical field has the value E_y, and all along the the right-hand side it has a different value, $E_y + (\partial E_y/\partial x)\ dx$. The line integral may therefore be written

$$\oint \mathbf{E} \cdot d\mathbf{s} = \left(E_y + \frac{\partial E_y}{\partial x}\ dx \right) dy - E_y\ dy = \frac{\partial E_y}{\partial x}\ dx\ dy.$$

But Eq. I.2 states that

$$\oint \mathbf{E} \cdot d\mathbf{s} = -\int_S \dot{\mathbf{B}} \cdot d\mathbf{A}.$$

The right-hand side of this equation applied to the face of the cube for which we have evaluated the contour integral, shown in Fig. I.5, is simply $-\dot{B}_y\ dx\ dy$. Equating our results for the contour and surface integrals, we have

$$\dot{B}_z = -\frac{\partial E_y}{\partial x}. \tag{I.5}$$

Similarly, in dealing with the third term of Eq. I.4, we wish to identify $\dot{D}_y$ with $\dot{D}$ of the first equation of Eq. I.2. To do this, we consider a square surface of our volume having sides dx and dz at right angles to y, as shown in Fig. I.6. It is possible to show that, just as E_y was independent of y, so H_z is independent of z. The line integral to be evaluated becomes

$$\oint \mathbf{H} \cdot d\mathbf{s} = H_z\ dz - \left(H_z + \frac{\partial H_z}{dx}\ dx \right) dz = -\frac{\partial H_z}{\partial x}\ dx\ dz.$$

Equating this to the integral on the right of Eq. I.2, which applies to the face of the cube shown in Fig. I.6 is $D_y\ dx\ dz$, we get

$$-\frac{\partial H_z}{\partial x} = \dot{D}_y. \tag{I.6}$$

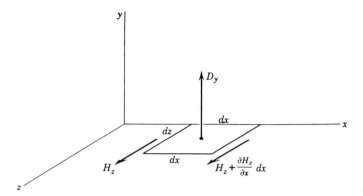

Fig. I.6   The evaluation of $\int H_t ds = \int_s \dot{D}_y \, dA$.

Our original expression for the rate of increase of the energy content of the volume element $dx \, dy \, dz$, in Eq. I.4, can now be expressed in the form

$$\frac{\partial U}{\partial t} = -\left(H_z \frac{\partial E_y}{\partial x} + E_y \frac{\partial H_z}{\partial x} \right) dx \, dy \, dz$$

or

$$\frac{\partial U}{\partial t} = -dy \, dz \left(\frac{\partial}{\partial x} E_y H_z \right) dx. \qquad (I.7)$$

We now give the quantity $E_y H_z$ a new name. It is the x component of the Poynting vector $\mathbf{S}$.

$$S_z \equiv E_y H_z.$$

The interpretation of Eq. I.7, and the general definition of the Poynting

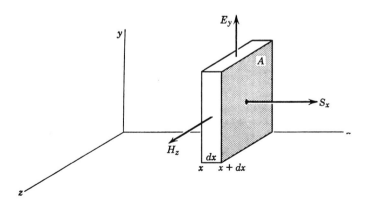

Fig. I.7   The Poynting vector.

vector **S** are facilitated by reference to Fig. I.7. In accordance with the above, the energy flow into the volume from the left is AS_z.

The energy flow out of the volume is $A[S_x + (\partial S_x/\partial x)dx]$, and the rate of accumulation of energy within the volume, $\partial U/\partial t$, is

$$\frac{\partial U}{\partial t} = AS_x - A\left(S_x + \frac{\partial S_x}{\partial x}dx\right)$$

$$= -A\frac{\partial S_x}{dx}dx.$$

But, equating this result with the result of our derivation, as summarized in Eq. I.7, we have

$$\frac{\partial U}{\partial t} = -dy\,dz\left(\frac{\partial}{\partial x}E_yH_z\right)dx$$

$$= -A\frac{\partial S_x}{\partial x}dx$$

or

$$S_x = E_yH_z.$$

This result may be generalized for fields in arbitrary directions in any coordinate systems. In vector notation, we may put

$$\mathbf{S} = [\mathbf{E} \times \mathbf{H}] \tag{I.8}$$

This is the general definition of the Poynting vector.

The energy flow vector **S** may be more pictorially described as follows. Suppose we have in some region of space an energy density u_s moving uniformly with a velocity **v**. The amount of energy crossing unit area normal to the flow in one second is simply $u_s\mathbf{v}$. We may therefore write

$$\mathbf{S} = u_s\mathbf{v}.$$

Notice that nothing we have said specifies that u_s must necessarily be the total energy density $u_e + u_m$. It is possible that the vector **S** should have its specified magnitude because all the energy in space is moving with a velocity $\mathbf{S}/(u_e + u_m)$. It is also possible, however, that only a part of the electric and magnetic energy in space moves, but with a greater velocity. In some cases, particularly when we are dealing with waves, it can be shown that indeed all the energy in space moves, but this is not a general property to be associated with the Poynting vector. It is only the product $u_s\mathbf{v}$ that we can in general specify.

This product, however, suffices for the specification of the momentum per unit volume that we must associate with the moving energy described by the Poynting vector. If mass is energy divided by c^2, then energy per unit volume divided by c^2 must be equivalent to mass per unit volume, or $u_s/c^2 = \rho_s$. But $\rho_s \mathbf{v}$ is simply a momentum per unit volume, and we therefore have

$$\frac{\mathbf{S}}{c^2} = \frac{u_s}{c^2}\, \mathbf{v} = \rho_s \mathbf{v} = \text{momentum per unit volume.} \qquad (I.9)$$

With moving energy there must be associated a momentum.

We shall now give examples of the Poynting vector. First we shall describe the flow of energy into a resistor in the form of a straight cylindrical wire of radius r carrying a constant current i (Fig. I.8). The current flows from a to b because of the presence of a longitudinal electric field of such magnitude that

$$EL = V_{ab} \qquad (I.10)$$

The magnetic field at the surface of the wire is tangential and perpendicular to the length

$$H = \frac{i}{2\pi r}.$$

The Poynting vector at the surface of the wire is directed inward, and its magnitude is given by

$$S = EH = \frac{iV_{ab}}{2\pi rL}.$$

The rate of flow of energy into the wire is the above multiplied by the

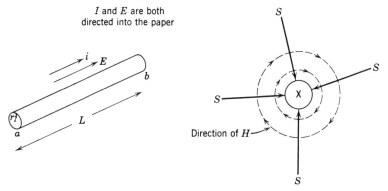

Fig. I.8   The flow of energy into a wire carrying a current.

surface area A of the wire

$$W = SA = S2\pi rL = iV_{ab}. \qquad (I.11)$$

This is just the rate of dissipation of electrical energy in the form of heat within the conductor.

As a further example, let us consider a parallel-plate capacitor being charged. Figure I.9 shows a cylindrical portion of the capacitor sufficiently far from the edges so that fringing fields may be neglected. We have, for the magnetic field H_b at the boundary of the cylindrical surface, from Eq. I.2

$$\oint \mathbf{H} \cdot \mathbf{ds} = H_b 2\pi r = \int_S \dot{\mathbf{D}}_n dA = \dot{D}\pi r^2. \qquad (I.12)$$

The magnitude of the Poynting vector, which is directed radially into the dielectric, is

$$S = EH = \frac{E\dot{D}}{2} r,$$

and the rate of flow into the cylindrical volume v under consideration is

$$SA = S2\pi rd = E\dot{D}\pi r^2 d = E\dot{D}v$$

which may be rewritten

$$SA = \frac{d}{dt}\left(\frac{\epsilon E^2}{2}\right) v. \qquad (I.13)$$

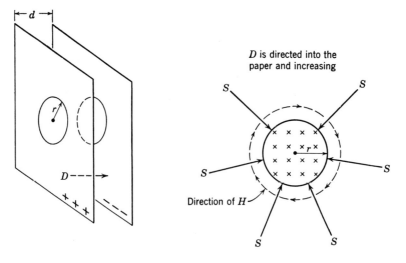

Fig. I.9   Energy flow into a capacitor.

In words, this equation says that the flow of energy into the dielectric, as given by the Poynting vector, is just equal to the rate of accumulation of electrostatic energy within the dielectric.

I.3 ELECTROMAGNETIC WAVES

We must now take up the question of the propagation of radiated waves. In the derivation of the Poynting vector we showed that the following expression might be derived from Maxwell's equations:

$$\mu \frac{\partial H_z}{\partial t} = - \frac{\partial E_y}{\partial x} \tag{I.14}$$

$$- \frac{\partial H_z}{\partial x} = \epsilon \frac{\partial E_y}{\partial t}. \tag{I.15}$$

Here we have substituted $\mu(\partial H_z/\partial t)$ for the $\dot{B}_z$ of Eq. I.5, and similarly $\epsilon(\partial E_y/\partial t)$ for $\dot{D}_y$ of Eq. I.6. These expressions involve relationships between the electric and magnetic fields. It is clear that electric and magnetic fields that vary with time are not independent, and that certain aspects of the one are necessarily associated with certain aspects of the other.

Upon differentiating Eq. I.14 with respect to the time, and Eq. I.15 with respect to x, we get

$$- \frac{\partial^2 E_y}{\partial x \partial t} = \mu \frac{\partial^2 H_z}{\partial t^2} \tag{I.16}$$

$$- \frac{\partial^2 H_z}{\partial x^2} = \epsilon \frac{\partial^2 E_y}{\partial x \partial t}. \tag{I.17}$$

Combining these, we find that

$$\frac{\partial^2 H_z}{\partial x^2} = \epsilon \mu \frac{\partial^2 H_z}{\partial t^2}. \tag{I.18}$$

Similarly, by differentiating Eq. I.14 with respect to x and Eq. I.15 with respect to the time and combining the resulting expressions, we see that

$$\frac{\partial^2 E_y}{\partial x^2} = \epsilon \mu \frac{\partial^2 E_y}{\partial t^2}. \tag{I.19}$$

These are the wave equations for electric and magnetic fields. They imply propagation with the velocity of light,

$$v = \frac{1}{\sqrt{\epsilon\mu}}.$$ (I.20)

Equations similar to Eqs. I.15 and I.18 may be written also for other coordinates. They can be combined into the two equations

$$\frac{\partial^2 H_z}{\partial x^2} + \frac{\partial^2 H_x}{\partial y^2} + \frac{\partial^2 H_y}{\partial z^2} = \epsilon\mu \frac{\partial^2 H}{\partial t^2}$$

$$\frac{\partial^2 E_y}{\partial x^2} + \frac{\partial^2 E_z}{\partial y^2} + \frac{\partial^2 E_x}{\partial z^2} = \epsilon\mu \frac{\partial^2 E}{\partial t^2}.$$

The left-hand sides of these equations can be written in a shorthand fashion:

$$\nabla^2 H = \frac{1}{c^2} \frac{\partial^2 H}{\partial t^2}$$ (I.21)

$$\nabla^2 E = \frac{1}{c^2} \frac{\partial^2 E}{\partial t^2}$$ (I.22)

where

$$\nabla^2 = \frac{\partial^2}{\partial x^2} + \frac{\partial^2}{\partial y^2} + \frac{\partial^2}{\partial z^2}$$

and where at the same time $\epsilon\mu$ has been replaced by $1/v^2$.

By far the most important electric and magnetic fields in space that we shall have to deal with are periodic functions of the time. We shall not be so much interested in the general solutions of the wave equation as in the particular solutions of the form

$$E_y = E_{y0} \sin \frac{2\pi}{\lambda} (x \pm ct).$$ (I.23)

This may be thought of as a plane wave, or an electric field which at any one time has the same value over planes at right angles to the x axis, and varying sinusoidally along this axis. This field may then be thought of as moving along the x axis without otherwise changing its form. The frequency of the oscillation at any one point is

$$\nu = \frac{v}{\lambda}.$$

A similar discussion could be given for the magnetic field H_z, which would be found to have the form

$$H_z = H_{z0} \sin \frac{2\pi}{\lambda} (x \pm ct). \tag{I.24}$$

The amplitudes of these two fields are however not independent, since Eqs. I.14 and I.15 must be satisfied as well as the wave equations. By differentiating the expressions for the fields we find that the conditions to be satisfied imply that

$$-\frac{\partial E_y}{dx} = -\frac{2\pi}{\lambda} E_{y0} \cos \frac{2\pi}{\lambda} (x \pm vt)$$

$$= \mu \frac{\partial H_z}{\partial t} = \pm \mu \frac{2\pi}{\lambda} v H_{z0} \cos \frac{2\pi}{\lambda} (x \pm vt)$$

or that, since $v = 1/(\epsilon\mu)^{1/2}$,

$$E_y = \pm \frac{\mu}{\sqrt{\epsilon\mu}} H_z$$

$$\sqrt{\epsilon} E_y = \pm \sqrt{\mu} H_z. \tag{I.25}$$

If we remember that E and H are perpendicular to each other, the subscripts y and z may be omitted. We have then for the impedance of free space

$$\frac{E}{H} = \sqrt{\frac{\mu_0}{\epsilon_0}} = \sqrt{\frac{4\pi \times 10^{-7}}{8.85 \times 10^{-12}}} = 377 \text{ ohms (approx.)} \tag{I.26}$$

PROBLEMS

1. A cubical box 1 cm on a side is located in uniform electric and magnetic fields. If the edges of the cube are parallel to the x, y, and z axes of a rectangular coordinate system, and the fields have the components

$$H_x = \frac{H}{\sqrt{2}} \quad H_y = \frac{H}{\sqrt{2}} \quad H_z = 0$$

$$E_x = 0 \quad E_y = 0 \quad E_z = E$$

compute the flow of energy into or out of the cube through each face and the net rate of accumulation of energy within the cube.

2. A copper wire, having a resistivity $\rho = 1.7 \times 10^{-8}$ ohmmeters, 4 mm

in diameter, carries a current of 10 amp. What is the heat dissipation per meter of wire? What are the magnitudes of E and H at the surface of the wire? What are the magnitudes of E and H at a point 1 mm from the axis of the wire? What is the magnitude and direction of the Poynting vector **S** at the above points? How much power per meter is dissipated in the central cylindrical section of the wire with a radius of 1 mm? How much power per meter length of the wire is supplied to the whole wire, and to the central core?

3. (*a*) Two tanks of water having masses M_1 and M_2 are connected by a straight pipe having a cross-sectional area A and a length L. The center of gravity of the system is a distance x from M_1, as shown in Fig. P.I.1. A pump P delivers water, flowing with a velocity v, from the first tank to the second at a rate

$$\frac{dM_2}{dt} = -\frac{dM_1}{dt}.$$

The total momentum of the moving water in the pipe is $\rho A L v$. This must be equal to the momentum of the entire system, or

$$(M_1 + M_2)\frac{dx}{dt}.$$

Prove that the momentum

$$\rho A L v = (M_1 + M_2)\frac{dx}{dt} = L\frac{dM_2}{dt}.$$

(*b*) A long cable having negligible resistance delivers power from a battery to a resistor. Prove that the momentum in the electromagnetic field is just equal to that which could be deduced from the velocity of the center of mass of the system.

4. Figure P.I.2 shows the central portion of length L of a long uniformly

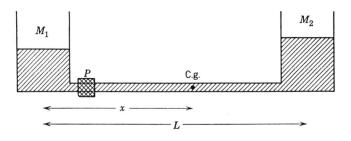

Figure P.I.1 (Problem 3)

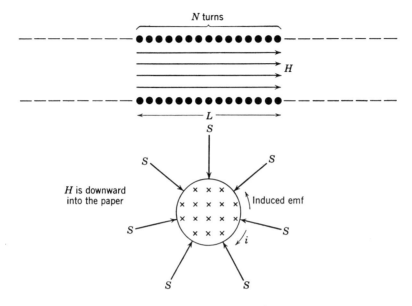

Figure P.I.2 (Problem 4)

wound solenoid, in which the current is increasing. The radius of the solenoid is r, and the volume v under consideration is $v = \pi r^2 L$. (*a*) What is the total magnetic energy in this section of the solenoid at any time? (*b*) What is the induced back emf $\mathcal{E}$ in the N turns of the section? (*c*) What is the value of the induced electric field E responsible for this emf? (*d*) What is the magnitude of the Poynting vector? (*e*) What is the total inward flow of energy through the surface into this portion of the solenoid?

Appendix II

The Special Theory of Relativity[1]

II.1. THE LORENTZ TRANSFORMATION

In 1905, within a span of about six months, the then 26-year-old patent examiner at the Swiss Patent Office in Berne, Albert Einstein, sent off five articles for publication in the German journal *Annalen der Physik*. Two of them (*Ann. Phys.* 17, 132 and 18, 639) contained the Special Theory of Relativity; the first was on the theory of light quanta and the second on that of Brownian motion. The tranquility of the working climate at the patent office—which Einstein occasionally called a "secular cloister"—left him enough time and energy to pursue vigorously his theoretical research, some of it even on "company time."

The Michelson-Morley experiment and other experiments have shown that light, regardless whether its source is at rest or in motion with respect to a particular frame of reference, propagates in vacuum always with the same speed c. In any frame of reference which moves without acceleration, and therefore has a constant velocity in relation to other such frames of reference, the speed of light always has the same value, or is invariant. This speed is therefore a universal constant. Frames of reference which move without acceleration are called inertial frames. The *special theory* of relativity is concerned only with this type, in contrast to the *general theory* of relativity. The experiments mentioned above demonstrate also that it is impossible to detect an ether drift. It makes therefore no sense to speak about absolute rest or absolute motion of a reference frame.

These facts are often stated as the *postulates* of relativity.

First postulate: The laws of physics are identical in all inertial reference systems.

Second postulate: The speed of light in a vacuum is the same in all in-

[1] This appendix should be studied after Sec. 1.6 of Chapter 1.

ertial reference systems. It is independent of the speed of the emitting source.

The Galilean transformation (Eq. 1.1) which is discussed in Sec. 1.5 yields incorrect results at high velocities. According to it, the velocity of the same light beam in a vacuum should be different for observers in different inertial reference frames. Another set of transformation equations is therefore needed, which for speeds small compared to the velocity of light should go over into the Galilean transformation laws. Hence, the latter retain their (approximate) validity for small velocities.

We consider two coordinate systems, S and S', moving relative to each other in the x direction with the velocity v. For S we use unprimed coordinates, that is x, y, z, t, for S' primed ones, that is x', y', z', t'. For the sake of simplicity, we set our systems such that corresponding axes are parallel to each other. The y and z coordinates are the same in both systems. At the time zero the origins are assumed to coincide, or

$$\text{at } t = t' = 0 \qquad x = x' = 0.$$

In both systems the velocity of light is equal to the universal constant c. The same light flash is observed in S and S' propagating spherically with the speed c. Therefore, we have for a light flash which starts at the time $t = t' = 0$ from the coordinate origin $x = x' = y = y' = z = z' = 0$ the following equations for the two systems:

$$x^2 + y^2 + z^2 = c^2 t^2 \tag{II.1}$$

$$x'^2 + y'^2 + z'^2 = c^2 t'^2. \tag{II.2}$$

The new transformation equations must be somewhat more general than the Galilean ones, but they still must be symmetric and linear. Symmetry means that the same transformation laws should apply for going from the unprimed to the primed system and in the opposite direction. Linearity means that x' must be proportional to $x - vt$ and that terms proportional to x^2 or $x^{1/2}$ or t^2, etc., must be excluded. However, the condition of the Galilean transformation that x' must be equal to $x - vt$ is dropped. The proportionality factor which we designate with γ must be determined. The time coordinate is different in both systems, and also this transformation must be a linear one. Therefore we set $t' = \delta x + \epsilon t$, where δ and ϵ are constants to be determined. Summarizing, we have thus as new transformations

$$x' = \gamma(x - vt)$$
$$y' = y$$
$$z' = z \tag{II.3}$$
$$t' = \delta x + \epsilon t.$$

Our next task is the determination of the coefficients γ, δ, and ϵ. For this we substitute Eq. II.3 in Eq. II.2, which yields

$$\gamma^2 x^2 - 2\gamma xvt + \gamma^2 v^2 t^2 + y^2 + z^2 = c^2\delta^2 x^2 + 2c^2\delta x\epsilon t + c^2\epsilon^2 t^2$$

or after collecting the terms containing x^2 and those containing t^2

$$(\gamma^2 - c^2\delta^2)x^2 + y^2 + z^2 - (v\gamma + c^2\delta\epsilon)2xt = (\epsilon^2 - v^2\gamma^2/c^2)t^2c^2. \quad \text{(II.4)}$$

This equation must be identical with Eq. II.1 for all values of x, y, z, and t. This is only possible if the coefficients of the terms containing x^2 or c^2t^2 are equal to unity, and if the last term of the left side vanishes. Therefore

$$\gamma^2 - c^2\delta^2 = 1$$

$$v\gamma + c^2\delta\epsilon = 0$$

$$\epsilon^2 - \frac{v^2}{c^2}\gamma^2 = 1.$$

These three equations with the unknowns γ, δ, and ϵ can be solved with some arithmetical gymnastics and yield

$$\gamma = \epsilon = \pm \frac{1}{\sqrt{1 - v^2/c^2}}$$

and

$$c\delta = \pm\sqrt{\gamma^2 - 1} = \pm \frac{v/c}{\sqrt{1 - v^2/c^2}}.$$

Using the signs which conform to physical reality we finally obtain the equations which are known as the *Lorentz transformation equations*:

$$x' = \frac{x - vt}{\sqrt{1 - v^2/c^2}}$$

$$y' = y$$

$$z' = z \quad \text{(II.5)}$$

$$t' = \frac{t - xv/c^2}{\sqrt{1 - v^2/c^2}}.$$

If we want to transform x', y', z', and t' of the primed system into x, y, z, and t of the unprimed system the transformation equations are similar as before, with the only difference being that the term which is proportional to v has its sign reversed, because the relative velocities of each of the systems as measured by the other system will have opposite directions. Therefore these Lorentz transformation equations are

$$x = \frac{x' + vt'}{\sqrt{1 - v^2/c^2}}$$

$$y = y'$$ (II.6)

$$z = z'$$

$$t = \frac{t' + x'v/c^2}{\sqrt{1 - v^2/c^2}} \, .$$

As we mentioned earlier, the Lorentz transformations must reduce to the Galilean transformations for speeds $v \ll c$. Indeed the factors $1/(1 - v^2/c^2)^{1/2}$ reduce then to 1, and the term xv/c^2 becomes negligible. We thus obtain for $v \ll c$ the Galilean transformation.

II.2. SIMULTANEITY

Whereas, from observations in our daily life, we are used to the possibility that different reference frames may yield different space coordinates and velocities, we do not have a similar intuitive feeling for the transformation of time coordinates. We shall first discuss the concept of simultaneity of two events. If the events happen at the same place there is no problem, but if they are separated in space we need clocks that are synchronized with each other. The synchronization of distant clocks can be accomplished using short light flashes. As long as the clocks do not move with respect to each other and therefore may be considered to belong to the same frame of reference, e.g. S, the problem can easily be solved. A clock on the earth and one on the moon can be synchronized by a light flash which is emitted on our planet, reflected on the moon, and whose return is again observed on earth. If the signal goes off exactly at 6 p.m. and returns after 2.6 seconds, we can tell an observer on the moon that he must have seen the flash at 1.3 seconds past six o'clock. Accordingly, the two clocks can be synchronized. Because earth and moon are at a practically fixed distance we may consider them to belong to the same inertial frame S.

Let us now imagine another inertial frame S' which moves with the velocity v with respect to S. The clocks within this system S' are synchronized in a similar manner.

In the system S two light signals flash simultaneously at locations with the coordinates x_1 and x_2, respectively; $y_{1,2} = z_{1,2} = 0$. The simultaneity of these events has been ascertained by readings of clocks located at x_1 and x_2 which have been synchronized. The same signals are also observed in the reference system S'. Here, these events appear at the coordinates x_1' and x_2', respectively. Clocks synchronized in this system which are located at these coordinates register for these events the times t_1' and t_2', respectively. The question now arises whether the two light flashes are simultaneous also in the primed system. According to the Lorentz transformation the times t_1 and t_2, where $t_1 = t_2 = t$, transform for the S' system into

$$t_1' = \frac{t - vx_1/c^2}{\sqrt{1 - v^2/c^2}}$$

and

$$t_2' = \frac{t - vx_2/c^2}{\sqrt{1 - v^2/c^2}}.$$

Because of the inequality of x_1 and x_2 the times t_1' and t_2' are different. In the primed system the two events are not simultaneous, although they are so in the primed system!

This puzzling result is related with the fact that the velocity of light in any inertial frame is invariant. Each observer, regardless whether he moves towards or from a light source will measure the same speed of light. Under such circumstances it is not surprising that strange effects will result if, for instance, two observers who approach each other with a velocity which is half the speed of light use the same light flash to synchronize the clocks of their respective systems and then perform the experiment on the simultaneity of events. In this example, the use of the same light source to synchronize the clocks within each system perhaps dramatizes the situation, but obviously is of no fundamental importance here.

The fact that two events can be simultaneous in one inertial frame, but not in another one demonstrates that there is no universal time which is valid for all inertial frames. According to the special theory of relativity, time is truly a relative quantity. On the other hand, the speed of light in vacuum is an absolute quantity.

II.3 LORENTZ CONTRACTION AND TIME DILATATION

The ends of a stick which is at rest in the unprimed system and is parallel to the x axis are at the coordinates x_1 and x_2. The length is therefore $\Delta x = x_2 - x_1$. This is called the proper length of the object, because the coordinate system and the object have no relative motion. An observer is in another, the primed, system which moves with constant velocity v in the x direction. As the observer passes along the stick, he measures its end points in his frame of reference, being careful to measure both ends at the same moment, according to his time. Under these conditions he will find the ends of the stick at the coordinates x_1' and x_2'. According to the Lorentz transformation equations the length of the stick transforms in the following way:

$$\Delta x = x_2 - x_1 = \frac{x_2' + vt'}{\sqrt{1 - v^2/c^2}} - \frac{x_2' + vt'}{\sqrt{1 - v^2/c^2}}.$$

Because t' is the same for the measurement of x_2' and x_1', this reduces to

$$x_2 - x_1 = \frac{x_2' - x_1'}{\sqrt{1 - v^2/c^2}}$$

or

$$\Delta x = \frac{\Delta x'}{\sqrt{1 - v^2/c^2}}.$$

Therefore

$$\Delta x' = \Delta x \sqrt{1 - v^2/c^2}. \tag{II.7}$$

This equation says that the length of the stick as measured by the observer in the primed system has contracted by a factor $(1 - v^2/c^2)^{1/2}$. In other words, the stick appears to be shorter. This is called the *Lorentz contraction*.

The time coordinate undergoes a similar change. An event appears in the unprimed system at the coordinate x_1. An observer with a clock, who is at rest in the unprimed system has measured the duration of this event and found $\Delta t = t_2 - t_1$. This is the so-called proper time interval of the event, because the clock did not move away from the place where the event took place. For an observer in the primed system which moves in the x direction with the velocity v the time appears as

$$\Delta t' = t_2' - t_1'.$$

This time interval transforms for an observer in the primed system which moves with the velocity v against the unprimed system in the following way:

$$\Delta t' = t_2' - t_1' = \frac{t_2 - xv/c^2}{\sqrt{1 - v^2/c^2}} - \frac{t_1 - xv/c^2}{\sqrt{1 - v^2/c^2}}$$

$$\Delta t' = \frac{\Delta t}{\sqrt{1 - v^2/c^2}}. \tag{II.8}$$

Thus the observer in the primed system measures a time interval which is lengthened by the factor $1/(1 - v^2/c^2)^{1/2}$. This is the *time dilation* or *time dilatation*.

II.4. MOMENTUM, MASS, AND ENERGY[2]

The relativistic mass change of an object moving with great velocity in some frame of reference is an effect which has to be taken into account by nuclear and particle physicists all the time.

The derivation of the mass change is very often done on the basis of a "thought experiment".[3] Two observers, W and E, ride on a highway in two cars (which are their frames of reference, W having unprimed coordinates, E having primed coordinates) in opposite lanes and directions, westbound and eastbound, respectively. The velocity of the cars relative to each other is v. The observer in each car throws a sphere, w and e, respectively, parallel to his y coordinate towards the other observer's traffic lane. The two objects collide elastically in the middle of the center strip and return to their observers. The whole arrangement is assumed to be completely symmetrical; the spheres are of equal mass and the speeds U_0, with which they are thrown, are equal. These speeds are supposed to be small compared to the velocity of light, whereas the relative speed of the cars, and therefore also the speed of the spheres as seen by the other observer, is very great.

An observer in the center-of-mass system (we assume for simplicity that both cars move on the highway with equal speeds) which is here the highway system sees the situation as illustrated in Fig. II.1.

How does observer W see the collision between the two objects? His ob-

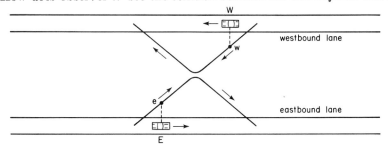

x: east-west, y: north-south.

Fig. II.1. The trajectory of the two colliding spheres as seen by an observer in the center-of-mass system, or stationed on the highway.

---

[2] The study of this section should be preceeded by the study of the first part of Sec. 1.7 of Chapter 1.

[3] G. N. Lewis and R. C. Tolman, *Philosophical Magazine* **18,** 510 (1909). See also W. Pauli, *Theory of Relativity*, Pergamon Press (1958), pp. 118 and 217.

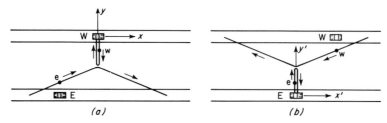

Fig. II.2. The collision of the two spheres (a) as seen by observer W, (b) as seen by observer E.

ject w moves in the negative direction from him and comes back to him, whereas the object e thrown by observer E moves with great speed towards him and then rebounds. This is illustrated in Fig. II.2(a), and Fig. II.2(b) shows the same collision from the viewpoint of observer E. The components of the velocities V and V', respectively, of the two objects in the two coordinate systems before and after the collision are given below:

Object	Observer W (unprimed system)		Observer E (primed system)	
	before the collision			
w	$V_x = 0$	$V_y = -U$	$V'_x = -v$	$V'_y = -U(1 - v^2/c^2)^{1/2}$
e	$V_x = v$	$V_y = U(1 - v^2/c^2)^{1/2}$	$V'_x = 0$	$V'_y = U$
	after the collision			
w	$V_x = 0$	$V_y = U$	$V'_x = -v$	$V'_y = U(1 - v^2/c^2)^{1/2}$
e	$V_x = v$	$V_y = -U(1 - v^2/c^2)^{1/2}$	$V'_x = 0$	$V'_y = -U$

For some of the y components of the velocity we have made use of the velocity transformation laws given in Eq. 1.7.1 for velocity components U which are transverse to the relative velocity v of the frames of reference.[4] Because the U_x component that enters this formula is zero, this equation reduces to the expressions in the table.

The whole collision process is obviously symmetric in the center-of-mass system, but also the observations of E and W are identical. Both observe that the other's sphere moves slower in the y direction than his own sphere. In spite of this, their own sphere returns with the original speed. Conservation of momentum requires therefore that the velocity decrease is compensated by a mass increase. Hence, we conclude that the mass of a par-

[4] Note that here this relative velocity is denoted by small v, not V, as in the original Eq. 1.7.1.

ticle depends on its velocity in the frame in which it is measured, or $m = m(v)$.

The conservation of momentum in the y direction, p_y, from the standpoint of observer W requires that

$$p_y = -m(U)U + \dot{m}(v)U\sqrt{1 - v^2/c^2} = m(U)U - m(v)U\sqrt{1 - v^2/c^2}$$

or

$$2m(U)U = 2m(v)U\sqrt{1 - v^2/c^2}$$

therefore

$$m(v) = \frac{m(U)}{\sqrt{1 - v^2/c^2}}.$$

We have made in the last steps the tacit assumption that the velocity U is small against v, certainly against c. If the velocity U is of a magnitude for which classical mechanics is a good approximation, the mass has not changed noticably, and we can set the mass $m(U)$ equal to the mass at rest, or the *rest mass*, m_0. We therefore have arrived at the important expression

$$m(v) = \frac{m_0}{\sqrt{1 - v^2/c^2}} \tag{II.9}$$

which shows the relativistic mass change of a moving body.

The kinetic energy, which we shall discuss next, is given in classical physics by $K = \frac{1}{2}mv^2$. Also this expression is revised in the theory of relativity.

From the work-energy theorem we know that the increase in kinetic energy is equal to the work done by the net force, or

$$\text{work} = K = \int_0^x F dx.$$

For the force we cannot use $F = mdv/dt$, because m is also a variable. However, the expression

$$F = \frac{d}{dt}(mv)$$

is suitable also in our case. The above equation can thus be written as

$$K = \int_0^x \frac{d}{dt}(mv)\,dx = \int_0^x \frac{d}{dt}\left(m\frac{dv}{dx}\,dx\right) = \int_0^v \frac{d}{dt}\frac{m_0v}{\sqrt{1 - v^2/c^2}}.$$

After integration we have

$$K = \frac{m_0 c^2}{\sqrt{1 - v^2/c^2}} - m_0 c^2. \tag{II.10}$$

Obviously for $v \ll c$ this expression has to become the familiar expression $\frac{1}{2} m v^2$. This is indeed so, because

$$(1 - v^2/c^2)^{-1/2} = 1 + \frac{1}{2}\frac{v^2}{c^2} + \frac{3}{8}\frac{v^4}{c^4} + \cdots$$

Inserting the first two terms of the expansion into Eq. II.10 yields

$$K = m_0 c^2 \left(1 + \frac{1}{2}\frac{v^2}{c^2} - 1 \right) = \frac{1}{2} m_0 v^2.$$

Eq. II.10 gives the kinetic energy as the difference between two energy terms, both being the product of a mass multiplied by the square of the speed of light. The term $m_0 c^2$, which has the dimension of an energy represents the energy of a body at rest in the appropriate reference frame. It is therefore called the *rest mass energy*. If the body is in motion, its mass and therefore its total energy E increases according to

$$E = \frac{m_0 c^2}{\sqrt{1 - v^2/c^2}} = m(v) c^2.$$

This leads to the *principle of the equivalence of mass and energy* expressed by the famous equation

$$E = mc^2. \tag{II.11}$$

Momentum in the theory of relativity is defined in the same way as in classical mechanics by

$$p = mv,$$

only that m is now the relativistic mass

$$m = \frac{m_0}{\sqrt{1 - v^2/c^2}}.$$

Therefore,

$$p = \frac{m_0 v}{\sqrt{1 - v^2/c^2}}. \tag{II.12}$$

Since

$$E = \frac{m_0 c^2}{\sqrt{1 - v^2/c^2}},$$

we can arrive at an important relation between the total energy, the momentum and the rest mass energy

$$E^2 = (pc)^2 + (m_0 c^2)^2, \qquad \text{(II.13)}$$

as substitution using the above expressions easily shows.

PROBLEMS

1. An event happens in the system S at $x = x_1$ at the time $t = t_1$, and a second event happens at $x = x_2$ at the time $t = t_2$. What must be the velocity of the system S' relative to S in order that the two events are simultaneous for a observer in S'?

2. A train travels through a station with a speed of $\frac{2}{3} c$. The train has just the length of the station platform, namely 200 m, as seen by an observer at the middle of this platform. At the instant when the train is lined up with the platform, light signals are emitted simultaneously at the two ends of the platform according to synchronized clocks located there. (a) If the station clocks read zero at the time when the signals go off, at which time do they reach the observer on the platform? (b) At what time do they reach an observer riding in the middle of the train according to the clocks on the platform? (c) What is the time interval between the arrivals of the two signals as measured by the observer on the train?

3. A 100 MeV electron passes through an apparatus of 1 m length. How long does the apparatus appear to the electron?

4. How far does a cosmic-ray neutron of an energy of 10^{14} eV travel if its lifetime, measured by its own clock (i.e. in proper time) is 11 minutes? ($m_0 c^2$ of a neutron 939.6 MeV)

5. In a number of particle-physics experiments a beam of K^+ mesons of 600 MeV kinetic energy is used. These K^+ mesons have a rest mass energy $m_0 c^2$ of 493.8 MeV and a mean lifetime of 1.2×10^{-8} sec as measured by their own clock (i.e. proper time). As measured by an observer in the laboratory: (a) What will be their mass? (b) Their lifetime? (c) The mean distance they can travel before they decay?

6. A muon in the cosmic radiation was created 10 km above sea level and decays in flight just before reaching ground. According to its own clock it lived for 2.2×10^{-6} sec, which is the mean lifetime for muons at rest (proper time). Assume that the muon was not slowed down by collisions in the atmosphere. (a) What must have been its kinetic energy? (b) How long does the flight path look to the muon?

7. A proton has a momentum of 10 GeV/c. (a) What is its velocity? (b) What is its kinetic energy? (c) What is its total energy? (d) What is its mass?

8. (*a*) What is the mass of an electron that has been accelerated by a potential of 511 kV? (*b*) What is its kinetic energy? (*c*) What is its total energy? (*d*) What is its momentum?

9. Show if in the relativistic energy range the formula for kinetic energy $K = \frac{1}{2} mv^2$ holds if m is the relativistic mass at the velocity v, instead of the rest mass.

10. Momentum and energy of a particle of known rest mass and charge can be determined from its radius of curvature in a magnetic field of known strength. Express the momentum of such a particle by the magnetic induction B and the radius of curvature ρ.

11. The radius of curvature of an electron in a magnetic field of 0.1 weber/m² is 0.03 m. What is its kinetic energy?

12. What is the radius of curvature of a proton (rest mass energy 938 MeV) of 3000 MeV kinetic energy in a magnetic field of 2 webers/m²?

13. Compute the rest mass energy in eV of an electron (mass 9.1×10^{-31} kg), of a proton (mass 1.67×10^{-27} kg).

14. (*a*) What is the energy of a proton whose mass is ten times its rest mass? (*b*) Of an electron?

15. In the fission of a uranium nucleus 200 MeV are set free as kinetic energy of the particles. What is the loss of rest mass of a quantity of 1 mole ²³⁵U, which has undergone fission?

16. In the chemical reaction $H_2 + \frac{1}{2}O_2$, 70.6 kcal are set free to produce one mole of water. What is the loss in rest mass and what fraction does it constitute?

17. Show that the value of $E^2 - (pc)^2$ for a particle is the same in all inertial reference frames and is therefore an invariant.

18. What is the momentum of a photon, or light quantum, of energy E? Of a neutrino of energy E? Neutrinos are elementary particles of zero rest mass.

Appendix III

The Complex Notation of Trigonometric Functions

In physics it is usually much more convenient to replace the trigonometric functions by appropriate exponential functions. These two kinds of
functions are connected by Euler's[1] relation

$$e^{i\alpha} = \cos \alpha + i \sin \alpha$$

where

$$i = \sqrt{-1} \qquad \text{and} \qquad i^2 = -1.$$

This relation can be derived from the Taylor expansion for the exponential
function

$$e^x = 1 + \frac{x}{1!} + \frac{x^2}{2!} + \frac{x^3}{3!} + \cdots$$

by substituting for x the value $i\alpha$. This yields

$$e^{i\alpha} = \left(1 - \frac{\alpha^2}{2!} + \frac{\alpha^4}{4!} - \frac{\alpha^6}{6!} + \cdots\right) + i\left(\frac{\alpha}{1!} - \frac{\alpha^3}{3!} + \frac{\alpha^5}{5!} \cdots\right)$$

$$= \cos \alpha + i \sin \alpha.$$

A complex number, such as $z = x + iy$, can be represented as a point in a
complex plane, as shown in Fig. III.1. If A is the distance of z from the
origin, we can write

$$x = A \cos \alpha \qquad \text{and} \qquad y = A \sin \alpha$$

[1] Leonard Euler (1707–1783), Swiss mathematician, professor of physics, later of
mathematics in St. Petersburg (Russia). Then went to Berlin to join the Academy of
Sciences. Returned after 25 years to St. Petersburg. Important contributions to fluid
dynamics, theory of gyroscopes and optics (wave theory of light, design of achromatic
lenses). Created the concept of the moment of inertia. In mathematics contributions
to the theory of differential equations and the theory of numbers.

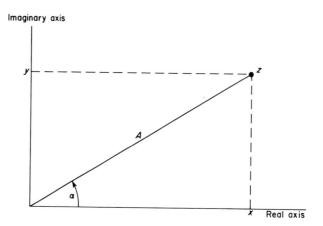

Fig. III.1   The complex plane.

or

$$z = A(\cos \alpha + i \sin \alpha).$$

Using Euler's relation we have

$$z = Ae^{i\alpha} = A(\cos \alpha + i \sin \alpha).$$

Instead of writing $A \cos \omega t$ we now write $Ae^{i\omega t}$ and take the real part of it. For $A \sin \omega t$ we take the imaginary part of $Ae^{i\omega t}$. Generally, the real part and the imaginary part each yield a solution.

A traveling wave which otherwise may be written

$$y(x, t) = A \cos(kx - \omega t)$$

is now written as

$$y(x, t) = Ae^{i(kx-\omega t)}.$$

This method is advantageous because the clumsy trigonometric addition theorems are replaced by formulas that are easier to handle.

The equivalence of the trigonometric and the exponential form is also seen from the following example.

Trigonometric form	Exponential form
$x = A(\cos \omega t + i \sin \omega t)$	$x = Ae^{i\omega t}$
$dx/dt = A\omega(-\sin \omega t + i \cos \omega t)$	$dx/dt = Ai\omega e^{i\omega t}$
$= Ai\omega(\cos \omega t + i \sin \omega t) = i\omega x$	$= i\omega x$

The connection between the exponential function and the sine or cosine function is also seen, for instance, in the behavior of oscillations. In an undamped or slightly damped oscillation, the oscillation can be described by a sine (or cosine) function or, alternatively, by an exponential function with an imaginary exponent. However, if the damping is very great, the oscillatory motion yields to a motion described completely by an exponential function.

The equation of motion for damped harmonic motion is the following differential equation

$$m \frac{d^2x}{dt^2} = -a \frac{dx}{dt} - kx.$$

The first term on the right-hand side represents the damping force which is assumed to be proportional to the velocity dx/dt, and a is a constant. (For $a = 0$ the equation reduces obviously to the one for simple harmonic motion.) A solution for this differential equation is, as one easily verifies by substitution (see also Problem 5),

$$x = be^{-(a/2m)t}e^{+\sqrt{(a^2/4m^2)-(k/m)}\,t}$$

(Another solution differs from this one by a minus sign in front of the square root sign and a different value for b. The general solution is a super-position of these two solutions.)

As long as $k/m > a^2/4m^2$, the second exponent is imaginary and represents, according to Euler's relation, a sinusoidal motion. The amplitude, given by the first exponential function and the constant b, decreases exponentially with time. If, however, $k/m < a^2/4m^2$, the second exponent becomes real too: We have only an exponential decrease of the deflection without oscillation.

PROBLEMS

1. The differential equation for simple harmonic motion is $m(d^2x/dt^2) = -kx$. Show, by substituting, that $x = Ae^{i\omega t}$ is a solution of this equation and determine ω.

2. Show that $\sin x = (e^{ix} - e^{-ix})/2i$ and $\cos x = (e^{ix} + e^{-ix})/2$.

3. If $y = \tan x$ show that $e^{2ix} = (1 + iy)/(1 - iy)$.

4. Express $e^{i(\alpha+\beta)}$ by the ordinary addition theorems.

5. The differential equation of a damped harmonic motion is

$$m \frac{d^2x}{dt^2} + a \frac{dx}{dt} + kx = 0.$$

Determine ω and the amplitude. Hint: Starting with $x = Ae^{\lambda t}$, determine λ and A.

6. Show that the square of the amplitude, A^2, is given by

$$A^2 = zz^*$$

whereby $z^* = A(\cos \alpha - i \sin \alpha)$ is called the complex conjugate of z which results from replacing i by $-i$ in z.

7. Plot for $\psi = Ae^{-i\omega t}$ and its complex conjugate (see problem 6) $\psi^* = Ae^{-i\omega t}$ (a) the real parts of ψ and ψ^* as a function of t, (b) the imaginary parts, (c) $\psi\psi^*$.

Appendix IV

Elements of Statistical Mechanics; Boltzmann, Bose, and Fermi Statistics

Statistical mechanics designates that field of theoretical physics which is concerned with the statistical behavior of a big number of particles. The study of the velocity distribution of the molecules of a gas is a typical and classical example. Experiments tell us that at a given temperature of the gas the individual molecules do not have a uniform velocity, but that their velocity extends over a broad range which results in a distorted bell-shaped velocity distribution curve, as indicated in Fig. IV.1. Due to collisions of the molecules among each other and with the walls of the vessel containing the gas, the individual molecules change their velocity and hence their kinetic energy, but the sum of the kinetic energies of all molecules remains constant, as long as we assume that there is no change in volume or temperature and that the system is in equilibrium. The experiments also tell us that with increasing temperature the kinetic energy and the velocity of the molecules increase and that the maximum in the velocity distribution moves to higher velocities, which is also shown in Fig. IV.1.

Other properties of atoms can also be described in statistical terms.

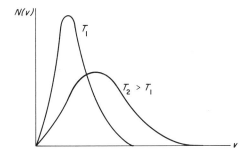

Fig. IV.1   The velocity distribution of the molecules of a gas at two different temperatures.

This method is particularly appropriate when dealing with a great number of atoms. Some atoms, for example, may be in their ground state or in one of many excited states. The methods of statistical mechanics can provide us with answers to questions like the one about the percentage of the atoms in a given state. Most atomic processes are not observed as individual events, but only as the combined effect from many individual events. For example, a spectral line which a spectroscopist sees or which a photographic plate registers is the cumulative effect of transitions of millions of atoms. Statistical mechanics is hence a link between the microscopic, or individual, events and the macroscopic, or bulk, phenomena.

We will not attempt here to present a rigorous theory of statistical mechanics, but rather will investigate the behavior of a system of very few particles under different conditions. Let us assume that we have a system in which A atoms share N units of energy ϵ.[1] We also stipulate that each of the atoms can be distinguished from the others. If we were satisfied with a system of a few hundred atoms, we could chose the approximately one hundred different elements. Since most of them have several isotopes we could in principle have a system of several hundred different distinguishable components, as stated above. (Alternatively, we might consider following the individual molecules of a gas, which now may be all of the same kind, with an electron microscope, a feature which in a few years might well be technologically possible. We therefore can assume that the molecules are in principle distinguishable.) The units of energy, which the atoms can take up or give off, however, are all alike. We now wish to solve the problem of how many different ways we can distribute the N units of energy among the A different atoms. Although this problem can be solved in a general way with the usual methods of mathematical combinations,

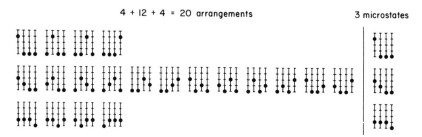

4 + 12 + 4 = 20 arrangements   3 microstates

Fig. IV.2   Four atoms sharing three energy units ϵ, resulting in 20 arrangements which can be combined into 3 microstates.

[1] A somewhat realistic example might be a system of oscillators, for example, atoms fixed in a crystal lattice and oscillating. As shown in Chapter 3 an oscillator can accept or release energy only in units of $h\nu$, where ν is the natural frequency of the oscillator.

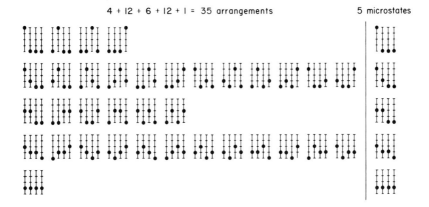

Fig. IV.3   Arrangements and microstates for a system of four atoms and four energy units.

we will attack it in a much more direct and elementary way, limiting ourselves to a system of very few atoms.

We shall discuss a system of four atoms which at first share three energy units ϵ. In Fig. IV.2 these atoms are represented by vertical lines, with their energy content indicated by the position of the dot along this line. An atom in its ground state, for example, has the dot at the bottom end. It might now happen that one of the four atoms has all the three energy units and the other atoms have nothing, or that the available energy is in some way distributed among two or three atoms. Since we have assumed that the atoms are distinguishable, it matters with regard to the second example if atom 1 has two units and atom 2 has one unit, or if it is vice versa. Each of these individual arrangements is different. Further arrangements which are similar because they have two units of energy in one atom and one unit in another involve atoms 1 and 3, 1 and 4, 2 and 3, and 3 and 4. All these arrangements are said to belong to the same *microstate*. The arrangements and their microstates are listed in the first row of Fig. IV.2. The other microstates and their arrangements are given on the subsequent rows. It is important to remember that in all cases there are four atoms which share three units of energy.

We now increase the energy of our system of four atoms to four units of energy. Obviously, the combinations will increase, but their number is still easily manageable, as Fig. IV.3 shows. There are now five microstates which split into a total of 35 arrangements. It is left as an exercise for the reader to list the microstates and arrangements for one and two units of energy.

Maxwell-Boltzmann Statistics

The basic assumption of statistical mechanics is that each different combination is equally likely to occur. Because we assume that the atoms are distinguishable, each individual arrangement must be considered as one such combination. In our example with four energy units distributed over four atoms, all the 31 arrangements are therefore equally probable. We can now easily calculate from the graph the probability for finding an atom, regardless which one of the four, in a state in which it contains, for example, three units of energy. We only have to count which fraction of the $4 \times 35 = 140$ atoms represented in Fig. IV.3 meet our criterion. We find altogether 12 atoms with three energy units, or 8.6% of the 140 atoms. Similarly, we find 60 atoms, or 43%, having zero energy, and so on. Thus we can construct a graph of the probability for an atom to be in a certain energy state. Such a plot is given in Fig. IV.4. Note that the shape of the curve connecting the data points fits fairly closely an exponential curve. For total energies of the system other than four units we obtain similar curves, some of which are shown in Fig. IV.5.

In all these curves the lowest energy state has the highest probability to be populated, and with increasing total energy the curves become flatter and extend to higher energies. Calculations for many more atoms and units of energy would have resulted in exponential curves that can be represented by a function proportional to $e^{-E/\epsilon}$, where ϵ must obviously have the dimension of an energy. A more detailed theory also would show that $\epsilon = kT$ where k is the Boltzmann constant, which is a constant of nature with the value 1.380×10^{-23} joules/K $= 8.617 \times 10^{-5}$ eV/K. This function is

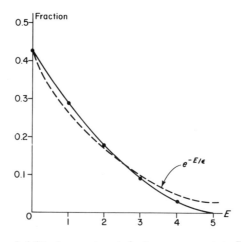

Fig. IV.4   The probability for an atom to be in an energy state E if the number of atoms is 4 and the total energy of the system is 4ϵ. The dashed line is an exponential function proportional to $e^{-E/\mathcal{E}}$.

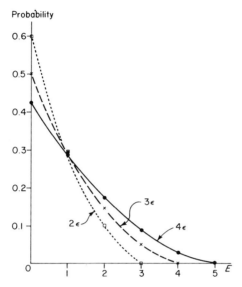

Fig. IV.5   The probability for an atom to be in an energy state E if the number of atoms is 4 and the total energy of the system is 2ϵ, 3ϵ, or 4ϵ.

known as the Boltzmann distribution function or probability function. In our example, we had divided the total available energy in equal portions. This procedure was chosen for convenience only and is not necessary. Any division, or an infinitely fine division, of the total energy would have given the same functional dependence.

The assumptions on which we have based our considerations up to this point and our results are those of the Maxwell-Boltzmann statistics, or simply Boltzmann statistics. This statistics is appropriate for assemblies of particles which in principle are distinguishable, whereby the words "in principle" may be interpreted very liberally. The Boltzmann statistics is the statistics to describe properties and behavior of particles which follow the laws of classical physics, because with some microscope we could always follow the path of such a particle.[2]

Bose-Einstein Statistics

Another type of statistics is known as the Bose-Einstein statistics, or simply Bose statistics. This is one of the two kinds of statistics which are appropriate for quantum-mechanical systems (the other one is the Fermi-Dirac statistics discussed below). In contrast to the Boltzmann statistics

[2] Readers only interested in the Maxwell-Boltzmann distribution may proceed directly to p. 663.

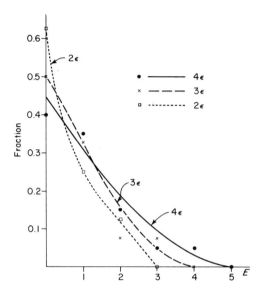

Fig. IV.6 The Bose-Einstein distribution for four particles sharing 2, 3, and 4 energy units ϵ.

in both of these statistics the particles are indistinguishable. Hence, it makes no more sense to speak about arrangements. We only have microstates, and each microstate represents a configuration that has the same probability of occurring as any other microstate of the same energy. In our earlier example of four atoms and four units of energy the resulting five microstates all have equal probability in the Bose statistics. We can construct graphs analogous to Figs. IV.4 and IV.5 using now the microstates of Figs. IV.2 and IV.3 in place of the arrangements. The resulting distribution functions are shown in Fig. IV.6. Due to our new counting procedure the number of atoms is now considerably smaller and the points on the graph scatter somewhat more, but the curves still display the same trend as in the Boltzmann distribution.

An example where the Bose statistics is the appropriate one is the cavity radiation which is discussed in Chapter 2. The quanta in the cavity constitute a "photon" gas which obeys this type of statistics.

Fermi-Dirac Statistics

It is known that particles of half-integer spin, such as electrons, protons, or neutrons, obey the Pauli exclusion principle; on the other hand, for particles of integer spin, as photons or α particles, there is no such restriction. As a consequence, in assemblies of particles of half-integer spin certain combinations are excluded, which would be permitted for the other category of particles. Because certain combinations now do not enter into the picture, the distribution function is different from the Bose distribution function, leading to the Fermi-Dirac statistics, or Fermi statistics in short. Particles which obey this statistics are called *fermions*; they have half-integer spin. Conversely, particles which follow Bose statistics are called *bosons*; they have integer spin and do not obey the exclusion principle.

Particles with spin $\frac{1}{2}$ can be in two possible spin orientations, "spin up" and "spin down." A state that is described by a spatial wave function can therefore be occupied by two like particles. It is consequently not possible that all particles of a system are in the lowest existing state described by a spatial wave function; only two particles can occupy it. In its ground state a system composed of fermions, hence, must have many of its constituents in higher states. A system of 14 particles in its lowest possible energy state is shown in Fig. IV.7(a). For simplicity's sake we assume again that the energy levels are equally spaced. The particles in the left column of each configuration shall have their spins "up" and in the right column "down." If one unit of energy is fed into this system, one of the two uppermost particles can move up into an unoccupied level, as shown in Fig. IV.7(b). Although the particles are indistinguishable, as they are also in the Bose statistics, the state of the system will be different due to their spin orientation. Consequently two states of our system of 14 fermions with an excitation energy of one unit are possible. For simplicity we assume here that no particle can change its spin direction.

If two units of energy are available, the five microstates of Fig. IV.7(c) can be formed: Either one of the uppermost particles moves up two steps, or one particle from the row just below the top, or both particles at the top move up by one step each. With four units of energy the number of micro-

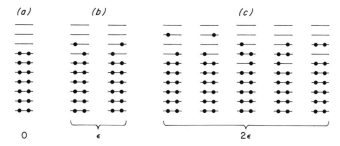

Fig. IV.7 A system of 14 fermions a) in its lowest energy state, b) with one additional unit of energy c) with two additional units of energy.

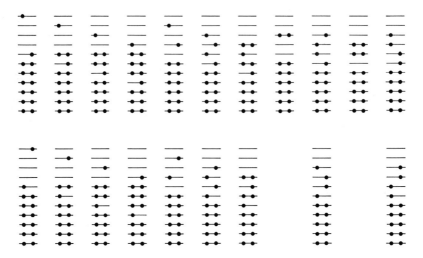

Fig. IV.8   A system of 14 fermions of spin $\frac{1}{2}$ with an excitation of four units of energy ϵ.

states increases to 18 (Fig. IV.8). Each one has the same probability to occur. As before in the case of the Boltzmann and Bose statistics we sum all the particles in a particular energy state and plot their number as a function of their energy. This is done in Fig. IV.9 for different excitation energies of the system. For low energies the Fermi distribution function is completely different from the distribution functions of the Boltzmann and Bose statistics. At higher excitation energies, however, the Fermi distri-

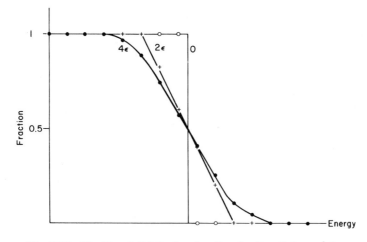

Fig. IV.9   The Fermi distribution function for $E = 0$, 2ϵ, and 4ϵ.

bution approaches the other two distributions. This is because the proportion of configurations which are ruled out by the exclusion principle becomes smaller because the particles spread out over an increasing number of states.

Distribution Functions

By refraining from an analytical derivation of the distribution functions for the different types of statistics, but following instead a more empirical approach, we cannot expect to obtain analytical formulations. We shall, however, present them here and refer the interested reader to the literature.

The Maxwell-Boltzmann distribution function f_{MB} is, as mentioned earlier

$$f_{MN} \propto \frac{1}{e^{E/kT}} \, .$$

The Bose-Einstein distribution function, f_{BE}, is

$$f_{BE} \propto \frac{1}{e^{E/kT} - 1} \, .$$

At higher temperatures and for big energies the -1 can be neglected against $e^{E/kT}$. The Bose-Einstein distribution function then approaches the one for the Maxwell-Boltzmann statistics. Only at low temperature and small energies are the two distributions much different. The properties of ^{4}He at low temperature whose monatomic molecules have spin zero are strongly determined by the Bose statistics.

The Fermi-Dirac distribution function is

$$f_{FD} = \frac{1}{e^{(E - e_F)/kT} + 1}$$

where e_F is called the Fermi energy. This is the energy at which one half of the states of this energy are occupied. From the shape of this distribution function at zero temperature, it follows that all states below the Fermi energy at this temperature[3] are fully occupied. At low temperatures $e^{(E-e_F)/kT}$ becomes for energies slightly smaller than e_F very soon negligibly small against 1, and the Fermi function is then 1. On the high-energy side of e_F, because the exponential becomes very big, f_{FD} soon becomes zero. Only within an energy range approximately equal to $2\,kT$, straddling both

---

[3] The Fermi energy is slightly temperature-dependent, but this shall not concern us.

sides of e_F, is f_{FD} appreciably different from 1 or 0. If e_F is small against kT and against E, so that it can be neglected, the exponential term dominates the denominator making the quantity $+1$ negligible. Thus also the Fermi distribution approaches the Boltzmann distribution. As we said earlier this trend is not so surprising because the Pauli exclusion principle has little to exclude when so many vacant states are accessible.

At high energies the Boltzmann, the Bose, and the Fermi distributions tend therefore to converge.

Throughout our previous discussion we have assumed that the states which our system could assume were evenly distributed over the whole energy range. Consequently, the probability of finding an occupied state in a certain energy interval (which was chosen big enough to contain a number of levels) was just proportional to the probability to find a given state in this energy region occupied. However, in most physical systems the number of available states per energy interval varies with the excitation energy, in contrast to the special, although important, case of the one-dimensional harmonic oscillator.[4] In a three-dimensional box the density of energy states ρ which a particle can occupy increases with increasing energy and is schematically illustrated in Fig. IV.10.

An example in classical physics is the speed distribution of molecules of a gas. These molecules have three degrees of freedom for translational motion. This means that they can move independently in the x, y, and z directions, for example. Figure IV.11 illustrates for two dimensions that a given speed can be realized in various ways. It is also clear that the bigger one chooses the speed $|v|$, the more different possibilities will exist. The shaded region in the figure which represents the endpoints of the velocity vectors falling into a speed interval $|\Delta v|$ increases linearly with the speed in the two-dimensional case, but if we consider three dimensions it increases

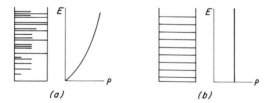

(a) *(b)*

Fig. IV.10 States and density of states ρ: *(a)* in a three-dimensional well, length of lines proportional to degeneracy (*cf.* Fig. 3.4.3); *(b)* in a one-dimensional harmonic oscillator.

[4] Also a three-dimensional harmonic oscillator has regularly spaced energy levels, but most of its levels are degenerate. Therefore the number of available states varies with the excitation energy.

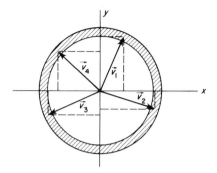

Fig. IV.11 Equal speeds $|v|$ realized in different ways in two dimensions. The shaded region represents all speeds falling into the interval between $|v|$ and $|v + \Delta v|$.

with the square of the speed, because the volume of a spherical shell is $4\pi v^2 \Delta v$. In a gas the number of realizable possibilities increases therefore with the square of the speed. The Boltzmann probability distribution function, on the other hand, tells us what the probability is for the realization of a given possibility. The number of actually realized possibilities is therefore given by the product of the possibilities times the probability for each such possibility, or

$$N(v) \propto v^2 \frac{1}{e^{E/kT}} = v^2 e^{-mv^2/kT}.$$

This is just the shape of the curves in Fig. IV.1. In a similar way we can treat the occupation of levels in a three-dimensional box. This is done in Chapter 5.

PROBLEMS

1. Three harmonic oscillators share three units of energy. (a) List the arrangements and microstates. (b) Plot the Maxwell-Boltzmann distribution function. (c) Plot the Bose-Einstein distribution function.

2. A system contains N oscillators. These oscillators have $n_1, n_2, n_3 \cdots n_N$ units of energy. (a) Show that the formula $(N!)/(n_1! n_2! \cdots n_N!)$ expresses the number of arrangements which compose a microstate. (b) Derive this formula.

3. N identical oscillators share n units of energy. (a) Verify on a few examples that the formula $[(N + n - 1)!]/[n!(N - 1)!]$ gives the number of microstates. (b) Derive this formula.

4. Assume a system of five spin-$\frac{1}{2}$ particles, all having "spin up," in a

harmonic oscillator potential. (a) List the possible states for an excitation of five quanta. (b) Plot the Fermi distribution function.

5. A system of twelve particles of spin $\frac{3}{2}$ is excited by three equal energy units. (a) List the possible states. (b) Plot the distribution function.

6. Five units of excitation energy are shared by 14 fermions of spin $\frac{1}{2}$. (a) List the possible states and draw the distribution function. (b) Compare this with Fig. IV.9.

7. Fig. IV.6 shows the Bose-Einstein distribution for four particles sharing four units of energy ϵ. Assume now that the same amount of energy is divided into two, now bigger, units ϵ. (a) Compare the new energy distribution with the old one. In particular, comment on how the ratio of atoms in the ground state to atoms in an excited state has changed. (b) How would this ratio be affected if the energy units were smaller than ϵ? (c) What effect does the quantization of energy have on the relative occupation of different energy states?

8. The maximum in the velocity spectrum (like the one in Fig. IV.1) of N_2 molecules at 290 K is at a velocity of 400 m/sec. At what temperature has this maximum shifted to 700 m/sec?

References Recommended for Further Study

GENERAL

M. Born, *Atomic Physics*, 8th ed., Hafner, New York, 1969.

R. M. Eisberg, *Fundamentals of Modern Physics*, Wiley, New York, 1961.

R. P. Feynman, R. B. Leighton, and M. Sands, *The Feynman Lectures on Physics*, Addison-Wesley, Reading, Mass., 1963.

R. B. Leighton, *Principles of Modern Physics*, McGraw-Hill, New York, 1959.

D. L. Livesey, *Atomic and Nuclear Physics*, Blaisdell, New York, 1966.

J. D. McGervey, *Introduction to Modern Physics*, Academic Press, New York, 1971.

J. G. Powles, *Particles and Their Interactions*, Addison-Wesley, Reading, Mass., 1968.

F. K. Richtmyer, E. H. Kennard, and J. N. Cooper, *Introduction to Modern Physics*, McGraw-Hill, New York, 1969.

SPECIFIC SUBJECTS

Electricity and Magnetism

R. S. Elliot, *Electromagnetics*, McGraw-Hill, New York, 1966.

E. M. Pugh and E. W. Pugh, *Principles of Electricity and Magnetism*, 2nd ed., Addison-Wesley, Reading, Mass., 1970.

W. T. Scott, *The Physics of Electricity and Magnetism*, 2nd ed., Wiley, New York, 1966.

Theory of Relativity

M. Born, *Einstein's Theory of Relativity*, Dover, New York, 1962.

A. Einstein, *Relativity, the Special and the General Theory*, Crown, New York, 1961.

J. L. Synge, *Talking about Relativity*, North-Holland, Amsterdam, 1970.

E. F. Taylor and J. A. Wheeler, *Spacetime Physics*, Freeman, San Francisco, 1966.

Optics

F. A. Jenkins and H. E. White, *Fundamentals of Optics*, 3rd ed., McGraw-Hill, New York, 1957.

A. Sommerfeld, *Optics*, Academic Press, New York, 1964.

Quantum Mechanics

W. H. Cropper, *The Quantum Physicists*, Oxford Univ. Press, New York, 1970.

W. Heitler, *Elementary Wave Mechanics*, 2nd ed., Oxford Univ. Press, New York, 1956.

N. F. Mott, *Elements of Wave Mechanics*, Cambridge Univ. Press, New York, 1962.

L. Pauling and E. B. Wilson, *Introduction to Quantum Mechanics*, McGraw-Hill, New York, 1935.

E. H. Wichmann, *Quantum Physics*, Berkeley Physics Course, Vol. 4, McGraw-Hill, New York, 1971.

Atomic Physics

G. Herzberg, *Atomic Spectra and Atomic Structure*, Dover, New York, 1944.

B. W. Shore and D. H. Menzel, *Principles of Atomic Spectra*, Wiley, New York, 1968.

Solid State Physics

J. S. Blakemore, *Solid State Physics*, Saunders, Philadelphia, Pa., 1969.

A. J. Dekker, *Solid State Physics*, Prentice Hall, Englewood Cliffs, N.J., 1957.

C. Kittel, *Elementary Solid State Physics*, Wiley, New York, 1966.

R. A. Levy, *Principles of Solid State Physics*, Academic Press, New York, 1968.

Nuclear and Particles Physics

B. L. Cohen, *Concepts of Nuclear Physics*, McGraw-Hill, New York, 1971.

H. Enge, *Introduction to Nuclear Physics*, Addison-Wesley, Reading, Mass., 1966.

P. Marmier and E. Sheldon, *Physics of Nuclei and Particles*, Vols. 1 and 2 (Vol. 3 to be published), Academic Press, New York, 1969.

E. B. Paul, *Nuclear and Particle Physics*, North-Holland, Amsterdam, 1969.

E. Segrè, *Nuclei and Particles*, Benjamin, New York, 1964.

HISTORY OF PHYSICS

M. Fierz and V. F. Weisskopf, ed., *Theoretical Physics in the Twentieth Century*, A Memorial Volume to Wolfgang Pauli, Interscience, New York, 1960.

W. Heisenberg, *Physics and Beyond, Encounters and Conversations*, Harper Torch Books, New York, 1972.

A. Hermann, *The Genesis of Quantum Theory*, MIT Press, Cambridge, Mass., 1971.

M. Jammer, *The Conceptual Development of Quantum Mechanics*, McGraw-Hill, New York, 1966.

M. J. Klein, *Paul Ehrenfest*, North-Holland, Amsterdam, 1970.

M. S. Livingston, *Particle Accelerators; a Brief History*, Harvard University Press, Cambridge, Mass., 1969.

G. Ludwig, *Wave Mechanics*, Pergamon, New York, 1968.

Nobel Lectures Physics, Elsevier, Amsterdam, 4 Vols.: *1091–1921*, 1967; *1922–1941*, 1965; *1942–1962*, 1964; *1963–1970*, 1972.

W. Pauli, ed., *Niels Bohr and the Development of Physics*, McGraw-Hill, New York, 1955.

E. Segrè, *Enrico Fermi, Physicist*, University of Chicago Press, Chicago, Ill., 1970.

Answers to Selected Problems

Chapter 1

3. $S_0 = E_0 H_0 / 2$

7. (a) 5×10^7, 10^8, and 1.5×10^8 Hz,   (b) 2.5×10^7, 7.5×10^7, and 1.25×10^8 Hz

9. (a) 1.82 A,   (b) 600 Hz, 3.37×10^5 m,   (c) 91.5 W

11. (a) 30, 10, 1 m,   (b) 3×10^6, 3×10^9, 10^{11} Hz

13. 15.9 A

15. (a) $90°$,   (b) $14°29'$, $48°35'$,   (c) $7°11'$, $22°1'$, $38°41'$, $61°3'$ from the normal to the line joining the antennas

17. $33°33'$, $60°$, $80°24'$, $99°36'$, $120°$, $146°27'$

19. Principal maxima at $0°$, $19°28'$, $41°49'$, $90°$. Secondary maxima at $9°36'$, $30°$, $56°27'$. Minima at $6°23'$, $12°50'$, $26°22'$, $33°43'$, $51°$, $62°38'$.

23. 30.4 s   29. 2.96×10^8 m/s

31. (a) $-0.10021\,c$,   (b) $+0.10021\,c$,   (c) 0.21%

34. $0.93\,c$ 38. $12.7'$

41. (a) -18.53 Å,   (b) $+18.61$ Å,   (c) 0.0355 Å

Chapter 2

2. (a) $I = \dfrac{I_0}{2} \cos^2 \theta$,   (b) $I = \dfrac{I_0}{8} \sin^2 2\psi$

4. $A(\cos \omega t - \tfrac{1}{9} \cos 3\omega t + \tfrac{1}{25} \cos 5\omega t - \ldots)$

8. would become broader   10. 2.5×10^{20} s^{-1}, 10^{15} s^{-1}

12. (a) 0.33×10^{-6} N, (b) $\tfrac{1}{4}°$

14. (a) 1.03×10^3 V/m,   (b) 4.65×10^{-6} N/m^2,   (c) 5.26×10^8 N

20. $\left(\dfrac{\sqrt{K_e} - 1}{\sqrt{K_e} + 1}\right)^2$ 23. 7.4%

24. 3 ft   25. 25 ft, red light on the left

28. At a point $nR/(n - 1)$ beyond the first vertex if $n > 2$. At a point $\dfrac{2 - n}{2(n - 1)} R$ beyond the second vertex if $n < 2$.

29. (a) $A^2/2 + B^2/2 + AB \cos[k(x_1 - x_2) + \alpha - \beta]$,   (b) $A^2/2 + B^2/2$,   (c) $2A^2, 0$

30. 0.546, 1.09, 1.64, 2.10, 2.73 cm;   5.46, 11.0, 16.6, 22.6, 28.3 cm

31. 367, 37   32. 0.05 mm, 0.5 mm

33. 6705 Å   36. 4700 Å, 6000 Å reflected

38. 6.65 m

39. (a) dark, (b) 4.24 × 10⁻⁴ m, (c) 3 × 10⁻⁴ m

41. (a) dark, (b) 0.25 mm, (c) point of wedge is bright, spacing of fringes is reduced

42. (a) $1.55 \times 10^{-3} \sqrt{n}$ m, (b) 0.55 m, 1.67 m, ∞.

43. one maximum only; 0, ±0.258 m, ±0.374 m, ±0.482 m, ±0.610 m; $(\alpha/\lambda) + 1$

44. (a) 0°, 10°, 20°20′, 31°20′, 44°, 60°10′,   (b) 4075 Å

45. (a) 5.88 × 10⁻⁷ m, (b) 8.9 × 10⁻¹¹ m   46. ±36°5′; 66°5′; −6°5′

47. 1   49. maxima at 4.49, 7.72, 10.89, 14.1

50. 5880 Å   51. 8.9°, overlap by 6.9°

52. 4 mm, 12 mm   53. (a) 2.6°, (b) 3.6°

54. (a) T, (b) T, (c) F, (d) F, (e) T, (f) T

55. (a) T, (b) T, (c) F, (d) T, (e) F, (f) T

56. >3.07 cm   57. 7.27 m

58. 6.7 × 10⁻⁷ rad

59. (a) 5.95 × 10⁻² seconds of arc,   (b) 2.73 × 10¹⁰ m

60. 152.5 km   61. 6.4 × 10⁻³ mm

62. 16 m   65. 4; 3.62 Å, 2.56 Å

69. (111): 2.12 Å, (220): 1.28 Å

70. (111): 17°51′, 1°45′; (220): 14°29′, 1°26′

71. (111): 13°50′, 1°22′; (220): 22°59′, 2°14′

73. 0.05 eV, 3 × 10³ m/s   74. (111), 50 eV, 90°

75. (a) 0.29 Å,   (b) 5 × 10⁵ Å, 4.4 × 10⁻³⁸ kg

77. 1.2 × 10⁻¹⁴ m, 1.2 × 10⁻¹⁴ m; 12.2 Å, 0.39 Å

78. (a) yes, (b) ³He: $v = 5.75 \times 10^7$ m/s, (c) 2.3 × 10⁻¹⁵ m, (d) 6 × 10⁻¹⁵ m

80. (a) 579.4 Å, (b) 5794 Å, (c) 5220 K

84. 1.68 × 10¹² quanta/m³; 1.68 × 10¹⁸ quanta/λ³

85. 134 quanta/m³; 1.34 × 10⁻²⁸ quanta/λ³

90. 3060 Å, 5830 Å

91. 5.3 × 10⁵ m/s for Ni, 9.7 × 10⁵ m/s for Li

92. 2.6, 4.14, 2.07, 1.83, 5.39 eV   94. 4050 Å

95. 0.717, 0.733, 0.755 Å   96. 114°, 134°, 165°; 0.23, 0.61, 0.91 keV

97. (a) 0.172 Å, (b) 2.8 × 10⁴ eV

101. 1.989 MeV, almost 3 × 10⁸ m/s, in fact, $v/c = 0.979$

104. (a) 182 MeV, (b) yes, no, (c) 180°, 98°

106. (a) 2.4 Å, (b) 1.24 Å, (c) 0.124 Å 108. same order of magnitude

109. 0.51 MeV

111. (a) 0.49 Å, (b) 1.5 × 10⁻³ Å, 2 × 10²¹ s⁻¹

112. (a) 1.6 × 10¹⁵, (b) 3.45 × 10² V/m, (c) 1.5 m

114. (a) 5.3 × 10⁻⁷ m,   (b) 0.05°

Chapter 3

2. (a) C/r^2, (b) $(n/v)\,dr$ 3. v_2/v_1, v_2/v_1

4. $w/2$ 5. (a) 0.23 m/s, 1.7 × 10⁻² m, (b) w

6. 1.82 × 10⁸ m/s, 1.55 × 10⁸ m/s

7. (a) 1.87 × 10⁶ m/s, 4.8 × 10¹⁰ m/s, (b) c^2

10. (a) yes, (b) no   13. >7 × 10⁻²⁰ kg-m/s, >1.5 × 10⁴ MeV

18. 1/12, ±5 Hz; 1/1200, ±0.05 Hz   19. $\sqrt{\dfrac{2}{L}} \sin (n\pi x/L)$

23. (a) 0.092, (b) 0.25, (c) 0.303, (d) 0.25

24.
$$\left(\frac{2}{L}\right)^{3/2} \begin{array}{c} \sin \\ \text{or} \\ \cos \end{array} \left(\frac{s_x \pi x}{L}\right) \begin{array}{c} \sin \\ \text{or} \\ \cos \end{array} \left(\frac{s_y \pi y}{L}\right) \begin{array}{c} \sin \\ \text{or} \\ \cos \end{array} \left(\frac{s_z \pi z}{L}\right)$$

The sin is to be used if s is even, and the cos is to be used if s is odd.

$$\frac{h^2}{8mL^2}(s_x{}^2 + s_y{}^2 + s_z{}^2)$$

25. (a) 6.18×10^2, 1.24×10^3, 1.85×10^3 MeV
27. No degeneracies 49 E_0, 61 E_0, 76 E_0, 81 E_0, 88 E_0, 108 E_0, $E_0 = (h^2)/(288mL_0{}^2)$
33. 0.025, 0.975   41. 5×10^{26}
43. 1, 3, 6, 10   45. $2^{-1/2}$
52. 6.4×10^8

Chapter 4

1. (a) $Z^{3/2}(\pi a_0{}^3)^{1/2}e^{-Zr/a_0}$, (b) 54.4, 121 eV, (c) 0.029, 0.017, 0.009 Å
3. 0.76 a_0, 5.24 a_0
5. (a) 1.88 eV, 2.54 eV,   (b) $n = 3$ to 2, 4 to 2
6. 6070 Å, 4860 Å; 1220 Å, 1030 Å   7. 3.41 eV
9. -6.8 eV, -1.7 eV, -0.43 eV, ...
10. (a) 2.42 MeV, 8.5×10^{-15} m, 4.75×10^{-15} m, (b) 3×10^{-15}, 19.4 MeV, 7×10^{-15} m
12. (a) 1.4×10^{-3} eV, (b) 3.3 eV   14. $(me^4)/(4\epsilon_0 h^3)$
20. 4   22. 490 gauss/cm
24. 1, 2, 3, 4, 5   27. 2, 3/2
38. 0.39 eV, 0.125 eV   44. 2536.064, 2536.000, 2535.936 Å
45. (a) 19 weber/m², (b) >20 weber/m² 48. (a) 6×10^4 eV, (b) 8×10^{-13} m
50. 0.0736 weber/m²   52. 120 W/m
53. 30, 33, 41, 54, 66, 109, 164, 328 Å   54. $Z^* = Z - 7$
55. (a) 2×10^{-6}, (c) upwards   59. 20.1 keV, same
64. 560 newton/m   65. (a) 0.535 eV, (b) 0.267 eV
67. 2.44×10^{12}, 3.66×10^{12}, 4.88×10^{12} Hz

Chapter 5

3. 3°   5. 4.4×10^{12} Hz
8. $\omega L^2/(\pi u^2)$
10. (a) approx. 420 K, (b) approx. $6.2 \times 10^{-6} \, T^3$
17. 1.4×10^{-10} s   19. (a) 1.4×10^5 km, (b) 0.74×10^{-10}
22. 1.4×10^{12} m, 7.7×10^{21} m   24. $C_H B/\rho$
28. 2.3×10^{11} electrons/m³   32. 81,200 K
37. 9.0×10^{-7} eV
39. (a) $e_F + kT \ln 3$ (b) e_F (c) 8.7×10^3 K

43. (a) length, (b) $\dfrac{\hbar}{m_0}(1 - 4 k^2 s^2)\mathbf{k}$

44. $h^2 2^{1/2}/(a^2 E_0)$, $2h^2/(a^2 E_0)$, $-2h^2/(a^2 E_0)$, $-h^2/(a^2 E_0)$

45. $-\dfrac{1}{\hbar}E_0a2^{-1/2}$ 46. (b) $5a/4$, $4\hbar/(5a)$

50. (a) -0.0094eV, (b) 64Å, (c) 5.7×10^4, (d) 5.2×10^8, (e) negative, (f) 115 K

51. 2.3×10^3 Å, 18.4×10^3 Å

Chapter 6

1. (a) 7.1×10^{-15} m, (b) 2.3×10^{14} g/cm³, (c) 2.4 fm, (d) 87 MeV
2. 12.4 km, 6.5×10^{-4} s   3. (a) 9.52 MeV, (b) 4.27×10^7 m/s
5. (a) 28.4 MeV, (b) yes   8. one in 7.9×10^7
11. (a) 18 or 19, (b) approximately 85, approximately 155
20. (a) 3.65×10^{-15} m, (b) 1.49×10^{-15} fm

23. $-0.86\dfrac{Q}{2M}$ 26. (a) $-\frac{5}{2}$, (b) $-\frac{5}{2}$, (c) $T \geq \frac{5}{2}$

31. (a) 2.14 ± 0.16 MeV, (b) yes   33. (a) yes, (b) 1/12, (c) $(25\pi^2)/(36a^2)$
34. (a) $c = (2\pi\rho)^{-1/2}$, (b) 0.323   35. H_2 molecule: 0.4, deuteron: 35
41. (b) $\frac{3}{2}$ 42. no, yes, yes, no, no, yes, no
43. (a) no, (b) 0.669 MeV, (c) approximately 2 MeV, (d) approximately -1.06 MeV
46. (b) 2×10^{-54} kg-m², rigid sphere: 5.1×10^{-54} kg-m²
47. (a) 12.3 MeV, (b) 10.6, 13.6 MeV, (c) 14.4, 11.4 MeV
50. 92%   51. (a) ^{206}Pb, (b) 8, (c) 6
55. (a) 0.78 MeV, (b) 0.78 MeV   63. 18.6, 4.9, 2.4, -6.7 MeV
65. $_4{}^9$Be $(n, \alpha)\ _2{}^6$He with 0.74-MeV neutrons, $_4{}^9$Be $(n, \gamma)\ _4{}^{10}$Be or $_4{}^9$Be $(d, p)\ _4{}^{10}$Be gives 6.3-MeV gamma rays or 3.4-MeV protons, $_4{}^9$Be $(p, \gamma)\ _5{}^{10}$B or $_4{}^9$Be $(d, n)\ _5{}^{10}$B gives 6.1 MeV-gamma rays or 3.2-MeV neutrons.
68. (a) 280 MeV, (b) 203 MeV
69. (a) 85 collisions, (b) 9.19×10^9 neutrons, (c) 1.09 neutrons per fission
72. 3.125×10^{16} fissions/s, 9.4 days
74. (a) 1.445 kg/sec, (b) 7.0×10^{-14}/year, (c) $2.0 \times 10^6 x$ years

Chapter 7

2. (a) $0.9909\,c$, (b) $m = 7.4\,m_0$ 6. 5.7 GeV
8. neutrino   10. $\mu^+\nu$, $\mu^-\bar{\nu}$
12. (a) impossible, (b) impossible, (c) possible
13. (a) 29.6 MeV/c, (b) 420 MeV, forwards
14. (a) 6.8°, (b) 212 MeV   24. 66 MeV
29. yes   36. (a) same direction, (b) same direction
38. (a) opposite direction of μ^+
44. (a) $M(\Sigma^-) - M(\Sigma^+) + M(n) - M(p)$,   (b) $\Delta_{\text{calculated}} = 6.6$ MeV

APPENDIX I

2. 0.135 W/m, 1.35×10^{-2} V/m, 7.96×10^2 A/m, 1.35×10^{-2} V/m, 3.98×10^2 A/m, 10.74 W/m², 5.37 W/m², 0.0338 W/m, 0.135 W/m, 0.0338 W/m.

4. (a) $\mu_0 \dfrac{H^2}{2} \pi r^2 L,$ (b) $\pi r^2 N (dB/dt),$ (c) $\frac{1}{2} r(dB/dt),$ (d) $\frac{1}{2} r(dB/dt) H,$

(e) $\pi r^2 L \dfrac{d}{dt} \left(\dfrac{\mu_0 H^2}{2} \right).$

APPENDIX II

3. $L = 0.508$ m
7. (a) $0.9956\, c,$ (b) 9.106 GeV,   (c) 10.044 GeV,   (d) $10.7\, m_0$
11. 0.523 MeV   16. 2.66×10^{-12} kg, 1.48×10^{-10}

APPENDIX IV

8. 770 K

Index